CELL CHEMISTRY

CELL CHEMISTRY

A COLLECTION OF PAPERS DEDICATED TO

OTTO WARBURG

ON THE OCCASION OF HIS

70TH BIRTHDAY

EDITED BY

DEAN BURK

ELSEVIER PUBLISHING COMPANY

AMSTERDAM  HOUSTON (TEXAS)

LONDON NEW YORK

1953

SOLE DISTRIBUTORS FOR THE U.S.A. AND CANADA:
ELSEVIER PRESS INC., 402 LOVETT BOULEVARD,
HOUSTON (TEXAS) AND 155 EAST 82ND STREET,
NEW YORK 28 (N.Y.) – FOR THE BRITISH COMMON-
WEALTH EXCEPT CANADA: CLEAVER-HUME PRESS
LTD., WRIGHT'S LANE, KENSINGTON, LONDON, W.8.

Library of Congress Catalog Card Number: 53-7253

THE ORIGINAL EDITION OF THIS BOOK
APPEARED AS AN ISSUE OF BIOCHIMICA ET BIOPHYSICA ACTA
VOL. 12 NO. 1/2 (1953)

PRINTED IN THE NETHERLANDS BY
DRUKKERIJ MEIJER N.V., WORMERVEER AND AMSTERDAM

CONTENTS

OTTO WARBURG

INTRODUCTION

OTTO WARBURG, ARTISAN OF CELL CHEMISTRY

by

DEAN BURK

*Foreign Member, Max Planck Institute for Cell Physiology, Berlin-Dahlem (Germany),
and Head of Cytochemistry Section, National Institutes of Health,
United States Public Health Service, Bethesda, Md. (U.S.A.)*

OTTO HEINRICH WARBURG was born on October 8, 1883 in Freiburg in Baden. In 1896 he came with his parents to Berlin, where his father, EMIL WARBURG, had been called to the Chair of Physics in the University of Berlin and was later appointed to the Presidency of the *Physikalische Reichsanstalt* (Imperial Bureau of Physical Standards). The mother of OTTO WARBURG stemmed from a family of public officials and soldiers, and her brother fell as a general in World War I. In two large official residences of his parents—the first at the Marschallbrücke in Berlin, the second in Marchstrasse in Berlin-Charlottenburg, and both built from plans prepared by Frau VON HELMHOLTZ— OTTO WARBURG grew up during the culminating period of splendor of the Germany of Wilhelm II, in personal touch with many leading circles in the capital.

In the home of his parents, THEODOR WILHELM ENGELMANN told him about *Bacterium photometricum* and photosynthesis; EMIL FISCHER about plans to fathom the secret of enzymes; and VAN 'T HOFF about the maximum work obtainable in chemical reactions. Thus the course of his life was already set in childhood.

Later, at the university, he learned chemistry from EMIL FISCHER, with whom he worked for three years; medicine in the clinic of LUDOLF VON KREHL, to whom he was an assistant for three years; thermodynamics from WALTER NERNST, with whom he worked on oxidation-reduction potentials in living systems in 1914; and physics and photochemistry from his father, with whom he worked on the quantum requirement of photosynthesis in 1920 in the *Physikalische Reichsanstalt*. In 1913 he became a Member of the newly founded Kaiser Wilhelm Society. Since then, without interruption except for World War I, he has contributed increasingly to the fame and renown of this scientific organization, from 1931 on as Director of the Institute whose name is known to all biochemists.

He has never given a course of lectures to students. He is no administrator. He is no member of committees. Among the forty rooms in his institute he has no office, conference room, or writing room, apart from the general library. He selects his staff on a basis of technical ability and talent. In his opinion, the building of a research institute in the natural sciences must have for its main foundation a permanent staff of technically trained assistants.

He is best characterized as an artisan, or even, by his own frequent say so in public, as a technician. He believes that, in the natural sciences, one can find out something new when one does something with one's hands that nobody did before. Thus, the fermentation of tumors was discovered when in the surrounding Ringer-solution the bicarbonate concentration was raised 20-fold. Iron-oxygenase was discovered when in biological experimentation with carbon monoxide the CO-pressure was raised 1000-fold. Acyl phosphate was discovered when in the oxidation-reaction of fermentation the phosphate concentration was raised 20-fold. The energy cycle and one-quantum reaction of photosynthesis was discovered when the light-dark time intervals measured in manometry were shortened from 5 minutes to 1 minute. Or, to mention an earlier classic example: the discovery of PLANCK's energy quanta was initiated when in 1899 LUMMER and PRINGSHEIM placed KURLBAUM's bolometer before a black body heated to different temperatures.

Although OTTO WARBURG endeavors to advance science mainly through his own experimental works, it cannot be said that he fails to look out for the future of scientists. Thus, he very early recognized the native gifts of RICHARD KUHN and ADOLF BUTENANDT, and assisted notably in their obtaining research institutes of the Kaiser Wilhelm Society at relatively youthful ages, and he is at present similarly concerned for younger colleagues. For all positions obtained by OTTO MEYERHOF in Germany—in Kiel, in Berlin, and in Heidelberg—he labored, successfully, against widespread opposition. After 1933, he helped scores of political refugees to leave Germany and to obtain haven and positions elsewhere.

But, like the Cowardly Lion of Oz, he was no "resistance-fighter": he was not prepared to die as a defenceless scientist in combat with political dictators. Yet he has been ever ready to lose his life as a soldier in the army. In World War I, as an officer in the Prussian Horse Guards on the Russian front, he rode in many field patrols in advance of the infantry, and was eventually wounded in action. In the early years of this fighting, he was, by the by, armed with both pistol and—less effective but more sinister—mediaeval lance!

He has spent the greater part of his life in Berlin, the most restless city in a restless world. Here he was ever favored with luck. In World War II, during the years 1939 to 1945, he and his entire staff enjoyed the singular privilege of continuing to work on purely scientific problems without reference to war work (see appended table). In 1943, as Berlin became dangerous because of air attacks, Prince von Eulenberg placed at his disposal the nearby castle of Liebenberg, where he and his staff lived and worked, with transported equipment, undisturbed until 1945. In that year the Red Army took possession of the Island of Rügen in the Baltic, and immediately provided a military guard for his estate there, making it possible for him to continue his studies still undisturbed.

His only misfortune was that in June 1945 the Russians removed all the equipment from his institutes. It appears that this took place at the instigation of the local Dahlem communists, for shortly thereafter Marshal Zhukov, Commander-in-Chief of the Russian-occupied zone, invited WARBURG for a visit to tell him, in the name of the Russian government, that the dismantling of his institutes had been a mistake, and a misfortune for science. The Marshal issued an order that the apparatus and books be returned, but alas, everything had already been scattered to the four winds.

After the Yalta-Tehran agreements it became doubtful whether WARBURG

belonged to the Russian or to the American occupation zone, since he was domiciled partly in the Russian zone, on the Island of Rügen, and partly in the American sector of west Berlin; and, furthermore, his Liebenberg institute lay in the Russian zone, while the mother research institute was in the American sector of Berlin. WARBURG decided for the Americans, and in 1948 began anew to re-establish at Dahlem the Kaiser Wilhelm Institute* for Cell Physiology, the building of which had remained undamaged. From all sides he received help, as reward for not fleeing from Berlin, from neither Hitler nor Stalin. His efforts during the war years and after, to maintain his laboratory and experimental work, bore fruit in the uniquely early reconstitution of his institute, which, already in 1949, had become well equipped with apparatus and books.

Max Planck Institute for Cell Physiology, will Emil Fischer Memorial Statue, Berlin-Dahlem

It was during this year of the re-equipment of his Dahlem institute that he availed himself of an opportunity to visit his American friends. Through the courtesy and generous support of the National Institutes of Health, United States Public Health Service, at Bethesda, Maryland, he was enabled, in cooperation with the staff of the Cytochemistry Section there, and with STERLING HENDRICKS of the United States Department of Agriculture at nearby Beltsville, to develop modern methods of photo-synthetic experimentation, and to "rediscover" the high efficiency of photosynthesis. As a conclusion to this important and memorable visit, the experimental set-up at Bethesda was transferred for the summer of 1949 to the Marine Biological Laboratory at Woods Hole, Massachusetts, where he had the privilege of demonstrating for many weeks, through the hospitality of Professor E. S. GUZMAN-BARRON, the new methods to the rising generation of American biologists. Since these Woods Hole days he has

---

* Since July 1953: Max Planck Institute.

been a member of the Institute for Muscle Research founded by ALBERT SZENT-GYÖRGYI and STEPHEN RATH.

On May 8, 1950, General MAXWELL D. TAYLOR, then Military Commandant of the American Sector of Berlin, officially reopened the Dahlem institute. The rebirth of the Kaiser Wilhelm Institute for Cell Physiology, celebrated with ceremony on that day, the fifth anniversary of the cessation of hostilities, was a signal event both for science and for the promotion of good relations among men of good will everywhere. Today, the Institute stands at the crest of the biochemical institutes of the world, and, in addition, is probably the finest photochemical institute in existence. Its director expects to do his greatest and boldest experiments, as did his distinguished father before him, after passing the three score and ten mark. His genius may be likened to a positive first order reaction with an extended half-time, attained only after the Half-Century of Biochemical Discovery listed below. His prescription for such continued scientific production is provided by the photograph concluding this Introduction, taken at the turn of his sixty-ninth birthday.

It would be superfluous here to give an extended list of the many honors received by Professor WARBURG, such as the Nobel Prize in Medicine (1931, for iron-oxygenase), Foreign Membership in the Royal Society of London (1934), and, most recently (1952), Knighthood in the Order of Merit founded originally by Frederick the Great and restricted to thirty of Germany's most distinguished citizens.

A scientific appreciation of his work is probably best realized by the following appended table, which contains a list of experimental contributions regarded by him as his most important discoveries. Most of these were accomplished and accepted only after long struggle, but this was no disadvantage. For the greater the resistance to a discovery, the more is the discoverer forced to fortify the new domain of knowledge; and the greater is the final victory. At the moment, battle rages over the energetics of photosynthesis. But the termination of this battle can no longer be in doubt when one reads the two communications concluding this volume. Indeed Time, the sovereign judge, has shown that all his published experiments have been right. Most of them were ahead of their time. Thus, their significance is still increasing.

A Half-Century of Biochemical Discovery

1904   Splitting of racemic leucine ethyl ester by pancreatin (first publication).

1905   (EMIL FISCHER AND OTTO WARBURG) Splitting of racemic leucine into its optically active components by means of formyl derivatives.

1910–1914 Respiration of sea-urchin eggs, red blood cells, and grana.

1918–1920 Development of biochemical manometry.

1921–1924 Iron catalyses on surfaces. Narcotic action: displacement of substrates from surfaces. Cyanide action: chemical reaction with iron.

1920–1924 Quantum requirement of photosynthesis.

1923   Tissue slice technique ($d = (8C_{O_2}D/A)^{1/2}$).

1923–1925 Metabolism of tumors.

1924   Iron, the oxygen-transferring constituent of the respiration enzyme ("iron-oxygenase").

1925–1926 Inhibition of cell respiration by carbon monoxide.

1927–1932 Action spectrum of iron-oxygenase.

1932–1933 Discovery of the yellow enzymes.

1932   First crystallization of a flavin ("luminoflavin").

1935   Discovery of nicotinamide as the active group of hydrogen-transferring enzymes.

1935   Nature of coenzyme action ($- dc/dt = k \cdot E \cdot c/C$).

1935–1937 Development of the optical methods based upon the ultraviolet absorption band of dihydro-nicotinamide.

1936   Mechanism of alcohol formation in nature:
          Dihydro-nicotinamide + acetaldehyde = nicotinamide + ethyl alcohol.

1936–1937 Stepwise oxidative degradation of phosphorylated hexoses to trioses.

1937   Discovery of the copper of phenol oxidases, and its action through valence change.

1938   Isolation and crystallization of flavin adenine dinucleotide.

1939   Crystallization of the oxidizing fermentation enzyme, and mechanism of the oxidation reaction of fermentation:
          Glyceric aldehyde diphosphate + nicotinamide = phosphoglyceric-*acyl-phosphate* + dihydro-nicotinamide.

1941   Crystallization of enolase, and chemistry of fluoride inhibition of fermentation.

1942   Crystallization of muscle zymohexase.

1942   In vitro Pasteur Reaction with hexosediphosphate and yeast zymohexase.

1943   Crystallization of the reducing fermentation enzyme from tumors and comparison with the homologous crystallized fermentation enzyme from muscle.

1943   Fermentation enzymes in the blood of tumor-bearing animals.

1944   Quinone and green grana.

1946–1947   *"Heavy Metals as Active Groups of Enzymes"* and *"Hydrogen-Transferring Enzymes"*. Arbeitsgemeinschaft Medizinischer Verlage, Berlin, 1946 and 1947.

1948   The manometric actinometer.

1949   (With DEAN BURK) Maximum efficiency of photosynthesis.

1950   DEAN BURK AND OTTO WARBURG. The one-quantum reaction and energy cycle in photosynthesis.

1951   Crystallization of the hemin of iron-oxygenase.

1952   Zymohexase and ascites tumor cells.

1953   Chemical constitution of the hemin of iron-oxygenase.

THE BIOSYNTHESIS OF GLUCOSAMINE*

by

LUIS F. LELOIR AND CARLOS E. CARDINI

Instituto de Investigaciones Bioquímicas, Fundación Campomar,
Buenos Aires (Argentina)

After the isolation of uridine-diphosphate-glucose (UDPG)[1], a very similar compound (UDPAG) containing acetylglucosamine instead of glucose was found in yeast[2]. Considering the structural similarity of the two compounds and the coenzymic function of UDPG in the transformation of galactose-1-phosphate into glucose-1-phosphate, it has been considered that UDPAG might be involved in the metabolism of hexosamine phosphates. Part of the plan of investigation consisted in a search for enzymes in some organism with a high hexosamine metabolism. Since molds should synthesize large amounts of glucosamine in order to build their cell walls, which contain chitin, experiments have been carried out with *Neurospora crassa*. While no information on a coenzymic function of UDPAG has been obtained several enzymes have been found. Besides a chitinase, the *Neurospora* extracts were found to contain the enzymes required for the following sequence of reactions:

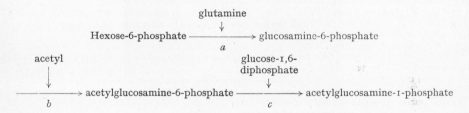

Reaction *a* and some preliminary studies on reaction *b* will be dealt with in this paper. As to reaction *c*, it has been detected by using synthetic acetylglucosamine-1-phosphate. *Neurospora* extracts were found to catalyze the transformation of this substance into acetylglucosamine-6-phosphate, but no such activity could be detected in rabbit muscle extracts. The interconversion of the acetylglucosamine phosphates is accelerated by glucose-1,6-diphosphate, a fact which bears a resemblance to its action on the mannose-[3] and on the ribose-phosphates[4]. Further studies designed to decide whether the phosphoglucomutase and phosphoacetylglucosaminemutase actions are due to one or two enzymes, and to clarify the mechanism of the stimulation by glucose-diphosphate are being carried out.

* This investigation was supported in part by a research grant (G-3442) from the National Institutes of Health, Public Health Service and by the Rockefeller Foundation.

References p. 22.

I

The synthesis of glucosamine-6-phosphate can also be brought about by a mechanism different from reaction *a*. Thus HARPUR AND QUASTEL[5] discovered that glucosamine is phosphorylated by ATP in the presence of brain extracts, and from further studies by BROWN[6] and GRANT AND LONG[7], it has been concluded that the phosphorylation is catalysed by hexokinase and that the reaction product is glucosamine-6-phosphate. It is difficult to decide whether this synthesis is a physiological process or simply an unspecific effect.

Similar events have been found to occur with galactosamine. Liver and yeast extracts containing galactokinase were found to phosphorylate galactosamine to a product which appears to be galactosamine-1-phosphate[8]. In this case, as with glucosamine, the corresponding hexose inhibits the phosphorylation of the hexosamine.

The formation of glucosamine by a process such as reaction *a* would explain the results of TOPPER AND LIPTON[9], who found that in *Streptococcus* the glucosamine formed from glucose-1-^{14}C contained nearly all the label in the 1-position.

METHODS

Analytical. The following methods were used: BLIX[10] for glucosamine. KUNITZ AND MCDONALD[11] for protein. Glutamate was estimated with ninhydrin after paper chromatography with phenol[12]. Amide nitrogen by estimation of the ammonia liberated after heating eleven minutes at 100° in 1 N acid[13]. Ammonia by distillation in Conway units[14] and nesslerization.

For the estimation of acetylglucosamine the method of MORGAN AND ELSON[15] was slightly modified in order to make it less sensitive to buffers and to reduce the time needed for colour development. The *p*-dimethylamino benzaldehyde (DAB) reagent was prepared by adding 0.5 g of DAB to 10 ml of concentrated HCl and completing to 100 ml with glacial acetic acid. The analytical procedure was as follows: the neutralized unknowns and standards containing 0.1–0.5 μmoles of acetyl glucosamine were taken to 0.5 ml with water. After adding 0.1 ml of 1 M sodium carbonate the tubes were heated 5 minutes in a boiling water bath. After cooling 2.5 ml of the DAB reagent were added and mixed immediately with a suitably glass rod. The optical density at 544 mμ was measured after 3 to 5 minutes with a Beckman spectrophotometer. The colour increases during 2 minutes and begins te decrease slowly after 3 minutes. If the time elapsing between the addition of the DAB reagent and the colorimetric reading is equal in all the samples a good proportionality between concentration of acetylglucosamine and optical density is obtained.

Preparation of the enzyme. A wild type *Neurospora crassa* E-5297a was grown for three days on "minimal medium"[16] at 30° under forced aeration. The mycelium was separated by filtration, washed with water, lyophilized and stored over calcium chloride in an evacuated desiccator at 5°. Extraction of the dried mycelium was effected by homogenizing 0.8 g in 16 ml of water at 0°, followed by centrifugation. The supernatant containing about 40 mg of protein per ml is referred to as crude extract.

Partial purification was carried out as follows: 6.5 ml of acetone were added to 13 ml of the crude extract at 0°. The inactive precipitate was centrifuged off at 0°. To the supernatant 3.9 ml of acetone were added. The precipitate was separated by centrifugation, washed three times with acetone and dried in an evacuated desiccator. The yield was about 60 mg of a white powder.

The formation of "glucosamine" was found to be greater in the presence of 8-hydroxyquinoline, and this fact was attributed to protection of the enzyme from metal inactivation. Therefore, 8-hydroxyquinoline was added to the acetone used in the purification (about 10 mg %) and the buffer (pH 6.5) used for dissolving the enzyme was saturated with 8-hydroxyquinoline.

The enzyme in solution was found to lose activity in a few hours at 5° and in a few days at —10°

The ratio: μmoles of glucosamine formed/mg protein per hour, was about 0.04 for the crude enzyme and usually about 0.3 for the acetone fractionated enzyme.

Acetylation experiments. The enzyme preparation used was a crude extract which had been dialyzed about two hours against running water. The enzyme system was similar to that used by KAPLAN AND LIPMANN[17]. The CoA solution was an aqueous extract of rat liver. In every case controls in which the reaction was stopped at time = 0 were run simultaneously. The reaction was stopped by immersing the tubes in boiling water followed by centrifugation.

Acetylglucosamine was estimated in the supernatant as described above. In some cases the phosphoric esters were precipitated by adding 0.3 ml of 5% zinc sulphate and 0.3 N barium hydroxide until the suspension gave a rose colour with phenolphthalein.

References p. 22.

RESULTS

The formation of "glucosamine". Incubation of hexose-6-phosphate with glutamine and the enzyme gave rise to an increase in the glutamine content. As shown in Fig. 1, hardly any increase took place when glutamine or hexose-6-phosphate were omitted.

The results of an analysis of the chemical changes occurring during the reaction appear in Table I. The increase in "glucosamine" was approximately equal to the decrease in amide nitrogen of glutamine and to the increase in glutamate. There occurred also a small increase in ammonia in the complete system as well as in the controls without glutamine.

An experiment carried out at different temperatures appears in Table II. At 37° glucosamine formation was faster than at 30° in the beginning, but slower afterwards.

In many experiments it was observed that the enzyme solutions became rapidly inactivated at room temperature. On the other hand, in the experiments of Fig. 1 the enzyme in the pres-

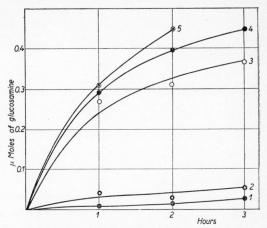

Fig. 1. The formation of glucosamine. Incubation at 30° of 1 mg of purified enzyme and 0.05 ml of trishydroxymethylaminoethane acetate buffer of pH 6.4 with substrates. Total volume, 0.2 ml.
Curve 1, 0 μmoles of hexose-6-phosphate
+ 2 μmoles of glutamine
Curve 2, 2 μmoles of hexose-6-phosphate
+ 0 μmoles of glutamine
Curve 3, 1 μmoles of hexose-6-phosphate
+ 5 μmoles of glutamine
Curve 4, 4 μmoles of hexose-6-phosphate
+ 2 μmoles of glutamine
Curve 5, 4 μmoles of hexose-6-phosphate
+ 5 μmoles of glutamine

TABLE I

BALANCE EXPERIMENT

The aliquots of the complete system taken for analysis contained: 1.3 μmoles of glutamine, 1.3 μmoles of glucose-6-phosphate and 0.6 mg of purified enzyme and citrate buffer. pH 6.4. Total volume, 0.1 ml. Incubated 3 hours at 30°.

	Δ "glucosa-mine"	Δ amide	Δ NH$_3$	Δ glutamate
Complete system	0.42	—0.39	0.17	0.36
No glutamine	0.03	—0.07	0.14	0.08
No hexose-6-phosphate	0.03	—0.04	0.22	0.10

TABLE II

FORMATION OF "GLUCOSAMINE" AT DIFFERENT TEMPERATURES
Complete system as in Table I. Results in μmoles.

Temperature	Time of incubation (minutes)			
	30	*60*	*120*	*180*
24°	0.08	0.20	—	0.46
30°	0.13	0.24	0.40	0.52
37°	0.16	0.20	0.34	0.40

References p. 22.

ence of the substrates was still active after 3 hours at 30°. An experiment was therefore carried out in order to ascertain which of the substrates exerted a stabilizing action. Samples of the enzyme were preincubated 30 minutes at 30° with or without substrate, and then the enzyme system was completed.

The glucosamine formed in one hour was as follows (the amount formed during preincubation was subtracted):

Preincubated without substrate	0.50
Preincubated with glutamine	0.76
Preincubated with hexose-6-phosphate	0.70
No preincubation	0.80

Thus both substrates, and specially glutamine, exerted a considerable stabilizing action.

Specificity. Glucose-6-phosphate could be replaced by fructose-6-phosphate, but not by any of the following substances: maltose, glucose, mannose, fructose, fructose-1,6-diphosphate, glucose-1,6-diphosphate, a-galactose-1-phosphate, fructose-1-phosphate, glucose-2-phosphate, xylose-5-phosphate, dihydroxyacetone or glyceraldehyde.

The enzyme preparation was found to contain considerable amounts of the enzyme which catalyzes the interconversion of fructose-6-phosphate into glucose-6-phosphate. The activity of this isomerase was estimated by measuring the disappearance of fructose phosphate with ROE's[18] method. It was found that under the conditions used for measuring glucosamine formation the equilibrium values for the glucose-fructose esters was attained in about 5 minutes. Therefore, it has not been possible to decide whether the reactant is glucose-6-phosphate or fructose-6-phosphate.

"Glucosamine" was formed when glucose-1-phosphate was used instead of hexose-6-phosphate with the crude enzyme, but not with the purified preparations. Under the conditions of the test and with the purified enzyme the phosphoglucomutase activity was very weak.

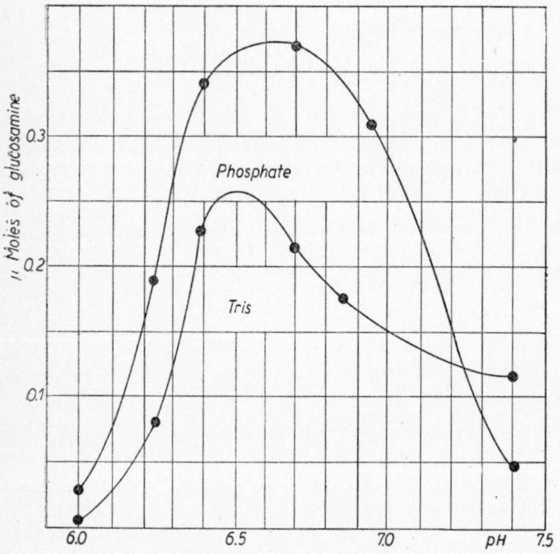

The substances which were tested with negative results as possible substitutes for glutamine were the following: asparagine, glutamic and aspartic acids, arginine, putrescine, urea, ammonium acetate, alanine, glycine, butyramide, serine, cysteine, lysine, ornithine, valine, leucine and citrulline. Pairs such as ammonium salts with ATP, asparagine and glutamate, etc., also gave negative results.

pH optimum. As shown in Fig. 2, the reaction has a sharp pH optimum at pH 6.4–6.8.

Study of the "glucosamine" ester. 100 μmoles each of glutamine and hexosemonophosphate plus 50 mg of enzyme in 10 ml of 0.025 M tris-acetate buffer (pH 6.4) were

Fig. 2. pH optimum curve. System composed of 2 μmoles each of hexose-6-phosphate plus 1 mg of enzyme and 0.1 ml of 0.1 M phosphate or tris-hydroxymethylaminoethane acetate buffers. Incubated 2 hours at 30°. The pH was determined on aliquots with a glass electrode.

References p. 22.

incubated 3 hours at 30°. The proteins were removed by heat coagulation. Barium acetate was added to the clear liquid and the pH was adjusted to 8. The mixture was centrifuged and the precipitate was washed twice with 1 ml of water. Three volumes of ethanol were added to the pooled supernatants. The precipitate was redissolved in 10 ml of water, a small precipitate centrifuged off and three volumes of ethanol were again added. The precipitate was then dried with ethanol and ether. Yield, 29 mg. These were dissolved in 2 ml of water. The solution contained 41 μmoles of total phosphate, 36 μmoles of reducing substance calculated as glucose, and 5.5 μmoles of "glucosamine". Direct paper chromatography of this ester mixture in different solvents gave irregular results, so that it was decided to remove the phosphate group.

0.5 ml of the above solution was made 0.01 M in respect to Mg^{+2}, and 10 mg of a kidney phosphatase preparation and a drop of toluene were added. After 16 hours at 37°, about 70% of the phosphate was hydrolysed. The mixture was then deproteinized with trichloroacetic acid, washed with ether and used for paper chromatography. A sample of glucosamine-6-phosphate was run simultaneously. One of the solvents used was a mixture of ethyl acetate-pyridine-ammonia[2] with which it is possible to separate glucosamine from galactosamine. The other solvent was phenol-water[19] with ammonia. Phenol without ammonia was used with paper which had been immersed in 0.1 M zinc sulphate and dried in air. This procedure was based on a previous observation which disclosed that zinc ions greatly retard the migration of hexosamines but only have a small influence on other sugars. It was also observed that with an alkaline solvent there was no retardation by zinc ions.

TABLE III

PAPER CHROMATOGRAPHY OF THE "GLUCOSAMINE" ESTER AFTER TREATMENT WITH PHOSPHATASE

	Ethyl acetate-pyridine-NH$_3$		$R_{glucose}$ Phenol-NH$_3$		Phenol-SO$_4$Zn treated paper	
Ex-"glucosamine" ester	0.99, 0.62, 1.39		1.0, 1.73, 1.54		1.01, 0.13, 1.19	
Ex-glucosamine-6-phosphate*	0.61		1.69		0.14	
Glucosamine	0.61		1.69		0.14	
Galactosamine	0.36		1.87		0.15	
Fructose		1.42		1.47		1.45
Mannose		1.35		1.47		1.15

* Prepared from glucosamine with ATP and hexokinase[6].

The results of the chromatography are shown in Table III. The ex-ester sugar mixture gave spots which migrated like glucose and glucosamine. The position of the substances was revealed with the aniline phthalate reagent[20], and that of hexosamines was checked with the modified ELSON AND MORGAN reagent[19]. Besides glucose and glucosamine, the ex-ester mixture contained small amounts of another hexose which migrated like mannose. In some cases a very faint spot with the $R_{glucose}$ value of fructose was observed. The presence of these sugars is not surprising since the sample of hexose-6-phosphate used was obtained by the action of yeast enzymes.

Acetylation. As shown in Table IV, *Neurospora* extracts, when suitably supplemented, are able to bring about the acetylation of glucosamine. These extracts are also able to catalyze the phosphorylation of glucosamine (Table V) and contain phosphatase.

References p. 22.

TABLE IV

THE ACETYLATION OF GLUCOSAMINE

Complete system: 2 μmoles of glucosamine, 4 μmoles of ATP, 0.05 ml of 1 M sodium acetate, 0.05 ml of 0.1 M cysteine, 0.05 ml of 0.2 M sodium citrate of pH 7, 0.1 ml of CoA solution, 0.05 ml of 0.1 M magnesium chloride and 0.2 ml of crude dialyzed enzyme. Final volume, 0.7 ml. Incubated 2 hours at 37°.

	μmoles of acetylglucosamine formed
Complete system	0.38
No glucosamine	0.025
No CoA	0.075
No ATP	0.025
No Mg++	0.070

TABLE V

THE PHOSPHORYLATION OF GLUCOSAMINE

Complete system as in Table III, but without CoA. The difference in glucosamine or acetyl-glucosamine content between samples incubated with an without ATP was considered to be due to phosphorylation. The estimations were carried out after precipitation of proteins and phosphoric esters with zinc sulphate and barium hydroxide.

Substrate	μmoles of substrate phosphorylated	
	No Mg++	With Mg++
Glucosamine	0.8	1.80
Acetylglucosamine	0	0

TABLE VI

THE ACETYLATION OF GLUCOSAMINE PHOSPHATE

Complete system as in Table III. The acetylglucosamine content of the supernatants after zinc sulphate-barium hydroxide precipitation was considered as free acetylglucosamine.

Substrate	Time of incubation (minutes)	μmoles of acetylglucosamine formed Total	Free
Glucosamine	30	0.26	0.18
	60	0.40	0.28
	120	0.38	0.25
Glucosamine-6-phosphate	120	0.60	0.49

TABLE VII

THE ACETYLATION OF THE "GLUCOSAMINE" ESTER

The "glucosamine" ester was obtained by incubation during 3 hours at 30° of 2 μmoles each of glutamine and hexose-6-phosphate with the purified enzyme. The controls contained the same substances plus glucosamine (0.5 μmoles) or glucosamine-6-phosphate (1 μmol), and the reaction was stopped at $t = 0$. The acetylating system described in Table III was then added.

	μmoles of acetylglucosamine formed
"Glucosamine" ester	0.21
Control with glucosamine	0.20
Control with glucosamine-6-phosphate	0.31

References p. 22.

The result of the action of this set of enzymes is that starting with free glucosamine or with glucosamine-6-phosphate, the reaction products are similar. Most of the acetyl-glucosamine appears free and a part precipitates with zinc sulphate-barium hydroxide as would acetylglucosamine phosphate (Table VI). If acetylglucosamine phosphate was formed, it could not have arisen by phosphorylation of acetylglucosamine, since this process is not catalyzed by the extracts (Table V). Therefore, it seems logical to conclude that glucosamine-6-phosphate can be acetylated directly to acetylglucosamine phosphate.

Table VII shows the results of the action of the acetylating system on the "glucosamine" ester formed from hexose phosphate and glutamine. This substance gave rise to acetylglucosamine, as did glucosamine or glucosamine-6-phosphate.

DISCUSSION

The substance formed from hexose-6-phosphate and glutamine gives the ELSON AND MORGAN and DISCHE[21] reactions for hexosamines. It can be prepared as the barium salt admixed with hexosemonophosphates. It behaves like glucosamine-6-phosphate when incubated with the acetylating system of *Neurospora*, and after dephosphorylation with phosphatase glucosamine can be identified by paper chromatography with selected solvents.

All this is considered as evidence proving that the product is glucosamine phosphate. The ester gives positive reactions for hexosamines, so that a 1-ester can be excluded, and since a migration of the phosphate during the reaction appears unlikely, the product should be glucosamine-6-phosphate.

No evidence for the necessity of a cofactor for the formation of glucosamine phosphate was obtained. Thus, no stimulation was obtained by the addition of different ions, ATP, pyridoxal phosphate, UDPAG, etc. The mechanism of the reaction cannot be discussed until it is decided whether the reactant is fructose-6 or glucose-6-phosphate. In order to settle this point it will be necessary to obtain enzyme preparations free from isomerase.

Further investigation will also be necessary in order to decide whether the acetylation step takes place on free glucosamine, on glucosamine-6-phosphate or on both. In connection with this point, it may be mentioned that CHOU AND SOODAK[22] extracted an enzyme from pigeon liver which catalyzed the acetylation of free glucosamine and galactosamine, but that the corresponding phosphates were not tested.

SUMMARY

A partially purified enzyme has been prepared from *Neurospora crassa* which catalyzes the formation of glucosamine phosphate from hexose-6-phosphate and glutamine. The glucosamine phosphate was identified by colour reactions, by dephosphorylation and paper chromatography and by its behaviour towards an acetylating system.

Quantitative analysis of amide nitrogen, glutamate, and hexosamine agreed with the following equation:

$$\text{Hexose-6-phosphate} + \text{glutamine} \longrightarrow \text{glucosamine-6-phosphate} + \text{glutamate}$$

Crude *Neurospora* extracts were found to phosphorylate glucosamine in the presence of ATP and, when suitably supplemented, to acetylate glucosamine or glucosamine phosphate.

References p. 22.

RÉSUMÉ

Les auteurs ont préparé et partiellement purifié, à partir de *Neurospora crassa*, un enzyme qui catalyse la formation de glucosamine phosphate à partir d'hexose-6-phosphate et de glutamine. Le glucosaminephosphate a été identifié par ses réaction colorées, par la déphosphorylation, par la chromatographie sur papier et par son comportement en présence d'un système acétylant.

L'analyse quantitative de l'azote amidé, du glutamate et de l'hexosamine est en accord avec l'équation suivante:

$$\text{Hexose-6-phosphate} + \text{glutamate} \longrightarrow \text{Glucosamine-6-phosphate} + \text{glutamate}$$

Les extraits bruts de *Neurospora* phosphorylent la glucosamine en présence d'ATP et écatylent la glucosamine et le glucosaminephosphate, quand on les supplémente convenablement.

ZUSAMMENFASSUNG

Ein teilweise gereinigtes Enzym, das die Bildung von Glucosaminphosphat aus Hexose-6-phosphat und Glutamin katalysiert, wurde aus *Neurospora crassa* dargestellt. Das Glucosaminphosphat wurde durch Farbreaktionen, Desphosphorylierung und Papierchromatographie und durch sein Verhalten gegenüber einem acetylierten System identifiziert.

Die quantitative Analyse von Amidstickstoff, glutaminsaurem Salz und Hexosamin stimmte mit der folgenden Gleichung überein:

$$\text{Hexose-6-phosphat} + \text{Glutamin} \longrightarrow \text{Glucosamin-6-phosphat} + \text{Glutaminsaures Salz}$$

Es wurde gefunden, dass rohe *Neurospora*-extrakte Glucosamin in Gegenwart von ATP phosphorylieren und, wenn sie geeignet ergänzt werden, Glucosamin oder Glucosaminphosphat acetylieren.

REFERENCES

[1] C. E. CARDINI, A. C. PALADINI, R. CAPUTTO AND L. F. LELOIR, *Nature*, 165 (1950) 191; R. CAPUTTO, L. F. LELOIR, C. E. CARDINI AND A. C. PALADINI, *J. Biol. Chem.*, 184 (1950) 333.
[2] E. CABIB, L. F. LELOIR AND C. E. CARDINI, *Ciencia e invest. (Buenos Aires)*, 8 (1952) 469; *J. Biol. Chem.* (in press).
[3] L. F. LELOIR, in *Phosphorus Metabolism, A Symposium on the Role of Phosphorus in the Metabolism of Plants and Animals*, Johns Hopkins Press; Baltimore, 1951, p. 67.
[4] H. KLENOW AND B. LARSEN, *Arch. Biochem. Biophys.*, 37 (1952) 488.
[5] R. P. HARPUR AND J. H. QUASTEL, *Nature*, 164 (1949) 693.
[6] D. H. BROWN, *Biochim. Biophys. Acta*, 7 (1951) 487.
[7] P. T. GRANT AND C. LONG, *Biochem. J.*, 50 (1952) xx.
[8] C. E. CARDINI AND L. F. LELOIR, unpublished results.
[9] Y. J. TOPPER AND M. M. LIPTON, *Federation Proc.*, 11 (1952) 299.
[10] G. BLIX, *Acta Chem. Scand.*, 2 (1948) 467.
[11] M. KUNITZ AND M. McDONALD, *J. Gen. Physiol.*, 29 (1945) 411.
[12] J. AWAPARA, *J. Biol. Chem.*, 178 (1949) 113.
[13] J. F. SPECK, *J. Biol. Chem.*, 179 (1949) 1387.
[14] E. J. CONWAY, *Micro-Diffusion Analysis and Volumetric Error*, Crosby Lockwood & Son Ltd., London, 1939.
[15] W. T. J. MORGAN AND L. A. ELSON, *Biochem. J.*, 28 (1934) 988.
[16] G. W. BEADLE AND E. L. TATUM, *Am. J. Botany*, 32 (1945) 678.
[17] N. O. KAPLAN AND F. LIPMANN, *J. Biol. Chem.*, 174 (1948) 37.
[18] J. H. ROE, *J. Biol. Chem.*, 107 (1934) 15.
[19] S. M. PARTRIDGE, *Biochem. J.* 42 (1948) 238.
[20] S. M. PARTRIDGE, *Nature*, 164 (1949) 443.
[21] Z. DISCHE AND E. BORENFREUND, *J. Biol. Chem.*, 184 (1950) 517.
[22] T. CHOU AND M. SOODAK, *J. Biol. Chem.*, 196 (1952) 105.

Received February 16th, 1953

CORRELATION BETWEEN PHOTOSYNTHESIS AND LIGHT-INDEPENDENT METABOLISM IN THE GROWTH OF *CHLORELLA**

by

H. TAMIYA, T. IWAMURA, K. SHIBATA, E. HASE AND T. NIHEI

The Tokugawa Institute for Biological Research, Tokyo (Japan)

The growth of green plants in general may be regarded as being composed of two main processes, the light-dependent process, photosynthesis, and the light-independent processes which involve an immense variety of biochemical and biophysical events by which the primary photosynthetic products are converted into cell materials. Despite the vast amount of work devoted to the analysis of specific reactions involved in the growth of plants, few attempts have been made to correlate quantitatively photosynthesis and the dark process as a whole. Obviously, this is due to the enormous complexity of the relationship between them, which is especially complicated in the higher plants which have highly differentiated structures and grow under conditions difficult to control experimentally.

The matter appears in a somewhat different light when we deal with the simplest form of green plant, such as *Chlorella*, which has been recognized as excellent experimental material for the study of photosynthesis ever since it was first used by WARBURG in his pioneer work in the field. Working with the culture of *Chlorella ellipsoidea*, we[1] have recently observed that the cells assume, in the course of their growth, two distinct forms possessing widely different characters. The form, which we named "dark cells", is much smaller in size, richer in chlorophyll, and more photosynthetically active than the other form called "light cells". The dark cells with their well-organized photosynthetic apparatus are strongly disposed toward photosynthesis, and, if provided with light and adequate nutrient substances, grow into the light cells which in turn, under adequate conditions, divide into a number of dark cells. This latter process occurs entirely independently of light, thus embodying the essential feature of the light-independent phase of growth mentioned above. The over-all growth process of the algae is accomplished by the repetition of the mutual change between these two kinds of cells, and it may be expressed most simply by the following formulae:

$$D \xrightarrow{\text{light}} L$$

$$L \xrightarrow{\text{dark}} nD$$

---

* This work was supported by grants from the Ministry of Education, the Ministry of International Trade and Industry, and the Mainichi Shimbun, Inc. A part of the theory described in this paper was worked out by the senior author during his stay in Stanford, California, as a guest investigator of Carnegie Institution of Washington. The writers' warm thanks are due to the members of the Institution for their interest and advice in the preparation of this paper.

References p. 40.

where D and L represent dark and light cells, respectively, and n the number of dark cells produced from one light cell. The two essential aspects of growth, the increase in mass and the increase in cell number, are succinctly represented by the two processes: the former process occurs in the light, and the latter in the dark.

The present work was carried out with a view to investigating more in detail the properties of the two kinds of cells, the nature of their interconversion, and the correlation of the two processes in the over-all phenomenon of algal growth under different conditions.

METHOD

Culture. Chlorella ellipsoidea was cultured in a flat flask shown in Fig. 1, using a medium which had the following composition unless otherwise stated for particular experiments; per liter of solution: 5.0 g KNO_3, 2.5 g $MgSO_4 \cdot 7H_2O$, 1.25 g KH_2PO_4, 0.003 g $FeSO_4 \cdot 7H_2O$, 1 ml each of ARNON's A5 and B6 solutions (2). (pH: 5.3–5.4).

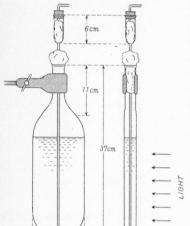

Fig. 1. Front and side views of the culture flask used.

The flask, which had a inner thickness of 2.8 cm and a total capacity of 600 ml, was filled with 500 ml of the medium, and after autoclaving and seeding with algae, the main body of the flask was immersed in a thermostated water bath having glass walls, and illuminated from outside of the thermostat in the direction perpendicular to the flat surface of the flask. During the culture, air containing 5% CO_2 was constantly bubbled through the cell suspension with a velocity of 200–300 ml per minute, by which the cells were kept evenly suspended in the medium. Before entering the culture flask, the CO_2-enriched air was saturated with water vapor at the same pressure as the culture medium by being scrubbed through the gas wash-bottles containing a solution having the same composition and temperature as the culture medium.

The illumination was furnished by a projector lamp or reflector flood lamp operated at 70–85 volts using a voltage stabilizer and variable transformer. The intensity of the light supplied was in the range between 140 and 50,000 lux (at the position of the flasks in the thermostat water), which was checked and regulated 2 or 3 times a day using a photometer having a submergible photo-receiver.

Measurement of growth. The growth of algae was followed by measuring both the packed cell volume in ml (V) and cell number (N) per liter of culture. In the alga used, the ratio between the packed cell volume (in ml) and the dry weight (in g) was on the average 1:0.256. This ratio varied only in a narrow range between 0.252 and 0.263 without showing any systematic change according to the ratio of dark and light cells.

Two kinds of experiments were performed: in one series, the *transitory phenomena* of formation of dark cells from light cells or *vice versa* were investigated; and in the other, the *steady state* of growth, *i.e.* the state in which the growth rate as well as the ratio of dark and light cells was constant during the course of growth. Such a steady state obtained only when the culture was kept longer than about 4 days under each specified set of conditions*.

Steady state experiments were performed with the following special precautions.

1. To assure the establishment of the steady state, the actual measurement of growth was begun only after a preliminary culture lasting 4–7 days under each condition.

---

* As has been described elsewhere[1], our alga shows, under certain experimental conditions, the peculiar phenomenon that, in the course of culture, the change of dark cells to light cells and *vice versa* occur almost in unison in all cells existing in the culture, and, interestingly enough, it takes place at a fairly definite interval of about 30 hours. Such a periodic "bursting division" occurred especially markedly when the inoculum was made from a rather old and starved culture and the culture was subjected suddenly to high light intensity. However, on continuing the culture for several days with frequent refreshment of medium, the phenomenon ceases to occur and the cells begin to grow and divide "individually", showing as a whole a definite ratio of dark and light cells in the culture.

References p. 40.

2. To make practically all cells in the culture receive directly the measured intensity of light, in other words, to avoid as much as possible the mutual shading of cells in the suspension, the population density of the culture was kept always below 0.1 ml packed cell volume per liter during the experiment*.

This was effected by diluting frequently** the culture with fresh medium, by which also the constancy of the nutrient medium during the culture could be assured.

The relative rate (k_g) of growth was calculated according to

$$k_g = \frac{1}{t_2 - t_1} \log_{10} \frac{V_2}{V_1}$$

where V_1 and V_2 are packed cell volume per liter at the times t_1 and t_2, respectively, measured in terms of days. At steady states of growth, the ratio V_2/V_1 is equal to the ratio of dry weights of cells (W_2/W_1) or of cell number (N_2/N_1).

Measurement of cell size and the ratio of dark and light cells. At each stage of culture, the diameter of algal cells was measured either by the projection method adopted by KETCHUM et al.[4] or by direct microscopic observation using a calibrated micrometer; the latter method was preferred in most cases because it gave sufficiently accurate results in a short time when conducted by a practiced observer. With each sample, the sizes of 200 to 300 individual cells were measured***, and by grouping the diameters into classes of 0.55 micron span, their distribution was represented by percentage frequency polygons (see, *e.g.*, Figs. 3 and 5). The dark and light cells were distinguished according as the cell diameter was shorter or longer than 4.5 microns, and to represent the size distribution of cells in quantitative terms, the ratio of the number of dark cells ([D]) to the total cell number (N) was calculated. This ratio ([D]/N) will be called "dark cell ratio" and denoted by Δ in the following.

Measurement of photosynthetic rate. The rates of photosynthesis and respiration were measured with the WARBURG-BARCROFT differential manometer with a rotary motion of vessels in a circle of 6–10 mm in diameter and at 250–300 r.p.m. The cells were suspended in 16 ml of $M/50$ phosphate buffer (potassium salt) of pH 5.4 containing per liter: 2.5 g $MgSO_4 \cdot 7H_2O$, 0.003 g $FeSO_4 \cdot 7H_2O$ and 1 ml each of ARNON's A5 and B6 solutions, and the gas space of the vessel was filled with air containing 5% CO_2. The cell suspension, 1.0 cm in thickness, was illuminated from below with the arrangement which was virtually the same as that employed by TAMIYA AND CHIBA[5]. To make the effect of mutual shading of cells negligible, the concentration of cell suspension was kept below 0.4 ml per liter (= 6.5 cmm cells per 16 ml of suspension). The rate of photosynthetic O_2-output was determined by taking into consideration the rate of respiration in the dark, the ratio CO_2/O_2 in both processes being regarded as unity.

To compare the rate of photosynthesis with that of growth (k_g) on a common basis, the former was expressed by the weight (in g) of organic photosynthate CHOH produced by 1 g dry weight of cells per day. The rate (k_p) expressed in this manner may be calculated from the ordinary expression of photosynthetic rate, *e.g.*, the O_2-output in mm^3 per mm^3 of cells per 10 minutes, by the following equation:

$$k_p = 0.327 \times (O_2\text{-output in cmm per cmm of cells per 10 minutes}).$$

Determination of some cell constituents. The chlorophyll content of algal cells was measured by the following procedure. The pigment was extracted from measured amounts of cells with cold methanol and treated with hydrochloric acid to give phaeophytin. The latter was transferred into benzene, which was thoroughly washed with water, and after removing the water layer, the benzene extract was further dehydrated with a small quantity of solid Na_2SO_4, then decanted and made up to a definite volume with further addition of benzene. The quantity of phaeophytin in this solution was determined spectrophotometrically at 666 mμ (1 mg phaeophytin corresponds to 1.026 mg of chlorophyll).

The phosphorus and nitrogen contents of cells were determined by ALLEN's method[6] and semi-micro-KJELDAHL method, respectively.

---

* Both by experiments and by statistical considerations it was ascertained that, under the condition of our experiments (thickness of culture solution: 2.8 cm; average diameter of cells: 3–5.5 microns), the light-diminishing effect of mutual shading of cells may practically be neglected when the population density of cell suspension is less than 0.1 ml packed cell volume per liter. (*Cf.* TAMIYA et al.[3]).

** The interval of refreshment of culture medium varied according to the rapidity of growth; it was 1/2 or 1 day at higher temperatures and stronger light intensities, and several days when both temperature and light intensity were low.

*** One of the characteristics of our algal strain is that it contains some elliptic cells with the ratio of axes of about 1:0.85 to 1:0.75. The percentage of elliptic cells is, however, about 10% in well illuminated culture and about 20% in weakly illuminated culture, the rest being almost perfectly spherical cells as it is the case with other *Chlorella* strains. For elliptic cells the mean of both axes was determined and the cells were regarded as spheres having diameters of that magnitude.

References p. 40.

RESULTS

Characteristics of dark cells and light cells

Stationary cultures grown under a moderate intensity of light usually show the dark cell ratio of 0.4 to 0.8, the value being, as a rule, higher in weakly illuminated cultures than in strongly illuminated ones. By fractional centrifugation of these cultures we can obtain cell suspensions which consist practically entirely of dark cells or light cells. In Fig. 2 are shown the microphotographs of the two kinds of cells in such suspensions.

Microscopic observation shows that the light cells may further be divided, according to the grade of ripening, into two categories, sporulated and non-sporulated, but they can hardly be separated by such a technique as fractional centrifugation. On the other

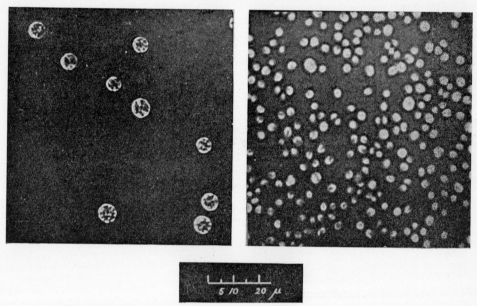

Fig. 2. Microphotographs of two types of cells at the same magnification.

hand, the dark cells, in so far as they are defined by their cell diameters less than 4.5 microns, appear under the microscope to be quite uniform in appearance. During the course of the present study, however, it was found that among dark cells there are also two distinct categories which can be obtained separately by a certain procedure.

The one category, which we call "nascent dark cells" in the following, consists of cells which represent the nascent state of dark cells derived from light cells. These cells can be obtained from light cells by incubating the latter in the dark while being well aerated. The other category, which we call "active dark cells", consists of dark cells derived from nascent dark cells by illuminating the latter for a few hours. Since the transformation in the light of the nascent dark cells into active dark cells takes place relatively rapidly, the dark cells contained in continuously illuminated cultures are mostly in the active form.

References p. 40.

Using the samples containing practically 100% of each type of cells, some of their physiological and chemical characteristics were compared*. The results obtained are summarized in Table I.

The following facts emerge from the data given in the table.

1. In respect to average cell size and respiratory activity, the order is: Light cells > Active dark cells > Nascent dark cells.

2. The photosynthetic rate (both under light-saturated and -limited conditions), and the contents of chlorophyll and nitrogen in cells increases in the order: Light cells < Nascent dark cells < Active dark cells.

TABLE I

CHARACTERISTICS OF DARK AND LIGHT CELLS

	Average cell diameter (μ)	Light-saturated photosynth. rate at 25° C	Light-limited photosynth. rate (α)*	Respiratory activity (Q_{O_2}) at 25° C	Chlorophyll content (%)	Nitrogen content (%)	Phosphorus content (%)
Dark { active	3.1–3.4	1.7–1.9	0.36–0.54	4.6–6.1	2.4–5.2	7.0–9.5	1.7–1.8
cells { nascent	2.3–2.5	1.0–1.6	0.23–0.29	2.9–4.6	0.9–2.0	5.5–7.0	1.8
Light cells	5.5–5.9	0.26–0.32	0.10–0.16	7.7–9.3	0.8–1.3	5.2–5.7	1.2–1.8

* The light-limited photosynthetic rate is expressed by $\alpha = (dk_p/dI)_{I \to 0}$ (in terms of 1/day-kilolux), where k_p is photosynthetic rate and I the light intensity.

3. Regarding phosphorus content, no significant difference is found among different kinds of cells.

Most remarkable was the difference in light-saturated photosynthetic rate between active dark cells and light cells, the activity of the former being about 6 times that of the latter. Significant also was the difference in light-limited photosynthetic rate and chlorophyll content, which was about 3.5 times higher in active dark cells than in light cells.

Transformation of dark cells into light cells

The process of transformation of dark cells into light cells, which takes place only in the light, was followed in detail using cell samples rich in active dark cells as starting material. In Figs. 3 and 4 are shown various aspects of the transformation which occurred when the cell suspension (in normal nutrient medium and provided with CO_2-enriched air), was illuminated with 2,000 lux light at 9°–10° C. The starting population, consisting of 90% dark cells, gradually changed its dark cell ratio and within 100 hours 90% of its population were transformed into light cells. During this period the cell number remained unchanged, while the packed cell volume and the average cell volume increased

* The effective way of collecting light cells is to take advantage of the occurrence of periodical "bursting division" which was mentioned in the footnote on p. 24. During the period of repeated "bursting divisions", there are stages in which almost 90% of the whole population are light cells. In separating these cells, adequate timing of harvesting and fractionation is necessary, because they will divide, sooner or later, bursting into dark cells. The division can be prevented by keeping the suspension in an ice box under anaerobic conditions (see later). Nascent dark cells can easily be obtained from light cells, by keeping the latter in the dark, for 2 or 3 days, under *aerobic condition*. There are two ways to obtain active dark cells: either subject the nascent dark cells to illumination for several hours, or collect the cells grown under weak light (about 150 lux or less) at relatively high temperatures such as 25° C.

References p. 40.

remarkably. At about the 100th hour, however, the light cells began to divide, which was reflected in a sudden increase in cell number and dark cell ratio as well as the decrease in average cell volume.

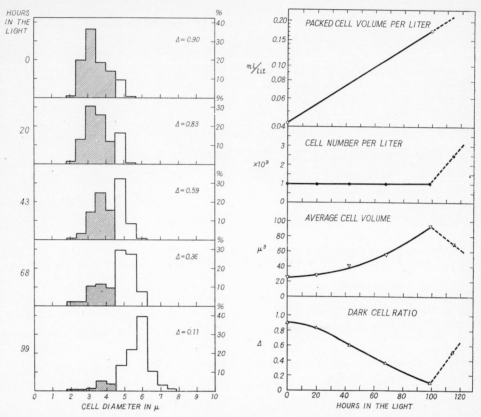

Fig. 3. Distribution polygons of cell diameter showing the transformation of active dark cells into light cells in the light. Shaded portions of polygons indicate dark cells. The starting material of dark-cell-rich culture was prepared by growing the alga at 25°, first under 10,000 lux light for 1 weak, then under 400 lux for 3 days.

Fig. 4. Change of packed cell volume, cell number, average cell volume and dark cell ratio during the transformation of dark cells into light cells. Measurements were made with the same material as that illustrated in Fig. 3.

The culture was placed in the dark for 1 day, before the cells were transferred into fresh medium for the main experiment. Main experiment was conducted at 9°–10° C, with 2000 lux light, under provision of CO_2-enriched air.

From other experiments, which we shall not reproduce here to save space, it was found that the transformation of dark cells into light cells in the light, at least within first 20 hours of illumination, was not affected markedly by the deprival of nitrogen or phosphorus or of whole nutrient salts from the culture medium. But later the transformation was more or less markedly affected by nutrient deficiency; in distilled water and in P-deficient medium it was halted completely at a certain stage, and in N-deficient medium it was increasingly retarded with the progress of incubation. It was also revealed that, during the course of transformation, the chlorophyll content of cells decreased, whereas the total amount of chlorophyll in the culture[*] increased in normal medium, but not in P- or N-free medium and in distilled water.

***

[*] Calculated from the chlorophyll content of cells and the packed volume of cells contained in the suspension.

References p. 40.

During the course of transformation in normal medium, the packed cell volume of the suspension increased (in terms of k_g) at first rapidly and later more slowly. The initial velocity of increase of packed cell volume corresponds to that of photosynthesis; for example, a suspension which contained 2.55 ml per liter of active dark cells ($\Delta = 0.90$), increased its packed cell volume up to 6.16 ml per liter within the first 6 hours of illumination with 20,000 lux light at 25° C, during which time the cell number remained unchanged. This increase corresponds to the relative growth rate of $k_g = 1.53$, which is almost equal to the rate of photosynthesis ($k_p = 1.81$) shown by active dark cells under the same condition.

The data presented above show clearly that photosynthesis forms the key event occurring in the transformation of dark cells into light cells. It must, however, be noted that the process—especially at its later stages—involves also other metabolic processes, which is evidenced by the effect of N- and P-deprivation[*] as well as the formation of chlorophyll during the process in normal medium.

Transformation of light cells into dark cells

While the dark cells remain unchanged when they are not illuminated, the light cells are rather labile and under ordinary conditions, regardless of whether they are in the light or in the dark, they change sooner or later into dark cells. Using a suspension of light cells it was found that the light (at least up to the intensity of 20,000 lux) does not exert any influence upon the process of their transformation into dark cells. In Figs. 5 and 6 is shown the process of transformation taking place in the dark. The light cells which formed 85% of the total population at the beginning gradually decreased to give rise to dark cells, and within about 50 hours more than 90% of the whole population had turned into dark cells. Noteworthy is the fact that the transformation occurred only under aerobic conditions[**] and was completely halted when the cell suspension was deprived of oxygen[***]. (See Fig. 6.)

It is apparent from the figure that, while the cell number and the dark cell ratio had increased during the process, the packed cell volume remained almost unchanged or, actually, slightly decreased, which may be attributed to the consumption of cell materials by respiration. From the data given in the figure, and other data not presented here, it was found that the number of dark cells produced by the division of one light cell was between 6 and 7. This fact indicates that the actual number of n in the process $L \longrightarrow nD$ is 4 or 8 in most cases[†]. By comparing the frequency polygons given in Fig. 5 with those in Fig. 3 it will be noticed that the dark cells derived from light cells *in the dark* were smaller in size than those taken from continuously illuminated cultures. The former are what we call *nascent* dark cells and the latter the *active* dark cells.

In the experiment given in Figs. 5 and 6, the cells were suspended in normal culture medium. It was found in other experiments that the transformation (under aerobic conditions) was not markedly affected by deprival of phosphate from the medium, but was considerably retarded, although eventually proceeded to completion, on deprival of nitrate, and was most strongly suppressed in distilled water. The dark cells produced in distilled water or in N-deficient medium showed a

---

[*] Photosynthesis, in the ordinary sense, can proceed for an appreciable length of time without provision of any nutrient substances. It was ascertained that the dark cells can photosynthesize in distilled water at a rate of 90–95% of normal rate (observed in ordinary phosphate buffer), and this activity lasted more than two hours without showing any sign of decrease.

[**] It was confirmed by other experiments that the provision of CO_2 is not necessary for provoking the transformation.

[***] The light cells which had been subjected to anaerobiosis for 67 hours showed quite normal growth when supplied with CO_2-air and light, indicating that they had remained intact during the anaerobiosis.

[†] This was borne out by microscopic observation of a large number of cells in the dividing state.

References p. 40.

considerably weaker photosynthetic activity and lower chlorophyll content than the normal nascent dark cells. It is evident that the transformation of light cells into dark cells involves, although not manifested as a substantial increase *in mass*, an important anabolic and formative metabolism coupled with the energy yielding aerobic metabolism, in which not only the endogenous substances, but also certain inorganic materials taken from the circumambient solution are used as building blocks.

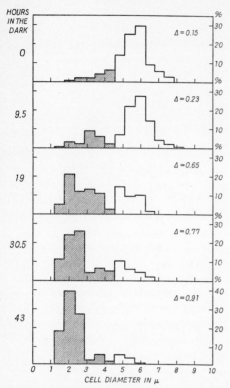

Fig. 5. Distribution polygons of cell diameter showing the transformation of light cells into nascent dark cells in the dark. The starting material was prepared from a dark-cell-rich culture ($\Delta = 0.99$) which was illuminated with 2000 lux light at 9°–10° C for 7 days. The resulting light-cell-rich culture ($\Delta = 0.15$) was resuspended in normal culture medium, and the main experiment was conducted in the dark at 15° C with provision of CO_2-enriched air.

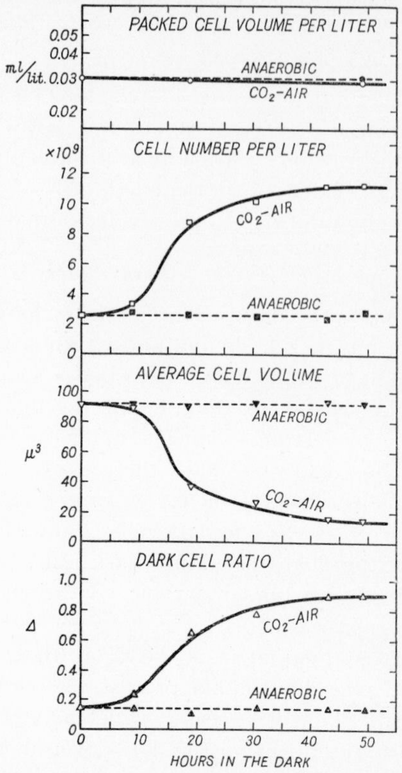

Fig. 6. Change of packed cell volume, cell number, average cell volume and dark cell ratio during the transformation of light cells into dark cells under aerobic and anaerobic conditions. The data of the aerobic experiment are the same as those shown in Fig. 5. The anaerobic experiment was performed by evacuating the cell suspension in THUNBERG's tubes; otherwise the condition was the same as in control experiment.

Some aspect of such constructive events occurring in the process was studiedin the experiment reproduced in Fig. 7. In this experiment the contents of chlorophyll and phosphorus in cells were followed during the transformation occurring in normal medium and in the dark. As may be seen, the chlorophyll content in cells as well as the total amount of chlorophyll in the culture increased appreciably during the dark process[*]. On the other hand, both the phosphorus content in cells and the total amount of assimilated phosphorus in the culture remained unchanged during the process, indicating that the anabolic metabolism of phosphorous compounds had been accomplished using the phosphorus which had pre-existed in light cells.

At the 53th hour of the dark experiment, when the transformation of light cells into *nascent* dark cells seemed to have completed, the suspension was suddenly subjected to illumination (20,000

---

[*] It has been known that *Chlorella* can synthesize chlorophyll in the dark when it is grown heterotrophically with provision of sugar as carbon source.

References p. 40.

lux). Within the first several hours of illumination, there occurred a slight increase of cell volume and a sudden increase in chlorophyll content of cells, while the cell number remained unchanged. The resulting cells had the typical characteristics of *active* dark cells which are encountered in ordinary (continuously illuminated) cultures. This state, however, did not last long on continued illumination, because the active dark cells further turned into light cells, which is evidenced by the decrease in dark-cell ratio as well as in chlorophyll content of cells. It is worth noticing that both the total amount of chlorophyll and assimilated phosphorus in the culture suddenly increased on illumination. This may suggest two possibilities; either the anabolic metabolism has been accelerated considerably by abundant supply of photosynthate, or the anabolic metabolism might have involved some photochemical process other than photosynthesis in the ordinary sense.

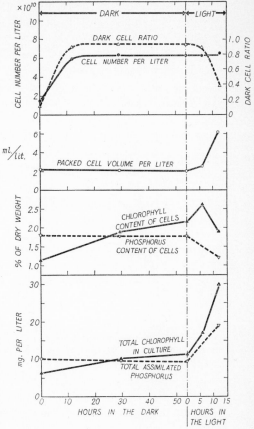

Fig. 7. Increase in chlorophyll content (and apparent constancy of phosphorus content) of cells during the transformation of light cells into dark cells in the dark. The starting material was prepared from a dark-cell-rich culture ($\Delta = 0.99$) which was illuminated with 22,000 lux at 14° C for 55 hours. The resulting light-cell-rich culture ($\Delta = 0.11$) was resuspended in normal medium, and the main experiment was conducted at 25° C, with provision of CO_2-enriched air, first in the dark for 53 hours, and then in the light (20,000 lux) for 12 hours.

The rate of growth in steady state as compared with photosynthetic rate at different temperatures and under different light intensities

Effects of temperature and the light intensity upon the steady-state rate of growth were investigated with the special precautions described already. In parallel, the photosynthetic rate as it is affected by the same environmental factors were determined using exclusively active dark cells as material.[*]

The conditions applied in both series of experiments were the same except for the point that the medium used in the photosynthetic measurements was deprived of nitrogen in order to prevent the occurrence of growth during the measurement. The temperatures investigated were 7°, 15° and 25° C.

The results of a large number of measurements are summarized in Fig. 8, in which the growth rate (k_g) and photosynthetic rate (k_p) are plotted, on a common scale, against the light intensity. Each value presented is the average of several measurements. These results lead us to the following conclusions:

1. As far as the shape of the curves is concerned, the rate-light intensity relationships at different temperatures are fundamentally the same for photosynthesis and

---

[*] In all photosynthetic measurements, cell samples showing the dark cell ratio of 0.95 to 1.00 were used.

References p. 40.

2

growth; namely, at lower light intensities there exists a linear relationship between the rate and light intensity, while at higher light intensities the rate becomes independent of light intensity.

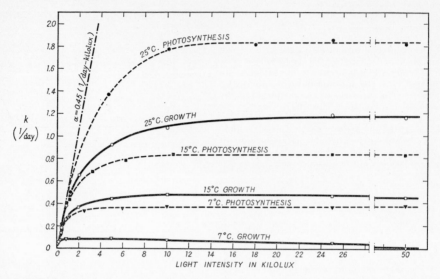

Fig. 8. Relative rates of growth and photosynthesis as a function of light intensity at different temperatures. Photosynthetic rate was measured with active dark cells and expressed in terms of g organic photosynthate formed by 1 g dry weight of cells per day, so that it is directly comparable with the growth rate defined by: $k_g = 1/\Delta t \times \log_{10}(W_2/W_1)$, where t is the time in days, and W the dry weight of cells in unit volume of culture.

2. In both photosynthesis and growth, the light-saturated rate is temperature-dependent, while the light-limited rate a, *i.e.*, the tangent of the rate-light intensity curve at sufficiently low light intensity, is temperature-independent.

3. The value of a is quite the same for photosynthesis and growth.

4. At saturating light intensity, the growth rate is always lower than the photosynthetic rate. The temperature dependency of the former is more conspicuous than that of the latter.

It ought to be remarked that the growth rate tended to be lowered at extremely high light intensities, which was especially notable at lower temperatures. Such a tendency was not observed in photosynthesis, at least up to the light intensity of 50,000 lux in the experiments lasting for 3 hours. At 7° C, the growth was retarded even when the light intensity was about 10,000 lux, and at 50,000 lux the cells completely ceased to grow within a few days, with a symptom of complete bleaching of cells. The tendency of color-fading of cells was observed, though to a minor extent, also at higher temperatures. In all cases, the cell suspensions grown under weaker light were dark green in color, and with the increase of light intensity the color changed into light green and then into brownish pale green. It is interesting to note that the occurrence of such a fading in color was dependent on temperature; for example, the light intensity under which the light green cells were formed increased with temperature as follows: 2000 lux at 7°, 25,000 lux at 15° and 50,000 lux at 25° C.

It was found that these color changes, except for the extreme case observed at 7°, reflect the change of relative abundance of dark and light cells in the culture. In Fig. 9 are shown the dark cell ratios (Δ) found in the steady state of growth under different conditions.

References p. 40.

At each temperature, the Δ-value decreased with increase of light intensity, and except in the culture at 7°, it tapered off gradually to a certain constant value at higher light intensities. At 7° the Δ-value decreased up to 800–2000 lux and then increased in a peculiar manner with further increase of light intensity, which is obviously due to the injurious effect of stronger light at that temperature. The minimum value of Δ attained at higher light intensities was larger at higher temperatures than at lower ones, and, what is worth noticing, the light intensity at which Δ attained its minimum value approximately coincided with the light intensity at which the growth rates reached their light-saturated values. To illustrate visually the relative abundance of dark and light cells in the culture under different conditions, the frequency polygons of cell diameter found in some representative cases are presented in Fig. 10.

The main quantitative data brought out by the experiments described above are summarized in Table II.

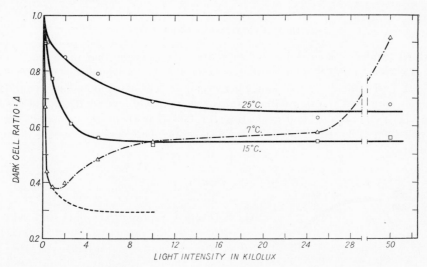

Fig. 9. Dark cell ratio of cultures at different temperatures and under different light intensities. The values given are the means of several readings obtained during the culture. The curve for 7°-culture bent in a peculiar manner at higher light intensities, which is obviously due to the injurious effect of strong light at that temperature. If there were no such effect, the curve might have followed the course as represented by the dashed line.

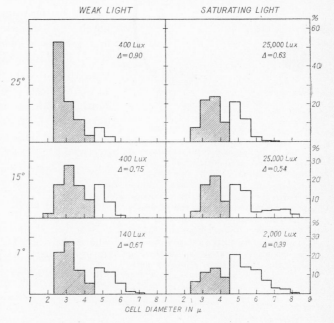

Fig. 10. Size distribution of cells grown under limiting and saturating lights at different temperatures. The polygons represent the mean values of several distribution data obtained during the steady states of growth.

References p. 40.

TABLE II

MAIN QUANTITATIVE DATA REGARDING THE EFFECT OF LIGHT AND TEMPERATURE UPON THE RATES OF
PHOTOSYNTHESIS AND GROWTH AS WELL AS THE DARK CELL RATIO IN THE CULTURE

Temperature (C)	Light-limited rate: a (1/day-kilolux)		Light-saturated rate (1/day)		Half-saturating light intensity (lux)		Dark cell ratio (Δ) at saturating light intensity
	Photosynthesis	Growth	Photosynthesis	Growth	Photosynthesis	Growth	
25°			1.79	1.19	2400	1600	0.66
15°		0.45	0.86	0.49	1200	600	0.55
7°			0.40	0.09	500	110	0.38

THEORETICAL CONSIDERATIONS

All the evidence described above supports the conclusion that the growth process —increase in cell number and in total mass—of *Chlorella* is accomplished by a repetition of the "life cycle" involving the change between dark cells (nascent and active) and light cells (non-sporulated and sporulated) as it is schematically represented by the diagram in Fig. 11. Symbolically, and neglecting the fact that there are two kinds each of dark and light cells, the process may most simply be expressed by the following formulae:

$$D \xrightarrow{k_L} L \qquad (1)$$

$$L \xrightarrow{k_D} nD \qquad (2)$$

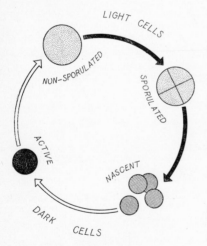

where D and L represent the dark and light cells respectively, k_L the rate constant of the *increase of cell mass* in the formation of light cells from dark cells, and k_D the rate constant of the *increase in cell number* in the transformation of a light cell into a number (*n*) of dark cells. Since the key part of the first process is photosynthesis and the photosynthetic activity of dark cells is several times stronger than that of light cells, it is not unreasonable to substitute for k_L in the above formula the photosynthetic rate k_p which we have determined with dark cells[*]. Then, the rates of change in the number of light and dark cells in processes (1) and (2) are expressed by

$$\frac{d[L]}{dt} = \frac{1}{n-1}(k_p[D] - k_D[L]) \qquad (3)$$

$$\frac{d[D]}{dt} = \frac{1}{n-1}(nk_D[L] - k_p[D]) \qquad (4)$$

Fig. 11. Schematic representation of the mutual transformation between light and dark cells in the life cycle of growing *Chlorella* cells. White arrows indicate the light processes, while black arrows show the processes that can occur both in the light and in the dark. Sizes of circles correspond approximately to the relative sizes of cells and the extent of darkening indicates the relative photosynthetic activity.

where [L] and [D] are the numbers of light and dark cells, respectively, in unit volume of culture[**]. The total number (*N*) of cells in unit volume of

---

[*] and [**] See the footnotes on page 35.

culture is $N = [L] + [D]$. In steady state of growth, the ratio $[D]/[L]$ is constant, and the relative growth rate (k_g) assumes the same value whether it is calculated in terms of increase of cell number (N) or packed cell volume (V) or dry weight of cells (W) per unit volume of culture, namely

$$k_g = \frac{1}{N}\frac{dN}{dt} = \frac{1}{V}\frac{dV}{dt} = \frac{1}{W}\frac{dW}{dt} \tag{5}$$

The solution of differential equations (3) and (4), with due considerations of above mentioned relations, leads to the following expression for the relative rate of growth in steady state:

$$k_g = \frac{1}{2(n-1)}\left\{\sqrt{(k_p - k_D)^2 + 4nk_pk_D} - (k_p + k_D)\right\}$$

This expression is too complicated to be used for practical purposes, but if we restrict our considerations to the cases in which k_p is sufficiently small or sufficiently large compared with k_D, then it may be replaced by the simpler form:

$$k_g = \frac{k_pk_D}{k_p + k_D} \tag{6}$$

As is well known, the photosynthetic rate as a function of light intensity (I) may most simply, though rather approximately, be expressed by an equation of a rectangular hyperbola, namely

$$k_p = \frac{ak_pI}{k_p + aI} \tag{7}$$

---

* Strictly speaking, this substitution postulates some modification in our concept of light cells and of the dark process. As we have shown, the rate of growth of dark cells in process (1) was equal to k_p only at the earlier stages of the process, and it decreased gradually owing to the decrease of photosynthetic activity accompanying the enlargement of cells. If we denote the rate constant corresponding to k_p by k_L, and the smaller rate constant corresponding to the decreased photosynthetic activity at later stages by k'_L, then the course of events occurring in the whole process may be expressed symbolically by

$$\left.\begin{array}{l} D \xrightarrow{k_L} L' \\ L' \xrightarrow{k'_L} L \xrightarrow{k_D} nD \end{array}\right\} \tag{i}$$

where L' is a cell which is larger than dark cell but smaller than the light cell according to our definition. From the kinetic point of view, the above process may be described as

$$\left.\begin{array}{l} D \xrightarrow{k_L} L' \\ L' \xrightarrow{k'_D} nD \end{array}\right\} \tag{ii}$$

where k'_D is the rate constant of the reaction step which involves a certain photosynthetic process, though consisting mainly of dark processes. In a strict sense, the whole theory developed in the following should be construed as dealing with the kinetic picture represented by formula (ii).

** If the rate constants of processes (1) and (2) are expressed in terms of the *number of cells undergoing the transformations*, these constants (denoted by k_1 and k_d, respectively) are related to k_L and k_D in the following manner:

$$k_1 = k_L/(n-1); \qquad k_d = k_D/(n-1)$$

Explanation: Denoting the weight of a single dark cell by w, the rate of increase (in weight) of organic substance (W) in process (1) is given by $dW/dt = k_Lw[D]$. Since the weight of a light cell is n-times that of a dark cell, the net increase in weight occurring in the formation of a light cell from a dark cell is $(n-1)w$. Therefore, we may also write: $dW/dt = (n-1)k_1w[D]$. Comparing this equation with the above one, we have: $k_L = (n-1)k_1$.

On the other hand, the rate of increase in cell number in process (2) is given by $dN/dt = k_D[L]$, where $N = [L] + [D]$. Using k_d we may write the relations: $d[D]/dt = nk_d[L]$, $-d[L]/dt = k_d[L]$; therefore, $dN/dt = (n-1)k_d[L]$, which, compared with the above equation, shows that $k_D = (n-1)k_d$.

References p. 40.

where k_P is the light-saturated value of k_p and α is a constant which corresponds to the value of dk_p/dI at $I \to 0$. Substituting (7) in (6), we have

$$k_g = \frac{\alpha k_P k_D I}{k_P k_D + \alpha(k_P + k_D)I} \tag{8}$$

or

$$k_g = \frac{\alpha k_G I}{k_G + \alpha I} \tag{9}$$

where k_G is the light-saturated rate of growth, namely

$$k_G = \frac{k_P k_D}{k_P + k_D} \tag{10}$$

The rate constant (k_D) of the dark process is given by

$$k_D = \frac{k_P k_G}{k_P - k_G} \tag{11}$$

Eqs. (8) and (9), which are the counterpart of Eq. (7) for photosynthesis, show that

$$\left(\frac{dk_g}{dI}\right)_{I \to 0} = \alpha \tag{12}$$

indicating, in agreement with our observation, that the light-limited rate of growth is the same as that of photosynthesis. If the half-saturating light intensities for photosynthesis and growth are denoted by μ_p and μ_g, respectively, we have from (7), (8) and (9),

$$\mu_p = \frac{k_P}{\alpha} \quad \text{and} \quad \mu_g = \frac{k_P k_D}{\alpha(k_P + k_D)} = \frac{k_G}{\alpha} \tag{13}$$

From Eqs. (3) and (4) we can derive the relation

$$\frac{dN}{dt} = k_D \left\{ N - [D] \right\} \quad \text{or} \quad \frac{dN}{dt} = k_D N(1 - \varDelta)$$

Therefore,

$$k_g = \frac{1}{N} \frac{dN}{dt} = k_D(1 - \varDelta) \tag{14}*$$

and

$$\varDelta = \frac{k_D - k_g}{k_D} = \frac{\alpha k_D I + k_P k_D}{k_P k_D + \alpha(k_P + k_D)I} \tag{15}$$

This equation shows that, in conformity with our observations, the dark cell ratio is unity when $I = 0$, and decreases with the increase of I till it attains, at sufficiently high light intensity, a final value $(\varDelta_s)$ which is given by

$$\varDelta_s = \frac{k_D}{k_P + k_D} = \frac{k_G}{k_P} \tag{16}$$

---

* This equation shows that, at a given temperature, we can estimate k_g from $\varDelta$ and *vice versa*, if the value of k_D at that temperature is known. Provided that the cellular characteristics of dark and light cells are known, the value $\varDelta$ also allows us to gauge the properties of the whole algal population in a given culture.

References p. 40.

It also follows from Eq. (15) that the light intensity at which $1 - \Delta$ becomes a half of

$1 - \Delta_s$ is $\dfrac{k_P k_D}{a(k_P + k_D)}$, a value which is equal to the half-saturating light intensities for

growth rate (Eq. 13). This deduction is also corroborated by our experiment.

It should be remarked that all the k-values used in the above theory are those referred to the natural logarithms (see Eq. 5), whereas in our experiments they have been expressed in terms of BRIGGsian logarithms. However, the equations (6) to (16) may all be applied as such to our experimental values.

By applying the experimental values of k_P (0.40 at 7°, 0.86 at 15°, and 1.79 at 25°) and a(0.45) to Eq. (8), the value of k_D was estimated to be 0.12 at 7°, 1.32 at 15° and 5.38 at 25° C. Fig. 12 shows to what extent the value of k_g calculated by Eq. (8) with these

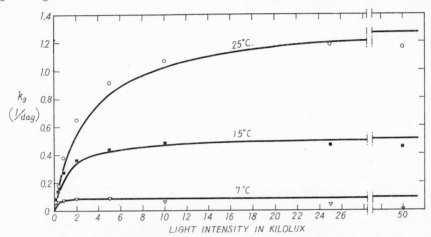

Fig. 12. Comparison of the calculated and observed values of relative growth rate (k_g) at different temperatures and under different light intensities.

values of k_P, k_D and a coincides with the experimental data.[*] By applying the same values of k_P, k_D and a in Eqs. (10), (13) and (16), the values of k_G, μ_p, μ_g and Δ_s were calculated and they are compared with observed values in Table III.

As may be seen, the agreement between calculated and observed values is fairly good for k_G, but not quite satisfactory for μ_p, μ_g and Δ_s. The discrepancy regarding the μ-values is attributable to the fact that both Eqs. (6) and (7) are simplified to fit only with cases of sufficiently high or sufficiently low light intensities. As to the discrepancy concerning Δ_s, it is probably due to the situation we have mentioned in the footnote on page 35.

TABLE III

CALCULATED AND OBSERVED VALUES OF k_G, μ_p, μ_g AND Δ_s

Temperature (C)	k_G		μ_p (in lux)		μ_g (in lux)		Δ_s	
	obs.	cal.	obs.	cal.	obs.	cal.	obs.	cal.
25°	1.19	1.34	2400	3980	1600	2980	0.66	0.75
15°	0.49	0.52	1200	1910	600	1160	0.55	0.61
7°	0.09	0.09	500	890	110	200	0.38	0.23

[*] The phenomenon of growth retardation at very high light intensities, which was especially notable at lower temperatures, was not taken into consideration in our theory.

References p. 40.

An interesting fact is revealed when we compare the temperature dependency of k_P, k_D and k_G. In Fig. 13 are plotted the logarithms of these values against the reciprocals of absolute temperature. At $25°$, k_D is about 3 times larger than k_P, which indicates that, at that temperature, the (light-saturated) growth rate (k_G) is largely determined by the process of photosynthesis. At $7°$, on the contrary, k_D is less than $1/3$ of k_P; therefore, the dark reaction represents the main rate-determining step in the over-all growth process. At $15°$ the (light saturated) growth rate is almost equally dependent upon the rates of photosynthesis and the dark reaction. In Fig. 13 are given the magnitudes of the apparent activation energy (in kcal.) of each process, calculated from the inclination of the curves in each temperature range. Of great interest is the remarkable temperature dependency of the dark process, and especially that at lower temperature, which corresponds to an apparent activation energy of as much as 49 kcal.

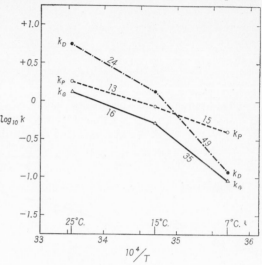

Fig. 13. Temperature dependency of the rate of the dark process and the light-saturated rates of growth and photosynthesis. The figures given on the curves indicate the apparent activation energies in kcal. calculated from the inclination of curves at the respective temperature spans.

The physico-chemical implication as well as the physiological significance of this remarkable phenomenon is indeed a problem which is worth while to be studied in the future.

SUMMARY

1. Observations on the culture of *Chlorella* have revealed that the algal cells assume two distinct forms in the course of their growth. One form, which we called "dark cells", is smaller in size, richer in chlorophyll content, and stronger in photosynthetic activity than the other, which we referred to as "light cells". When illuminated, dark cells grow and, with a substantial increase in mass, turn into light cells; the latter, when ripened, bear autospores in themselves (on the average 6–7 per cell) and eventually burst setting free the autospores which then become individual dark cells. The transformation of light cells into dark cells involves no increase of cell mass and occurs only under aerobic conditions, irrespective of whether the cells are in the light or in the dark. The dark cells freshly born from light cells are somewhat smaller in size and contain less chlorophyll than the "active" dark cells, into which the former turn rapidly under the influence of light.

2. The processes of transformation between these types of cells were investigated separately under various experimental conditions, and it was concluded that (i) the main event occurring in the transformation of dark cells into light cells is photosynthesis, although it is accompanied by some other metabolic processes, which are to be distinguished from the photosynthetic process in the ordinary sense; and that (ii) the transformation of light cells into dark cells involves a light-independent and aerobically endergonic anabolic metabolism, although, when illuminated, the transformation is accompanied also by some photosynthetic processes.

3. The steady state of growth, as it is affected by light intensity and temperature, was investigated in detail, and its rate was compared with the photosynthetic rate using a common unit of measurement, *i.e.*, in terms of weight of organic matter synthesized per unit time and per unit weight of cells.

References p. 40.

It was found that under weak light the rate of growth is exclusively determined by the photosynthetic process, whereas under strong light the light-independent metabolic processes become more or less significant in determining the rate of over-all growth. It was observed that the relative abundance of dark and light cells in the cultures varies considerably according to the culture condition, and indeed that the proportion of dark cells becomes larger in weaker light and at higher temperatures.

4. Based on the experimental evidence mentioned above, the following formulae were set forth to describe symbolically the course of events occurring in the growth of algae.

$$D \xrightarrow[k_p]{\text{light}} L \qquad\qquad L \xrightarrow[k_D]{\text{dark}} nD$$

where D and L represent dark and light cells, respectively, k_p the rate constant of photosynthesis, by which dark cells are changed into light cells, k_D the rate constant of increase in cell number in the dark process, and n the number of dark cells arising from one light cell. Steady state kinetics based on this scheme lead to the formulae representing the over-all growth rate and the relative abundance of dark and light cells in the culture as functions of (i) light intensity, (ii) the rate of dark process, and (iii) the light-saturated and light-limited rates of photosynthesis. Correspondence between the theory and the observations was found to be, by and large, satisfactory.

5. It was revealed by this analytical study that the dark process involved in the algal growth has a remarkably large temperature coefficient, especially in the range of lower temperatures.

RÉSUMÉ

1. L'observation de cultures de *Chlorella* montre que les cellules de l'algue se présentent sous deux formes distincts au cours de la croissance. L'une, appelée cellules "dark" est plus petite, plus riche en chlorophylle et présente une photosynthèse plus active que l'autre, appelée cellules "light". Les cellules "dark", quand on les éclaire, croissent et, avec une cette augmentation de masse, deviennent des cellules "light"; ces dernières, quand elles sont mûres, renferment des autospores (en moyenne 6 à 7 par cellule), qu'elles peuvent libérer en éclatant. Chaque autospore devient alors une cellule "dark". Le passage des cellules "light" aux cellules "dark" n'entraîne pas d'augmentation de la masse des cellules et a lieu seulement en aérobiose, que les cellules soient à la lumière ou à l'obscurité. Les cellules "dark", à leur naissance, sont un peu plus petites et contiennent moins de chlorophylle que les cellules "dark" "actives". Le passage à la forme active s'opère rapidement sous l'influence de la lumière.

2. Les phénomènes qui accompagnent le passage d'un type de cellules à l'autre ont été étudiés dans diverses conditions expérimentales, et l'on peut conclure que: (i) ce qui caractérise la transformation des cellules "dark" en cellules "light" est avant tout une photosynthèse, quoique quelques autres phénomènes métaboliques aient lieu, qui n'appartiennent pas à la photosynthèse au sens habituel; (ii) la transformation des cellules "light" en cellules "dark" met en jeu un anabolisme endergonique aérobie, indépendant de la lumière, quoique, si on éclaire, elle s'accompagne d'une certaine photosynthèse.

3. La marche de la croissance en période végétative a été étudiée en détail en fonction de l'intensité de la lumière et de la température et sa vitesse comparée à celle de la photosynthèse à l'aide d'une même unité de mesure: le poids de matière organique synthétisé par unité de temps et par unité de poids de cellules. Sous faible lumière, la vitesse de la croissance est exclusivement déterminée par la photosynthèse, tandis que sous éclairage intense, les réactions du métabolisme indépendantes de la lumière jouent un rôle plus ou moins important. Les proportions des cellules "dark" et "light" varient considérablement en fonction des conditions de culture et, en particulier, les cellules "dark" sont plus fréquentes sous faible éclairage et à température élevée.

4. Les résultats expérimentaux décrits plus hauts conduisent aux formules suivantes qui symbolisent la marche de la croissance des algues:

$$D \xrightarrow[k_p]{\text{lumière}} L \qquad\qquad L \xrightarrow[k_D]{\text{obscurité}} nD$$

D et L représentent respectivement les cellules "dark" et "light", k_p la constante de vitesse de la photosynthèse par laquelle les cellules "dark" sont transformées en cellules "light"; k_D la constante de vitesse de l'accroissement du nombre de cellules à l'obscurité; n étant le nombre de cellules "dark" qui naissent d'une cellule "light". La cinétique de l'état végétatif fondée sur ce schéma, conduit à des formules qui donnent la vitesse de croissance globale et les proportions relatives de cellules "dark" et "light" dans les cultures en fonction de (i) l'intensité de la lumière (ii) la vitesse de la réaction obscure et (iii) les vitesses de photosynthèse en lumière saturante et au seuil d'éclairement.

5. Cette étude analytique montre que la phase obscure de la croissance des algues a un coefficient de température remarquablement élevé, particulièrement aux basses températures.

References p. 40.

ZUSAMMENFASSUNG

1. Beobachtungen an *Chlorella*kulturen zeigten, dass die Algenzellen zwei verschiedene Formen im Laufe ihres Wachstums annehmen. Eine Form, die wir "dunkle Zellen" nannten, hat eine geringere Grösse, grösseren Chlorophyllgehalt und eine stärkere photosynthetische Aktivität als die andere, die wir als "helle Zellen" bezeichneten. Bei Beleuchtung wachsen die dunklen Zellen und verwandeln sich unter wesentlicher Massenzunahme in helle Zellen. Wenn die letzteren reif sind, tragen sie Autosporen (im Durchschnitt 6–7 pro Zelle) und platzen schliesslich unter Freisetzung der Autosporen, welche dann dunkle Einzelzellen werden. Die Umwandlung von hellen Zellen in dunkle Zellen geht nicht mit einer Zunahme an Masse einher und vollzieht sich nur unter aerobischen Bedingungen, gleichgültig ob die Zellen sich im Hellen oder im Dunklen befinden. Die aus den hellen Zellen neu erstandenen dunklen Zellen haben eine etwas geringere Grösse und enthalten weniger Chlorophyll als die "aktiven" dunklen Zellen, in welche die ersteren sich rasch unter dem Einfluss von Licht umwandeln.

2. Der Prozess der Umwandlung dieser beiden Zelltypen wurde getrennt unter verschiedenen experimentellen Bedingungen untersucht und es wurde daraus geschlossen, dass (i) die Photosynthese, obwohl sie von anderen Stoffwechselvorgängen begleitet ist, von denen der photosynthetische Prozess im gewöhnlichen Sinn unterschieden werden muss, das Hauptereignis bei der Umwandlung von dunklen Zellen in helle Zellen ist, und dass (ii) die Umwandlung von hellen Zellen in dunkle Zellen einen lichtunabhängigen und aerobisch verlaufend anabolischen Stoffwechselvorgang enthält, obgleich bei Beleuchtung die Umwandlung ebenfalls von einigen photosynthetischen Prozessen begleitet ist.

3. Der stationäre Wachstumszustand und seine Beeinflussung durch die Lichtintensität und die Temperatur wurde eingehend untersucht und seine Geschwindigkeit wurde mit der Geschwindigkeit der Photosynthese verglichen, unter Benutzung einer gemeinsamen Masseinheit, nämlich des Gewichts der pro Zeiteinheit und Gewichtseinheit der Zelle synthetisierten organischen Substanz. Es wurde gefunden, dass bei schwachem Licht die Wachstumsgeschwindigkeit ausschliesslich durch den photosynthetischen Vorgang bestimmt wird, während bei starkem Licht die lichtunabhängigen Stoffwechselvorgänge mehr oder weniger bedeutend werden bei der Bestimmung der allgemeinen Geschwindigkeit. Es wurde beobachtet, dass die relative Menge der dunklen und hellen Zellen in der Kultur beträchtlich je nach den Kulturbedingungen schwankt und dass in der Tat der Anteil der dunklen Zellen bei schwachem Licht und hohen Temperaturen grösser wird.

4. Gegründet auf den oben erwähnten experimentellen Beweis wurden die folgenden Formeln gegeben, um den Verlauf der während des Wachstums der Algen vor sich gehenden Ereignisse symbolisch zu beschreiben,

$$D \xrightarrow[\ k_p\ ]{\text{Licht}} L \qquad\qquad L \xrightarrow[\ k_D\ ]{\text{Dunkelheit}} nD$$

in denen D und L die dunklen, bzw. hellen Zellen, k_p die Geschwindigkeitskonstante der Photosynthese mit der die dunklen Zellen in helle Zellen umgewandelt werden, k_D die Geschwindigkeitskonstante der Zunahme der Zellenzahl im Dunkelprozess, und n die Zahl der dunklen Zellen, die aus einer hellen Zelle hervorgehen bezeichnet. Die auf dieses Schema gegründete Kinetik des stationären Zustandes führte zu den Formeln, die die Gesamtwachstumsgeschwindigkeit und die relative Menge der dunklen und hellen Zellen in der Kultur in Abhängigkeit (i) von der Lichtintensität, (ii) der Geschwindigkeit des Dunkelprozesses und (iii) der Geschwindigkeiten der Photosynthese bei Lichtsättigung und mit Licht als begrenzendem Faktor bezeichnen. Die Übereinstimmung zwischen der Theorie und der Beobachtung war im Grossen und Ganzen zufriedenstellend.

5. Es wurde durch diese analytische Untersuchung gezeigt, dass der Dunkelprozess beim Algenwachstum einen bemerkenswert hohen Temperaturkoeffizienten hat, besonders im Bereich niedrigerer Temperaturen.

REFERENCES

[1] H. TAMIYA, K. SHIBATA, T. SASA, T. IWAMURA, AND Y. MORIMURA, *Monograph on Algal Culture*, Carnegie Institution of Washington, Publication No. 598 (in press).
[2] D. I. ARNON, *Am. J. Bot.*, 25 (1938) 322; *Science*, 92 (1940) 264.
[3] H. TAMIYA, E. HASE, K. SHIBATA, A. MITSUYA, T. IWAMURA, Y. NIHEI, AND T. SASA, *Monograph on Algal Culture*, Carnegie Institution of Washington, Publication No. 598 (in press).
[4] B. H. KETCHUM AND A. C. REDFIELD, *J. Cellular Comp. Physiol.*, 33 (1949) 281.
[5] H. TAMIYA AND Y. CHIBA, *Studies from Tokugawa Inst.*, 6, No. 2 (1949) 1.
[6] R. J. L. ALLEN, *Biochem. J.*, 34 (1940) 858.

Received February 25th, 1953

GROWTH AND PHAGE PRODUCTION OF B. *MEGATHERIUM*

IV. KINETICS OF CELL GROWTH, PHAGE PRODUCTION, AND PROTEIN AND NUCLEIC ACID SYNTHESIS IN LYSOGENIC *MEGATHERIUM* CULTURES

by

JOHN H. NORTHROP

(with the technical assistance of MARIE KING)

The Laboratory of the Rockefeller Institute for Medical Research, Department of Bacteriology, University of California, Berkeley (U.S.A.)

KRUEGER AND NORTHROP found that the increase in phage in the presence of a susceptible organism followed a logarithmic curve just as does the increase in the cell concentration of the suspension. That is,

$$\frac{dP}{dt} = K_p P \quad \text{and} \quad \frac{dB}{dt} = K_g B \tag{1}$$

K_p = growth rate (constant) of phage
K_g = growth rate (constant) of cells

Therefore,

$$\frac{dP}{P} = \frac{dB}{B}\frac{K_p}{K_g} \tag{2}*$$

In these experiments, the amount of phage added was small compared to the number of cells. The increase in the amount of phage occurs in the cells and each infected cell liberates several phage particles. The reaction, therefore, is exactly the same in general as that of the multiplication of the cells, except that one infected cell forms many phage particles, but one normal cell forms only two cells. It is to be expected, therefore, that the reactions will follow the same course, but with different rates. In both cases the growth constant (fractional rate of increase per unit of time) is independent of the concentration. This is true whether the concentration increase during the course of the reaction, or whether it is increased by adding more P or B from an outside source. In either case the results agree with the logarithmic equation.

It has recently been found (NORTHROP[2]) that the same relation between phage production and bacterial growth holds in the case of sensitive B. *megatherium* + C phage when all the cells are infected at the beginning of the experiment. In this system, a dilute cell suspension continues to grow for 2–3 cell divisions after infection and before lysis occurs. The number of phage particles liberated per original infected cell at the end of the reaction is predicted by equation (2). (In the case of resting cells, the increase in RNA must be used instead of the increase in cells.) Under these conditions the multipli-

---

* This is the same equation as that found empirically by HUXLEY [23, 24] to represent the relationship between the size of various organs in growing animals or plants. (Any pair of value each of which varies logarithmically with t, must be related by equation (2); the reverse statement, however, is not true. Values of P and B which satisfy equation (2) do not necessarily have any simple relation to the time).

cation of the phage cannot be followed continuously, since it occurs inside the cells and an infected cell gives rise to one plaque, no matter how many phage particles it contains. The original and final number of phage particles is therefore all that can be determined. All the cells liberate phage at about the same time. The variation of the phage yield with the rate of growth of the cells must, therefore, be due to changes in the number of particles formed per cell, and not to changes in either the fraction of the total number of cells which liberate phage or to variation in the time at which the phage is liberated. In this case the rate of increase is not proportional to the free phage concentration and adding different amounts of phage has no effect on the yield, provided all the cells are infected at the beginning of the experiment.

In the present experiments it has been found that the same relation between phage growth and cell division holds for lysogenic *megatherium* cultures (Megatherium 899a) (DE JONG[3]).

During the lag period, the growth rate of the phage is much higher than that of the cells, as in the case with the phage-sensitive cell system. As soon as the lysogenic culture enters the range of log growth, however, the phage growth rate suddenly drops to exactly that of the cells, so that, after this, the ratio of P/B remains constant as long as the system remains in log growth.

EXPERIMENTAL RESULTS

Resting cells of lysogenic *B. megatherium* 899a were added to 5% peptone and the suspensions shaken at 34° C. The free phage, cells, cellular protein and cellular RNA per ml of the suspension were determined at various times.

The results of such an experiment are shown in Fig. 1 in which the various values have been plotted (on a log scale) against the time.

The curves for protein per ml and cell count per ml are nearly parallel throughout, so that the protein per cell remains nearly constant (*cf*. CALDWELL, MACKOR AND HINSHELWOOD[4], PRICE[5]). The RNA/ml increases more rapidly at first than the cell count and the P/ml very much more rapidly. All the curves become parallel during the log-growth phase and then flatten out. The first part of the phage curve is autocatalytic (logarithmic)* and has a much steeper slope than do the other curves. The increase in phage, in this part of the curve, may, therefore, be written $dP/dt = K_pP$, where P is the external phage. If the value of P is varied by adding more from an outside source, however, the equation fails, since the added phage has no effect on the rate of formation of new phage (Fig. 2). Since the value for P/ml

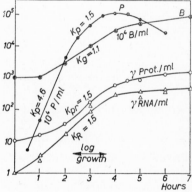

Fig. 1. Concentration of free phage (P), RNA, protein, and cells in a suspension of *megatherium* 899a, growing in 5% peptone. Cells from an 18 h 5% peptone-agar slant suspended in 10 ml 5% peptone, centrifuged, the cells added to 100 ml 5% peptone. 10 ml suspension put in each of 10 2 × 20 cm test tubes and the tubes shaken at 34°. 1 ml samples taken from each tube at the time indicated and combined. The combined sample was then analyzed in duplicate sets as described under experimental prodecure.

---

* This fact does not contradict the assumption that individual cells liberate phage particles in bursts (*cf*. BURNET[25], NORTHROP[2]).

References p. 50.

appears in the equation as the catalyst, but does not act as the catalyst when added from
an outside source, it follows that the P/ml formed
during the course of the reaction must be proportional
to the catalyst, although it is not the catalyst itself.

The conclusion that the ratio of P/B, RNA/B
and protein/B is constant during the log growth period
is only approximately correct in the experiment just
described, since this period exists over a small part of
the curve. Theoretically, a true "steady state" exists
only when the composition of the medium remains
constant. This condition can be strictly fulfilled by the
addition of more medium at a constant rate exactly
equal to that required to maintain a constant cell
concentration. It can be approximated by working in
the range of very low cell concentrations or by repeated dilution of the growing culture. (Very dilute cell
suspensions are impractical owing to the difficulty of
collecting enough cells for analysis.)

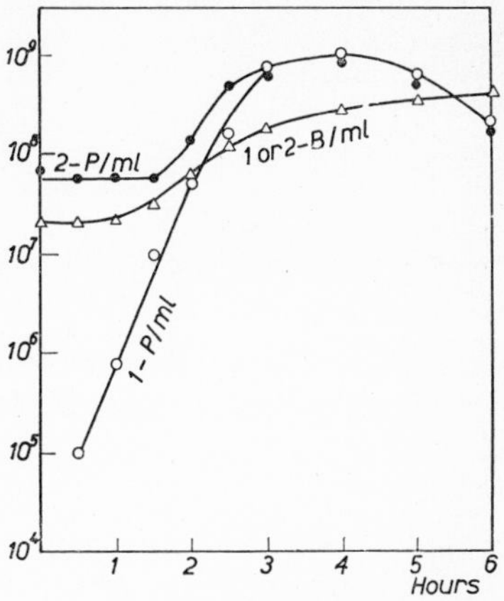

Fig. 2. Effect of addition of phage
on the rate of production of
phage by *megatherium* 899a. Cell
suspension prepared as in Fig. 1
and 10 ml placed in each of 2
tubes, 8×10^7 "T" phage/ml
added to one tube and both tubes
shaken at 34°.

Preliminary experiments showed that the culture
remains in log growth if the cell concentration is
maintained between $1 \cdot 10^7$/ml and about $8 \cdot 10^7$/ml by
repeated dilution. The growth is the same if the cells
are centrifuged and suspended in fresh media, or if the suspension is simply diluted
1/5 in fresh media.

The results of an experiment in which resting cells were grown in 5% peptone and
diluted 1/2 as soon as they reached a concen-
tration of $8 \cdot 10^7$/ml is shown in Fig. 3. The
phage growth rate is 6–9 per h for the first 2.5
h, while the cell growth rate gradually increases from 1.3 to 1.7 per h where it remains
constant. The cells are now in log growth. As
soon as this occurs the phage rate also drops
to 1.7 so that, from this point on, the ratio of
phage/cells is constant. The results are still
somewhat irregular, as only one plaque count
was made on each sample, and the cells did
not reach the log growth until near the end of
the experiment.

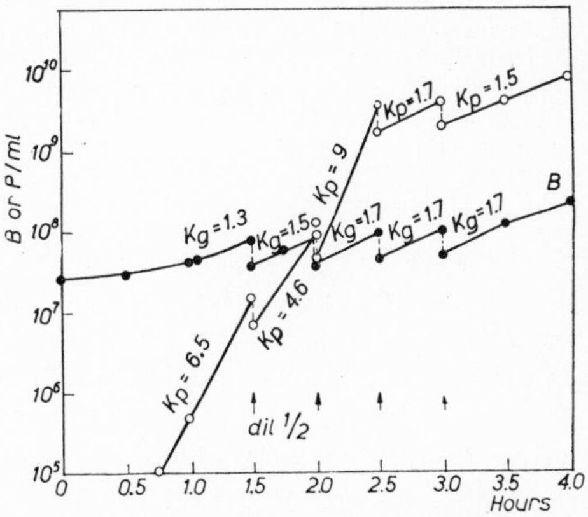

Fig. 3. Changes in P/ml and B/ml in
culture of 899a, kept in log growth by
repeated dilution. Cell suspension prepared
as in Fig. 1 and shaken at 34°. Diluted
1/2 with fresh 5% peptone when $B/ml =$
$8 \cdot 10^7$ and every half hour thereafter.

The experiment shown in Fig. 4 was
started by allowing a suspension containing
about $1 \cdot 10^5$ B/ml to stand at 25° for 18 h.
The cells grow very slowly during this time,
owing to lack of oxygen, but pass through
most of the lag phase. The tube was then shaken at 34°. The free P/ml and cells/ml of
the suspension and the RNA and protein of the washed cells were determined at intervals. As soon as the cell concentration reached $5 \cdot 10^7$/ml, the suspension was diluted 1/5
with fresh 5% peptone, and this cycle repeated 3 times.

References p. 50.

The results show that the cells reached log growth in about an hour and a half. The phage growth rate and cell growth rate are already equal and remain equal through

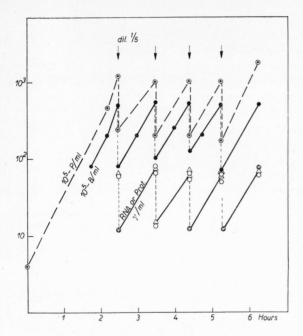

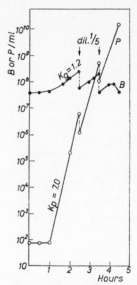

Fig. 5. Changes in free phage and B/ml in suspensions of *megatherium* sensitive + phage T. Cells from 18 h 5% peptone agar slant washed off in 5% peptone and diluted to $4 \cdot 10^7$ cells/ml. 80 "T" phage particles/ml added and then tubes shaken at 34°. Suspension diluted 1/5 when B/ml = $2 \cdot 10^8$.

Fig. 4. Changes in P/ml, B/ml, RNA/ml, and protein/ml in suspensions of lysogenic *megatherium* 899a in 5% peptone kept in log growth by repeated dilution. Cells from 18 h 5% peptone slant washed in 5% peptone, diluted to $1 \cdot 10^6 B$/ml. Stand 25°, 18 h and then shake at 34°. Suspension diluted 1/5 with fresh 5% peptone as soon as B/ml = $500 \cdot 10^5$.

all the successive growth steps. The RNA and protein growth rates are also equal to the cell and phage growth rates. In other words, the composition of the cells remained exactly the same with respect to phage, protein and RNA throughout the experiment and would continue to do so indefinitely until some change in the media occurred, or a new type of cell appeared. The fact that such a constant ratio of P/B would result in a lysogenic culture was pointed out by DELBRÜCK[6].

Rate of phage production and cell growth with sensitive cells

The results of an experiment in which T phage was added to a culture of *megatherium* sensitive, growing in 5% peptone, are shown in Fig. 5. In this case, the phage growth rate remains at its original high value throughout, and as a result the ratio of P/B continues to increase very rapidly. When this ratio reaches about 50/1, lysis occurs. Lysis caused by such high P/B ratios is not accompanied by an increase in the number of phage particles (NORTHROP AND KRUEGER[1]), (NORTHROP[7]), (DELBRÜCK[6]). This explains the fact that there is no change in slope of the P curve when lysis starts.

References p. 50.

DISCUSSION

1. *The growth curve*. The curves shown in Fig. 1 consist, as usual, of three more or less overlapping parts: the lag period during which the medium remains nearly constant, but the cell composition changes; the log growth period when both medium and cells remain nearly constant in composition; and the terminal lag period or stationary phase, in which the composition of both medium and cells is changing. These various stages of the growth cycle have been discussed in detail by HINSHELWOOD[20], and the present discussion applies principally to the log growth or steady state phase.

The decrease in rate towards the end of the reaction is due to depletion of the medium, in this case*. The usual method of correcting for this effect is to write the equation as $\dfrac{dx}{dt} = K_x\, x\, (x_e - x)$ where $x = x_e$ when $\dfrac{dx}{dt} = 0$; *i.e.*, when the reaction stops. This equation fits nearly 90% of the cell growth curve, whereas the simple log equation holds for about 50%. This is a surprisingly good fit, when it is recalled that almost all "simple" enzyme reactions show as great or greater discrepancies, when compared to simple kinetic theory. In the case of enzymes, also, it is the substrate term (corresponding to $(x_e - x)$ in the present instance) which causes the difficulty**.

2. *Relation between free phage concentration and phage growth rate*. The growth rate of the phage for the first two hours is accurately described by the autocatalytic equation $\dfrac{dP}{dt} = K_p \cdot P$, where P is the free phage *formed during the experiment*. It does not hold if the free phage is added from an outside source (Fig. 2). It follows that the free phage formed during the experiment must be proportional to the catalyst, but added free phage is not.

Exactly the same peculiarity occurs during the autocatalytic formation of trypsin from trypsinogen (KUNITZ[8]). In this reaction trypsin, and also an inert protein, are formed from trypsinogen and the time curves of the reactions are accurately predicted by the equations $\dfrac{dI}{dt} = K_I I$ trypsinogen and $\dfrac{dTr}{dt} = K_{Tr} Tr$ trypsinogen, where $I = $ concentration of inert protein and $Tr = $ concentration of trypsin.

The inert protein, however, is not the catalyst (although it appears as such in the equation) since addition of more inert protein has no effect on the reaction rate just as the addition of phage has no effect on the reaction rate in the present example. The explanation is that, in the trypsinogen experiment, the concentration of inert protein is proportional at all times to the concentration of trypsin which is the true catalyst.

The kinetics of the phage reaction may be accounted for by the following assumptions:

a. The rate of formation of the phage is proportional to the concentration of intracellular phage; *i.e.*, $\dfrac{dN}{dt} = K_p N$, where N is the intracellular P/ml. (3)

---

* The decrease in P/ml at the end of the reaction is due to some cellular activity, possibly the formation of an inhibitor (BURNET[26]) since the decrease does not occur in the supernatant from the culture, at this time.

** In this form the reaction is bimolecular and the rate of the reaction depends on the product of the concentrations of x and $(x_e - x)$. Diluting the system, therefore, will slow the rate in direct proportion. As a result, if a cell is disintegrated in a relatively large volume of media, all the autocatalytic reactions must decrease enormously in rate.

This effect may account, in part, for the difficulty of causing such reactions to take place in vitro

b. A constant, small fraction of the intracellular P is liberated per unit of time,
$i.e., \dfrac{dP}{dt} = \dfrac{FdN}{dt}$ or $P = FN$, where F = fraction of total phage per ml, liberated per unit
of time. Also $N = MB$, where M = phage per cell and B = cells/ml. Substituting the
value of $N = \dfrac{P}{F}$ and $\dfrac{dN}{dt} = \dfrac{Pd}{Fdt}$ in (3) $\dfrac{dP}{dt} = K_p P$.

If F or N is known, then the other variable can be calculated. For instance, LWOFF
AND GUTMAN[9] (cf. also CLARK AND COWLES) have found that lysis of B. megatherium
in a hanging drop preparation liberates about 100 phage particles per cell. During the
log phase the ratio of free phage to cells, P/B, is about 2/1 (Fig. 4). If each cell contains
100 phage particles, $F = P/MB = 0.02$. In the early stages of the reaction where the
cells are in the resting state, the ratio of P/B is 1/500. Since $F = 0.02$ and $M = P/FB$,
$M = 0.1$, i.e., only one cell in 10 liberates an active phage particle.

It is immaterial, as far as the derivation of the equation is concerned, whether or
not the cells lyse at the time of liberation of the phage. If the fraction of cells liberating
phage is constant, the cell concentration-time curve will still be logarithmic.

It may be noted that, since $P = FN$, variation in P could be ascribed mathe-
matically, to variation in F (or to variation in $F \times N$), the fraction of phage appearing
as extracellular, rather than to variation in N alone. Experimentally, however, this
appears to be unlikely, as it would be necessary to assume that F increases logarithmically with time, in the early part of the reaction, and also that even at the end of the
reaction it must remain small compared to 1, otherwise all the phage would be outside
at the end of the experiment and the cell curve would no longer be logarithmic.

The assumption that F is constant is also indicated by the fact that the lysis time
of infected megatherium cells is nearly independent of the growth rate or phage content
of the cells NORTHROP[6].

If log P is plotted against t, the slope is $\dfrac{\Delta \log P}{\Delta t}$ and $K_p = 2.3 \times$ slope = growth
rate. In the first part of the reaction the P has a growth rate of 4.6 (Fig. 1), while the
cells (or protein) have a growth rate of 1.1. The percentage increase in phage is therefore
4 times that of the cells. So far this result is the same as that in the phage-sensitive cell
system (NORTHROP)[2], and the relative rates are also about the same in both systems.
This relation cannot exist for long, as the cell would soon be all phage and would be
destroyed. In the sensitive system, this is what happens and the reaction is stopped by
the lysis of the cells (cf. Fig. 5), but in the lysogenic system, the growth constant of the
phage suddenly drops to that of the cells, so that after this point is reached, the ratio
P/B remains constant.

If the phage particle is formed from a precursor* in the bacterial cell, as suggested
by BORDET[11] (cf. also NORTHROP[12]; KRUEGER AND MUNDELL[13]; KRUEGER, MECRAKEN
AND SCRIBNER[14]), the result may be predicted, at least qualitatively. Suppose that, in the

---

* The assumption that viruses may be derived from precursors has been criticized on the grounds
that the nature of the active virus would then be determined by the nature of the host (TOPLEY
AND WILSON[27]). This is not a necessary corollary of the assumption of a precursor, but it is a probable
one. It must be remembered in this connection that there are at present no really accurate means of
identifying bacterial viruses so that small changes may be overlooked. On the other hand, recent work
of KRUEGER AND RALSTON[25], ROUNTREE[29] and BERTANI AND WEIGLE[31] has shown that such changes
in the virus after a change of hosts actually occur.

References p. 50.

resting cell, very few (1 ?) active phage particles exist. As the cell starts synthesis, more precursor is synthesized at a rate similar to that of RNA synthesis. The phage reaction also starts and is regulated, at first, only by its own velocity constant, since the substrate (precursor) is present in excess. This is the original rate observed. Since this rate is much higher than that of the formation of the precursor, the precursor will soon be greatly reduced in concentration and the reaction will slow down until the rote of formation of the phage is just equal to the rate of formation of the precursor. This is now a steady state and the reaction can proceed indefinitely. This mechanism may also account for the observation (WEED AND COHEN[15]) that the first phage liberated from *B. coli* containing ^{14}C pyrimidines contains more of the labelled pyrimidine than does phage liberated later. It predicts that, in a lysogenic culture, phage produced during the lag phase will contain more host C or P than phage produced during the log phase.

It may also explain the fact (KRUEGER AND MUNDELL[13], NORTHROP[16]) that infected sensitive cells in the log phase produce more phage than resting cells. Such infected sensitive cells do not divide, as a rule, but continue to form RNA (PRICE[17]) at nearly the same rate as uninfected cells. If the phage precursor is formed at a rate similar to that of RNA, log cells contain more than resting cells and, in addition, make more, during the phage production period, than do resting cells.

If the phage precursor is also the precursor of other cell constituents, then destruction of the sensitive cells may be due to the fact that, in these cells, the ratio of phage formation to precursor formation is so high that the concentration of precursor is reduced until it is insufficient to allow the formation of normal cell constituents at the minimum rate required for the life of the cell. In the lysogenic cell, on the other hand, the concentration of precursor, in the steady state, is high enough to provide the necessary normal cell constituents*.

Constant composition of cells and media during the steady state

Since bacteria continue to grow indefinitely without change of properties, if supplied with fresh media, it follows that their composition must remain exactly constant and the ratio of any component of the cell or medium to any other component, must also remain constant.

This condition is strictly fulfilled only if the medium is renewed at a constant rate exactly equal to that required to keep the cell concentration constant. A culture in log growth approximates this condition, but does not fulfil it, for the composition of the medium must change with the change in concentration of the cells.

Examples of such constant ratios during (approximate) steady state have been observed by many workers. NORTHROP[12] found that the relative concentration of phage and also of gelatinase, an extracellular enzyme, to the cells was nearly constant during log growth.

---

* The equations governing this relationship are $\dfrac{\mathrm{d}x}{\mathrm{d}t} = K_x A x$ where x = concentration of precursor, A = components of the medium (considered to be constant). The transformation of the precursor to normal cell constituents is $\dfrac{\mathrm{d}B}{\mathrm{d}t} = K_B B x$, $\dfrac{\mathrm{d}C}{\mathrm{d}t} = K_C C x$ ... at equilibrium $\dfrac{\mathrm{d}x}{\mathrm{d}t} = \dfrac{\mathrm{d}B}{\mathrm{d}t} + \dfrac{\mathrm{d}C}{\mathrm{d}t}$ ...
and $K_x A x - K_P B - K_C C \ldots = 0$.
  Evidently the addition of a new substance P such that $K_P P$ is smaller or of the same order of magnitude as $K_B B$ or $K_C C$ will not have much effect on the various other concentrations. If $K_P P$, however, is much larger than the other terms, the value of the other terms must decrease. (*Cf.* also MANDELSTAN[30]).

References p. 50.

3

WOODS AND TRIM[18] found the same result for deaminase of *C. welchii*.

PRICE[17] found that the protein, RNA and DNA per cell (staphylococcus) remained constant during log growth.

Constant ratio of P/B during log growth of lysogenic *megatherium* was found by CLARK AND COWLES[19].

The reverse of this condition is also true. If any cell component or product of metabolism is found to change its concentration relative to any other compound during the steady state of the culture, then a new type of cell must have appeared.

HINSHELWOOD[20] has pointed out that such extreme synchronization of reaction rates could hardly exist without some common regulating mechanism. He has shown that a series of reactions, each one dependent on the preceding, can furnish such a regulatory mechanism.

The derivation of all the substances used in cell synthesis, from a common precursor by a series of simultaneous reactions (NORTHROP[21]) also leads to synchronization of reaction rates. If any substance in the cells increased at a faster rate than the cells, no matter how slight, sooner or later the cell must be destroyed, while if it increased at a slower rate, sooner or later the last molecule would be lost and a new kind of cell appear, which contained none of the slow growing component*. Loss of plastids by plant cells, or of the Kappa particle of paramecium occur in this way and the loss of phage by lysogenic bacteria has been reported. The destruction of a cell by overgrowth of a component occurs when a susceptible cell is infected with phage.

It follows that any cell component which increases in amount per cell in passing from the resting cell to the log growth cell, must decrease in amount again as the cell returns to the resting stage; otherwise the cycle would not be complete.

The best conditions, therefore, for comparing various cultures growing in the same media, or the effect of various media on the growth of one culture, is during the "steady state".

EXPERIMENTAL PROCEDURE

Phage determination —0.2 ml suspension added to 1.8 ml ice cold normal saline and centrifuged at once for 10 min at 3500 R.P.M. Phage determined in supernatant as previously described (NORTHROP[22]). Control experiments showed that this procedure stopped phage production as soon as the cells were added to the cold normal saline and did not change the amount of the free phage.

Cell count — (NORTHROP[16]).

Protein and RNA — Sample removed from tube and 1/10 volume of formalin added. Suspension centrifuged, precipitate stirred up with 10 ml cold normal saline, centrifuged. Precipitate washed once more with normal saline and then washed 3 times with cold 5% trichloracetic acid. The rest of the determination was carried out as previously described (NORTHROP[16]).

Control experiments showed that the RNA and protein content of the cells was not changed by the formalin.

SUMMARY

1. The changes in the concentration of cells, free phage, cellular protein, and cellular RNA have been determined during the growth of cultures of lysogenic *megatherium* 899a, in peptone medium.

2. During the lag phase the RNA increases more rapidly than the cells, and the free phage much more rapidly.

---

* All autocatalytic equations express the paradox that, if none of the product formed is present, none can be formed. This difficulty may be circumvented by assuming that there is another, possibly very slow, reaction which results in the formation of the same product. In the case of the trypsinogen–trypsin reaction this secondary reaction is known to occur.

References p. 50.

3. The rate of increase of the free phage is autocatalytic (logarithmic) and is proportional at any time to the free phage formed during the reaction. The rate is not changed by the addition of free phage from an outside source.

4. This relationship may be derived by assuming: 1. The rate of increase of the free phage is proportional to the concentration of the intracellular phage. 2. A small constant fraction of the intracellular phage is released per instant of time. The free phage is therefore proportional to the intracellular phage at all times.

5. The rate of formation of phage, RNA, and protein, during the steady state, is exactly equal to the rate of growth of the cells. This must be true of all cell components or metabolites, if the culture continues in the steady state without the appearance of new cell types.

6. In the phage-sensitive cell system the rate of formation of the phage continues at 4–5 times the rate of increase of the cells until the ratio of phage/cells is about 50. Lysis then occurs without further increase in free phage.

RÉSUMÉ

1. Les auteurs ont déterminé les concentrations en cellules, en phage libre, en protéines cellulaires et en acide ribonucléique cellulaire au cours de la croissance de cultures de *Megatherium* 899a lysogène, en milieu peptoné.

2. Pendant le temps de latence, l'acide ribonucléique et surtout le phage libre augmentent plus rapidement que les cellules.

3. La vitesse d'accroissement du phage libre est celle d'une réaction autocatalytique (logarithmique). Elle est proportionnelle quel que soit le temps au phage libre formé pendant la réaction. La vitesse n'est pas affectée par l'addition de phage libre d'origine extérieure.

4. On peut rendre compte de cette relation en supposant que: 1. La vitesse d'accroissement du phage libre est proportionnelle à la concentration du phage intracellulaire. 2. Une petite fraction constante du phage intracellulaire est libérée dans l'unité de temps. Le phage libre est donc constamment proportionnel ay phage intracellulaire.

5. Les vitesses de formation du phage, de l'acide ribonucléique et des protéines, pendant la croissance, sont exactement égales à la vitesse de croissance des cellules; ceci doit être vrai de tous les constituants et métabolites cellulaires, si la culture continue à croître sans apparition de nouveau type de cellule.

6. Dans les cultures sensibles au phage, la formation du phage se poursuit avec une vitesse 4 à 5 fois plus grande que celle de l'accroissements des cellules, jusqu'à ce que le rapport phage/cellules soit environ 50. La lyse se produit alors sans augmentation du phage libre.

ZUSAMMENFASSUNG

1. Les auteurs ont déterminé les concentrations en cellules, en phage libre, en protéines cellulaires et en acide ribonucléique cellulaire au cours de la croissance de cultures de *Megatherium* 899a lysogène, en milieu peptoné.

2. In der Anfangsperiode des Wachstums vermehrt sich die RNS schneller und der freie Phage noch viel schneller als die Zelle.

3. Die Vermehrungsgeschwindigkeit des freien Phagen ist autokatalytisch (logarithmisch) und zu jeder Zeit proportional zu dem während der Reaktion geformten freien Phagen. Die Geschwindigkeit wird nicht verändert durch den Zusatz von freiem Phagen aus einer Quelle ausserhalb.

4. Diese Beziehung kann abgeleitet werden durch die Annahme, dass 1. die Wachstumsgeschwindigkeit des freien Phagen proportional ist zu der Konzentration des intracellularen Phagen und 2. dass ein kleiner konstanter Bruchteil des intracellularen Phagen pro Zeiteinheit freigesetzt wird. Der freie Phage ist daher zu jeder Zeit proportional zu dem intracellularen Phagen.

5. Die Geschwindigkeit der Bildung von Phage, RNS und Protein während des stabilen Zustands ist genau gleich der Wachstumsgeschwindigkeit der Zellen. Dies muss für alle Zellkomponenten oder am Stoffwechsel beteiligten Komponenten gelten, wenn die Kultur ihren stabilen Zustand ohne das Auftreten neuer Zelltypen beibehält.

6. In dem Phage-empfindlichen Zellsystem wird die Bildungsgeschwindigkeit des Phagen, die 4–5 mal so gross ist wie die Wachstumsgeschwindigkeit der Zellen, beibehalten bis das Verhältnis des Phagen zu den Zellen ungefähr 50 ist. Es tritt dann Lysis ein ohne eine weitere Zunahme des freien Phagen.

References p. 50.

REFERENCES

[1] A. P. KRUEGER AND J. H. NORTHROP, *J. Gen. Physiol.*, 14 (1930) 223.
[2] J. H. NORTHROP, *J. Gen. Physiol.*, 35 (1952) 471.
[3] D. DE JONG, *Zentr. Bakteriol. Parasitenk.*, Orig., 120 (1931) 1.
[4] P. C. CALDWELL, E. L. MACKOR AND C. N. HINSHELWOOD, *J. Chem. Soc.*, (1950) 3151.
[5] W. H. PRICE, *J. Gen. Physiol.*, 35 (1952) 741.
[6] M. DELBRÜCK, *J. Gen. Physiol.*, 23 (1940) 643.
[7] J. H. NORTHROP, *J. Gen. Physiol.*, 21 (1938) 335.
[8] M. KUNITZ, *J. Gen. Physiol.*, 22 (1939) 293, 429.
[9] A. LWOFF AND A. GUTMAN, *Ann. Inst. Pasteur*, 78 (1950) 711.
[10] N. A. CLARK AND P. B. COWLES, *J. Bact.*, 63 (1952) 177.
[11] J. BORDET, *Proc. Roy. Soc. B*, 107 (1931) 398.
[12] J. H. NORTHROP, *J. Gen. Physiol.*, 23 (1939) 59.
[13] A. P. KRUEGER AND J. H. MUNDELL, *Science*, 88 (1938) 551.
[14] A. P. KRUEGER, T. MECRACKEN AND E. J. SCRIBNER, *Proc. Soc. Exptl. Biol. Med.*, 40 (1939) 573.
[15] L. L. WEED AND S. S. COHEN, *J. Biol. Chem.*, 192 (1951) 693.
[16] J. H. NORTHROP, *J. Gen. Physiol.*, 36 (1953) 581.
[17] W. H. PRICE, *J. Gen. Physiol.*, 33 (1949) 17.
[18] D. D. WOODS AND A. R. TRIM, *Biochem. J.*, 36 (1942) 501.
[19] N. A. CLARK AND P. B. COWLES, *J. Bact.*, 63 (1952) 187.
[20] C. N. HINSHELWOOD, *Chemical Kinetics of the Bacterial Cell*, Oxford, 1946.
[21] J. H. NORTHROP, *Chemistry and Physiology of Growth*, edited by ARTHUR K. PARPART, Princeton Press, 1949.
[22] J. H. NORTHROP, *J. Gen. Physiol.*, 34 (1951) 715.
[23] J. S. HUXLEY, *Nature*, 114 (1924) 895.
[24] J. S. HUXLEY, *Problems of Relative Growth*, Methuen and Co., London, 1932.
[25] F. M. BURNET, *Biol. Rev.*, 9 (1934) 332.
[26] F. M. BURNET, *J. Pathol and Bacteriol.*, 38 (1934) 285.
[27] TOPLEY AND WILSON, *Principles of Bacteriology and Immunology*, 3rd ed., Williams & Wilkins, Baltimore, 1946, p. 337.
[28] A. P. KRUEGER AND D. RALSTON, *Proc. Soc. Exptl. Biol. Med.*, 80 (1952) 217.
[29] P. M. ROUNTREE, *J. Gen. Microbiol.*, 3 (1949) 153.
[30] J. MANDELSTAM, *Biochem. J.*, 51 (1952) 674.
[31] G. BERTANI AND J. F. WEIGLE, *J. Bact.*, 65 (1953) 113.

Received February 27th, 1953

KRISTALLISIERTES
3-CARBONSÄUREAMID-N1-D-RIBOSIDO-PYRIDINIUMBROMID
UND VERWANDTE VERBINDUNGEN

von

P. KARRER, M. VISCONTINI UND R. HOCHREUTER

Chemisches Institut der Universität, Zürich (Schweiz)

Bei der Konstitutionsaufklärung des Diphospho-pyridin-nucleotids (Codehydrase I) duch O. WARBURG[1] und des Triphospho-pyridin-nucleotids (Codehydrase II) durch VON EULER[2] spielten synthetische Modellversuche eine erhebliche Rolle[3]. Es gelang uns damals, als die den Codehydrasen im chemischen Aufbau am nächsten stehende Verbindung das Tetraacetat des 3-Carbonsäureamid-N1-glucosido-pyridiniumbromids (I) sowie das N1-D-Glucosido-*o*-dihydro-nicotinsäureamid (II) in kristallisierter, reiner Form herzustellen[4]. Dagegen schlugen alle Versuche fehl, auch die entsprechenden Nicotin-säureamidderivate mit Pentoseresten, d.h. N1-D-Ribosido-*o*-dihydro-nicotinsäure, 3-Carbonsäureamid-N1-D-ribosido-pyridiniumbromid (III) und die analogen Arabinose- und Xylose-Derivate kristallisiert zu erhalten.

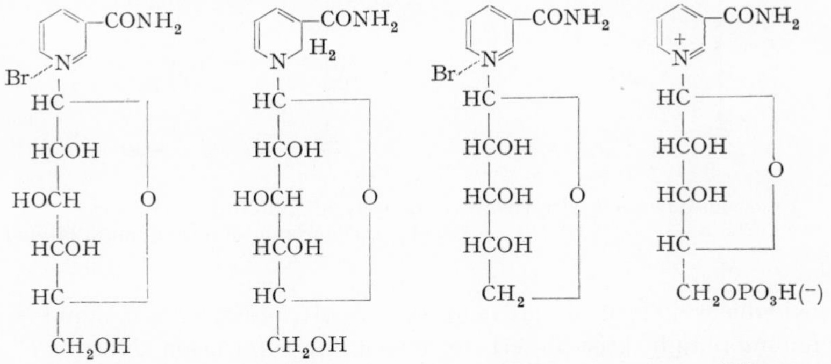

Vor nicht sehr langer Zeit haben HAYNES UND TODD[5] unsere früheren Arbeiten wieder aufgenommen, aber auch sie konnten nur die Glucosederivate des Nicotin-säureamids, die wir bereits kristallisiert in Händen gehabt hatten, in kristall. Zustand erhalten, während die von ihnen dargestellten Pentoseverbindungen keine Neigung zur Kristallisation aufwiesen.

Im Hinblick auf die Bedeutung einer Synthese eines N1-D-Ribosido-nicotinsäure-amid-phosphorsäureesters (IV) haben wir unsere früheren Untersuchungen auf diesem Gebiet wieder aufgenommen.

Literatur S. 55.

Zunächst haben wir eine Methode ausgearbeitet, das 3-Carbonsäureamid-N^1-D-glucosido-pyridiniumbromid (I) aus dem entsprechenden Tetraacetat in einfacher Weise zu erhalten, während es früher nur gelungen war, diese Substanz auf dem Umweg:

$$\text{N-D-Tetracetyl-glucosido-}o\text{-dihydro-nicotinsäureamid} \xrightarrow{\begin{subarray}{c}\text{alkalische}\\ \text{Verseifung}\end{subarray}}$$

$$\text{N-D-Glucosido-}o\text{-dihydro-nicotinsäureamid (II)} \xrightarrow[\text{(J}_2\text{)}]{\text{Oxydation}}$$

$$\text{3-Carbonsäureamid-N}^1\text{-D-glucosido-pyridiniumbromid (I)}$$

darzustellen. Das nunmehr benutzte Verfahren besteht in der Verseifung der Acetat-gruppen des 3-Carbonsäureamid-N^1-D-tetracetylglucosido-pyridiniumbromides (Tetra-acetat von I) durch wässerige Bromwasserstoffsäure. Analog war früher[6] N-D-Glucosido-trimethylammoniumbromid [(CH$_3$)$_3$N·C$_6$H$_{11}$O$_5$]Br aus dem entsprechenden Tetracetat dargestellt worden.

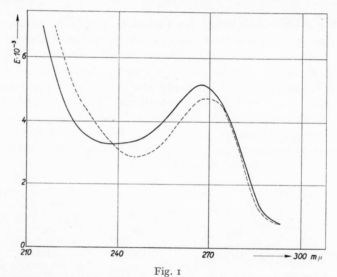

Fig. 1

——————   3-Carbonsäure-amid-N^1-D-ribopyranosido-pyridiniumbromid (Wasser)
– – – – –   3-Carbonsäure-amid-N^1-2′,3′,4′-triacetyl-D-ribopyranosido-pyridinium-bromid (Wasser)

Das N^1-Glucosido-nicotinsäureamid-bromid (I) (3-Carbonsäureamid-N^1-D-gluco-sido-pyridiniumbromid) kristallisiert in feinen, nadelförmigen Kristallen, die sich zwischen 151°–152° zersetzen. [α]$_D^{20}$ = +28.64° (Wasser).

C$_{12}$H$_{17}$O$_6$N$_2$Br   Ber. C 39.46 H 4.68 N 7.67 Br 21.91%
(365)   Gef. C 39.51 H 4.79 N 7.89 Br 22.15%

Zur Herstellung einer entsprechenden D-Ribosidoverbindung (III) ist Tetracetyl-D-ribose Ausgangsmaterial. Diese kommt, wie neuere Arbeiten[7] zeigten, in zwei Isomeren vom Smp. 110° und 85° vor. Wir benutzten zunächst die Form vom Smp. 110°, die in üblicher Weise in Acetobromribose verwandelt wurde. Letztere reagierte unter bestimm-ten Versuchsbedingungen mit Nicotinsäureamid unter Bildung von N-[Triacetyl-D-ribosido]-nicotinsäureamid (Triacetat von III), das nach der Reinigung mittels Ver-

Literatur S. 55.

teilungschromatographie prachtvoll kristallisierte. Es bildet feine Nadeln, die bei 142° schmelzen und nicht hygroskopisch sind. $[\alpha]_D^{20} = -4.5°$ (Wasser).

Durch Verseifung mittels wässeriger Bromwasserstoffsäure gewannen wir aus diesem Triacetat zwei verschiedene Substanzen, die sich durch Verteilungschromatographie trennen liessen. Die eine ist ein 3-Carbonsäureamid-N-D-ribopyranosido-pyridiniumbromid der Formel (III), die andere ein Monoacetat der Verbindung III. Erstere kristallisiert in zu Büscheln vereinigten Prismen und schmilzt bei 147° unter Zersetzung. $[\alpha]_D^{20} = +1°$ (Wasser).

$C_{11}H_{15}O_5N_2Br$ Ber. C 39.41 H 4.51 N 8.36 Br 23.85%
(335)   Gef. C 39.68 H 4.57 N 7.95 Br 23.40%

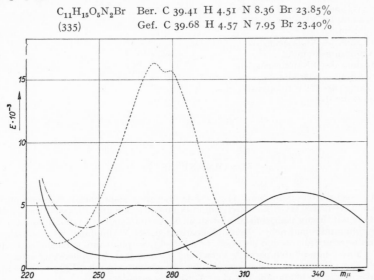

Fig. 2 —·—·— 3-Carbonsäure-amid-N¹-D-glucosido-pyridiniumbromid (Wasser)
———— Dieselbe Substanz in 0.01 N-NaOH nach der Reduktion mit Natriumdithionit
········· Reduzierte Substanz in N-Salzsäure.

Das Monoacetat von III, mit vorläufig noch unbekannter Stellung des Acetylrestes, schmilzt bei 170° und ist ebenfalls gut kristallisiert. $[\alpha]_D^{20} = +10°$ (Wasser).

$C_{13}H_{17}O_6N_2Br$ Ber. C 41.38 H 4.53 N 7.42 Br 21.20%
(377)   Gef. C 41.39 H 4.34 N 7.14 Br 21.64%

Unser 3-Carbonsäureamid-N¹-D-ribopyranosido-pyridiniumbromid (III) besitzt pyranoside Structur, denn es verbrauchte bei der Oxydation mit Natriummetaperjodat nach MALAPRADE[8] pro Mol 2.0 Mol Perjodsäure, wobei 1.01 Mol Ameisensäure gebildet wurden. Das Monoacetat von III beanspruchte 0.97 Mol Perjodsäure pro Mol; hierbei entstand keine Ameisensäure.

Offen ist noch die Frage, ob die Bindung des Riboserestes am Ring-stickstoff des Nicotinsäureamids in der Substanz (III) β oder α-glucosidisch ist.

Durch Phosphorylierung des 3-Carbonsäureamid-N¹-D-ribopyranosidopyridinium-bromids (III) mit Metaphosphorsäure erhielten wir einen Triphosphorsäureester, in welchem die 3 Phosphorsäurereste eine Kette $-OPO_2H-O-PO_2H-O-PO_3H_2$ bilden. Die vorsichtige Hydrolyse dieses Triphosphates führte zu einem 3-Carbonsäureamid-N¹-D-ribosido-pyridinium-monophosphorsäureester, in welchem die Stellung des Phosphorsäurerestes noch zu beweisen bleibt.

Literatur S. 55.

TABLE I

R_F-WERTE EINIGER VORBESCHRIEBENER PYRIDINDERIVATE.

Verwendet wurde die aufsteigende Methode bei einer Temperatur von 18°.

Verbindung	Lösungsmittelgemisch		
	Butanol-Eisessig-Wasser 4:1:5	Butanol mit H_2O gesattigt-Äther 4:1	Butanol-Eisessig-Wasser 8:1:5
Nicotinsäureamid	0.76	0.60	0.61
Nicotinsäureamidhydrobromid	0.32		0.15
3-Carbonsäureamid des N^1-D-Tetraacetyl-glucosidopyridinium-bromids	0.58		
3-Carbonsäureamid des N^1-D-Glucosido-pyridiniumbromids	0.14		
3-Carbonsäureamid des N^1-Triacetyl-D-ribosidopyridinium-bromids	0.35	0.12	0.29
3-Carbonsäureamid des N^1-Monoacetyl-D-ribosidopyridinium-bromids	0.20		0.09
3-Carbonsäureamid des N^1-D-ribopyranosido-pyridinium-bromids	0.16	0.03	0.04

ZUSAMMENFASSUNG

Aus Tetracetyl-D-ribose vom Smp. 110° wurde über die entsprechende Acetobrom-D-ribose 3-Carbonsäureamid-N^1-D-triacetylribosidopyridiniumbromid in schön kristallisierter Form erhalten. Bei dessen Verseifung mit Bromwasserstoffsäure entstand das kristallisierte 3-Carbonsäureamid-N^1-D-ribopyranosido-pyridiniumbromid neben einem Monoacetat dieser Verbindung. 3-Carbonsäureamid-N^1-D-ribopyranosido-pyridiniumbromid liess sich mittels Metaphosphorsäure in einen Triphosphorsäureester überführen und dieser durch partielle Verseifung in einen Monophosphorsäure-ester.

Schliesslich wurde aus dem Tetracetat des 3-Carbonsäureamid-N^1-D-glucosido-pyridiniumbromids die acetylfreie Verbindung durch saure Verseifung erhalten.

SUMMARY

Well-defined crystals of 3-carboxamide-N^1-D-triacetylribosidopyridinium bromide have been obtained from tetra-acetyl-D-ribose (m.p. 110°) through the intermediary of the corresponding aceto-bromo-D-ribose. On saponification with hydrobromic acid this compound gives crystallised 3-carbox-amide-N^1-D-ribopyranosidopyridinium bromide together with a monoacetate. This bromide can, with the aid of metaphosphoric acid, be transformed into a triphosphoric ester and this latter, by partial saponification, into a monophosphoric ester.

Finally, starting from the tetra-acetate of 3-carboxamide-N^1-D-glucosido-pyridiniumbromide, the authors have obtained the de-acetylated compound by means of acidic saponification.

RÉSUMÉ

Les auteurs ont obtenu à partir du tétra-acétyl-D-ribose (p.F. 110°), par l'intermédiaire de l'acétobromo-D-ribose correspondant, le bromure de 3-carboxamide-N^1-D-triacétylribosidopyridinium bien cristallisé. Par saponification à l'acide bromhydrique ce dernier donne le bromure de 3-carbox-amide-N^1-D-ribopyranosidopyridinium cristallisé, accompagné d'un monoacétate. Le bromure de 3-car-boxamide-N^1-D-ribopyranosidopyridinium peut être transformé à l'aide d'acide métaphosphorique en ester triphosphorique et ce dernier, par hydrolyse partielle, en ester monophosphorique.

Enfin, à partir du tétra-acétate du bromure de 3-carboxamide-N^1-D-glucosido-pyridinium, les auteurs ont obtenu le composé désacétylé par saponification acide.

Literatur S. 55.

LITERATUR

[1] O. WARBURG, W. CHRISTIAN UND A. GRIESE, *Biochem. Z.*, 275 (1934) 212, 464; 282 (1935) 157.

[2] H. VON EULER, H. ALBERS UND F. SCHLENK, *Z. physiol. Chem.*, 234 (1935) 1; 237 (1935) 1; H. VON EULER UND E. ADLER, *Z. physiol. Chem.*, 238 (1936) 233.

[3] P. KARRER UND O. WARBURG, *Biochem. Z.*, 285 (1936) 297; P. KARRER, G. SCHWARZENBACH, F. BENZ UND U. SOLMSSEN, *Helv. Chim. Acta*, 19 (1936) 811; P. KARRER, B. H. RINGIER, J. BÜCHI, H. FRITZSCHE UND U. SOLMSSEN, *Helv. Chem. Acta*, 20 (1937) 55, sowie verschiedene weitere Abhandlungen.

[4] *Helv. Chim. Acta*, 20 (1937) 55.

[5] *J. Chem. Soc.*, (1950) 303.

[6] P. KARRER UND J. TER KUILE, *Helv. Chim. Acta*, 5 (1922) 870.

[7] G. A. HOWARD, B. LYTHGOE UND A. R. TODD, *J. Chem. Soc.* (1947) 1052; H. ZINNER, *Chem. Ber.*, 83 (1950) 153.

[8] L. MALAPRADE, *Bull. soc. chim.*, [4] 43 (1928) 683; [5] 1 (1934) 833. Vgl. ferner B. LYTHGOE UND A. R. TODD, *J. Chem. Soc.* (1944) 592.

Eingegangen den 4. März 1953

ON THE MECHANISM OF ENZYME ACTION. LV.

A STUDY OF THE INTERACTION BETWEEN CALCIUM AND TRYPSIN

by

F. F. NORD AND M. BIER

Department of Organic Chemistry and Enzymology*, Fordham University, New York 58 (U.S.A.)

The role of certain metallic cations in chemical processes occurring in living matter has received considerable attention since the early days of physiology and enzymology. The most characteristic aspect of these phenomena is the specificity of the ions and enzymes involved. In recent years it became increasingly evident that these biologically important effects of metallic ions are but a particular case in the much broader range of more or less specific interactions between proteins and other macromolecular compounds on the one side and smaller molecules such as cations, anions, dyes, etc. on the other.

In the particular case of trypsin it has long been known that calcium augments the extent of its formation from trypsinogen[1]. Recently there were discussed further examples of the specific interaction of calcium and certain other ions with trypsin[2]. Notably, calcium protects the enzyme against selfdigestion and it also slightly increases its proteolytic activity. It was therefore suggested that calcium is an integral part of a more stable trypsin molecule as it causes a shift towards the active form in the existing equilibrium between the native and denatured enzyme. It is proposed to call this form *calcium-trypsin*.

Most of these manifestations of the interaction of trypsin and calcium were observed in the pH range 6 to 9, the region of the proteolytic activity of the enzyme. A more direct evidence for the formation of a calcium-trypsin complex was obtained through the study of the dissociation of trypsin. Calcium ions, in contrast to magnesium, sodium or potassium ions, give rise to a shift in the titration curves of the enzyme in the region of the dissociation of the carboxyl groups towards lower pH values. The acidity of the carboxyl groups of the enzyme is evidently increased by the specific binding of calcium. This is also a unique example of a difference in the effect of calcium and magnesium ions upon the dissociation curves of a protein.

The present communication explores the stability zones of trypsin over the entire practicable pH scale. The effect of calcium ions on the dissociation curves prompted an electrophoretic investigation of the enzyme in the same pH region and it resulted therefrom that trypsin is electrophoretically inhomogeneous. In the presence of calcium two well-defined peaks appear on electrophoretic examination. In the absence of calcium,

---

* Communication No. 277.—Read at the Symposium on *Frontiers in Enzymology* held at the autumn meeting of the Am. Chem. Society, 1953.—For the previous paper of this series see *Arch. Biochem. Biophys.*, 45 (1953) No. 1.

References p. 66.

trypsin appears to be a homogeneous protein due to the interaction of the two trypsin components. This interaction causes an aggregation which was evidenced by ultra-centrifugal measurements[3]. The nature of these reversible aggregates is indicated by the experiments to be described, a temperature rise to only 30° C preventing their formation. Calcium ions also prevent the interaction and thus give rise to a normal sedimentation behaviour[4].

EXPERIMENTAL

Enzyme preparation

In this study a number of different samples were used. Commercial crystalline trypsin (Worthington Biochemical Laboratory, Freehold, N.J.) which contains about 50% of $MgSO_4$ was employed in some experiments where the presence of this salt did not appear to be critical or could be taken into account. Most experiments were performed, however, with salt-free preparations of the enzyme either using the commercial salt-free product, prepared by dialysis of crystalline trypsin at pH 2.3 and freeze-drying, or alcohol precipitated trypsin, prepared according to our previously described procedure[5]. Due to the fact that magnesium ions seem to have no specific effect on the electrophoretic or ultracentrifugal behaviour of trypsin, the three preparations were fully identical in their behaviour. Similarly, no differences in properties were observed between successive batches of the various preparations.

Electrophoretic analyses

A Perkins Elmer Model No. 38 apparatus was used as in the previous studies[6]. The experiments were carried out in a pH range of reasonable stability of the enzyme and all the samples were equilibrated against the buffer by overnight dialysis in the cold on a slowly rotating shaker. An aliquot of a stock solution of the buffer was mixed with a fixed volume of solution, containing the desired amount of the various neutral salts. In all experiments the final composition of the buffer is reported.

Ultracentrifugal determinations

A Spinco analytical centrifuge, model E, was used in the sedimentation studies on the enzyme. The trypsin samples were dissolved in the appropriate buffers always immediately prior to the actual run except in those experiments where the effect of prolonged digestion was under investigation. In this case, aliquots of the same solution were analyzed at different times.

Usually five exposures at 32 min intervals were taken in each experimental run, using the 1.2 cm cell. In a few instances the 0.4 cm cell was also utilized. The sedimentation constants were calculated by measuring the displacement of the sedimenting boundary between two successive exposures. All the sedimentation constants are reported as $s_{20, w}$, namely, corrected for the temperature and density of the medium according to SVEDBERG AND PEDERSEN[7] as well as the values of LANDOLT AND BÖRN-STEIN. The temperature of the rotor was measured before and after each run and the average of these two readings is reported as the temperature of the experiment. By appropriate application of refrigeration it was possible to maintain the temperature during the run within less than 1° C, in most of the experiments. In a few cases where the difference exceeded the above limits, an individual correction for each time interval was applied, assuming a linear change in temperature.

pH measurements

All pH values were determined with a Cambridge Instrument pH meter, research model, using potassium acid phthalate as reference buffer.

Activity of the enzyme

As in previous communications the activity was determined by measuring the absorption at 280 mμ of a hemoglobin digest.

RESULTS

Electrophoresis

It is between pH 4 and 5 that the shift in the dissociation curves of trypsin caused by the addition of calcium ions is the most evident[5]. This is why we have searched in the same pH region for a specific effect of calcium ions on the electrophoretic mobility of the enzyme. Preliminary experiments have shown that, rather than giving rise only to a

References p. 66.

difference in electrophoretic mobility, calcium ions cause a change in the appearance of the electrophoretic pattern. Whereas in the absence of calcium trypsin presents patterns characteristic of a homogeneous compound as shown by the photographs in series A, Fig. 1, two well-defined peaks appear upon the addition of calcium. We have studied the conditions of maximal separation of the two components. Two factors are found to influence the separation of the two components: pH and concentration of calcium. In Fig. 1, series B and C, the electrophoretic patterns obtained in the presence of 0.01 and 0.033 M CaCl$_2$ respectively are presented. It is evident that at the lower concentration of the calcium ions the separation of the two components is not yet complete. A further increase of concentration of calcium ions gives rise to no other changes in pattern and therefore the concentration of 0.033 M was applied in the comparison of all chlorides of divalent cations. To study the effect of monovalent cations a concentration of 0.10 M was chosen to keep the ionic strength constant. Because of the relatively high requirements of calcium ion concentration, advantage could not be taken of the observed better separation of electrophoretic components at very low ion concentrations[8, 8a]. As expected from the dissociation curves of trypsin, the separation of the two components is best evidenced between pH 4 and 5. At pH 3.5 and 5.5 the two peaks remain partially superimposed, even after prolonged electrophoresis.

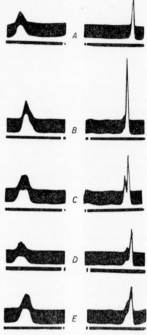

Fig. 1

    In Table I are listed all the cations, applied as chlorides, the effect of which on the electrophoretic patterns of trypsin was investigated. Besides calcium, only manganese and cadmium cause a separation of peaks to occur, whereas all other cations give rise to patterns characteristic of an electrophoretically homogeneous protein. The electrophoretic patterns obtained in the presence of manganese and cadmium are also included in Fig. 1, series D and E.

TABLE I

EFFECT OF VARIOUS IONS ON THE ELECTROPHORETIC PATTERNS OF TRYPSIN

Separation of components not observed in presence of:	*Components separated in presence of:*
Li$^+$, Na$^+$, K$^+$, NH$_4^+$, Mg^{++}, Ba^{++}, Sr^{++}, Co^{++}, Cu^{++}, Ni^{++}.	Ca^{++}, Mn^{++}, Cd^{++}.
All cations were added as chlorides	Ionic strength 0.10; pH 4.75–5

    The mobilities and relative areas of the components of trypsin in the presence of various ions are recorded in Table II. It can be seen that of the two boundaries the larger one moves with a mobility characteristic of trypsin in absence of calcium ions whereas the smaller boundary moves at a slightly lower rate.

    It was of importance to obtain small samples of electrophoretically separated faster and slower moving components to test their respective proteolytic activity. Due to the

References p. 66.

TABLE II

ELECTROPHORETIC BEHAVIOUR OF TRYPSIN IN PRESENCE OF VARIOUS IONS

Buffer			Mobilities $\times$ 10^5				Relative composition[*]
Sodium acetate-acetic acid	Neutral salt	pH	Component I Asc.	Desc.	Component II Asc.	Desc.	Ratio of areas Comp. I: Comp. II ascending boundaries
0.04 M	CaCl$_2$ 0.03 M	4.74	5.43	5.35	4.92	4.76	2.1
0.04 M	MgCl$_2$ 0.03 M	4.74	5.48	4.95	—	—	No separation
0.04 M	CaCl$_2$ 0.03 M	4.44	6.04	5.25	5.44	4.60	Separation not sufficient for calculation
0.04 M	MgCl$_2$ 0.03 M	4.44	5.97	5.43	—	—	No separation
0.04 M	CdCl$_2$ 0.033 M	4.75	6.03	—	5.56	—	2.3
0.04 M	MnCl$_2$ 0.033 M	4.76	6.83	—	6.22	—	2.9

* The ratio of areas of the two ascending boundaries was calculated as 2.3 $\pm$ 0.3, in 10 measurements carried out under varying conditions.

high concentrations of trypsin required in these analyses (0.5–1%) only a few drops of each of the two components are required for the determination of their proteolytic activity, carried out at a hundredfold dilution. By using a larger cell (6 ml) and a very slow flow of buffer into the electrode vessel on the ascending side arm of the electrophoresis cell, the separation of the two components could be extended to 24 hours at the end of which period small samples of the two components became available using a syringe. In Table III the relative activities of the components obtained in four independent

TABLE III

COMPARISON OF THE PROTEOLYTIC ACTIVITIES OF THE TWO COMPONENTS OF CRYSTALLINE TRYPSIN

Experiment	Slower component		Faster component	
	Opt. Dens.[*] of sample	Activity[**]	Opt. Dens.[*] of sample	Activity[**]
1	0.045	0.100	0.090	0.340
2	0.045	0.500	0.095	0.900
3	0.040	0.230	0.070	0.415
4	0.040	0.320	0.105	0.700

* Optical density at 280 mμ of the electrophoretically separated samples, diluted to 4 ml.
** Activity expressed in arbitrary units (optical density at 280 mμ of hemoglobin digests after hundredfold dilution of the separated samples).

experiments, together with the protein concentration in each as measured by the ultra-violet adsorption at 280 mμ, are reported. Whereas no exact comparison of the specific activities of the two components can be made on the basis of these experiments, there is no doubt that both possess proteolytic activity.

There was another opportunity to compare the properties of the two components of trypsin, namely by subjecting trypsin solutions to selfdigestion at pH 8 in the presence or absence of calcium. This ion, of course, considerably diminishes the rate of self-digestion. Aliquot samples from the two solutions were taken at 24 hour intervals and examined electrophoretically after dialysis with calcium buffer at pH 5 under conditions giving the best separation of the two components. At the same time the tryptic activity was determined. Due to dialysis at pH 5 most breakdown products were eliminated and a

References p. 66.

comparison of the relative concentration of the two components and the tryptic activity of the solution at different stages of selfdigestion could be evaluated. The data are presented in Fig. 2 and Table IV.

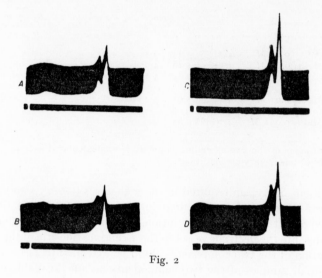

Fig. 2

TABLE IV

EFFECT OF SELFDIGESTION OF TRYPSIN ON ITS COMPOSITION

Run	Incubation time	Residual proteolytic activity %	Residual protein concentration from area measurements %	Ratio Components I : II (ascending areas)
A	1 day[*]	54	42	2
B	2 days[*]	43	34	2.4
C	2 days[**]	89	74	1.7
	3 days[**]	75	71	2.1
D	5 days[**]	63	63	1.9

[*] Digested in 0.1 M sodium acetate, 0.05 M MgCl$_4$, pH 7–7.5
[**] Digested in 0.1 M sodium acetate, 0.05 M CaCl$_4$, pH 7–7.5

Ultracentrifugation

The ultracentrifugal behaviour of trypsin was investigated in several arbitrarily differentiated pH-stability regions. At pH 2.3 where the enzyme is most stable, sedimentation diagrams characteristic of a homogeneous protein were obtained as is exemplified by the photographs in series A of Fig. 3. The dependence of the sedimentation constant on the concentration of the enzyme is presented in Table V. No significant concentration dependence of the sedimentation constant below 1% protein concentration was observed and the average of the values obtained was $s_{20,w} = 2.4\ S$.

Freshly prepared solutions of trypsin in a borate buffer, pH 8, present similar patterns as shown in series B of Fig. 3. From the data in Table V it can be seen that the sedimentation constants are not significantly higher at this pH, giving an average value of $s_{20,w} = 2.5\ S$. Two runs performed on trypsinogen in the acid and alkaline buffer present identical patterns and sedimentation constants as trypsin.

References p. 66.

Below pH 2.3 trypsin becomes increasingly unstable, the rate of inactivation following a monomolecular course[10]. In series C

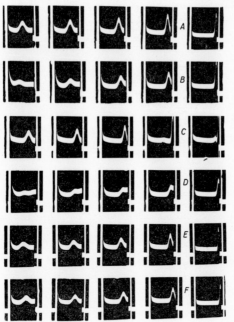

Fig. 3

of Figure 3 are presented the sedimentation patterns of trypsin after 24 hour digestion in a 0.1 HCl, 0.1 NaCl buffer. The faster sedimenting components which have appeared are due to the aggregation of denatured protein, not interfered with by any proteolysis. A similar behaviour was also observed in the denaturation of other proteins. At pH 8, in the absence of calcium, trypsin is also quite unstable and in series D of Figure 3 are recorded the sedimentation diagrams of trypsin after 24 hour digestion at pH 8 in 0.1 M borax buffer. Instead of the heavier components, observable upon acid inactivation, some lighter ones appear which are products of the self-digestion of trypsin. It is important to note that the presence of either the aggregation products or of the breakdown products does not change in a significant way the sedimentation rate of the remaining unchanged enzyme.

It was reported[3] that between the two extreme pH regions trypsin is subject to aggregation with a maximum occurring at pH 5. This is in agreement with our results as evidenced from the values recorded in Table V. Depending on the conditions of the experimental runs at pH 5, sedimentation constants ranging from 2.4 S to over 3.5 S can be obtained. The sedimenting boundary remains however at all times rather symmetrical and there is no appearance of two components as is the case in acid or alkaline digestion. A typical series of sedimentation patterns is presented under E in Fig. 3. Whereas this aggregation was shown to be concentration dependent[3] it seems to have been overlooked that the aggregation is also strongly temperature dependent, the aggregation decreasing with temperature. This is evident from Fig. 4 and is a further example of the importance of temperature in all aggregation phenomena[9].

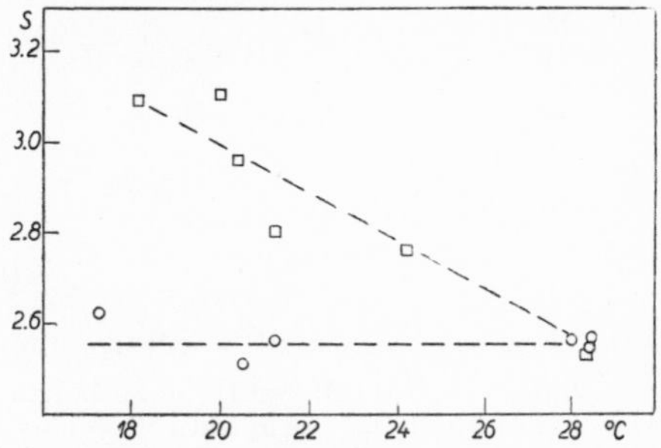

The aggregation occurs in the pH range where the effect of calcium on the electrophoretic patterns of trypsin was observed. It is natural that we have also investigated the effect of calcium on the sedimentation behaviour of trypsin. The presence of 0.05 M. $CaCl_2$ completely prevents the aggregation of trypsin as can be recognized in Fig. 4. The concentration of $CaCl_2$ used was chosen on the basis of the results of the electrophoretic analyses,

Fig. 4. □ — In absence of calcium, pH 5.2.
○ — In presence of calcium, pH 5.2.

these having indicated that a concentration of 0.01 M is not sufficient for full characterization of its effect. A typical pattern is reproduced in Series F, Fig. 3.

References p. 66.

TABLE V

SEDIMENTATION BEHAVIOUR OF TRYPSIN (Tr) AND TRIPSINOGEN (Tren)

No. of experiment	Enzyme preparation	Buffer	pH	Temp. °C	Concentration of enzyme mg/ml	$s_{20,w}$ S
1				24.7	10	2.20
2				22.7	10	2.48
3				20.2	10	2.43
4	SF Tr	A	2.4	24.2	9	2.32
5				23.5	8	2.43
6				23.4	5	2.40
7				24.6	2.5	2.36
8				22.6	2.5	2.44
9	Cr Tr	A	2.4	23.7	10	2.57
10	Tren	A	2.4	22.7	10	2.47
11				24.2	10	2.32
12	SF Tr	B	1.3	21.0	10	2.49
13				20.3	10	2.32
14				25.1	10	2.53
15	SF Tr	C	8.1	25.0	10	2.49
16				21.9	–	2.53
17	SF Tr	D	7.9	23.4	10	2.60
18	Tren	D	7.9	18.8	10	2.43
19				17.2	10	2.62
20				20.5	10	2.51
21	SF Tr	E	5.2	21.2	10	2.56
22				28.0	10	2.56
23				28.4	10	2.55
24				28.4	10	2.56
25				18.2	10	3.09
26				20.0	10	3.10
27	SF Tr	F	5.2	20.4	10	2.96
28				21.2	10	2.80
29				24.2	10	2.76
30				28.3	10	2.53
31			5.6	25.7	10	2.73
32			5.4	27.2	10	2.97
33	Cr Tr	G	5.2	26.2	10	3.04
34			5.0	26.8	10	2.94
35			4.8	24.9	10	3.27
36			4.8	19.2	10	3.45

REMARKS

Enzyme preparation: SF = salt free; Cr = crystalline.

Buffers: A = 0.1 M NaCl + 0.01 M HCl; B = 0.1 M NaCl + 0.1 M HCl; C = 0.1 M Na$_2$B$_4$O$_7$; D = 0.01 M Na$_2$B$_4$O$_7$ + 0.1 M NaCl; E = 0.05 M CaCl$_2$ + 0.1 M CH$_3$CO$_2$Na — CH$_3$CO$_2$H; F = 0.05 M MgCl$_2$ + 0.1 M CH$_3$CO$_2$Na — CH$_3$CO$_2$H; G = 0.1 M CH$_3$CO$_2$Na — CH$_3$CO$_2$H.

Experiments: No. 1–9: Average sedimentation rate at pH 2.4 = 2.40 ± 0.07 S; No. 12–13: After 24 and 48 h incubation. Heavier components appear, with $s > 20$ S; No. 16: After 24 hr. self-digestion. Slower sedimenting components appear; No. 14–18: Average sedimentation rate at pH 8 = 2.52 ± 0.04 S; No. 19–24: Average sedimentation rate at pH 5.2 in presence of CaCl$_2$ = 2.56 ± 0.02 S; No. 25–36: Sedimentation rate in absence of calcium ions is strongly temperature dependent.

References p. 66.

DISCUSSION

The properties of the trypsin molecule studied in the present series of experiments are summarized in Fig. 5 in which the behaviour of the enzyme at different pH ranges is presented schematically.

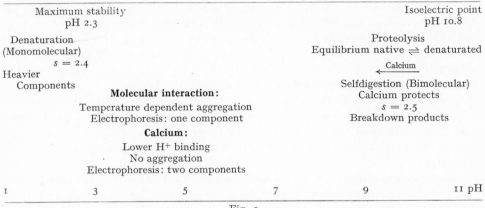

Fig. 5

The enzyme is most stable at about pH 2.3 and presents an ultracentrifugal behaviour characteristic of a homogeneous protein with a sedimentation constant $s_{20,w} = 2.4$ S. At lower pH values the enzyme becomes increasingly unstable and the denaturation causes the appearance of faster sedimenting aggregation products. The proteolytic activity of the enzyme is exerted between pH 6 and 9 and in this pH range it is known that its native and denaturated forms are in equilibrium[10]. Due to the digestion of the latter by the native enzyme, its solutions rapidly lose their activity and slower sedimenting breakdown products appear. Calcium and manganese ions when present reduce the rate of self-digestion considerably and also slightly increase the activity of the enzyme. It is assumed that these ions are integral parts of a more stable trypsin molecule, *i.e.* that they cause a shift in the equilibrium between the native and denaturated enzyme towards the active form. Taking advantage of the protective effect of calcium ions it was possible also to establish that the iso-electric point of the enzyme is in the neighborhood of pH 10.8[6].

It is between the above two extreme pH ranges that a number of other interesting phenomena occur. The formation of a specific calcium-trypsin complex was proven by the study of the electrometric titration curves of the enzyme. In the pH range 2 to 5 where the dissociation of the carboxyl groups of the enzyme takes place, calcium ions, in contrast to magnesium, sodium or potassium ions, induce a shift in the dissociation curves towards the more acid pH values. This is evidence of a specific binding of the calcium ions by the carboxyl groups of the enzyme which results in a decrease of their dissociation constants. In this pH range, therefore, the net charge of the enzyme is reduced by the addition of calcium ions. It would follow therefrom that its electrophoretic mobility should be lower when calcium ions are added as compared to magnesium. Experiments have shown, however, that the effect of calcium ions is more complex. Whereas in the absence of these ions the enzyme gives rise to an electrophoretic pattern characteristic of a homogeneous protein, the presence of calcium induces the separation

References p. 66.

4

of the moving boundary into two well-defined peaks, the larger of the two moving with the mobility of the enzyme in absence of calcium whereas the smaller moves at a slightly lower rate.

This fact cannot be understood without a detailed analysis of our ultracentrifugal results. It was already noted that in the same pH range the sedimentation constant of trypsin increases, the concentration-dependent aggregation being maximal at about pH 5[3]. This observation was left, however, without a rational explanation. But we have noticed that the aggregation is strongly temperature dependent. It is significant that by varying the three factors, *e.g.* concentration, temperature as well as the pH, sedimentation constants can be obtained ranging from 2.4 S, the normal value, to 3.5 S, the protein presenting a single sedimenting boundary at all times[4].

This is in contrast to the appearance of faster sedimenting boundaries upon acid denaturation of the enzyme or of slower sedimenting boundaries during the self-digestion at pH 8. In both cases the appearance of the faster or slower sedimenting boundaries does not affect the rate of sedimentation of the remaining unchanged enzyme to a significant extent.

A continuous variation of the sedimentation constant can only be explained by the existence of a *reversible* equilibrium between monomeric and dimeric or polymeric forms of the enzyme, the time necessary for the establishment of the equilibrium being small in comparison to the sedimentation rate. The rate of sedimentation will then depend on the relative proportion of the various forms present and it is evident that in the case of trypsin the equilibrium is shifted towards the monomeric form by an increase of temperature or decrease in concentration.

The addition of calcium ions in sufficient concentration fully prevents the aggregation reducing the sedimentation constant to its normal value, namely that of the monomeric enzyme. It appears, therefore, that calcium, bound to the carboxyl groups of the enzyme, prevents the interaction of enzyme molecules which results in the formation of dimeric or higher polymeric forms. On the basis of this interpretation it must also be considered that the electrophoretic patterns obtained when calcium is present correspond to the actual molecular distribution of the protein, namely that trypsin is electrophoretically heterogeneous and contains two components. The apparently homogeneous patterns obtained in the absence of calcium are but an artefact, resulting from the interaction of the two components, enhanced by the low temperature at which electrophoretic measurements are carried out. It is, of course, open to speculation whether the interaction is limited to a combination of the two different types of trypsin molecules or whether, which seems the more probable case, it is a random combination of any two or more molecules present.

As in the case of sedimentation, the electrophoretic mobility of such a system existing in reversible equilibrium would be a weighed average of the mobilities of the various forms coexisting at the equilibrium. The apparent identity of the mobilities of the total trypsin in absence of calcium and of the major component of trypsin in the presence of calcium is, therefore, purely coincidental. The average mobility of trypsin when calcium is added is lower than in the absence of calcium in accordance with the smaller net charge of the calcium-trypsin.

The properties of the two components of trypsin were further analyzed. Besides calcium ions, manganese and cadmium ions also give rise to the appearance of the two characteristic components in electrophoretic analysis. The same ions, together with

References p. 66.

cobalt, magnesium and barium, enumerated in order of decreasing effect, are also reported as slightly increasing the activity of the enzyme[11]. Whereas the first three ions are about equivalent in their effect, the second group of ions exerts a much smaller effect. On electrophoresis the ions of the second group, even at higher concentrations, do not give rise to the separation of the moving boundary into its two components. Instead, a single boundary is obtained. The binding of these ions, resulting in an increased activity of the enzyme, is apparently more loose than that of the first group of ions and falls therefore below the threshold value apparently necessary to prevent the interaction of enzyme molecules resulting in the formation of polymeric forms.

It was, of course, uncertain whether both of the components are actually trypsins or whether one is an inactive impurity or product of a denaturation of the enzyme. The results of the direct assay of the two components, reported in Table III, clearly show that they possess comparable proteolytic activity. Furthermore, experiments depicted in Fig. 2 and Table IV indicate that both components show closely similar stabilities, namely they are self-digested at about the same rate, either in presence or absence of calcium. It is obvious, therefore, that calcium offers an equally protective effect to both components and that we may therefore consider that both are trypsins. This would be in agreement with the behaviour of another example of a multi-component protein all fractions of which have the same biological activity, namely the antitryptic factor of eggwhite, ovomucoid[8].

ACKNOWLEDGEMENT

This study was carried out under the aegis of the U.S. Atomic Energy Commission. – We also wish to record the assistance of L. TERMINIELLO.

SUMMARY

1. In the neighbourhood of pH 5 the electrophoretic analysis of crystalline trypsin results in patterns characteristic of a homogeneous protein, while the addition of calcium, manganese or calcium ions (0.033 M) causes the moving boundary to separate into two distinct peaks. The two components of trypsin have comparable stability both in the presence or absence of calcium ions and, if separated electrophoretically, possess similar proteolytic activity.

2. Trypsin has a sedimentation constant of 2.4–2.5 S at the pH values of 2.3 and 8. On the acid side of pH 2.3, the denaturation causes a slow appearance of faster sedimenting components, whereas at pH 8, the self-digestion prompts the appearance of slower sedimenting breakdown products. The rate of sedimentation of the remaining unaltered trypsin appears unaffected by the presence of either the faster or the slower sedimenting components.

3. In the intermediate pH range, around pH 5, the sedimentation constant may increase up to 3.5 S, depending upon the conditions, while the enzyme sediments as a homogeneous protein. This is due to a reversible aggregation equilibrium which is strongly temperature dependent. Calcium prevents the aggregation.

4. Trypsin has to be viewed as a heterogeneous protein consisting of two components. In the absence of calcium, manganese or cadmium, in the neighbourhood of pH 5, the reversible molecular interaction of the two components induces the aggregation and results in apparently homogeneous electrophoretic and ultracentrifugal patterns. The addition of calcium or of the other two ions prevents the interaction, restores the normal sedimentation behaviour, and reveals the true electrophoretic heterogeneity of the enzyme.

RÉSUMÉ

1. Au voisinage de pH 5, la trypsine cristallisée se comporte, à l'électrophorèse, comme une protéine homogène, tandis qu'après addition des ions de calcium, manganèse ou cadmium (0.033 M), elle se sépare en deux constituants distincts. Les deux constituants ont une stabilité comparable à la fois en présence et en absence des ions de calcium et, après séparation par électrophorèse, possèdent des activités protéolytiques semblables.

References p. 66.

La constante de sédimentation de la trypsine est de 2.4 à 2.5 S à pH 2.3 et 8. A pH inférieur à 2.3, la dénaturation entraîne l'apparition lente de corps à sédimentation plus rapide, tandis qu'à pH 8, l'autolyse provoque l'apparition de produits de dégradation à sédimentation plus lente. La vitesse de sédimentation de la trypsine qui reste intacte n'est pas modifiée par la présence des corps à sédimentation lente ou rapide.

3. A des pH intermédiaires, aux environs de 5, la constante de sédimentation peut augmenter jusqu'à 3.5 S selon les conditions, l'enzyme se sédimentant alors comme une protéine homogène. Ceci est dû à une aggrégation équilibrée réversible, qui dépend étroitement de la température. Le calcium empêche cette aggrégation.

4. On doit considérer la trypsine comme une protéine hétérogène formée de deux constituants. En l'absence de calcium, de manganèse ou de cadmium, au voisinage de pH 5, l'interaction moléculaire réversible des deux constituants entraîne la formation d'aggrégats et donne le comportement apparent, à l'ultracentrifugation et à l'électrophorèse, d'une protéine homogène. L'addition de calcium ou des deux autres ions empêche l'interaction, rétablit le comportement normal à la sédimentation et met en évidence l'hétérogénéité réelle de l'enzyme à l'électrophorèse.

ZUSAMMENFASSUNG

1. Bei ungefähr pH 5 ergibt die elektrophoretische Analyse von kristallisiertem Trypsin, das für ein homogenes Protein charakteristische Bild, während der Zusatz von Calcium, Magnesium oder Cadmiumionen (0.033 M) eine Trennung der beweglichen Grenzlinie in zwei unterschiedliche Spitzen verursacht. Die beiden Komponenten des Trypsins haben eine vergleichbare Stabilität sowohl in Gegenwart als auch in Abwesenheit von Calciumionen und besitzen nach elektrophoretischer Trennung eine ähnliche proteolytische Aktivität.

2. Trypsin hat eine Sedimentationskonstante von 2.4–2.5 S bei den pH-Werten 2.3 und 8. Auf der sauren Seite von pH 2.3 verursacht die Denaturierung ein langsames Auftreten von sich schneller absetzenden Komponenten, während bei pH 8 die Selbstverdauung zum Auftreten von sich langsamer absetzenden Abbauprodukten verursacht. Die Sedimentationsgeschwindigkeit des zurückbleibenden unveränderten Trypsins scheint durch die Gegenwart von sich sowohl schneller als auch langsamer absetzenden Komponenten nicht beeinflusst zu werden.

3. In dem Zwischenbereich von ungefähr pH 5 kann je nach den Bedingungen die Sedimentationskonstante zu 3.5 S ansteigen, und das Enzym sich als homogenes Protein absetzen. Dies ist einem reversiblen Aggregationsgleichgewicht zuzuschreiben, das streng temperaturabhängig ist. Calcium verhindert die Aggregation.

4. Trypsin muss als ein aus 2 Komponenten bestehendes heterogenes Protein angesehen werden. Bei Abwesenheit von Calcium, Magnesium oder Cadmium bei ungefähr pH 5 verursacht die reversible molekulare Reaktion der beiden Komponenten die Aggregation und ergibt ein elektrophoretisch und nach Untersuchungen mit der Ultrazentrifuge scheinbar einheitliches Bild. Die Zugabe von Calcium oder der zwei anderen Ionen verhindert die Reaktion, stellt das normale Sedimentationsverhalten wieder her und verrät die wahre elektrophoretische Uneinheitlichkeit des Enzyms.

REFERENCES

[1] M. C. DELEZENNE, *Compt. rend. soc. biol.*, 59 (1905) 476; M. R. MCDONALD AND M. KUNITZ, *J. Gen. Physiol.*, 25 (1941) 53.

[2] M. BIER AND F. F. NORD, *Nature*, 171 (1953) 1022.

[3] H. NEURATH et al., *Discuss. Faraday Soc.*, 13 (1953) 58.

[4] M. BIER, L. TERMINIELLO AND F. F. NORD, *Arch. Biochem. Biophys.*, 41 (1952) 238.

[5] J. A. DUKE, M. BIER AND F. F. NORD, *ibid.*, 40 (1952) 424.

[6] M. BIER and F. F. NORD, *ibid.*, 31 (1951) 335; 33 (1951) 320.

[7] T. SVEDBERG AND K. O. PEDERSEN, *The Ultracentrifuge*, Oxford, Clarendon Press, 1940.

[8] M. BIER, J. A. DUKE, R. J. GIBBS AND F. F. NORD, *Arch. Biochem. Biophys.*, 37 (1952) 491.

[8a] E. A. ANDERSON AND R. A. ALBERTY, *J. Phys. Coll. Chem.*, 52 (1948) 1361.

[9] F. F. NORD AND O. M. v. RANKE-ABONYI, *Science*, 75 (1932) 54; F. F. NORD, M. BIER AND S. N. TIMASHEFF, *J. Am. Chem. Soc.*, 73 (1951) 289.

[10] M. KUNITZ AND J. H. NORTHROP, *J. Gen. Physiol.* 17 (1934) 591.

[11] M. M. GREEN, J. A. GLADNER, J. W. CUNNINGHAM, JR., AND H. NEURATH, *J. Am. Chem. Soc.*, 74 (1952) 2122.

Received, March 11th, 1953

ON THE PHOTOCHEMICAL REDUCTION OF NITRATE BY ALGAE

by

C. B. VAN NIEL, M. B. ALLEN AND B. E. WRIGHT

Hopkins Marine Station of Stanford University, Pacific Grove, California (U.S.A.)

"Punkte 1 und 2 (*viz.* that in the primary reaction O_2 is not evolved, and that no substances are produced from which O_2 is spontaneously liberated) sind das einzige Sichere, was sich über den Primärvorgang aussagen lässt; sie machen es wahrscheinlich, dass der Primärvorgang nicht das Kohlensäuremolekül betrifft." (O. WARBURG[1], p. 206.)

INTRODUCTION

Thirty-three years ago WARBURG AND NEGELEIN[2] found that suspensions of algae, illuminated in nitrate-containing solutions, could produce O_2 even in the absence of CO_2. This phenomenon was interpreted by relating it to the fact, established by the same authors, that in darkness the algae can oxidize some of their organic components to CO_2 with the simultaneous reduction of nitrate, presumably to NH_3. Consequently, an algal suspension in the presence of nitrate can never be considered as strictly free of CO_2, and O_2 production during a period of illumination could be ascribed to the occurrence of a normal photosynthetic reaction. Schematically, this interpretation may be represented by the following equations:

In darkness $\qquad 2\,C + HNO_3 + H_2O \rightarrow 2\,CO_2 + NH_3 \qquad\qquad$ (a);

In light $\qquad\qquad 2\,CO_2 + 2\,H_2O \rightarrow 2\,C + 2\,O_2 \qquad\qquad\qquad$ (b).

The above formulation implies that, at sufficiently high light intensities, the rate of O_2 production is determined by the rate of CO_2 formation, and can never exceed the rate of reaction (b). It was, however, observed that O_2 evolution in CO_2-free suspensions of algae supplied with nitrate might proceed as much as ten times faster than CO_2 production in darkness. In order to make these results compatible with the suggested explanation the additional hypothesis was proposed that the rate of oxidation of organic cell constituents to CO_2 with concomitant reduction of nitrate was considerably accelerated by light.

Considering the state of our knowledge of the photosynthetic reaction in 1920, it must be granted that WARBURG AND NEGELEIN's interpretation of the photochemical nitrate reduction appeared the most feasible one. But later developments in this field gradually led to the conclusion that the process in question could also be understood on the basis of an entirely different mechanism.

Studies with green and purple sulfur bacteria had revealed the existence of photosynthetic processes that differ from normal green plant photosynthesis by the absence

References p. 73/74.

of O_2 production and the requirement for an external supply of reducing agents[3,4]. Together with the fundamental contributions of KLUYVER AND DONKER[5], describing all biochemical reactions as special cases of hydrogen (electron) transfer, these findings resulted in the formulation of photosynthesis as a photochemical conversion of CO_2 into organic matter with the simultaneous oxidation of any one of a number of hydrogen (electron) donors, in accord with the general equation:

$$CO_2 + 2\ H_2A \xrightarrow{\text{light}} (CH_2O) + H_2O + 2\ A.$$

This concept of photosynthesis suggested that the evolution of O_2 by green plants during illumination is the result of a photochemical dehydrogenation of H_2O, a possibility which received strong experimental support, if not confirmation, from the studies of RUBEN et al.[6], and of VINOGRADOV AND TEIS[7], carried out with oxygen-18 labeled H_2O and CO_2. The results showed convincingly that the O_2 evolved is derived exclusively from H_2O.

A further consequence of this interpretation is that the actual assimilation or reduction of CO_2 in photosynthesis should be considered as the result of enzymic, non-photochemical reactions. That such an assimilation of CO_2 in the absence of light can be accomplished had been definitively shown by WINOGRADSKY's discovery of the chemo-autrotrophic bacteria, as early as 1890[8]. That also in green plant photosynthesis CO_2 does not participate directly in the primary photochemical reaction was unequivocally demonstrated when HILL[9–11] succeeded in separating the photochemical mechanism from the non-photochemical enzyme systems in his epoch-making experiments with isolated chloroplasts. These organs can produce O_2 when illuminated, but completely lack the ability to reduce CO_2.

This need for relegating the assimilation of CO_2 to non-photochemical reactions suggested the possbliity that in photosynthesizing organisms reduction processes might occur in which compounds other than CO_2 are involved. In that event the photo-chemical reduction of nitrate could be interpreted as a reaction essentially analogous to the photochemical reduction of CO_2, with nitrate replacing CO_2 as the final hydrogen acceptor. This idea was expressed in 1941 in the following passage:

"Green plant photosynthesis is thus considered as a complex of photochemical and dark reactions in which the former consist of a photodecomposition of water, with the aid of chlorophyll and enzymes of unknown nature. One series of dark reactions proceeds from here by transferring hydrogen to the ultimate acceptor (CO_2, nitrate, hydroxylamine, etc.), while a second series results in the formation of a peroxidic compound and its decomposition with the liberation of oxygen". (12, p. 323).

RABINOWITCH[13], in discussing the production of O_2 by illuminated algae suspensions in the presence of nitrate, also offered this interpretation as a possible alternative to the one advanced by WARBURG AND NEGELEIN. And WARBURG himself, in the second edition of his book, "Schwermetalle als Wirkungsgruppen von Fermenten"[14], has revised his earlier explanation in a passage which reads, in part, as follows:

"Betrachtet man jedoch die photochemische Wirkung der Chlorella auf Chinon und auf Nitrat als analoge Vorgänge, so wird man annehmen, dass auch die photochemische Nitratreduktion nicht durch Vermittlung der Kohlensäure, sondern direkter erfolgt. Es wäre also zu untersuchen, ob grüne Granula, in Nitratlösung suspendiert, bei Belichtung Sauerstoff entwickeln ... Entwickeln die Granula Sauerstoff, so ist der Weg über die Kohlensäure, geradeso wie oben in Fall des Chinons, aus-geschlossen, da die Granula Kohlensäure nicht reduzieren können". (p. 184).

In spite of these attempts to formulate a concept of the photochemical nitrate reduction that is integrated with present knowledge of various aspects of the photo-

References p. 73/74.

synthetic mechanism, experiments designed to support the "alternate hypothesis" have not been carried out. The following statement of RABINOWITCH[13] accurately represented the stage when the experiments discussed below were undertaken:

"More detailed experiments, with specific inhibitors of the type of hydroxylamine, could help to analyze the mechanism of photochemical nitrate reduction and establish its relation to ordinary photosynthesis. Unfortunately, this subject has not received further attention since 1920, although it is certainly worth renewed study". (p. 540).

BASIS OF THE EXPERIMENTAL APPROACH

Instead of following the experimental procedure suggested by WARBURG, we have chosen a different one. There is a twofold reason for this. In the first place, it is altogether likely that the enzyme system involved in the reduction of nitrate is not present in the chloroplasts or grana, just as that for CO_2 assimilation must be deemed missing in these structures .But more important, the study of nitrate reduction was one phase of a more general investigation, concerned with the determination of intermediate products in CO_2 assimilation proper. The approach rests on the following considerations.

The most general formulation of green plant photosynthesis, in keeping with present knowledge, can be schematically represented by the diagram[15]:

$$\text{HOH} \xrightarrow[\text{Pigments}]{\text{Light}} \quad \begin{matrix} \text{H} \left({\small \begin{matrix} \text{E}' \\ \text{E}'\text{H} \end{matrix}} \right) \!\!\times\!\! \left({\small \begin{matrix} \text{BH}_2 \\ \text{B} \end{matrix}} \right) \\[2em] \dot{\text{H}}\text{O} \left({\small \begin{matrix} \text{E}'' \\ \text{E}''\text{OH} \end{matrix}} \right) \rightarrow \text{O}_2 \end{matrix}$$

We consider the photochemical reaction to be limited to the formation of the entities, E'H and E"OH; the further transformations represent enzyme-controlled dark reactions. From present information about the effects of light intensity and temperature on the rate of photosynthesis it is reasonable to postulate that at a sufficiently high intensity of illumination the rate of O_2 production is governed by one of the dark reactions.

In normal photosynthesis the function of B, the hydrogen acceptor participating in the regeneration of E' from E'H, is exhibited by CO_2 or, more probably, by some of its early transformation products, such as carboxylic acids enzymically generated by CO_2-addition to other compounds. Hence, at high light intensities the rate of photosynthesis will be limited either by an enzyme concerned in the formation and reduction of these substances, or by a component of the enzyme system responsible for the regeneration of E" and the liberation of O_2. In the former case it should then become possible to bring into operation additional enzyme systems which can transfer hydrogen from E'H to a different acceptor, B', and therefore to increase the rate of O_2 evolution at light intensities greater than that required for saturation of the CO_2 assimilating mechanism.

Since it appeared an almost foregone conclusion that the enzymes involved in nitrate reduction are different from those concerned with the reduction of CO_2, these deductions would imply that the rate of O_2 evolution in the presence of both CO_2 and nitrate might be greater than that obtainable in the absence of nitrate. Theoretically, the relation between rate of O_2 production, CO_2 assimilation, and light intensity could then be expressed by the curves in Fig. 1.

From this figure it may be concluded that the linear relationship between rate of

O_2 production and light intensity should persist over a longer range when two simul-

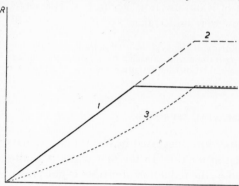

taneously reducible substrates are present than when either one alone is available. Ideally, one might expect to observe an additive effect.

Less can be said with any degree of certainty about the quotient CO_2/O_2 during photosynthesis at different light intensities. This ratio will depend upon the relative efficacy of the enzyme systems involved in the reduction of the different hydrogen acceptors, competing for the hydrogen from E'H. It should, however, be clear that at a sufficiently high light intensity the rate of reduction of each of the components will become independent of the presence of others.

Fig. 1. Relation between rate of photosynthesis (R) and light intensity (I) in the presence and absence of nitrate. Curve 1: Nitrate absent; O_2 production or CO_2 assimilation. Curve 2; Nitrate present; O_2 production. Curve 3: Nitrate present; CO_2 assimilation.

APPLICATION TO THE PROBLEM OF NITRATE REDUCTION

There are some reports in the literature which clearly show that photosynthesizing algae can reduce nitrate and CO_2 simultaneously, and that, even in experiments of short duration, the nitrate reduction may attain considerable magnitude. Particularly the studies of CRAMER AND MYERS[16, 17] have contributed much in this direction, having demonstrated that the quotient CO_2/O_2, measured at low intensities of illumination, is very much smaller in the presence (0.6–0.8) than the absence of nitrate (0.94–1.0). It was established that under these conditions the rate of O_2 production was identical in the two cases[16]. This is in agreement with the above considerations.

Furthermore, the fact that the CO_2/O_2 ratio in the presence of nitrate increased from 0.7 at low, to 0.86 at high light intensity[17] indicates that the rate of nitrate reduction was relatively greater in the former case. But measurements of the absolute rate of O_2 evolution at high light intensity were not reported. From the point of view of an interpretation of the mechanism underlying the phenomenon of photochemical O_2 production in the presence of nitrate it is, however, especially this value that is of great significance. As the analysis of the hypothetical situation in which two different acceptors compete for the hydrogen from E'H has shown, one might predict that in strong light the rate of O_2 evolution in the presence of both nitrate and CO_2 should exceed that measured in the presence of CO_2 alone. Such a result would effectively eliminate the possibility that O_2 liberation in nitrate solutions is the result of CO_2 production from cell material and nitrate, since measurements could be conducted under conditions of CO_2 saturation. An extension of the observations of Cramer and Myers therefore seemed desirable.

A pure culture of *Chlorella pyrenoidosa* was used for the experiments. The algae were grown in Gaffron's medium or in modified Knop's solution, as described by MYERS[18]. In both cases nitrate was the only nitrogen source, since it is well known that many micro-organisms, potentially capable of reducing nitrate, fail to do so when they have been harvested from cultures in media containing reduced nitrogen compounds, and since the studies of MYERS AND CRAMER[17] provide evidence that this may be true also for *Chlorella*.

The cultures were aerated with a continuous stream of 5% CO_2 in air. Some of the cultures were grown in the intense red light from a neon grid, others in white light of 35–40 f.c. In order to obtain constant rates of photosynthesis at a given light intensity it was found desirable to place the cells at low light intensity (*ca* 20 f.c.) for the last 10–12 hours of growth. Cells were harvested after 3–4 days' incubation.

Most experiments were carried out with cells suspended in $M/100$–$M/15$ KH_2PO_4; nitrate, when present, was added in a concentration of 0.1%. Measurements of O_2 evolution and CO_2 assimilation were performed by two different procedures with concordant results. The methods employed were: A. The two-vessel method of WARBURG, based on the different solubilities of O_2 and CO_2, and requiring simultaneous readings of pressure changes in two flask-manometer combinations, identical except for the relative volumes of the liquid and gas phases. The gas phase in these experiments was 5–10% CO_2 in air. B. An alternative two-vessel method, in which the gas phase consisted of 5% CO_2 in N_2. CO_2 assimilation was determined directly in one vessel which contained a $CrCl_2$ solution ("Oxsorbent") in its side arm, while O_2 production was calculated from the concurrently recorded pressure changes produced by a duplicate suspension in the absence of Oxsorbent.

It was observed that absorption of O_2 by the $CrCl_2$ solution lags behind its liberation into the gas phase. Hence a small amount of O_2 is present as long as the suspensions are illuminated. By measuring the pressure decrease immediately after darkening it was established that, under the conditions ordinarily used, approximately 4–8 μl O_2 remained unabsorbed during the period of illumination. The inaccuracy resulting from this phenomenon was eliminated by taking into account only the pressure changes recorded after a situation of equilibrium had been reached, which required about 15 minutes.

Comparison of the rate of O_2 production by the cells in the acidic suspensions simultaneously with that in $M/10$ carbonate-bicarbonate buffer at pH 9.5 generally showed the former to be higher, indicating lack of CO_2 saturation under the conditions of low (0.2%) CO_2 concentration, as also reported by WARBURG *et al.*[19–21]. The reduction of nitrate by cell suspensions in KH_2PO_4 solution did not lead to the accumulation of nitrite, even in experiments with CO_2-N_2 mixtures as the gas phase; this is in agreement with the results described by KESSLER[22].

Illumination of the suspensions was achieved by means of a bank of 50–100 Watt Mazda bulbs, placed below a glass window in the bottom of the thermostat. Care was taken to ensure a homogeneous light field at the place where the vessels were suspended in the water bath. Variations in light intensity were produced by changing the capacity of the light bulbs, or the distance between the lights and the reaction flasks, or by attaching calibrated neutral filters to the bottoms of the reaction vessels. In order to obtain clear-cut results, especially at low light intensities, it was found desirable to use suspensions sufficiently thin (less than 2.5 μl cells per ml suspension) to avoid mutual shading of the cells.

Originally it was the intention to study in detail the relation between the assimilatory rates in the presence and absence of nitrate as a function of light intensity. The results of numerous experiments showed, however, that the photosynthetic characteristics of the cell suspensions did not remain constant during the course of a run involving determinations at several different light intensities. Generally, the photosynthetic rates

References p. 73/74.

determined at one specific intensity during the early part of an experiment differed considerably from those measured at the same intensity after the cell suspension had meanwhile been subjected to different intensities of illumination. This should be ascribed to the fact that such experiments extended over many hours, especially with dilute suspensions, where rates were calculated from measurements taken during a 2-hour exposure at one light intensity in order to insure reliable data for computations. The present report is therefore restricted to observations made at high light intensity, with one companion experiment permitting comparison with rates at a light intensity below saturation.

A summary of the results is presented in Table I.

TABLE I

RATES OF O_2 PRODUCTION AND CO_2 ASSIMILATION IN THE ABSENCE AND PRESENCE OF NITRATE, IN μL PER HOUR

Light Intensity	O_2 produced		CO_2 assimilated		CO_2/O_2	
		KNO$_3$		KNO$_3$		KNO$_3$
	Absent	Present	Absent	Present	Absent	Present
High	98.5	121.7	96.1	100.7	0.98	0.83
High	70.4	83.9	63.3	70.5	0.90	0.84
High	51.7	82.6	48.8	52.2	0.95	0.63
High	49.2	72.3	42.7	49.0	0.86	0.68
High	78.0	85.2	71.1	72.1	0.91	0.84
High	68.5	79.8	64.7	65.0	0.95	0.81
High	50.4	67.4	47.2	57.8[*]	0.94	0.86
High	36.5	40.3	33.3	33.8	0.92	0.83
Low	34.8	34.0	33.4	27.8	0.96	0.82

[*] This experiment was carried out with a cell suspension in tapwater; it is probable that the relatively high value for CO_2 assimilation is the result of the formation of alkali during the nitrate reduction, with the consequent absorption of CO_2 by the suspension fluid. An experimental determination of a possible increase in bicarbonate was not made.

It will be seen that at high light intensities the rate of O_2 production is greater in the presence than in the absence of nitrate, while the rate of CO_2 assimilation is approximately the same. Consequently, the quotient, CO_2/O_2, is invariably lower in the former than in the latter case. In contrast, under conditions of light limitation the rate of O_2 evolution appears not to be affected by the presence of nitrate; now its influence expresses itself in a lower rate of CO_2 assimilation. This last result is in complete agreement with the earlier and more extensive data of CRAMER AND MYERS[16].

From these results it can be concluded that the photochemical nitrate reduction cannot be explained by invoking the production of CO_2 from cellular constituents and nitrate because in all cases photosynthesis was measured in the presence of sufficient CO_2 to eliminate this component as a limiting factor.

One might postulate a conversion of organic cell material with nitrate as oxidant to substances other than CO_2 which could compete with the latter as hydrogen acceptors in photosynthesis and thus cause an increased rate of O_2 production at high light intensities. Such a postulate does not seem warranted, however, since it involves the hidden assumption that the enzymic oxidation of cell constituents with nitrate yields oxida-

References p. 73/74.

tion products different from those formed in the normal oxidation in the presence of O_2. For this assumption there is at present not the slightest evidence.

Hence it seems logical to infer that our results support the contention that the photochemical nitrate reduction represents a process in which nitrate acts directly as an alternate hydrogen acceptor in photosynthesis.

SUMMARY

At high light intensity suspensions of *Chlorella pyrenoidosa*, supplied with non-limiting concentrations of CO_2, produce oxygen at a greater rate when nitrate is simultaneously present. In that case the photosynthetic quotient, CO_2/O_2, is considerably lower than in the absence of nitrate, even though the rate of CO_2 assimilation is not reduced. From these results it is concluded that the photochemical nitrate reduction, discovered by WARBURG AND NEGELEIN in 1920, cannot be explained on the basis of a dark reaction which yields CO_2 by the oxidation of cell material with the concomitant reduction of nitrate. It can best be interpreted as a process in which nitrate acts directly as an alternate and additional hydrogen acceptor in photosynthesis.

RÉSUMÉ

La vélocité de l'évolution d'O_2 dans une suspension de *Chlorella pyrenoidosa* en présence d'une quantité suffisante d'acide carbonique peut être augmentée considérablement si l'on ajoute en même temps du nitrate, pourvu que l'intensité de l'illumination soit élévee. Dans ce cas le quotient assimilatoire, CO_2/O_2, est réduit; néanmoins l'assimilation de l'acide carbonique reste à peu près la même. Les résultats de nos expériences démontrent que la réduction photochimique du nitrate, découverte en 1920 par WARBURG ET NEGELEIN, ne constitue point un processus dans lequel en premier lieu des substances cellulaires des algues sont transformées en acide carbonique par voie d'une réaction enzymatique non-photochimique, suivi d'une assimilation "normale". Plutôt doit-elle être envisagée comme une réaction dans laquelle les nitrates ils-mêmes font concurrence à l'acide carbonique pour l'hydrogène résultant de la photodécomposition de l'eau.

ZUSAMMENFASSUNG

Bei genügend hoher Beleuchtungsintensität bildet eine mit Kohlensäure reichlich versehene Suspension von *Chlorella pyrenoidosa* pro Zeiteinheit mehr Sauerstoff, wenn gleichzeitig Nitrat anwesend ist. Obgleich in diesem Falle die Geschwindigkeit der Kohlensäureassimilation nicht geringer ist als in einer Nitrat-freien Suspension, so ist doch der assimilatorische Quotient, CO_2/O_2, bedeutend kleiner. Hieraus wird geschlossen, dass die 1920 von WARBURG UND NEGELEIN entdeckte photochemische Nitratreduktion nicht durch die Annahme, dass in einer Dunkelreaktion aus Zellsubstanz Kohlensäure gebildet wird bei gleichzeitiger Reduktion des Nitrats, erklärt werden kann. Vielmehr weisen die Versuchsergebnisse darauf hin, dass Nitrat neben Kohlensäure als selbständiger Wasserstoffakzeptor bei der Photosynthese dienen kann.

REFERENCES

[1] O. WARBURG, *Biochem. Z.*, 103 (1920) 188.
[2] O. WARBURG AND E. NEGELEIN, *Biochem. Z.*, 110 (1920) 66.
[3] C. B. VAN NIEL, *Arch. Mikrobiol.*, 3 (1931) 1.
[4] C. B. VAN NIEL, *Cold Spring Harbor Symposia Quant. Biol.*, 3 (1935) 138.
[5] A. J. KLUYVER AND H. J. L. DONKER, *Chem. Zelle u. Gewebe*, 13 (1925) 134.
[6] S. RUBEN, M. RANDALL, M. KAMEN AND J. L. HYDE, *J. Am. Chem. Soc.*, 63 (1941) 877.
[7] A. P. VINOGRADOV AND R. V. TEIS, *Compt. rend. acad. sci., U.S.S.R.*, 33 (1941) 490.
[8] S. WINOGRADSKY, *Microbiologie du Sol*, (Oeuvres complètes), Masson et Cie., Paris, 1949; 861 pp.
[9] R. HILL, *Proc Roy. Soc., B*, 127 (1939) 192.
[10] R. HILL AND R. SCARISBRICK, *Proc. Roy. Soc., B*, 129 (1940) 238.
[11] R. HILL, *Symposia Soc. Exptl. Biol*, V (1951) 222.
[12] C. B. VAN NIEL, *Advances in Enzymol.*, 1 (1941) 263–328.
[13] E. I. RABINOWITCH, *Photosynthesis and related processes*. Vol. I. Interscience Publ., Inc., New York, 1945; XIV plus 599 pp.

[14] O. WARBURG, *Schwermetalle als Wirkungsgruppen von Fermenten*. 2. Aufl., W. Saenger, Berlin, 1948, 195 pp.
[15] C. B. VAN NIEL, *Bacterial photosyntheses*. In: *The Enzymes*, edited by J. B. SUMNER AND K. MYR-BÄCK, Vol. II, 1074–1088. Acad. Press, Inc., New York, 1952.
[16] M. CRAMER AND J. MYERS, *J. Gen. Physiol.*, 32 (1948) 92.
[17] J. MYERS AND M. CRAMER, *J. Gen. Physiol.*, 32 (1948) 103.
[18] J. MYERS, *Plant Physiol.*, 22 (1947) 590.
[19] O. WARBURG, H. GELEICK AND K. BRIESE, *Z. Naturforsch.*, 6b (1951) 285.
[20] O. WARBURG, H. GELEICK AND K. BRIESE, *Z. Naturforsch.*, 7b (1952) 141.
[21] O. WARBURG, *Naturwiss.*, 39 (1952) 337.
[22] E. KESSLER, *Z. Naturforsch.*, 7b (1952) 280.

Received March 16th, 1953

THE REACTION OF THE CARCINOGENIC DIBENZCARBAZOLES AND DIBENZACRIDINES WITH PURINES AND NUCLEIC ACID

by

J. BOOTH AND E. BOYLAND

The Chester Beatty Research Institute, Royal Cancer Hospital, London, S.W.3 (England)

Polycyclic compounds without polar groups are only slightly soluble in water and the solubilities usually decrease with increase in molecular size. The solubility of such substances is however much greater in the presence of caffeine (BROCK, DRUCKREY AND HAMPERL[1]). WEIL-MALHERBE[2] measured the solubility of a number of hydrocarbons in many different purine solutions and found that the efficiency of purines as solubilising agents increased with increasing oxidation and N-methylation, $1:3:7:9$-tetramethyluric acid being the most efficient purine examined.

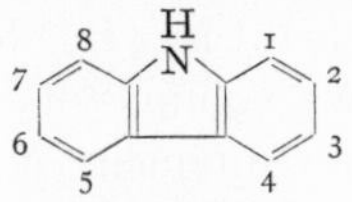

Carbazole

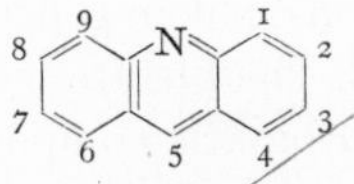

Acridine

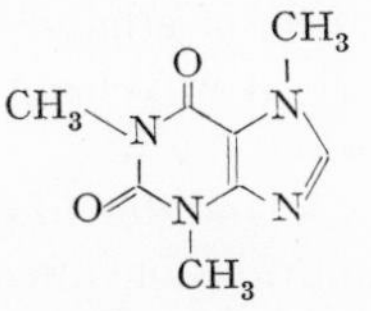

Caffeine

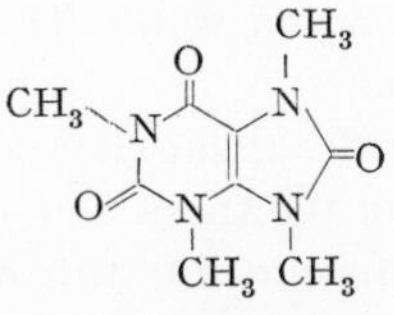

$1:3:7:9$-Tetramethyluric acid

The increased solubilities may be due to the formation of molecular compounds or complexes, and well-defined crystalline compounds containing one molecule of pyrene and one molecule of tetramethyluric acid, and containing one molecule of $3:4$-benz-pyrene and two molecules of tetramethyluric acid were prepared by WEIL-MALHERBE[2].

The solubilities of carcinogenic aromatic amines such as 2-naphthylamine, 2-aminofluorene, 2-anthramine, 4-aminostilbene, 4-aminoazobenzene and benzidine in water are also greatly increased by the addition of caffeine or tetramethyluric acid (NEISH[3]).

This work has been extended to the dibenzocarbazoles which had been shown to be carcinogenic by BOYLAND AND BRUES[4], $1:2$-$6:7$- and $3:4$-$6:7$-dibenzacridines which are known to be carcinogenic (BARRY, COOK, HASLEWOOD, HEWETT, HIEGER AND KENNAWAY[5]) and $1:2$-$8:9$-dibenzacridine which is being tested by LACASSAGNE (personal communication).

References p. 87.

EXPERIMENTAL

All absorption measurements were made with a Unicam SP.500 photoelectric spectrophotometer, readings being taken at intervals of 1 mμ. Whatman No. 42 paper was used for filtration except when stated to the contrary.

The solubility of polycyclic compounds

Preparation of suspensions. Polycyclic compounds were ground in a hand homogeniser with water until the particles became wet and finely divided. The suspensions were filtered and the solids washed several times with water. The solid material was then washed off the filter paper and diluted with water to make a suspension containing approximately 200 mg/100 ml. After diluting a sample with ethanol to dissolve the solid, the concentration was estimated by comparing the absorption at a wavelength of maximum absorption for the particular compound with a standard absorption curve.

Solubility in water. A mixture of 1 l water and 1 ml of the previously prepared suspension of the aromatic compound was shaken gently at 22° for 3 hours. After filtration the filtrate was extracted with three 50 ml portions of benzene. The combined benzene extracts were dried over Na_2SO_4, evaporated to a small volume and made up to 10 ml with benzene. The concentration increased thus 100 times was measured with the photoelectric spectrophotometer.

Solubility in purine solutions. The 0.2% suspension (1 ml) was added to 9 ml of aqueous purine solution, shaken gently at a constant temperature (22°) for the required time and then filtered. The filtrate was diluted with known volumes of ethanol and the concentration of the aromatic compound estimated by measurement of the absorption at the wavelength of one of the maxima of the substance concerned. The standard optical density measurements used for these determinations were made in the same concentrations of ethanol as the unknown solution, because absorption differs in different proportions of ethanol and water. The lowest concentration of ethanol used was 50%. This method is restricted to those substance which absorb at wavelengths greater than 330 mμ since the purines themselves absorb below this wavelength.

The solubilities of the three isomers of dibenzcarbazole and dibenzacridine at room temperature were determined in this way in saturated solutions of caffeine (0.07 M) and of tetramethyluric acid (0.08 M). These aromatic compounds were also soluble in sodium deoxyribonucleate (DNA) (0.1%). More concentrated solutions of DNA were too viscous to filter and could not be used for determinations by this method.

The Molecular Ratio (M.R.) is calculated as

$$\frac{\text{Mols. of purine in solution}}{\text{Mols. of aromatic compd. in solution}}$$

i.e. the number of mols. of purine required to dissolve 1 mol. of aromatic compound (*cf.* WEIL-MALHERBE[2]). In calculating the M.R. for the deoxyribonucleate solution an arbitrary mol. wt. of 391 (equivalent to that of the sodium salt of adenylic acid) was used.

Change in solubility with time of shaking. By adding 5 ml of the 0.2% suspension of aromatic substance to 45 ml of saturated purine solution, suspensions of excess solid in 0.063 M caffeine or 0.072 M tetramethyluric acid were obtained. These were shaken at a constant temperature: samples (2 ml) withdrawn at various intervals of time after mixing were filtered and the concentration of the substance under examination estimated in the filtrates as before.

In the case of the hydrocarbons studied in this way (*e.g.* 3:4-benzpyrene and pyrene), the concentration of hydrocarbon in the filtrate increased during the first 15 to 30 min to a constant value.

The solubilities of the three dibenzcarbazoles in caffeine solution, however, increased to a maximum and then decreased to a steady level. When 3:4:5:6-dibenzcarbazole was added to a tetramethyluric acid solution under these conditions, the decrease in concentration started immediately, presumably because the maximum concentration was reached within a few seconds of mixing (but see page 79).

Of the three dibenzacridines studied in tetramethyluric acid solution at 37°, only the 1:2-8:9-isomer showed a slow decrease in concentration after the initial rise (Table I and Figs. 1 and 2). When the whole of the mixture was filtered, after shaking for the

TABLE I

SOLUBILITY OF AROMATIC COMPOUNDS IN PURINE SOLUTIONS

	Solubilities										
	Water	Caffeine (0.063 M)				Tetramethyluric acid (0.072 M)				DNA (0.0025 M)	
Aromatic compound		At maximum		At equilibrium		At maximum		At equilibrium			
	Conc.	Conc.	M.R.	Conc.	M.R	Conc.	M.R.	Conc.	M.R.	Conc.	M.R.
3:4-5:6 DBC	0.20	338	210	113	630	1120	71	82	975	13	190
1:2-5:6 DBC	<0.05	172	406	38	1840	1060	75	128	625	8	310
1:2-7:8 DBC	<0.05	300	230	139	502	840	95	45	1780	—	—
3:4-6:7 DBA	0.25	840	84	840	84	1760	45	1760	45	165	14
1:2-6:7 DBA	<0.05	11	6350	11	6350	84	955	84	955	3	835
1:2-8:9 DBA	0.07	19	3600	15	4660	150	530	97	830	11	230

DBC = Dibenzcarbazole.
DBA = Dibenzacridine.
DNA = Deoxyribonucleic acid (M.R. calculated on Mol.Wt. of sodium salt of adenylic acid).
(Concns. shown in table are for M concn. of aromatic compound.)

time required to obtain maximum concentration, a small amount of crystalline material separated from the filtrate on standing. This was due to formation of molecular compounds identical with those described below (page 80).

Effect of pH on the 3:4-5:6-*dibenzcarbazole-caffeine complex.* The solutions were buffered with McIlvaine's sodium phosphate-citric acid standard buffer solutions for pH 2–8, and 0.05 M sodium carbonate-sodium borate mixtures for pH 9–11. Mixtures of 8 ml 0.087 M caffeine, 1 ml buffer solution and 1 ml 0.2% 3:4-5:6-dibenzcarbazole suspension were added to each of ten 25 ml flasks giving suspensions of solid in 0.07 M caffeine.

The mixtures were shaken at 22° for 20 min to give maximal concentrations and excess 3:4-5:6-dibenzcarbazole removed by filtration. Immediately after filtration 1 ml was removed from each filtrate for estimation of dibenzcarbazole concentration (F_1). The remainder of the filtrates were shaken for a further 18 hours at 22°, again filtered and the dibenzcarbazole concentration in these filtrates estimated (F_2). Thus the differ-

References p. 87.

ence between F_1 and F_2 gave the amount of dibenzcarbazole precipitated as a molecular complex for each pH value.

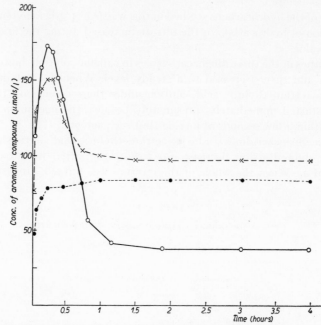

Fig. 1. Relationship between conc. of aromatic compound and time of shaking. O————O, 1:2-5:6-dibenzcarbazole in 0.063 M caffeine; ×————×, 1:2-8:9-dibenzacridine in 0.072 M tetramethyluric acid; ●·········●, 1:2-6:7-dibenzacridine in 0.072 M tetramethyluric acid.

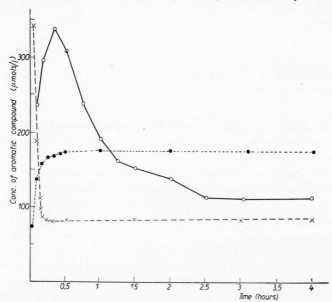

Fig. 2. Relationship between conc. of aromatic compound and time of shaking. O————O, 3:4-5:6-dibenzcarbazole in 0.063 M caffeine; ×————× 3:4-5:6-dibenzcarbazole in 0.072 M tetramethyluric acid; ●·········● 3:4-6:7-dibenzacridine × 10^{-1} in 0.072 M tetramethyluric acid.

References p. 87.

The effect of pH on the amount of 3:4-5:6-dibenzcarbazole remaining in solution after the precipitation of the molecular complex is almost negligible, but the amount which dissolves before precipitation begins, and therefore, the amount precipitated as a molecular compound increases with an increase in pH (Fig. 3).

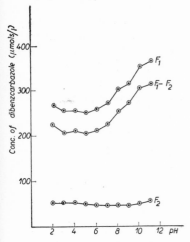

Fig. 3. Effect of pH on the precipitation of the 3:4-5:6-dibenzcarbazole-caffeine complex. F_1 conc. of dibenzcarbazole in 0.07 M caffeine before precipitation of the complex; F_2 conc. of dibenzcarbazole in 0.07 M caffeine after precipitation of the complex; F_1–F_2, dibenzcarbazole precipitated as complex.

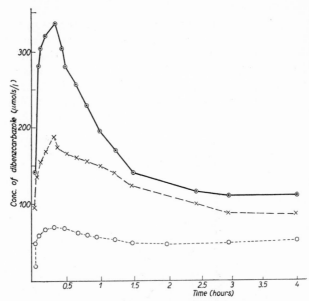

Fig. 4. Effect of purine conc. on precipitation of 3:4-5:6-dibenzocarbazole-caffeine complex. ⊙——⊙, conc. of dibenzcarbazole in 0.07 M caffeine; ×----×, in 0.046 M caffeine; ○········○, in 0.023 M caffeine.

Effect of purine concentration on the precipitation of the 3:4-5:6-*dibenzcarbazole-caffeine complex.* The concentration of dibenzcarbazole at various intervals of time after mixing was estimated, using 0.07, 0.046 and 0.023 M solutions of caffeine. The results showed that the maximum concentration of dibenzcarbazole, the amount of complex precipitated and the dibenzcarbazole remaining in solution when the equilibrium had been reached increased with increase of caffeine concentration. The time required to reach the maximum concentration of dibenzcarbazole and to reach equilibrium however was not affected (Fig. 4).

Effect of amount of dibenzcarbazole added on the precipitation of the complex. In these experiments suspensions of 20, 50, 100 and 200 mg/l of 3:4-5:6-dibenzcarbazole in 0.07 M caffeine solution were examined. The more concentrated suspensions produced a greater maximum concentration of dibenzcarbazole in solution before precipitation of the complex and a shorter time was required for the equilibrium to be reached.

Similarly, by reducing the amount of dibenzcarbazole added to a 0.08 M solution of tetramethyluric acid from 200 mg/l, when the maximum dibenzcarbazole concentration was reached too quickly for detection, to 50 mg/l, an increase to a maximum occurred followed by a decrease (Fig. 5).

Effect on purine concentration on the solubility of 3:4-6:7-*dibenzacridine.* (*No precipitation of complex.*) 3:4-6:7-Dibenzacridine was chosen for this investigation because

References p. 87.

5

its comparatively high solubility in purine solutions enabled measurements to be made over a wide range of concentrations. The effect of different concentrations of caffeine and deoxyribonucleic acid was investigated and an interesting difference observed. The molecular ratio decreased with increasing concentration in the case of caffeine and increased in the case of DNA.

The solubilities were determined as before using caffeine concentrations ranging from 0.0014 M to 0.07 M and sodium deoxyribonucleate concentrations equivalent to 0.00023 M to 0.0042 M nucleotide. The suspensions were shaken at 22° for 1 h since preliminary experiments had shown that there was no increase in solubility after this time. When measuring the concentration of dibenzacridine in the sodium deoxyribonucleate, it was necessary to add 0.1 ml of 2 N NaOH to the filtrate on diluting, since

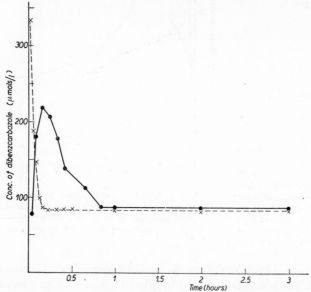

Fig. 5. Effect of amount of 3:4:5:6-dibenzcarbazole added on precipitation of the dibenzcarbazole-tetramethyluric acid complex. ×----× 200 mg/l dibenzcarbazole in 0.08 M tetramethyluric acid; ●——● 50 mg/l dibenzcarbazole in 0.08 M tetramethyluric acid.

ionisation of the dibenzacridine occurred and the ion has a different absorption spectrum from the unionised molecule. The results are shown in Table II (M.R. values for deoxyribonucleate are calculated as before).

In the case of hydrocarbons dissolved in caffeine and tetramethyluric acid solutions studied by WEIL-MALHERBE[2] the M.R. was either constant or decreased with increase in purine concentrations. NEISH[3], however, had observed that the M.R. for the solubility of 2-naphthylamine, 2-aminofluorene and benzidine in caffeine, increased with increase in caffeine concentration.

Preparation of molecular compounds. Saturated ethanolic solutions of the dibenzcarbazole or dibenzacridine were added to aqueous caffeine (0.07 M) or tetramethyluric acid (0.08 M) solutions with gentle shaking, until excess of the compound was precipitated. The excess solid was immediately removed by filtration through Whatman No. 1 paper. In some cases the filtrate was slightly turbid, but on standing (0.5–6 h) small amounts of crystalline precipitates were formed. These were filtered off, washed once with water

References p. 87.

TABLE II

SOLUBILITY OF 3:4-6:7-DIBENZACRIDINE IN CAFFEINE AND SODIUM DEOXYRIBONUCLEATE SOLUTIONS

Caffeine			Sodium Deoxyribonucleate		
Caffeine conc. (μ mols/$_1$)	DBA conc. (μ mols/$_1$)	M.R.	DNA conc. (μmols/$_1$)	DBA conc. (μmols/$_1$)	M.R.
14,000	59	237	230	56	4
21,000	130	162	460	75	6
28,000	204	138	920	114	8
35,000	276	126	1,380	126	11
42,000	377	111	1,840	136	14
49,000	477	103	2,300	165	14
56,000	600	93	2,760	165	17
63,000	702	90	3,220	158	20
70,000	840	84	3,700	144	26
			4,200	136	31

and dried. The properties of compounds prepared in this way are shown in Table III. I:2-6:7-Dibenzacridine was not sufficiently soluble in ethanol to prepare a molecular compound by this method.

Spectrophotometric analysis of the molecular compounds. Absorption spectra of benzene or ethanol solutions of the molecular compounds of hydrocarbons prepared by WEIL-MALHERBE (*e.g.* 1 mol. 3:4-benzpyrene + 2 mols. tetramethyluric acid) and of the dibenzcarbazole and dibenzacridine complexes were found to be the sum of the ab-

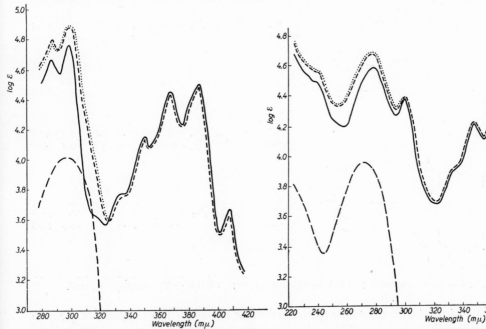

Fig. 6. Absorption spectra of 3:4-benzpyrene-tetramethyluric acid compound and its components in benzene. ———, 3:4-benzpyrene; — —, tetramethyluric acid; -----, molecular compound; ---------, calculated curve for 1 mol. 3:4-benzpyrene + 2 mols. tetramethyluric acid.

Fig. 7. Absorption spectra of 3:4-5:6-dibenz-carbazole-caffeine compound and its components in ethanol. ———, 3:4-5:6-dibenzcarbazole; — — caffeine; -----, molecular compound; ---------, calculated curve for 1 mol. 3:4-5:6-dibenz-carbazole + 1 mol. caffeine.

References p. 87.

TABLE III

PROPERTIES OF MOLECULAR COMPOUNDS FORMED BY COMBINATION OF
DIBENZCARBAZOLES AND DIBENZACRIDINES WITH PURINES

Polycyclic compound	Purine	M.P. and description		Analysis (%) C	H	N	DBC or BDA
I mol. 3:4-5:6 DBC	I mol. caffeine	158° plates	$C_{28}H_{23}O_2N_5$ requires Found	72.9 72.7	5.0 5.0	15.2 15.2	57.9 57.3
I mol. 1:2-5:6 DBC	I mol. caffeine	197° small prisms	$C_{28}H_{23}O_2N_5$ requires Found	72.9 72.4	5.0 5.0	15.2 14.8	57.9 57.6
I mol. 1:2-7:8 DBC	2 mols. caffeine	Softens 96° M.P. 170° small prisms	$C_{36}H_{33}O_4N_9$ requires Found	65.9 66.2	5.1 5.4	19.2 18.9	40.8 40.5
I mol. 3:4-5:6 DBC	I mol. TMUA	236° rect. plates	$C_{29}H_{25}O_3N_5$ requires Found	70.9 70.6	5.1 4.9	14.2 14.0	54.4 54.2
I mol. 3:4-6:7 DBA	I mol. TMUA	185° needles	$C_{30}H_{25}O_3N_5$ requires Found	71.6 71.9	5.0 5.4	14.0 14.2	55.5 56.6
I mol. 1:2-8:9 DBA	I mol. TMUA	198° plates	$C_{30}H_{25}O_3N_5$ requires Found	71.6 71.6	5.0 5.1	14.0 14.3	55.5 54.3

DBC = Dibenzcarbazole;   DBA = Dibenzacridine;   TMUA = Tetramethyluric acid.

sorption of the two components of the molecular compounds, (examples are given in Figs. 6 and 7).

Similar results have been found in the case of molecular compounds formed between hydrocarbons and trinitrobenzene (JONES AND NEUWORTH[6]), hydrocarbons and deoxycholic acid (FIESER AND NEWMAN[7]) and naphthalene and picric acid (HUNTER, QUREISHY AND SAMUEL[8]).

References p. 87.

The ultraviolet absorption spectra of 3:4-benzpyrene, 3:4-5:6-dibenzcarbazole and 3:4-6:7-dibenzacridine in saturated purine solutions, were compared with the absorption of the same compounds in 50% ethanol alone and saturated with caffeine or tetra-methyluric acid. In each case there was a depression of the maxima and a bathochromic shift in the purine solution (*e.g.* see Fig. 8). The greatest shift occurred in 3:4-benzpyrene when the maximum at 384 mμ was shifted to 391 mμ in tetramethyluric acid.

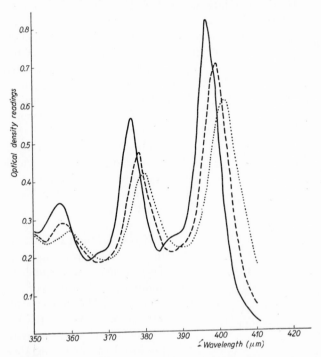

Fig. 8. Absorption spectra of 3:4-6:7-dibenzacridine in purine solutions. ——, in 50% ethanol; -----, 50% ethanol saturated with caffeine; ·········, in 50% ethanol saturated with tetramethyluric acid.

Similar changes in the absorption spectra of acriflavine dissolved in nucleic acid have been described (OSTER[9]). Such modifications of the spectra may be similar to the changes produced by using different solvents.

The purine components of the molecular compounds do not absorb at wavelengths above 300 mμ (caffeine) or 330 mμ (tetramethyluric acid), whereas all the dibenz-carbazoles and dibenzacridines studied have well defined maxima between 340–400 mμ. As the molecular extinctions of dilute solutions of the molecular compounds in this range are identical with those of the pure dibenzcarbazoles or dibenzacridines, such maxima are convenient for the estimation of the aromatic component in molecular compounds. Ethanolic solutions of known concentrations of the molecular compounds were prepared and optical density (Log I_0/I) at suitable maxima determined. The concentration, and hence the proportion of aromatic component in the complex could then be calculated by comparison with a similar determination on the pure aromatic substance, since if the concentrations used are such that the optical density readings are of the same order they are directly proportional to the concentration. The results of these estimations are shown in the last column of Table III.

Fluorescence of solutions. WEIL-MALHERBE[10] noticed that the fluorescence of solutions of hydrocarbons in aqueous caffeine was quenched by the addition of acid, the quenching agent being the caffeine ion and not the hydrogen ion, whereas substituted uric acids alone quenched the fluorescence in aqueous solutions and this quenching was independent of the pH of the solution. Similar results were obtained with the dibenzcarbazoles, the aqueous caffeine solutions possessing an intense blue fluorescence which was quenched on acidification and restored on neutralisation, whilst the aqueous tetramethyluric acid solutions were not fluorescent. Caffeine solutions of the dibenzacridines

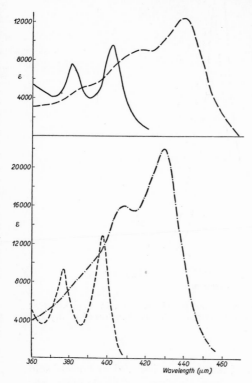

were colourless and possessed an intense blue fluorescence; acidification of these solutions quenched the fluorescence and produced a bright yellow colour owing to the ionisation of the dibenzacridine; the tetramethyluric acid solutions again showed no fluorescence in acid or alkali, but acidification produced bright yellow solutions.

Ionisation of the dibenzacridines. When 3:4-6:7-dibenzacridine was dissolved in a neutral solution of the sodium salt of DNA (pH 6.5) a bright yellow colour and a change in the absorption spectra were observed. These changes were similar to those brought about by the addition of acid to an ethanolic solution of the dibenzacridine (Fig. 9). The absorption curves in DNA show the typical bathochromic shift and reduction of maxima produced by dissolving these compounds in purines.

The degree of ionisation at any pH value is directly proportional to the height of the absorption maximum of the dibenzacridine ion at 435 mμ for solutions of the same concentration since this value is negligible for the unionised molecule. The pK_a values were determined spectrophotometrically for 3:4-6:7-dibenzacridine in 25%, 50% and 75% ethanol, aqueous caffeine, tetramethyluric acid and 50% ethanolic DNA solutions

Fig. 9. Effect of DNA on the absorption curve of 3:4-6:7-dibenzacridine. ----------, in 50% methanol pH = 6.2; —·—·—, in 50% methanolic 5N HCl pH < 1; — —, in 0.1% DNA solution pH = 6.5; —— in 0.1% DNA + 0.1 ml N NaOH, pH = 9.0.

(Fig. 10). The DNA apparently increases the pK_a of the dibenzacridine from approximately 3.5 in aqueous ethanol, caffeine and tetramethyluric acid to 6.8 in aqueous DNA and to 6.1 in 50% ethanolic DNA. Determination of the pK_a values of the other two isomers of dibenzacridine in tetramethyluric acid showed that they were weaker bases (Table IV).

The dissociation curve for 3:4-6:7-dibenzacridine dissolved in DNA is abnormal in that the slope is less steep than that of a normal ionisation curve.

References p. 87.

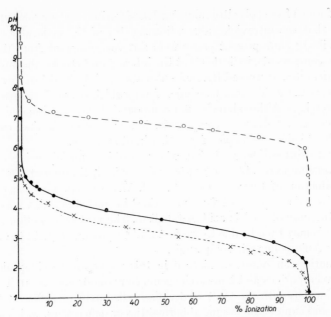

Fig. 10. Ionisation of 3:4-6:7-dibenzacridine in purine solutions. ●————●, in 0.063 M caffeine; ×·········×, in 0.072 M tetramethyluric acid; ○-----○, in 0.1% DNA.

TABLE IV

pKa VALUES OF THE DIBENZACRIDINES IN PURINE SOLUTIONS

Dibenzacridine	Solvent	pKa
3:4-6:7 DBA	25%, 50% or 75% ethanol	3.8
	0.1% DNA	6.8
	50% ethanolic 0.1% DNA	6.1
	0.063 M caffeine	3.5
	0.072 M tetramethyluric acid	3.1
1:2-6:7 DBA	0.072 M tetramethyluric acid	2.2
1:2-8:9 DBA	0.072 M tetramethyluric acid	−0.2

DISCUSSION

The molecular compounds formed between caffeine (or tetramethyluric acid) and one of the dibenzcarbazoles (or dibenzacridines), which have so far been isolated, resemble the hydrocarbon-purine complexes isolated by WEIL-MALHERBE, in that only small changes in light absorption are associated with their formation. In this way they differ from the molecular compounds formed between nitro-compounds and hydrocarbons or amines. The change or intensification of colour which takes place in these cases has been ascribed to the formation of a complex molecule, essentially ionic in character, involving an electron transfer from the unsaturated hydrocarbon to the poly-nitro compound (WEISS[11]; KRONBERGER AND WEISS[12]).

The infrared absorption spectra of the complexes of purines with hydrocarbons and with aromatic nitrogenous substances (BOOTH, BOYLAND AND ORR[13]) are similar to those of complexes formed from polynitro compounds as described by BURTON AND RICHARDS[14].

The fact that the ultraviolet absorption spectra of the molecular compounds in solution described in the present paper were not very different from the sum of the spectra of the components, indicates that the interaction between the two molecules is of a rather indefinite nature and the molecules are possibly held together by hydrogen bonds (in the case of the dibenzcarbazoles) or forces which are weak compared with those existing between ions. Although molecular compounds have been isolated only for some pairs of purines and polycyclic compounds, it seems probable that the increase in solubility is due to similar complex formation in other cases.

LEITER AND SHEAR[15] showed that when xanthine, nucleic acid, hypoxanthine, guanine and caffeine were added to 3:4-benzpyrene in lipoid solvents and injected into mice, the production of tumours was retarded. WEIL-MALHERBE[2] suggests that the affinity of polycyclic compounds for the purines in nucleo-proteins may cause interference with the normal nucleic acid metabolism. The protective action of the purines in carcinogenesis may then be due to the fact that they compete with the nucleoprotein for the carcinogenic polycyclic compounds.

The aromatic compounds considered in this paper are carcinogenic but similar reactions between purines and non-carcinogenic compounds also occur. The reaction of aromatic carcinogens with the DNA of dividing cells might be sufficient to distort the nucleoprotein and cause chromosome abnormalities or deficiencies, which are associated with the induction of mutations and of cancer. Whether the carcinogenic compounds produce more change of this kind than inactive analogues, and if such changes are sufficient to account for the biological effects produced is not known.

ACKNOWLEDGEMENTS

We are grateful to Messrs. F. Hoffmann-La Roche & Co Ltd. for the supply of samples of dibenzcarbazoles and to Mr F. H. OLIVER for the micro-analyses. This investigation has been supported by grants to the Royal Cancer Hospital and Chester Beatty Research Institute from the British Empire Cancer Campaign, the Jane Coffin Childs Memorial Fund for Medical Research, the Anna Fuller Fund and the National Cancer Institute of the National Institutes of Health, U.S. Public Health Service.

SUMMARY

1. The solubilities of three isomers of dibenzcarbazole and dibenzacridine (like those of other aromatic carcinogens) in caffeine and tetramethyluric acid solutions are much greater than in water.
2. The three dibenzcarbazoles examined and 1:2-7:8-dibenzacridine are precipitated from aqueous solutions of purines as molecular compounds formed between the aromatic substances and the purines.
3. A solution of sodium deoxyribonucleate also dissolves the dibenzcarbazoles and dibenzacridines. The apparent pK_a of 3:4-6:7-dibenzacridine is approximately 3.5 in 50% ethanol, caffeine and tetramethyluric acid solutions and 6.8 in a solution of sodium deoxyribonucleate.

RÉSUMÉ

1. Les trois isomères du dibenzcarbazole et de la dibenzacridine (de même que tous les cancérigènes aromatiques), sont beaucoup plus solubles dans des solutions de caféine et d'acide tétraméthylurique que dans l'eau.

References p. 87.

2. Les trois dibenzcarbazoles étudiés et la 1:2-7:8-dibenzacridine, dissous dans des solutions aqueuses de purines, précipitent sous forme de combinaisons moléculaires avec les purines.

3. Une solution de désoxyribonucléate de sodium dissout également les dibenzcarbazoles et les dibenzacridines. Le pK_a apparent de la 3:4-6:7-dibenzacridine est d'environ 3.5 dans des solutions éthyliques à 50 % de caféine et d'acide tétraméthylurique et de 6,8 dans une solution de désoxyribonucléate de sodium.

ZUSAMMENFASSUNG

1. Die Löslichkeit von 3 Isomeren des Dibenzcarbazols und Dibenzacridins ist wie die anderer aromatischer carcinogener Stoffe in Coffein und Tetramethylharnsäurelösungen viel grösser als in Wasser.

2. Die drei untersuchten Dibenzcarbazole und 1:2-7:8-Dibenzacridin werden aus der wässrigen Lösung der Purine als Molekülverbindungen der aromatischen Substanzen mit den Purinen ausgefällt.

3. Eine Lösung von desoxyribonucleinsaurem Natrium löst ebenfalls die Dibenzcarbazole und Dibenzacridine. Die scheinbare pK_a des 3:4-6:7-Dibenzacridins ist ungefähr 3.5 in 50 % Äthanol-, Coffein- und Tetramethylharnsäurelösungen und 6.8 in einer Lösung von desoxyribonucleinsaurem Natrium.

REFERENCES

[1] N. BROCK, H. DRUCKREY AND H. HAMPERL, *Arch. exptl. Path. Pharmakol.*, 189 (1938) 709.
[2] H. WEIL-MALHERBE, *Biochem. J.*, 40 (1946a) 351.
[3] W. J. P. NEISH, *Rec. trav. chim.*, 67 (1948) 361.
[4] E. BOYLAND AND A. M. BRUES, *Proc. Roy. Soc. B.*, 122 (1937) 429.
[5] G. BARRY, J. W. COOK, G. A. D. HASLEWOOD, C. L. HEWETT AND E. L. KENNAWAY, *Proc. Roy. Soc. B.*, 117 (1935) 318.
[6] R. C. JONES AND M. S. NEUWORTH, *J. Am. Chem. Soc.*, 66 (1944) 1497.
[7] L. F. FIESER AND M. S. NEWMAN, *J. Am. Chem. Soc.*, 57 (1935) 1602.
[8] R. F. HUNTER, A. M. QUREISHY AND R. SAMUEL, *J. Chem. Soc.*, (1936) 1576.
[9] G. OSTER, *Trans. Faraday Soc.*, 47 (1951) 660.
[10] H. WEIL-MALHERBE, *Biochem. J.*, 40 (1946b) 363.
[11] J. WEISS, *J. Chem. Soc.*, (1942) 245.
[12] H. KRONBERGER AND J. WEISS, *J. Chem. Soc.* (1944) 464.
[13] J. BOOTH, E. BOYLAND AND S. F. D. ORR, (1953). In preparation.
[14] W. R. BURTON AND R. E. RICHARDS, *J. Chem. Soc.*, (1950) 1316.
[15] J. LEITER AND M. S. SHEAR, *J. Natl. Cancer Inst.*, 3 (1942) 455.

Received March 20th, 1953

EFFECT OF THE PRESENCE OF LABILE METHYL GROUPS IN THE DIET ON LABILE METHYL NEOGENESIS

by

VINCENT DU VIGNEAUD, JOHN M. KINNEY, JOHN E. WILSON
AND JULIAN R. RACHELE

Department of Biochemistry, Cornell University Medical College, New York (U.S.A.)

Tissue slice experiments employing ^{14}C-labelled precursors[1-3] and experiments with germ-free animals receiving deuterium-labelled drinking water[4,5] have demonstrated that "biologically labile" methyl groups are synthesized in the tissues of the rat.

In the latter experiments the deuterium concentration of the body water of both germ-free and nonsterile animals was maintained at about 3 atom per cent. After a period of approximately 3 weeks the choline was isolated from the tissues of these rats and the deuterium concentration of the trimethylamine chloroplatinate prepared from the isolated choline was determined. The level of deuterium in the methyl groups of the choline of these animals was between 6.4 and 9.6% of that in the body water. These values agreed closely with the levels obtained in a much earlier experiment in which ordinary animals were given deuterium-labelled drinking water[6].

In interpreting these results it was reasoned that if synthesis of the labile methyl group did occur from some precursor in the presence of D_2O, then the methyl group so formed would have deuterium introduced into it during the synthetic process. From our previous experience that deuterium attached to the carbon of the labile methyl group did not exchange appreciably with the hydrogens of the body water[7-9], it appeared highly unlikely that in such experiments a direct exchange between the hydrogens of the methyl group and the deuterium of the D_2O in the body water had taken place to bring about the appearance of deuterium in the methyl group. Thus, the finding of deuterium in the methyl groups of choline under these conditions justified the conclusion that synthesis of the methyl group must have occurred.

In all of this work on the uptake of deuterium, the diet of the animals contained labile methyl groups, so that synthesis was apparently occurring to the extent observed, even in the presence of a dietary source of labile methyl groups. If the interpretation were correct that the appearance of deuterium in the labile methyl groups of the body is a reflection of the degree of neogenesis of methyl groups, then the appearance of a larger amount of deuterium in the methyl groups of choline should result under dietary conditions in which the animal was forced to synthesize its entire supply of labile methyl groups. The present paper reports a set of experiments designed to test whether this was the case. The amount of incorporation of deuterium from body water into the labile methyl group in animals receiving dietary methyl groups was compared with that in

References p. 91.

animals on a methyl-free diet. Both groups of animals received B_{12} and folic acid in sufficient amounts to ensure synthesis of labile methyl groups and promote growth when the labile methyl groups were not present in the diet.

The results fitted in with what would be predicted on the basis of the concept outlined. In the case of the animals on the methyl-containing diets, from 5.5 to 10.4% of the choline methyl was derived from the body water, whereas in the case of the animals on the methyl-free diet, the percentages ranged from 24.4 to 34.3. Thus the incorporation of deuterium into the methyl group of choline in the animals on the methyl-free diet was almost four times as great as that in the animals receiving diets containing labile methyl compounds.

EXPERIMENTAL

The eight rats used for these experiments were kept in raised cages equipped for urine collection. Drinking water was made continuously available. The animals were placed on an amino acid diet containing homocystine and choline, but no methionine. The composition of this diet, which was fed *ad libitum*, is shown in Table I. The weights

TABLE I

PERCENTAGE COMPOSITION OF INITIAL DIET

Sucrose	73
Salt mixture[10]	4
Amino acid mixture[*]	17.2
Water soluble vitamins[†§]	1
Corn oil	2
Vitamins E and K in corn oil[**]	1
Vitamins A and D conc.[***]	0.5 drop
DL-Homocystine	1
Choline chloride	0.8

[*] Glycine, 0.1; L-hydroxyproline, 0.1; L-proline, 0.2; DL-serine, 0.2; L-aspartic acid, 0.2; DL-alanine, 0.4; L-tryptophan, 0.4; L-arginine·HCl, 0.6; L-histidine·HCl·H_2O, 0.7; L-tyrosine, 1.0; DL-threonine, 1.4; DL-phenylalanine, 1.5; DL-*isoleucine*, 1.8; DL-valine, 2.0; L-glutamic acid, 2.0; L-leucine, 1.3; L-lysine·HCl, 1.9; sodium bicarbonate, 1.4.

[†] Biotin, 0.01 mg; folic acid, 0.1 mg (increased to 0.4 mg in the case of Rats 30, 31); thiamin chloride, riboflavin, pyridoxine hydrochloride, nicotinic acid, and *p*-aminobenzoic acid, 1 mg each; calcium d-pantothenate, 5 mg; inositol, 10 mg; Vitamin B_{12}, 20 µg (except for Rats 30 and 31, which received 15 µg); sucrose to make 1 g.

[§] In the case of Rats 30 and 31, the vitamins were removed from the diet on the 20th day and the following vitamin solution was given *per os* in two 0.5 ml portions daily (mg per ml of solution): thiamin chloride, riboflavin, nicotinic acid, pyridoxine hydrochloride, *p*-aminobenzoic acid, 0.8 each; calcium *d*-pantothenate, 0.40; inositol, 0.80; folic acid, 0.008; biotin, 0.0008, sucrose, 100 mg.

[**] Containing 4 mg of α-tocopherol acetate and 0.1 mg of 2-methyl-1,4-naphthoquinone.

[***] Containing 750 I.U. of vitamin A and 125 I.U. of vitamin D.

of the animals at various stages of the experiment are summarized in Table II, along with the days on which the dietary regimens were changed. Four of the rats (30, 31, 40 and 41) were maintained on a labile methyl-free diet throughout the experimental period. Two of the animals (42 and 43) received the diet given in Table I containing choline and the other two (44 and 45) received a diet in which the choline was replaced by a 1% level of methionine. After the animals had grown on these regimens for the times indicated in Table II, deuterium oxide was administered in the drinking water at a level of 10 atom per cent for 4 days and then at a level of 4 atom per cent. for the remainder of the 3-week experimental period. The animals were then sacrificed with chloroform and immediately frozen in dry ice.

TABLE II

WEIGHTS OF ANIMALS IN GRAMS

Day of Experiment		0	28	38	57	78
Rat No.	Sex	Weaned	Initial Diet	Choline* removed	D₂O begun	Sacrificed
30†	♂	41	41	121	214	238
31†	♂	39	39	121	208	234
40	♂	38	136	148	188	231
41	♂	32	104	122	192	226
42	♀	34	92	122	172	187
43	♀	26	93	120	164	170
44	♂	36	112	123	168	202
45	♀	33	98	119	162	176

* Rats 42 and 43 were continued on the initial choline-containing diet; rats 44 and 45 were placed on a diet in which the choline was replaced by methionine.

† Rats 30 and 31 were begun on the amino acid diet at weaning, choline was removed 30 days later, D₂O was begun 79 days later and the animals were sacrificed on the 100th day.

The choline was isolated as the chloroplatinate and degraded to trimethylamine according to procedures described previously[5]. The average deuterium content of the body water during the last 3 weeks of the experiment was determined by measuring by the mass spectrometer method[11,12] the deuterium content of water from the pooled urine of each animal for this period. The deuterium contents of the trimethylamine chloroplatinates were likewise determined. These values were then used to calculate the extent to which the deuterium of the body water had been incorporated into choline methyl groups. The experimental results are summarized in Table III.

TABLE III

ISOTOPIC CONTENTS OF BODY WATER AND CHOLINE METHYL GROUP

Rat No.	Average deuterium in body water (A)	Deuterium content		Per cent. of methyl hydrogen derived from body water (B/A × 100)
		TMA chloroplatinate	Methyl group of choline (B)	
	atom per cent. excess	atom per cent. excess	atom per cent. excess	
30*	2.71	0.84	0.93	34.3
31*	2.63	0.75	0.83	31.6
40*	2.95	0.65	0.72	24.4
41*	3.30	0.84	0.93	28.3
42	3.26	0.31	0.34	10.4
43	4.04	0.34	0.38	9.4
44	3.04	0.24	0.27	8.9
45	3.44	0.17	0.19	5.5

* These rats on the labile methyl-free diet.

References p. 91.

SUMMARY

The incorporation of deuterium from isotopically labelled body water into the methyl groups of body choline has been used as an indication of methyl synthesis in the rat *in vivo*. As a test of this concept the amount of isotope appearing in the body choline of rats on a methyl-free diet has been compared with that in rats receiving choline or methionine in the diet. The animals growing well without a source of methyl groups in the diet were found to incorporate approximately four times as much isotope into body choline as animals given choline or methionine.

RÉSUMÉ

L'incorporation de deuterium à partir de l'eau marquée dans les groupes méthyliques de la choline de l'organisme a été considérée comme un signe de la synthèse méthylique chez le rat *in vivo*. Pour vérifier la validité de cette hypothèse, les auteurs ont comparé la quantité d'isotope décelable dans la choline de l'organisme chez des rats carencés en groupements méthyliques et chez des rats recevant de la choline ou de la méthionine dans leur régime. Les animaux qui croissent normalement avec un régime sans groupements méthyliques incorporent environ quatre fois plus d'isotope dans la choline de leur organisme que ceux qui reçoivent de la choline ou de la méthionine.

ZUSAMMENFASSUNG

Der Einbau von Deuterium aus mit Isotopen markiertem Körperwasser in die Methylgruppen des Körpercholins wurde benutzt als ein Anzeichen der Methylsynthese in der Ratte *in vivo*. Zur Prüfung dieser Vorstellung wurde die Menge Isotop, die im Körpercholin der Ratten bei methylfreier Diät erscheint, verglichen mit derjenigen von Cholin oder Methionin in der Diät empfangenden Ratten. Es wurde gefunden, dass ohne eine Quelle für Methylgruppen in der Diät gut wachsende Tiere ungefähr 4 mal so viel Isotope in das Körpercholin einbauen, als Tiere, die Cholin oder Methionin erhielten.

REFERENCES

[1] W. SAKAMI AND A. D. WELCH, *J. Biol. Chem.*, 187 (1950) 379.
[2] W. SAKAMI, *Federation Proc.*, 9 (1950) 222.
[3] P. BERG, *J. Biol. Chem.*, 190 (1951) 31.
[4] V. DU VIGNEAUD, C. RESSLER AND J. R. RACHELE, *Science*, 112 (1950) 267.
[5] V. DU VIGNEAUD, C. RESSLER, J. R. RACHELE, J. A. REYNIERS AND T. D. LUCKEY, *J. Nutrition*, 45 (1951) 361.
[6] V. DU VIGNEAUD, S. SIMMONDS, J. P. CHANDLER AND M. COHN, *J. Biol. Chem.*, 159 (1945) 795.
[7] V. DU VIGNEAUD, M. COHN, J. P. CHANDLER, J. R. SCHENCK AND S. SIMMONDS, *J. Biol. Chem.*, 140 (1941) 625.
[8] E. B. KELLER, J. R. RACHELE AND V. DU VIGNEAUD, *J. Biol. Chem.*, 177 (1949) 733.
[9] V. DU VIGNEAUD, W. G. VERLY, J. E. WILSON, J. R. RACHELE, C. RESSLER AND J. M. KINNEY, *J. Am. Chem. Soc.*, 73 (1951) 2782.
[10] J. H. JONES AND C. FOSTER, *J. Nutrition*, 24 (1942) 245.
[11] J. GRAFF AND D. RITTENBERG, *Anal. Chem.*, 24 (1952) 878.
[12] H. W. WASHBURN, supplement to U. S. Naval Medical Bulletin, Bureau of Medicine and Surgery, U. S. Navy, Washington, D.C., p. 60 (1948).

Received March 23rd, 1953

L'ÉTUDE QUANTITATIVE DES ISOHÉMAGGLUTININES ET LE PROBLÈME DE LEUR FORMATION

par

R. WURMSER et S. FILITTI-WURMSER

Laboratoire de Biologie physicochimique de la Faculté des Sciences de Paris (France)

INTRODUCTION

L'étude quantitative de l'isohémagglutination qui a été poursuivie depuis 7 ans dans notre laboratoire a fait découvrir un assez grand nombre de faits qui échappaient aux techniques usuelles. En faisant la part de ce qui dépend de la quantité et de ce qui dépend de l'affinité des substances en jeu, cette étude a permis de les caractériser par des propriétés précises. La concentration des isohémagglutinines dans les sérums est extrêmement faible, de l'ordre de $10^{-9}M$ et l'on n'a pas réussi jusqu'à ce jour à les isoler. Mais leur combinaison avec les groupes agglutinogènes est réversible[1]. Il a donc été possible, grâce à une méthode de dosage par numération hématimétrique, de mesurer les chaleurs et les entropies de leurs combinaisons. Nous avons pu aussi mesurer des vitesses de sédimentation et obtenir ainsi des données sur les poids moléculaires.

Il est encore difficile de tirer de ces déterminations des informations sur les structures spécifiques. Par contre les différences qu'elles révèlent entre les isoagglutinines ont conduit à relier directement ces structures au génotype, ce qui soulève bien des questions sur le mécanisme de leur formation.

L'étude thermodynamique[2] de l'agglutinine repose sur la détermination hématimétrique de 3 nombres N_4, N_t, N_4'. N_4 est le nombre maximum d'hématies qui peuvent être agglutinées à 4° C par une certaine quantité de sérum contenu dans 1 mm³; N_t est le nombre total des hématies présentes dans 1 mm³ d'un mélange renfermant cette même quantité de sérum et agité à une température donnée jusqu'à ce que l'équilibre soit atteint; N_4' est le nombre maximum d'hématies qui peuvent être agglutinées à 4° C par 1 mm³ du liquide surnageant lorsque l'on a centrifugé ce mélange en équilibre. La différence $N_4 - N_4'$ donne un 4ème nombre N_f qui est proportionnel à l'agglutinine fixée.

La loi d'action de masse appliquée aux groupes agglutinogènes supposés sans interaction prévoit que l'on doit avoir:

$$\frac{N_t}{N_f} = \frac{6 \times 10^{17}}{m \, \varphi} + \frac{6 \times 10^{17}}{m \, K \, N_4'} \tag{1}$$

en appelant m le nombre de groupes agglutinogènes présents sur une hématie, K la constante intrinsèque de l'équilibre entre ces groupes et les molécules d'agglutinine, φ le coefficient d'équivalence entre le nombre N_4 et la molarité de l'agglutinine.

Effectivement cette relation linéaire entre (N_t/N_f) et $(1/N_4')$ s'est trouvé vérifiée dans toutes les isohémagglutinations d'hématies A ou B qui ont été étudiées[3, 4].

Bibliographie p. 97.

DIFFERENCIATION PHYSICOCHIMIQUE DES ISOHEMAGGLUTININES

Chaleur de réaction

Quand nous avons entrepris nos recherches on ne connaissait comme isohémagglutinines présentes régulièrement dans les sérums humains que les isoagglutinines a et a_1 se trouvant dans les individus des groupes sanguins B et O, et ce que l'on appelait l'isoagglutinine β existant dans les sérums des individus des groupes A et O. Or dès que les sérums du groupe A ont été soumis à une expérimentation systématique, il est apparu qu'ils ne se comportent pas tous de la même façon envers les hématies B, même lorsque l'on élimine par chauffage[2] ou absorption[5] le complément, qui existe en quantité variable dans les sérums et est un inhibiteur de l'agglutination. On obtient sans exception une relation linéaire entre (N_t/N_f) et $(1/N_4')$ pour le sérum d'un individu donné. Mais la pente de la droite représentative diffère parfois de la valeur que l'on trouve le plus fréquemment. Puisque cette pente est inversement proportionnelle à mK, et que m est le nombre de groupes agglutinogènes B présents sur une hématie BO ou AB et par conséquent en moyenne toujours le même[4], c'est donc que toutes les agglutinines n'ont pas la même affinité.

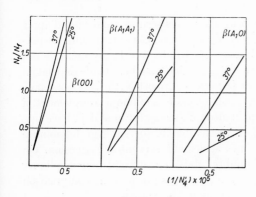

Fig. 1

Si d'autre part on mesure le rapport des pentes à deux températures (Fig. 1) afin d'en déduire la variation d'enthalpie ΔH on trouve que les sérums qui ont même pente à une certaine température l'ont également à une autre. En d'autres termes on parvient à un même classement des sérums que l'on se base sur l'affinité des agglutinines pour l'agglutinogène B ou sur la chaleur de leur réaction avec cet agglutinogène.

Les sérums sur lesquels avait porté notre étude provenaient de 27 individus du groupe A sans sélection de tel ou tel sous-groupe. Il était logique de rechercher si l'importance de chacune des classes caractérisées par une affinité et une enthalpie particulières ne correspondait pas à une fréquence d'un certain sous-groupe. C'est bien en fait ce que l'on peut constater. Par enquêtes sur l'origine de plusieurs sérums de chaque classe, on a vérifié leur attribution aux sous-groupes A_1, A_2 et A_3. En outre, parmi les sérums du sous-groupe A_1, un petit nombre, 2 sur 22, qui à première vue faisaient exception, furent reconnus provenir d'individus homozygotes A_1A_1, les autres provenant d'individus A_1O.

Ainsi les isoagglutinines β diffèrent entre elles suivant le génotype des individus qui les ont formées. Nous les désignons donc par les symboles $\beta(A_1O)$, $\beta(A_1A_1)$, $\beta(OO)$ $\beta(A_2)$ et $\beta(A_3)$, les valeurs de $(-\Delta H)$ correspondantes étant 16,000, 6500, 1700, 9000 et 3000 calories par mole.

Puisque toutes ces agglutinines se combinent avec les mêmes agglutinogènes B, on peut penser que les différences d'affinité et de chaleur de réaction, ne correspondent pas à des différences de structure dans la partie dela molécule qui réagit spécifiquement. Ce n'est toutefois qu'une probabilité. Admettons, comme le fait Pauling pour la formation des immun-anticorps, que la spécificité est surtout affaire de complémentarité de

Bibliographie p. 97.

forme: des affinités inégales pourront résulter de l'insertion dans un même "moule" de chaînes polypeptidiques dissemblables.

Poids moléculaire

En tout cas les molécules des diverses isoagglutinines se distinguent par des caractères qui ne sont pas limités à leur partie spécifique. Ceci résulte des déterminations de constantes de sédimentation[6] effectuées sur trois des isohémagglutinines β: $\beta(A_1O)$, $\beta(A_1A_1)$ et $\beta(OO)$.

Les constantes s_{20} à dilution infinie sont: $15.5 \cdot 10^{-13}$ pour $\beta(A_1O)$; $11 \cdot 10^{-13}$ pour $\beta(A_1A_1)$ et $6.6 \cdot 10^{-13}$ pour $\beta(OO)$. En faisant les hypothèses habituelles, les poids molé- $8 \cdot 10^6$ et $3 \cdot 10^6$ litre/mole.

Ainsi la totalité de la molécule d'agglutinine est intéressée dans la différenciation selon le génotype.

Entropie

Cette manière de voir est encore confirmée par d'autres données. Les constantes d'équilibre intrinsèques des agglutinines $\beta(A_1O)$, $\beta(A_1A_1)$ et $\beta(OO)$ à 25° C sont $2 \cdot 10^7$, $8 \cdot 10^6$ et $3 \cdot 10^6$ litre/mole.

Une remarque est à faire à ce sujet. On peut classer les sérums aussi bien d'après les chaleurs de combinaison que d'après le rapport N_4/N_{37} du nombre maximum d'héma- ties agglutinables à deux températures 4° C et 37° C. Tandis que la première de ces données ne concerne que l'union de l'agglutinine à l'agglutinogène, la seconde dépend en plus du processus secondaire d'agglutination. Le fait que le rapport N_4/N_{37} est plus élevé pour les sérums A_1O que pour les sérums OO, par exemple, s'explique simplement si l'adhésion de deux hématies se fait par la 2ème liaison d'une agglutinine déjà fixée une première fois. Pour des raisons géométriques il est vraisemblable que, sur le grand nombre de molécules d'agglutinine fixées, quelques unes seulement servent à l'adhésion. On peut donc les négliger dans les calculs de l'équilibre. Mais elle suffisent pour expliquer que le processus d'agglutination dépend, comme le processus primaire de combinaison de l'agglutinine, de la plus ou moins grande exothermicité de celui-ci.

En effet quel que soit le détail du mécanisme d'agglutination on peut admettre que les hématies qui s'agglutinent sont celles qui portent au moins un nombre critique de molécules d'agglutinine, variable d'ailleurs avec la concentration des hématies[2]. Considérons un sérum A_1O. Afin de fixer les idées nous prendrons une expérience où une même quantité de sérum dilué est mise en équilibre à 2 températures différentes avec $1 \cdot 10^6$ hématies par mm³. A 4° C il y a en moyenne 1000 molécules d'agglutinine fixées par hématie présente. Comme dans ces conditions le taux d'agglutination est 0.4, ce nombre, d'après la répartition statistique est très voisin de celui que doit porter une hématie pour être agglutinée à 4°. A 37° le nombre de molécules d'isoagglutinine fixées par hématie présente est 2000. Cette fois le taux d'agglutination est 0.16, si bien que 2000 est une limite inférieure du nombre de molécules que doit porter une hématie pour être agglutinée à 37° C. Si maintenant on considère l'agglutination par un sérum OO on trouve qu'une hématie agglutinée porte, à 4° C et 37° C, sensiblement le même nombre de molécules d'agglutinine, soit 10,000 et 12,000, pour une concentration en hématies de $1 \cdot 10^6$ par mm³, avec un taux de 0.4.

Ainsi ce que l'on peut appeler le pouvoir agglutinant d'une agglutinine varie forte- ment ou non avec la température suivant que la combinaison avec l'agglutinogène est

Bibliographie p. 97.

plus ou moins exothermique. C'est ce que l'on attend si les liens entre les deux hématies sont des molécules d'agglutinine ancrées par des assemblages identiques d'atomes. Il y a donc là un indice en faveur de la multivalence des agglutinines, quoique la question soit loin d'être tranchée.

Mais du point de vue qui nous occupe ici principalement et qui est la formation des isoagglutinines, la question de la valence est secondaire. Il y a plutôt lieu d'insister sur un autre résultat de nos mesures. Les variations d'entropie qui accompagnent la combinaison de l'agglutinogène avec les agglutinines $\beta(A_1O)$, $\beta(A_1A_1)$, $\beta(OO)$ ont été calculées à partir des constantes d'équilibre indiquées plus haut: elles sont respective-ment —20, +8 et +24 calories/degré.

Ayant toujours en vue que l'interaction entre les groupes spécifiques complémen-taires de l'agglutinogène et de l'agglutinine doit être la même pour toutes les agglutinines anti-B, la chaleur de cette réaction locale doit être la même. Les chaleurs mesurées diffèrent parce que des changements secondaires affectent le reste de la protéine. Leur effet thermique se superpose à celui de l'union des groupes spécifiques. Toutefois les changements restent probablement limités à l'entourage de ces groupes.

Les variations d'entropie, elles aussi, s'expliqueraient mal sans ces modifications, dont il n'est pas encore possible de préciser la nature, libération de molécules d'eau fixées aux surfaces mises en contact par la réaction, ou remaniements intramoléculaires ressemblant à un début de dénaturation réversible.

FORMATION DES ISOHEMAGGLUTININES

Un point saillant des résultats que nous avons obtenus est l'homogénéité des iso-agglutinines. Cette homogénéité ressort de la manière dont la loi d'action de masse s'applique à leur combinaison avec les groupes agglutinogènes, la relation linéaire[1] étant vérifiée avec une approximation de 5%.

Il y a là un caractère distinctif des isoagglutinines. On s'accorde en effet à trouver chez les anticorps provenant d'immunisation une pluralité de sortes moléculaires, allant parfois jusqu'à donner une répartition gaussienne des affinités avec de grands écarts moyens.

Rien de semblable dans le cas des isohémagglutinines. Leur homogénéité tient apparemment à ce qu'un mécanisme génique contrôle directement leur formation. Ce qui donne à penser que les isohémagglutinines peuvent être un matériel de choix pour l'étude d'un tel mécanisme.

Les caractères si nettement distincts des agglutinines $\beta(A_1O)$, $\beta(A_1A_1)$, $\beta(OO)$ mon-trent qu'il n'y a pas dans leur formation dominance d'un des gènes, mais coopération des deux allèles. L'agglutinine $\beta(A_1O)$ est chimiquement différente de $\beta(A_1A_1)$ et $\beta(OO)$. Le cas est donc tout autre que celui des hémoglobines trouvées chez les individus à hématies falciformes. Là, quand le sujet est hétérozygote, il y a présence à la fois de l'hémoglobine normale et de l'hémoglobine particulière découverte par Pauling, Itano, Singer et Wells[7].

Avant d'aller plus loin il faut toutefois éliminer la possibilité que les propriétés du sérum A_1O résultent de la présence d'une combinaison très peu dissociable des deux agglutinines $\beta(A_1A_1)$ et $\beta(OO)$. L'étude du mélange de ces agglutinines permet d'écarter l'objection[8].

Dans une série d'expériences on a mélangé deux sérums A_1A_1 et OO et trouvé que,

Bibliographie p. 97.

ajoutés l'un à l'autre, ils agglutinent ensemble un nombre d'hématies égal à la somme de ce qu'agglutinait chacun d'eux séparément.

Une autre série d'expériences a consisté à calculer le rapport (N_t/N_f) en fonction de $(1/N'_4)$ pour des mélanges de sérums A_1A_1 et OO de molarité connue, en admettant que les deux agglutinines se combinent avec les groupes agglutinogènes conformément aux constantes d'équilibre qui leur sont propres. Les points expérimentaux se placent bien sur la courbe calculée. Dans la région où celle-ci est quasi-linéaire, la pente est de $3 \cdot 10^5$, intermédiaire entre les pentes qui correspondent aux isoagglutinines $\beta(A_1A_1)$ et $\beta(OO)$ quand elles sont seules, et qui sont respectivement $2.3 \cdot 10^5$ et $4.0 \cdot 10^5$. L'agglutinine $\beta(A_1O)$ qui donne une pente de $1.5 \cdot 10^5$ ne peut donc être confondue avec un mélange de $\beta(A_1A_1)$ et $\beta(OO)$.

L'existence de la molécule hybride $\beta(A_1O)$ étant établie, comment peut-on s'en représenter la formation? Il faut expliquer la création d'une structure qui ne ressemble exactement ni à l'une ni à l'autre des structures responsables de sa formation. S'agit-il d'une perturbation produite directement par un des allèles sur l'autre pendant l'acte même où ils contrôlent la synthèse? Si le mécanisme reproductif repose, comme l'a imaginé JORDAN, sur un processus de résonance, il n'est pas tout-à-fait exclu que les deux structures modèles, identiques dans leur partie specifique interfèrent en ce qu'elles ont de dissemblable, et en cela seulement.

Mais la correspondance établie entre l'équipement génique et les dimensions moléculaires des agglutinines conduit à une image plus conforme aux vues habituelles. Elle respecte notamment l'idée de HALDANE qu'à chaque gène est associé un enzyme[9].

Sans faire une hypothèse trop précise sur le mécanisme, on conçoit qu'il peut comprendre deux stades: la formation d'un précurseur protéique et l'acquisition par ce précurseur de la configuration particulière qui lui permettra de réagir avec le groupe spécifique de l'agglutinogene.

Les gènes A_1 et O sont pléiotropes: ils interviennent à ces deux stades. Dans le premier stade chacun d'eux préside à la synthèse du précurseur. Les précurseurs O ont le poids moléculaire 170,000; les précurseurs A_1 ont le poids moléculaire 300,000. Chez les homozygotes A_1A_1 et OO, ces précurseurs subissent immédiatement une deuxième influence génique qui leur confère la spécificité anti-B proprement dite. Chez les hétérozygotes A_1O, les précurseurs formés par chaque allèle s'associent en un précurseur de poids moléculaire 500,000 avant de subir la deuxième intervention génique commune à toutes les agglutinines anti-B.

CONCLUSIONS

Les données que nous avons établies ne conduisent pas seulement à des problèmes concernant la structure des agglutinines et leur genèse. La complémentarité de configuration qui existe entre les groupes spécifiques des agglutinines et des agglutinogènes fait que la connaissance des uns est solidaire de celle des autres. Mais nos mesures apportent aussi des renseignements plus directs.

Par exemple il n'apparaît pas de différence notable dans la nature ou la quantité des groupes agglutinogènes présents sur les hématies BO et A_1B. Comme si les groupes agglutinogènes se formaient sous l'influence des gènes respectifs A, B et O en des points prédestinés de l'hématie.

Tels sont quelques uns des problèmes que l'étude quantitative de l'agglutination

Bibliographie p. 97.

aide à aborder. La méthode est laborieuse, car elle exige pour atteindre la précision désirable de très nombreuses numérations. Mais les informations qu'elle fournit ne peuvent jusqu'à présent être obtenus par aucune autre méthode.

RÉSUMÉ

L'étude quantitative de l'isohémagglutination a permis de découvrir de nouvelles agglutinines normales anti-B, caractérisées par les chaleurs et les entropies de leur réaction, aussi bien que par leurs poids moléculaires. Ces propriétés sont liées au génotype. En particulier il existe une agglutinine hybride $\beta(A_1O)$ dont la structure est différente de celles des agglutinines $\beta(A_1A_1)$ et $\beta(OO)$ provenant d'individus homozygotes. La méthode employée permet aussi de connaître le nombre des groupes agglutinogènes présents sur une hématie. Divers problèmes soulevés par ces résultats sont discutés spécialement au point de vue de la formation des isoagglutinines.

SUMMARY

The quantitative study of isohaemagglutination has led to the discovery of new normal anti-β agglutinines, characterised by the heats and entropies of reaction and also by their molecular weights. These properties are related to the genotype. In particular, there exists a hybrid agglutinine $\beta(A_1O)$, the structure of which is different from those of the $\beta(AA)$ and $\beta(OO)$ agglutinines, originating from individual homozygotes. The number of agglutinogen groups on a red blood corpuscle can be obtained by the method employed. Various problems arising from these results are discussed from the point of view of the formation of isoagglutinines.

ZUSAMMENFASSUNG

Die quantitative Untersuchung der Isohämagglutination erlaubte die Entdeckung von neuen normalen Anti-β-agglutininen, die durch die Reaktionswärme und -entropie und ebenfalls durch ihr Molekulargewicht gekennzeichnet wurden. Diese Eigenschaften sind mit dem Genotyp verbunden. Eigentümlicherweise besteht ein Agglutininhybrid $\beta(A_1O)$, dessen Struktur verschieden ist von der von homozygoten Individuen stammenden Agglutininen $\beta(A_1A_1)$ und $\beta(OO)$. Die verwendete Methode erlaubt auch die Zahl der anwesenden agglutinogenen Gruppen auf einem roten Blutkörperchen zu bestimmen. Verschiedene sich aus diesen Ergebnissen erhebende Probleme werden besonders im Hinblick auf die Bildung von Isoagglutininen besprochen.

BIBLIOGRAPHIE

[1] S. FILITTI-WURMSER ET Y. JACQUOT-ARMAND, *Arch. sci. physiol.*, 1 (1947) 151.
[2] S. FILITTI-WURMSER, Y. JACQUOT-ARMAND ET R. WURMSER, *Compt. rend.*, 226 (1948) 844; *J. Chim. Phys.*, 47 (1950) 419.
[3] S. MAVRIDÈS, *Compt. rend.*, 236 (1953).
[4] S. FILITTI-WURMSER, Y. JACQUOT-ARMAND ET R. WURMSER, *J. Chim. Phys.*, 49 (1952) 550.
[5] G. AUBEL-LESURE, *Compt. rend. soc. biol.*, 944 (1950) 472.
[6] R. WURMSER, S. FILITTI-WURMSER ET G. AUBEL-LESURE, *Compt. rend.*, 234 (1952) 2392; *J. Chim. Phys.*, sous presse.
[7] L. PAULING, H. A. ITANO, S. J. SINGER ET I. C. WELLS, *Science*, 110 (1949) 543.
[8] S. FILITTI-WURMSER, G. AUBEL-LESURE ET R. WURMSER, *J. Chim. Phys.*, sous presse.
[9] J. B. S. HALDANE, *New Paths in Genetics*, Allen and Unwin, London, 1942.

Reçu le 27 mars 1953

REVERSIBILITY OF GLUCOSE-6-PHOSPHATE OXIDATION

by

B. L. HORECKER AND P. Z. SMYRNIOTIS

*National Institute of Arthritis and Metabolic Diseases, National Institutes of Health,
United States Public Health Service, Bethesda, Maryland (U.S.A.)*

The work of WARBURG and his collaborators[1] has established that glucose-6-phosphate is oxidized by triphosphopyridine nucleotide (TPN) in the presence of an enzyme which they called *Zwischenferment*. The reaction product was identified as 6-phosphogluconate[2]. The oxidation of glucose-6-phosphate proceeds essentially to completion and can be used for the spectrophotometric determination of this substance[3]. Interest in the reversal of this reaction has been stimulated by the observation that CO_2 fixation can occur by the reversal of the oxidative decarboxylation of 6-phosphogluconate[4]. Recently CORI AND LIPMANN[5] have shown the primary product of *Zwischenferment* action on glucose-6-phosphate to be the δ-lactone of 6-phosphogluconic acid, rather than the free acid. As LIPMANN[6] has pointed out, from the thermodynamic standpoint, the lactone should be more readily reduced to the glucose level than the free carboxyl form. An analogy may be drawn with the oxidation of glucose. BENTLEY AND NEUBERGER[7] found the primary product of glucose oxidation by notatin (glucose oxidase) to be the δ-lactone. STRECKER AND KORKES[8] obtained the same product with liver glucose dehydrogenase and demonstrated the reversibility of the reaction. In the present paper the reduction of 6-phosphogluconolactone to glucose-6-phosphate by reduced triphosphopyridine nucleotide (TPNH) in the presence of *Zwischenferment* is reported.

METHODS

Crystalline barium glucose-6-phosphate. The barium salt of glucose-6-phosphate has previously been available only as an amorphous, water-soluble product. A crystalline heptahydrate has now been obtained* which has a very limited solubility in water and can be prepared in essentially pure form. The crystalline salt has a solubility of 0.5 mg per ml and crystallization is readily induced even in dilute solution by the addition of a small seed crystal. Barium glucose-6-phosphate synthesized according to SEEGMILLER AND HORECKER[3] or LARDY AND FISCHER[9] was purified by crystallization from water. Small amounts of fructose-6-phosphate present in one of these preparations[3] remained in the mother liquor. Recrystallization was carried out by solution of the crystals with the aid of dilute acetic acid followed by neutralization with dilute ammonium hydroxide. The following analytical data were obtained**.

$(C_6H_{11}O_9P\ Ba \cdot 7H_2O)$ Calculated Ba 26.2, P 5.94, H_2O 24.1
                              Found   Ba 25.9, P 5.79, H_2O 24.4

Enzymic assay with *Zwischenferment* and TPN gave a purity of 98 per cent.

The monopotassium salt of glucose-6-phosphate was prepared from the barium salt as previously described[3].

---

* A similar crystalline product has been obtained independently by the Schwarz Laboratories (personal communication).

** The analyses for Ba, P, and weight loss in high vacuum at 100° were carried out by the National Institutes of Health Microanalytical Laboratory under the direction of Dr WM C. ALFORD.

References p. 102.

6-Phosphogluconolactone. The oxidation of glucose with bromine at neutral pH yields the δ-lactone as the initial reaction product[10]. Glucose-6-phosphate, which has the pyranose structure, would under similar conditions be expected to yield the δ-lactone. The oxidation was carried out by adding an excess of bromine to a solution of the monopotassium salt in 0.2 M acetate buffer, pH 5.7. During the reaction the pH was maintained between 5.5 and 5.7 by the addition of NaOH; below pH 5.5 the rate of oxidation by bromine was very slow, while above pH 6 the lactone was rapidly hydrolyzed. The oxidation was 80–90% complete after about 10 minutes at room temperature and was stopped at this point to avoid extensive hydrolysis of the lactone. Excess bromine was removed by vigorous gassing with helium for 2 minutes and the solution used at once for the enzymic experiments. 6-Phosphogluconolactone, presumably the γ-lactone, was prepared by heating in acid according to ROBINSON AND KING[11].

Other preparations. Zwischenferment was prepared from dried brewers yeast by the method of KORNBERG[12] which yields a product free of phosphogluconic dehydrogenase. Phosphogluconic dehydrogenase. Phosphogluconic dehydrogenase was prepared from brewer's yeast as previously described[13]. This preparation is contaminated with Zwischenferment. TPN was a chromatographed product which was 79% pure[14].

Isocitric dehydrogenase was prepared from pig heart by the method of OCHOA AND WEISZ-TABORI[15].

Determinations. The concentration of lactone was estimated by the colorimetric hydroxamic acid method of LIPMANN AND TUTTLE[16], with D-glucono-δ-lactone as a standard. Sugar lactones were found to vary greatly in this reaction (Table I) and all gave less colour than equivalent amounts of acetyl phosphate. Because of this variation the values given for 6-phosphogluconolactone are only

TABLE I

REACTION OF LACTONES IN THE HYDROXAMIC ACID TEST

Substance	Absorption at 540 mμ[*] Density per μM
D-Glucono-δ-lactone[**]	0.081
D-Glucono-γ-lactone[***]	0.152
D-Galacto-γ-lactone[§]	0.143
D-Gulono-γ-lactone[§]	0.097
D-Mannono-γ-lactone[§]	0.113
D-Ribono-γ-lactone[§]	0.133
D-Rhamnono-γ-lactone[§]	0.106
Li acetyl-phosphate[◊]	0.214

[*] Measured with the Coleman Junior Spectrophotometer in 16 mm. I.D. tubes in final volume of 6.0 ml.

[**] A commercial sample (Pfizer) obtained from Dr F. LIPMANN.

[***] Furnished by Dr H. C. ISBELL.

[§] Furnished by Dr. N. K. RICHTMYER.

[◊] Furnished by Dr. E. R. STADTMAN.

approximate, although they are in the range expected from the amount of glucose-6-phosphate oxidized and the observed rate of hydrolysis of the lactone. With HESTRIN's modification[17] of the hydroxamic acid reaction lower values were obtained, presumably due to rapid hydrolysis of the lactone at alkaline pH.

Glucose-6-phosphate was determined spectrophotometrically by measurement of TPN reduction in the presence of Zwischenferment. The results herein reported depend on the validity of this assay. With the purified Zwischenferment preparation employed other substances which might be present in the reaction mixtures, such as 6-phosphogluconate, ribulose-5-phosphate and isocitrate are completely inactive. Phosphogluconolactone originally present in the reaction mixture does not interfere with the reduction of TPN since it is completely hydrolyzed by the time the determinations are made.

RESULTS

The reduction of 6-phosphogluconolactone to glucose-6-phosphate was observed in the presence of TPNH and *Zwischenferment*, with TPNH generated by reduction with 6-phosphogluconate in the presence of phosphogluconic dehydrogenase, according to the following equations:

References p. 102.

6-Phosphogluconate $+$ TPN $\rightarrow$ ribulose-5-phosphate $+$ CO_2 $+$ TPNH $+$ H$^+$
6-Phosphoglucono-δ-lactone $+$ TPNH $+$ H$^+$ $\rightarrow$ glucose-6-phosphate $+$ TPN
Sum: 6-phosphogluconate $+$ 6-phosphoglucono-δ-lactone $\rightarrow$ ribulose-5-phosphate $+$ CO_2 $+$ glucose-6-phosphate

The formation of glucose-6-phosphate in this system is shown in Table II. No reduction to glucose-6-phosphate could be detected in the absence of the lactone or if the lactone formed by heating in acid were added. Only catalytic amounts of TPN were required; 2 μM of glucose-6-phosphate were formed in the presence of 0.14 μM of TPN.

Similar results were obtained with *iso*citrate and *iso*citric dehydrogenase as the TPN reducing system (Table III). In a control experiment with no *iso*citrate added no glucose-6-phosphate was formed; the small decrease in glucose-6-phosphate can be attributed to oxidation by the TPN added.

TABLE II

THE REDUCTION OF 6-PHOSPHOGLUCONOLACTONE COUPLED WITH THE OXIDATION

OF 6-PHOSPHOGLUCONATE

In Experiment 1, the reaction mixture contained 17.7 μM of 6-phosphogluconate, 14.8 μM of which was present initially as the δ-lactone, 0.14 μM of TPN, about 0.25 mg of *Zwischenferment* and 3.5 mg of phosphogluconic dehydrogenase in 0.07 M glycylglycine buffer, pH 7.4, in a total volume of 1.1 ml. Experiment 2 was similar except that 0.28 μM of TPN and 14.5 μM of 6-phosphoglucono-δ-lactone were present. Samples for glucose-6-phosphate assay were diluted with 4 volumes of water heated for 2 minutes at 100°, and centrifuged. In Experiment 3, the reaction mixture was similar except that it contained 11.7 μM of 6-phosphogluconate, 3.8 μM of which was present initially as the γ-lactone.

Experiment	Time minutes	Glucose-6-phosphate micromoles
(1) With δ-lactone	0	3.51[*]
	10	5.54
	Δ	+2.03
(2) With δ-lactone	0	2.07[*]
	10	4.35
	Δ	+2.28
(3) With γ-lactone	0	0.39
	10	0.41
	Δ	+0.02

[*] Present initially in the phosphogluconolactone preparation.

TABLE III

THE REDUCTION OF 6-PHOSPHOGLUCONOLACTONE COUPLED WITH THE OXIDATION

OF d-*iso*CITRATE

The reaction mixture contained 17.6 μM of 6-phosphogluconate, 12.2 μM of which was present initially as the δ-lactone, 0.14 μM of TPN, 6 mg of *Zwischenferment*, 4 mg of *iso*citric dehydrogenase, 5.0 μM of d-*iso*citrate and 2 μM of $MnCl_2$ in 0.03 M glycylglycine buffer, pH 7.4. The total volume was 2.5 ml and the final pH was 6.9.

Experiment	Time (min.)	Glucose-6-phosphate μM
Complete system	0	1.24
	10	3.58
	Δ	+2.34
*Iso*citrate omitted	0	1.24
	10	1.02
	Δ	—0.22

In the oxidation of glucose-6-phosphate to ribulose-5-phosphate and CO_2 with purified *Zwischenferment* and phosphogluconic dehydrogenase the limiting step appears to be the hydrolysis of the lactone ring. In the presence of both dehydrogenases approximately 2 moles of TPN were reduced for each mole of glucose-6-phosphate present (fig. IA). The first equivalent, however, was reduced much more rapidly than the second,

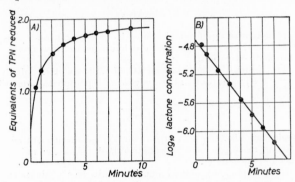

Fig. I. The oxidation of glucose-6-phosphate by TPN in the presence of *Zwischenferment* and phosphogluconic dehydrogenase. The reaction mixture (1.49 ml) contained 0.14 μM of TPN, 0.031 μM of glucose-6-phosphate, 50 μM of MgCl$_2$, 60 μM of glycylglycine buffer, pH 7.4, and 0.063 mg of phosphogluconic dehydrogenase, containing 0.23 units of *Zwischenferment* and 0.52 units of phosphogluconic dehydrogenase. TPN reduction was measured at 340 mμ in a 1.0 cm cell. B represents the logarithmic plot of the reaction from one-half minute to seven minutes.

although the phosphogluconic dehydrogenase activity was more than twice the *Zwischenferment* activity. With the amount of enzyme present in this experiment 6-phosphogluconate itself would be completely oxidized within the first minute; the relatively slow reaction observed must represent the hydrolysis of phosphogluconolactone. The second half of the reaction follows first order kinetics (fig. IB) from which it can be estimated that the half time for hydrolysis of the lactone ring under these conditions is about 1.5 minutes.

DISCUSSION

The experiments reported indicated that 6-phosphogluconaloctone (presumably only the δ-lactone) can be enzymically reduced to glucose-6-phosphate, in the presence of a source of reduced TPN. Together with evidence previously reported[4] for the reductive carboxylation of ribulose-5-phosphate to 6-phosphogluconate these results provide a mechanism for the direct fixation of CO_2 in hexose. The recent observations of VISHNIAC AND OCHOA[16] suggest that photosynthetic mechanisms are able to provide the reduced coenzyme, and thus the energy, for these reactions. The following reactions would be involved in the formation of hexosemonophosphate by a reversal of its oxidation:

$$\text{Ribulose-5-phosphate} + CO_2 + \text{TPNH} + H^+ \rightleftharpoons \text{6-phosphogluconate} + \text{TPN} \quad (1)$$

$$\text{6-Phosphogluconate} \rightleftharpoons \text{6-phosphogluconolactone} + H_2O \quad (2)$$

$$\text{6-Phosphogluconolactone} + \text{TPNH} + H^+ \rightleftharpoons \text{glucose-6-phosphate} + \text{TPN} \quad (3)$$

With the enzyme preparations used in these experiments reaction[2] appears to be the rate-limiting step. For this pathway for the oxidation of glucose-6-phosphate to have

References p. 102.

physiological significance, it becomes necessary to postulate the presence in intact cells of a lactonization enzyme which catalyzes reaction[2].

We are indebted to Dr. FRITZ LIPMANN for suggesting the method of preparation of 6-phosphoglucono-δ-lactone.

SUMMARY

1. The enzymic reduction of 6-phosphoglucono-δ-lactone to glucose-6-phosphate has been obtained with reduced TPN and glucose-6-phosphate dehydrogenase, thus demonstrating the reversibility of glucose-6-phosphate oxidation.

2. The half-life of 6-phosphoglucono-δ-lactone at pH 7.4 is about 1.5 minutes.

3. A purified crystalline preparation of barium glucose-6-phosphate is described.

RÉSUMÉ

1. La 6-phosphoglucono-δ-lactone peut être réduite enzymatiquement en glucose-6-phosphate en présence de TPN réduit et de glucose-6-phosphatedéshydrogénase, ce qui montre la réversibilité de l'oxydation du glucose-6-phosphate .

2. La moitié de la 6-phosphoglucono-δ-lactone est réduite en 1,5 minute environ à pH 7.4.

3. Une préparation pure cristallisée de glucose-6-phosphate de baryum est décrite.

ZUSAMMENFASSUNG

1. Die enzymatische Reduktion von 6-phosphoglucono-δ-lakton zu Glucose-6-phosphat wurde mit reduzierter TPN und Glucose-6-phosphatdehydrogenase erreicht und so die Umkehrbarkeit der Glucose-6-phosphatoxydation gezeigt.

2. Die Halbwertszeit des 6-Phosphoglucono-δ-laktons bei pH 7.4 ist ungefähr 1.5 Minuten.

3. Ein gereinigtes kristallines Bariumglucose-6-phosphatpräparat wird beschrieben.

REFERENCES

[1] O. WARBURG AND W. CHRISTIAN, *Biochem. Z.*, 242 (1931) 206; 292 (1937) 287; E. NEGELEIN AND E. HAAS, *Biochem. Z.*, 282 (1935) 206.
[2] O. WARBURG, W. CHRISTIAN AND A. GRIESE, *Biochem. Z.*, 282, (1935) 157.
[3] J. E. SEEGMILLER AND B. L. HORECKER, *J. Biol. Chem.*, 192 (1951) 175.
[4] B. L. HORECKER AND P. Z. SMYRNIOTIS, *J. Biol. Chem.*, 196 (1952) 135.
[5] O. CORI AND F. LIPMANN, *J. Biol. Chem.*, 194 (1952) 417.
[6] F. LIPMANN, in W. D. MCELROY AND B. GLASS, *Phosphorous Metabolism*, Vol. I, Baltimore, 1951, P. 158.
[7] R. BENTLEY AND A. NEUBERGER, *Biochem. J.*, 45 (1949) 584.
[8] H. J. STRECKER AND S. KORKES, *Nature*, 168 (1951) 913.
[9] H. A. LARDY AND H. O. L. FISCHER, *J. Biol. Chem.*, 164 (1946) 513.
[10] H. S. ISBELL, *Bur. Standards J. Res.*, 8 (1932) 615.
[11] R. ROBISON AND E. J. KING, *Biochem. J.*, 25 (1931) 323.
[12] A. KORNBERG, *J. Biol. Chem.*, 182 (1950) 805.
[13] B. L. HORECKER AND P. Z. SMYRNIOTIS, *J. Biol. Chem.*, 193 (1951) 371.
[14] A. KORNBERG AND B. L. HORECKER, *Biochemical Prepns.*, in press.
[15] S. OCHOA AND E. WEISZ-TABORI, *J. Biol. Chem.*, 159 (1945) 245.
[16] F. LIPMANN AND L. C. TUTTLE, *J. Biol. Chem.*, 159 (1945) 21.
[17] S. HESTRIN, *J. Biol. Chem.*, 180 (1949) 249.
[18] W. VISCHNIAC AND S. OCHOA, *J. Biol. Chem.*, 195, (1952) 75.

Received March 27th, 1953

AMINO ACID INTERACTIONS IN STRICT ANAEROBES
(CL. SPOROGENES)

by

R. MAMELAK AND J. H. QUASTEL

Research Institute, Montreal General Hospital, Montreal (Canada)

Following the demonstration by QUASTEL, STEPHENSON AND WHETHAM[1] and by QUASTEL AND STEPHENSON[2] that anaerobic growth of facultative anaerobes is secured by the presence in the nutrient medium of pairs of hydrogen donators and hydrogen acceptors (*e.g.* lactate-fumarate, or glycerol-aspartate) whose interaction provides energy for growth, and pyruvic acid for the synthetic requirements of the cell (QUASTEL[3]), STICKLAND[4, 5], and later WOODS[27], showed that similar considerations, with respect to energy formation, apply to strict anaerobes such as *Cl. sporogenes*. With these organisms, however, the hydrogen donators and acceptors are amino acids. For example, L-alanine and glycine form a pair of amino acids which interact in the presence of resting *Cl. sporogenes* to form acetic acid, ammonia and carbon dioxide.

Thus: $CH_3CHNH_2COOH + 2CH_2NH_2 \cdot COOH + 2H_2O = 3CH_3COOH + 3NH_3 + CO_2$.

Typical hydrogen donators are alanine, valine, leucine; typical hydrogen acceptors are glycine, proline, hydroxyproline. The interactions between pairs of these amino acids have been referred to as Stickland reactions, and it has been considered that α-ketonic acids are intermediates in these reactions. Neither STICKLAND, nor subsequent workers, however, have been able to prove that in the alanine-glycine interaction (for example) there is liberation of pyruvic acid.

STICKLAND[5] showed that pyruvate and glycine interact in the presence of resting *Cl. sporogenes*, the rate of pyruvate oxidation by glycine being greater than that of alanine under similar experimental conditions. Thus the lack of appearance of pyruvate, if it were formed, was held to be due to its high rate of reactivity with the amino acid hydrogen acceptors. KOCHOLATY AND HOOGERHEIDE[6, 7] using dyestuffs as hydrogen acceptors, studied the dehydrogenases of *Cl. sporogenes* concerned with the oxidation of alanine, pyruvic acid, ethanol, and showed that their activities were affected by the composition and pH of the culture medium, and by the age of the bacterial culture. They further observed that hydrogen absorption will occur with resting *Cl. sporogenes* in presence of amino acid hydrogen acceptors *e.g.* hydroxyproline, proline, glycine, ornithine, arginine and tryptophan, and also in presence of such substances as acetyl-methylcarbinol and diacetyl. They, and WOODS[27], also made clear the fact that certain amino acids *e.g.* ornithine, tryptophan, may act as both hydrogen donators and acceptors. Under such circumstances, an amino acid will break down anaerobically in presence of resting *Cl. sporogenes* to yield oxidation and reduction products *e.g.* two mols. tryptophan yield one mol. indolepyruvic acid, one mol. indolepropionic acid and two mols. ammonia.

References p. 120.

A variety of substances undergoes aerobic oxidation in presence of *Cl. sporogenes* *e.g.* pyruvate (NISMAN[8]), (though ROSENBERG AND NISMAN[9] report no aerobic oxidation of pyruvate by this organism), and amino acids such as alanine, leucine, threonine, serine, methionine, phenylalanine (NISMAN AND VINET[10]), the oxidation of amino acids being accompanied by ammonia liberation. The presence of arsenite exerts a much larger inhibitory effect on the amino acid reductases[11,12] than upon the amino acid oxidative enzymes. NISMAN AND VINET[12] conclude, from the kinetics of arsenite-inhibited reactions, that the enzymes in *Cl. sporogenes* responsible for the aerobic oxidation of amino acids are identical with those involved in the anaerobic amino acid interactions. Extracts of *Cl. sporogenes* in presence of pyruvate and phosphate give rise to acetyl phosphate[13] and, in presence of alanine, bring about the reduction of diphosphopyridine nucleotide[14]. Moreover such extracts will oxidise reduced diphosphopyridine nucleotide in presence of pyruvate and ammonium ions.

It is the purpose of this preliminary communication to throw further light on the mechanisms of amino acid interactions in *Cl. sporogenes* and to indicate how these mechanisms are linked with the phenomenon of oxygen toxicity to the strict anaerobes.

MATERIALS AND METHODS

Manometric technique. The conventional Warburg apparatus was used.

Nutrient media

Stock cultures of *Cl. sporogenes* were maintained on Brewer's meat with bi-weekly transfers to fresh media. A newly inoculated tube of media was heated at 80° C for 10 min prior to incubation at 38° C.

One ml of a suspension of organisms from the Brewer's meat was added to 1 litre of medium of the following composition.

> 15 g Bacto-casitone
> 1 g Sodium thioglycollate
> 1.25 g Sodium chloride
> 1.5 g Potassium chloride
> 0.75 g Cysteine hydrochloride
> 1 mg D-Biotin
> 1 litre water

The medium was adjusted to pH 7.0 before autoclaving.

Preparation of bacterial suspensions

One litre of a 14–17 hours culture (grown at 38°) was centrifuged and washed twice in 200 ml 0.15 *M* KCl. The cells were suspended in 8–16 ml 0.15 *M* KCl. One ml of a thick bacterial suspension, whose dry weight varied from 7.7–11.8 mg, was used in each experiment.

Preparation of bacterial extract

A bacterial crusher described by HUGHES[15] was used in these experiments and found to be very efficient. Two litres of bacteria were grown for 14–17 hours at 38°, washed once in 200 ml 1 % sodium thioglycollate and a second time in 10 ml of the same solution and the washed cells were frozen for 5–10 minutes in dry ice. The frozen cells were inserted into the crushing machine which had been cooled to —20° C. After crushing, the material was extracted with 7–9 ml 1% sodium thioglycollate and centrifuged in the cold at 20,000 *g* for 2 minutes. One ml of the supernatant was used in each experiment. In order to get good activity in the extract, the cells and the crushing machine must be kept very cold (—20° C). If this precaution is not observed and the cells thaw, the activity of the extract is very low. Sodium thioglycollate was used for washing and extraction to prevent the deleterious effects of exposure to oxygen.

Preparation of lyophylized bacteria

Cells of *Cl. sporogenes* were washed with 1% sodium thioglycollate and suspended in 20 ml 0.15 *M* KCl. The cell suspension was frozen in a mixture of dry ice and acetone and lyophilized for 5 hours. The dry cells were stored in a vacuum dessicator at 0°–10° C.

References p. 120.

Rat brain homogenate

Rats were killed by decapitation, the brains removed immediately and homogenized in 1% nicotinamide solution with a Potter-Elvehjem homogenizer. One g of brain was homogenized with 4 ml nicotinamide solution, 0.5 ml homogenate being used when required.

Pigeon liver acetone powder

Preparation. Pigeons were killed by decapitation and bled. The livers were removed and chilled. After mincing, each liver was homogenized in the cold. The homogenized tissue was poured into 10 times its volume of acetone. The dehydrated material was filtered on a Buchner funnel and was washed three times with acetone. The washed material was transferred to filter paper and dried in the air for approximately 5 minutes. Drying was completed in a vacuum dessicator over calcium chloride.

Extraction of liver acetone powder

The powder was ground in the cold with water or 0.2 M KF, using a Potter-Elvehjem homogenizer. After standing in ice for 10–15 minutes, it was centrifuged in the cold at 20,000 g for 2 minutes. To each vessel was added 0.5 ml of the supernatant. 50 mg of the crude powder was used for each vessel.

Estimation of the amino acids by paper chromatography

0.02–0.04 ml solution, to be analysed, was spotted on Whatman No. 1 filter paper. After drying at room temperature, the papers were chromatographed for 18 hours in butanol-ethanol-ammonia-water (20–60–7–13) by ascending chromatography. After drying, the papers were sprayed with 1% ninhydrin to locate the amino acids. The areas containing the amino acids to be analysed were cut out with a rim of 2 centimeters. The individual areas of filter paper were inserted into test-tubes, and saturated with 5% ninhydrin in butanol-water. Maximum colour was developed by incubation for 5 minutes at room temperature followed by 5 min at 55–60° C and 2 mins at 80° C. After cooling to room temperature, the coloured material was extracted twice with 10 ml 75% acetone for 20 mins. The combined extracts were collected and the colour was estimated at 525 mμ.

Estimation of ammonia

After incubation, the Warburg vessels were dismantled, and 0.2 ml 1.5 M H_2SO_4 on filter paper was inserted into the center well, and 0.3 ml saturated K_2CO_3 added to the side arm. After thermal equilibrium, the K_2CO_3 was tipped and the vessels incubated with shaking at 37° C. After 3 hours the filter papers were removed and the centre wells washed thoroughly with distilled H_2O. The filter paper and washings were collected in volumetric flasks, and aliquots were taken for NH_4 determinations (BRAGANCA, QUASTEL AND SCHUCHER[16]).

Pyruvate determination

The method of JOWETT AND QUASTEL[17] using 2:4 dinitrophenyl-hydrazine was adopted.

Lactate determinations

The method of BARKER AND SUMMERSON[18] as modified by UMBREIT[19] was used.

Sulfanilamide determinations

The method of BRATTON AND MARSHALL[20] was used. Acetyl sulfanilamide was determined by difference.

Manometric experiments

For measurements of CO_2 evolution, 0.028 M $NaHCO_3$ was used as buffer at a final pH of 7.0. The buffer was gassed with 7% CO_2 + 93% N_2 before use. The vessels were also gassed with this gas prior to measurements of CO_2 evolution. After gassing and thermal equilibrium (5 min) at 37° the substrate was tipped in. All substrates were neutralised, when necessary, with caustic soda. For oxygen absorption, in aerobic experiments 0.02 M sodium phosphate buffer at pH 7.3 was used. 0.2 ml of 20% KOH was placed in the centre well to absorb the CO_2. Air or O_2 formed the gas phase.

Hydrogen absorption

For hydrogen absorption, 0.02 M sodium phosphate buffer at pH 7.3, with KOH in the centre well, was used.

The vessels were gassed with nitrogen for five minutes and then with hydrogen for a further five minutes after which thermal equilibrium was allowed to take place.

Ferricyanide as terminal hydrogen acceptor

The technique of QUASTEL AND WHEATLEY[21] was followed.

References p. 120.

RESULTS

Competition of amino acids for a common reduction mechanism

Initial experiments were carried out to discover whether all the amino acid hydrogen acceptors are activated by the same enzyme or whether they are involved in a common reduction mechanism in *Cl. sporogenes*. Results given in Table I show that varying the concentration of L-proline from 0.005 M to 0.04 M has little or no effect on the speed of alanine-proline interaction, indicating saturation of the proline reductase at these concentrations. Similarly, it will be seen that in the alanine-glycine interaction, glycine reductase is saturated with its substrate at 0.02 M to 0.04 M. On adding a mixture of proline and glycine at these concentrations to alanine, an additive effect on the speed of carbon dioxide evolution is not observed, as would be the case if completely separate mechanisms were involved. The rate of formation of ammonia in the alanine-proline interaction is increased to a small extent by the addition of glycine, but a summation of effects is not demonstrable. If smaller concentrations of proline and glycine than those quoted are used, additive effects may be found, but it is easily shown that these are due to the fact that the proline becomes rapidly reduced, after which further glycine utilisation takes place. The results indicate that proline and glycine compete either for a common enzyme or for a common factor involved in the reduction of the amino-acids.

TABLE I

ALANINE-GLYCINE-PROLINE INTERACTIONS IN PRESENCE OF *Cl. sporogenes*

Mixtures of alanine and glycine, alanine and proline, or alanine, glycine and proline were incubated for various intervals of time with 1 ml freshly prepared *Cl. sporogenes* suspension made up in 0.15 M KCl in Warburg manometer vessels in 0.028 M NaHCO$_3$. Temp. 37°. Gas 93% N$_2$ + 7% CO$_2$. Total vol. 3.2 ml. Alanine placed in side tube and tipped at commencement of expt.

Expt.	Amino acids present	Time (min)	μM CO$_2$	μM NH$_3$
1	0.02 M L-alanine + 0.005 M L-proline	15	8.0	
	0.02 M L-alanine + 0.01 M L-proline	15	7.8	
	0.02 M L-alanine + 0.02 M L-proline	15	7.9	
	0.02 M L-alanine + 0.04 M L-proline	15	7.7	
2	0.02 M L-alanine + 0.01 M glycine	60	5.5	
	0.02 M L-alanine + 0.02 M glycine	60	6.2	
	0.22 M L-alanine + 0.04 M glycine	60	6.5	
3	0.02 M L-alanine + 0.04 M L-proline	80	31.2	40.5
	0.02 M L-alanine + 0.02 M glycine	80	6.7	24.0
	0.02 M L-alanine + $\begin{cases} 0.04 \ M \ \text{L-proline} \\ 0.02 \ M \ \text{glycine} \end{cases}$	80	30.7	49.5

Results obtained with lyophilised *Cl. sporogenes* show that the proline and glycine reductases are distinct from each other. With such a preparation, it is found that the rate of alanine-glycine interaction is negligible whilst that of alanine-proline proceeds rapidly.

It is, therefore, apparent that proline and glycine must normally compete, in intact *Cl. sporogenes*, for a common factor, possibly a hydrogen carrier, involved in their reduction.

Ferricyanide as a hydrogen acceptor with Cl. sporogenes

Typical results shown in Table II make it clear that ferricyanide is reduced by a variety of amino acids in presence of resting *Cl. sporogenes*. The amino acids that

References p. 120.

accomplish this reduction are those that normally act as hydrogen donators in the "Stickland" reaction. Amino acids that do not normally act as hydrogen donators have little or no activity with ferricyanide.

TABLE II

AMINO ACID-FERRICYANIDE INTERACTIONS IN PRESENCE OF *Cl. sporogenes*

Amino acids placed in Warburg manometer vessels in 0.028 M NaHCO$_3$ in presence of 93% N$_2$ + 7% CO$_2$. Final concn. amino acids 0.02 M (as L-form) (Temp. 37°, Time 45′). 1 ml fresh *Cl. sporogenes* suspension in 0.15 M KCl. 0.2 ml 8% K$_3$ Fe (CN)$_6$ placed in side tube.

Substrate	Amino acid		Amino acid + ferricyanide	
	μM CO$_2$	μM NH$_3$	μM CO$_2$	μM NH$_3$
Nil	1.0	—	5.4	—
DL-Alanine	3.0	—	47.5	—
DL-Methionine	13.5	—	55.5	—
L-Leucine	3.6	—	58.5	—
L-Ornithine	1.0	—	3.1	—
L-Glutamate	2.5	—	7.3	—
DL-Alanine	3.3	1.0	39.2	9.7
DL-Alanine + Glycine	6.2	23.5	40.0	8.9

During alanine-ferricyanide interaction in presence of *Cl. sporogenes*, ammonia is formed, but at a rate markedly less than that occurring in the alanine-glycine interaction. This is due largely to the fact that reduction of glycine gives rise to ammonia. On mixing ferricyanide with alanine and glycine, it is found that the rate of ammonia formation is that obtained in the alanine-ferricyanide reaction (see Table II). Thus glycine reduction is suppressed and it is evident, as has been confirmed by chromatographic evidence, that the utilisation of glycine is inhibited by the presence of ferricyanide. Ferricyanide, therefore, competes as a hydrogen acceptor with glycine and presumably with other amino acid hydrogen acceptors in *Cl. sporogenes*.

Hydrogen as a competitive hydrogen donator with Cl. sporogenes

As is well known[7], hydrogen is absorbed by resting *Cl. sporogenes* in presence of a variety of hydrogen acceptors. Ammonia is liberated when hydrogen is absorbed by the organism in presence of glycine but not in presence of proline, which is reduced to δ-aminovaleric acid[4]. Typical results showing rates of hydrogen uptake and ammonia formation are given in Table III.

TABLE III

INFLUENCE OF AMINO ACIDS ON HYDROGEN ABSORPTION BY *Cl. sporogenes*

Amino acids (0.02 M) added to phosphate buffer (0.02 M; pH 7.4) in Warburg manometer vessels in presence of 1 ml suspension freshly prepared *Cl. sporogenes* in 0.15 M KCl. Final vol. 3.2 ml. Gas = hydrogen. Temp. 37°. Time 125′ Proline placed in side tube and tipped at commencement of expt.

Amino acid	μM H$_2$ uptake	μM NH$_3$ formed
Nil	3.7	1.2
Glycine	11.3	18.0
L-Proline	14.2	3.5
L-Alanine + Glycine	4.0	39.0
L-Alanine + L-Proline	1.8	41.0
In presence of 0.028 M NaHCO$_3$ and 93% N$_2$ + 7% CO$_2$		
L-Alanine + Glycine	—	38.2
L-Alanine + L-Proline	—	39.0

References p. 120.

The addition of alanine to a hydrogen-glycine, or a hydrogen-proline, interaction completely suppresses hydrogen utilisation. The ammonia formation in alanine-glycine, or alanine-proline interaction in presence of hydrogen is practically identical with that obtained anaerobically in the absence of hydrogen (Table III).

Thus it is evident that hydrogen and amino acid hydrogen donators compete for a common mechanism involved in amino acid reductions in *Cl. sporogenes*.

The enzyme activating molecular hydrogen (hydrogenase) is not that concerned with the activation of alanine as hydrogen donator, for it may be shown that extracts of *Cl. sporogenes* that bring about amino acid interaction have no hydrogenase activity.

It must be concluded, therefore, that the suppression of hydrogen utilisation in the presence of alanine cannot be due to competition for a common enzyme and must therefore be due to competition for a common factor (presumably a hydrogen carrier) involved in the amino acid interactions.

Diphosphopyridine nucleotide (DPN), as a hydrogen carrier, in amino acid interactions in Cl. sporogenes

The addition of DPN to a cell free extract of *Cl. sporogenes* markedly stimulates amino acid interactions. Typical results with alanine-proline and leucine-proline are shown in Table IV. Similar results are obtained with leucine-ornithine, alanine-ornithine and serine. Such a stimulation is not seen with intact resting *Cl. sporogenes*.

TABLE IV

EFFECT OF DIPHOSPHOPYRIDINE NUCLEOTIDE (DPN) ON AMINO ACID INTERACTIONS
IN CELL FREE EXTRACTS OF *Cl. sporogenes*

Amino acids (0.02 M L-form) placed in Warburg manometer vessels in 0.028 M $NaHCO_3$ in presence of 93% N_2 + 7% CO_2 and 1 ml cell free extract of *Cl. sporogenes* in 1% sodium thio-glycollate solution and 0.002 M phosphate. Nicotinamide present 5.0 mg. Total volume 3.2 ml. Temp 37°. Time 120'. Alanine placed in side tube and tipped at commencement of expt.

Expt.	Amino acids	$\mu M\ CO_2$	$\mu M\ NH_3$
1	Nil	2.5	4.2
	Nil + 3 mg DPN	3.5	7.2
	DL-Alanine + L-Proline	19.2	23.0
	DL-Alanine + L-Proline + 3 mg DPN	34.5	36.0
2	L-Leucine + L-Proline	23.0	28.7
	L-Leucine + L-Proline + 2 mg DPN	30.0	37.0

The results with DPN make it evident that this substance plays an intermediary role in amino acid interactions. Moreover the facts that have been recorded concerning the competition of amino acid hydrogen acceptors and of ferricyanide for a common factor are all consistent with the view that DPN is the factor involved. It has been long known (QUASTEL AND WHEATLEY[21]) that ferricyanide is an oxidant of DPN linked dehydrogenase systems. It follows, too, from these observations that amino acid hydrogen donators, as well as molecular hydrogen, compete for the reduction of DPN. That alanine can accomplish this process is already clear from the evidence of NISMAN AND MAGER[14].

These conclusions, indicating the course of events in *Cl. sporogenes*, may be expressed as follows:

$$\begin{matrix}\text{Amino Acid} \\ \text{Hydrogen Donator}\end{matrix} + DPN + H_2O = \begin{matrix}\text{Corresponding} \\ \alpha\text{-Ketonic Acid}\end{matrix} + NH_3 + DPNH_2$$

References p. 120.

$$\genfrac{}{}{0pt}{}{\text{Amino Acid}}{\text{Hydrogen Acceptor}} + DPNH_2 = \genfrac{}{}{0pt}{}{\text{Reduced}}{\text{Amino Acid}} + DPN$$

As, however, α-ketonic acids do not accumulate in the anaerobic amino acid interactions, it follows that these, too, must undergo oxidation, presumably through the DPN system, the following reaction taking place:

$$\alpha\text{-Ketonic acid} + DPN + H_2O = \text{Lower fatty acid} + CO_2 + DPNH_2$$

Pyruvate, an intermediate in alanine-proline interaction in Cl. sporogenes

So far there has been no satisfactory evidence that pyruvate is an intermediate in the alanine-proline interaction, though the indirect evidence is in favour of this conclusion. Proof that pyruvate is an intermediate in this interaction is given in the typical results quoted in Table V.

TABLE V

LACTIC ACID FORMATION FROM ALANINE-PROLINE IN PRESENCE OF AN EXTRACT OF *Cl. sporogenes*

AND LACTIC DEHYDROGENASE OF BRAIN

Warburg manometer vessels contained 1 ml cell free extract of *Cl. sporogenes* (in 1% sodium thioglycollate and 0.002 M phosphate) and, where indicated, 0.5 ml of rat brain homogenate (1 g brain homogenized in 3 ml 0.002 M phosphate $+1$% nicotinamide solution) as source of lactic dehydrogenase. DPN present = 3 mg per vessel. 0.028 M NaHCO$_3$ present. Gas = 93% N_2 + 7% CO_2. Temp. 37°. Time 70 min. Total vol 3.2 ml. Amino acid 0.02 M L-form. Alanine tipped in.

Contents of vessel	μM CO_2	μM Lactate formed
Bacterial extract	3.5	0.3
Bacterial Extract + Brain homogenate	4.0	2.6
Alanine + Proline + Bacterial extract	30.0	1.5
Alanine + Proline + Bacterial extract + Brain homogenate	37.5	11.7
Alanine + Proline + Brain homogenate	4.7	0.3

The addition of a preparation of lactic dehydrogenase, in the form of a brain homogenate, to a cell free extract of *Cl. sporogenes*, containing alanine, proline and DPN, gives rise to high rate of lactate formation. This could only occur if the pyruvate formed normally as an intermediate is diverted by DPN and lactic dehydrogenase into lactate. It is noteworthy that in spite of the diversion of pyruvate into lactate by the added lactic dehydrogenase, the rate of evolution of carbon dioxide in the amino acid interaction is not diminished (Table V). Since the carbon dioxide is presumably wholly derived from the oxidation of pyruvate, it follows that pyruvate must be formed in sufficient amount from alanine to saturate the pyruvic oxidase-DPN system even in presence of lactic dehydrogenase.

Effect of DPN on pyruvic acid breakdown in presence of Cl. sporogenes

Sodium pyruvate undergoes anaerobic breakdown in presence of an extract of *Cl. sporogenes* giving rise to carbon dioxide but with little or no lactate formation. The speed of this process is markedly accelerated by the addition of DPN, so that there is little doubt that the initial anaerobic oxidation of pyruvate is DPN-linked (see Table VI). If a source of lactic dehydrogenase, in the form of a brain homogenate, is added to the pyruvate-DPN-bacterial extract system, lactate formation takes place (Table VI, Expt. 2). This result is to be expected if the reduced DPN formed by the oxidation of

References p. 120.

pyruvate, brings about reduction of pyruvate in presence of lactic dehydrogenase, and the regenerated DPN becomes available for further oxidation of the pyruvate.

TABLE VI

EFFECT OF DPN ON SODIUM PYRUVATE BREAKDOWN IN PRESENCE OF EXTRACTS OF *Cl. sporogenes*

Warburg manometer vessels contained 1 ml cell-free *Cl. sporogenes* extract in 1 % sodium thioglycollate + 0.002 M phosphate. 0.028 M NaHCO$_3$ present. Gas = 93 % N$_2$ + 7 % CO$_2$. Total vol. 3.2 ml. Temp. 37°.

Expt.	Contents of vessel	μM CO$_2$	μM Pyruvate disappeared	μM Lactate formed
1 (105 min)	No substrate + 3 mg DPN	1.6	—	
	0.02 M Pyruvate	9.6	19.5	
	0.02 M Pyruvate + 3 mg DPN	18.5	41.0	
2 (70 min)	0.01 M Pyruvate + 3 mg DPN + Brain homogenate	21.5	—	12.2
	0.01 M Pyruvate + 3 mg DPN + Brain homogenate, no bacterial extract present	5.0	—	2.4

Lactate formation from alanine in presence of Cl. sporogenes and lactic dehydrogenase, DPN, and arsenite

The fact that an alanine-proline mixture gives rise, in presence of *Cl. sporogenes* and lactic dehydrogenase, to lactate when proline reductase is inhibited by the addition of arsenite is shown in the results given in Table VII. Arsenite (0.005 M) almost completely eliminates carbon dioxide and ammonia formation from a mixture of alanine and proline in presence of an extract of *Cl. sporogenes*. When a brain homogenate is added to such an arsenite-inhibited system the rate of lactic acid formation is almost identical with that obtained in the absence of arsenite, whilst that of ammonia formation is greatly increased. Approximately equimolecular quantities of lactic acid and ammonia are produced (Table VII). These results are those expected if arsenite inhibits the proline reductase with relatively little effect on the following systems:

$$\text{Alanine} + \text{DPN} + \text{H}_2\text{O} = \text{Pyruvate} + \text{NH}_3 + \text{DPNH}_2$$
$$Cl.\ sporogenes$$
$$\text{Pyruvate} + \text{DPNH}_2 = \text{Lactate} + \text{DPN}$$
$$Lactic$$
$$Dehydrogenase$$

TABLE VII

EFFECT OF ARSENITE ON AMINO ACID INTERACTION IN EXTRACTS OF *Cl. sporogenes*

Warburg manometer vessels contained 1 ml cell-free *Cl. sporogenes* extract (in 1 % thioglycollate and 0.002 M phosphate); 0.028 M NaHCO$_3$ present. Amino acids = 0.02 M L-form. DPN = 3 mg/vessel. Sodium arsenite = 0.005 M. 0.5 ml Brain (rat) homogenate (1 % nicotinamide and 0.002 M phosphate). Gas = 93 % N$_2$ + 7 % CO$_2$. Total vol. 3.2 ml. Time 100′. Temp. 37°.

Contents of vessel	μM CO$_2$	μM NH$_3$	μM Lactate
Bacterial Extract	3.2	7.1	<1.0
Alanine + Proline + Bact. Extr.	32.0	39.5	1.8
Alanine + Proline + Bact. Extr. + Arsenite	4.7	10.0	2.0
Bacterial Extr. + Brain homog.	10.4	14.0	2.7
Alanine + Proline + Brain homog.	3.8	3.8	<1.0
Alanine + Proline + Bact. Extr. + Brain homog.	38.0	46.5	12.5
Alanine + Proline + Bact. Extr. + Brain homog. + Arsenite	8.0	22.5	12.0

References p. 120.

Effects of pyruvate addition on amino acid interaction in presence of Cl. sporogenes extract

In view of the conclusion that pyruvate must be produced in an alanine-proline interaction at a concentration sufficient to saturate pyruvic oxidase, even when pyruvate is being diverted to lactate by the presence of lactic dehydrogenase, it seems surprising that pyruvate does not accumulate normally in sufficient amounts to be isolated or even detected. The reason for this is that accumulation of pyruvate retards the process of alanine oxidation by DPN, either by substrate competition or through reversibility of action. Typical results showing this phenomenon are given in Table VIII. It will be seen that the rate of evolution of carbon dioxide is unaffected by a concentration of pyruvate that halves the rate of ammonia formation. It is evident that the pyruvic oxidase system is saturated at low concentrations of pyruvate, increase of which diminishes the rate of alanine oxidation. Clearly, a process that diverts pyruvate (*e.g.* to lactate) may prevent retardation of alanine oxidation and allow the amino acid interaction to proceed at an undiminished rate.

TABLE VIII

EFFECT OF SODIUM PYRUVATE ON AMINO ACID INTERACTION IN EXTRACTS OF *Cl. sporogenes*

Warburg manometer vessel contained 1 ml cell free *Cl. sporogenes* extract (in 1 % sodium thioglycollate and 0.002 % phosphate) 0.028 $NaHCO_3$. Gas = 93 % N_2 + 7 % CO_2. Amino acids = 0.02 M L-form, DPN = 3 mg/vessel. Total vol. 3.2 ml. Time 80′. Temp. 37°.

Contents of vessel	$\mu M\ CO_2$	$\mu M\ NH_3$
No substrate	3.4	7.0
Alanine + Proline	32.0	40.5
Alanine + Proline + 0.01 M Pyruvate	32.0	21.2
Alanine + Proline + 0.005 M Pyruvate	32.5	33.4
Alanine + Proline + 0.0025 M Pyruvate	32.5	39.5

Acetylation of sulfanilamide due to amino acid interaction in presence of Cl. sporogenes

The interaction of alanine and proline by an extract of *Cl. sporogenes* will bring about a disappearance of sulfanilamide in presence of an extract of pigeon liver powder, presumably by acetylation as acetic acid is a known product of the interaction.

Results given in Table IX show that a mixture of bacterial extract and pigeon liver extract, without added amino acids, accomplishes an acetylation of sulfanilamide, but that the rate of acetylation is markedly enhanced by the addition of a mixture of alanine and proline. Pyruvate may be substituted for alanine with a like effect on sulfanilamide acetylation. The presence of arsenite, which greatly inhibits amino acid interaction, also inhibits the increased sulfanilamide acetylation due to the amino acid interaction.

The addition of adenosine triphosphate has but little effect on the speed of acetylation of sulfanilamide by an amino acid interaction in presence of pigeon liver extract. This result, however, has little meaning, as extracts of *Cl. sporogenes* have a powerful ATP-ase activity, a concentration of 0.008 M ATP being completely decomposed in less than 20 minutes by an extract, under the experimental conditions quoted in Table IX.

In view of the high ATP-ase of *Cl. sporogenes* extracts it seems unlikely that the acetylation of sulfanilamide in such extracts is being mediated through the synthesis of ATP produced by amino acid interactions. It is more likely that the following reactions take place:

References p. 120.

7

TABLE IX

ACETYLATION OF SULFANILAMIDE DURING AMINO ACID INTERACTIONS IN PRESENCE OF

Cl. sporogenes EXTRACT

Warburg manometer vessels contained 1 ml extract of *Cl. sporogenes* (in 1 % thioglycollate and 0.01 M phosphate) and 0.5 ml extract of pigeon liver (500 mg acetone pigeon liver powder suspended in 5 ml 0.2 M KF and supernatant used), 0.028 M NaHCO$_3$ present. Gas = 93 % N$_2$ + 7 % CO$_2$. Temp.: 37°. Time 75'. DPN = 3 mg/vessel. Sulfanilamide = 200 μg/vessel (Expts. 1,3) and 400 μg/vessel (Expt. 2). Amino Acids = 0.02 M (L-form).

Expt.	Contents of vessel	μM CO$_2$	μg sulfanilamide acetylated
1	Bact. extr. + Pigeon liver extr.	11.0	117
	Bact. extr. + Alanine + Proline	32.0	12
	Pigeon liver Extr. + Alanine + Proline	4.0	44
	Bact. extr. + Pigeon liver Extr. + Alanine + Proline	35.0	180
2	Bact. ext. + Pigeon liver extract	6.0	183
	Bact. extr. + Pigeon liver extr. + Alanine + Proline	28.5	317
	Bact. extr. + Pigeon liver extr. + 0.005 M Arsenite	4.9	150
	Bact. extr. + Pigeon liver extr. + Alanine + Proline + 0.005 M Arsenite	5.4	172
3	Pigeon liver extr. + Pyruvate (.01 M) + Proline	6.1	37
	Bact. extr. + Pigeon liver extr. + Pyruvate (0.01 M) + Proline	47.0	183
	Bact. extr. + Pigeon liver Extr.	11.0	117

$$\text{Alanine} + \text{DPN} + \text{H}_2\text{O} = \text{Pyruvate} + \text{NH}_3 + \text{DPNH}_2$$

$$\text{Pyruvate} + \text{CoA} + \text{DPN} = \text{Acetyl-CoA} + \text{CO}_2 + \text{DPNH}_2$$

$$\text{Acetyl-CoA} + \text{Sulfanilamide} = \text{Acetylsulfanilamide} + \text{CoA}$$

Such a conclusion is supported by the experimental evidence that CoA is present in extracts of *Cl. sporogenes* (NISMAN AND MAGER[12]).

Effects of pyruvate on alanine oxidation by resting Cl. sporogenes

L-Alanine is oxidised aerobically by resting *Cl. sporogenes*, a vigorous rate of oxygen uptake, which falls off markedly with time, taking place. If pyruvate is an intermediate, as would be anticipated from the evidence given above, it would be expected that either pyruvate would be oxidised aerobically as vigorously as alanine or that it would accumulate during the oxidation. In fact, however, the rate of oxygen uptake by resting *Cl. sporogenes* in presence of pyruvate is remarkably feeble. Typical results for alanine and pyruvate are given in Table X. Moreover, estimation of the pyruvic acid indicates little or no disappearance in presence of *Cl. sporogenes* under aerobic conditions. During aerobic oxidation of alanine there is no accumulation of pyruvate, a fact noted by all previous workers. The problem arose, therefore, as to why pyruvate does not accumulate, if it does not undergo aerobic oxidation by *Cl. sporogenes*.

The following observations throw light on this phenomenon. The addition of pyruvate to DL-alanine markedly extends the interval during which vigorous aerobic oxidation of alanine takes place, so that in effect the oxygen uptake by *Cl. sporogenes* due to the alanine after a lengthy interval is greatly increased by the presence of pyruvate. Typical results are given in Table X. This phenomenon is also observed when a-ketoglutarate is substituted for pyruvate. During the period of marked stimulation of oxygen uptake due to the ketonic acid, little or none of the latter disappears. There is, however, a large increase of the rate of disappearance of alanine and of the rate of liberation of ammonia (see

References p. 120.

Table X). Approximately equimolar increases in oxygen uptake and ammonia formation take place (Expt. 4. Table X).

TABLE X

EFFECTS OF PYRUVATE AND α-KETOGLUTARATE ON OXYGEN UPTAKE OF RESTING
Cl. sporogenes IN PRESENCE OF ALANINE

Warburg manometer vessels contained 1 ml suspension (in 0.15 M KCl) freshly prepared *Cl. sporogenes* in 0.02 M phosphate buffer pH 7.3. DL-alanine = 0.04 M. Pyruvate = 0.01 M. α-Keto-glutarate = 0.01 M. Gas = air. Temp. 37°.

Expt.	Contents of vessel	Time	μM O₂ uptake	μM Alanine disappeared
I	No substrate	150′	2.0	
	Pyruvate	150′	3.6	
	Alanine	150′	9.9	
	Alanine + Pyruvate	150′	21.0	
2	No substrate	120′	1.0	
	Pyruvate	120′	2.0	
	Alanine	120′	13.8	12.4
	Alanine + Pyruvate	120′	34.4	35.0
3	α-Ketoglutarate	150′	1.0	
	Alanine	150′	6.5	
	Alanine + α-ketoglutarate	150′	14.5	
				μM NH₃ formed
4	No substrate	150′	1.0	3.7
	Pyruvate	150′	1.8	3.5
	Alanine	150′	6.3	9.5
	Pyruvate + Alanine	150′	17.1	19.5
	Alanine (Gas = O₂)	150′	3.6	7.0
	Pyruvate + Alanine (Gas = O₂)	150′	5.6	10.5

These results become immediately understandable on the following grounds: (a) hydrogen peroxide is formed during the aerobic oxidation of L-alanine (b) hydrogen peroxide is highly toxic to the amino acid oxidase (c) hydrogen peroxide is destroyed (non-enzymically) by pyruvate.

On this hypothesis, hydrogen peroxide is formed during the aerobic oxidation of the amino acid, much of it being destroyed by pyruvate which is formed simultaneously. Eventually, however, sufficient hydrogen peroxide accumulates to exert highly toxic effects, the corresponding quantity of undecomposed pyruvic acid being insufficient in quantity to be detected by ordinary chemical tests. The addition of pyruvate (or α-ketoglutarate) to the system, however, prevents the accumulation of hydrogen peroxide and the initial velocity of alanine oxidation proceeds unchecked, the pyruvate and hydrogen peroxide that are simultaneously formed interacting with each other. Thus the added pyruvate (or α-ketoglutarate) will not disappear (within experimental accuracy), whereas the rate of alanine oxidation will be increased.

It follows, from this view, that if oxygen is substituted for air, the rate of alanine oxidation by resting *Cl. sporogenes* will be diminished, as it is to be expected that the rate of hydrogen peroxide formation during the oxidation of the amino acid, by presumably the flavoprotein system, will be greater in oxygen than in air (see MANN AND QUASTEL[23]). The results of experiment (shown in Table X) verify this prediction. In the presence of oxygen, both the rates of oxygen uptake and of ammonia liberation by DL-alanine in presence of *Cl. sporogenes* are markedly retarded, and the stimulating effect of added pyruvate is decreased.

References p. 120.

Evidence that hydrogen peroxide is involved in aerobic oxidations by resting *Cl. sporogenes* is shown by the fact that the addition of catalase to the bacterial suspension brings about an increase in the rate of oxygen and of ammonia formation in presence of DL-alanine. For example, 1 ml bacterial suspension after exposure to air at 37° for 1 hour absorbed 9.5 μM oxygen in 90 minutes after addition of 0.02 M DL-alanine, whereas the same quantity of bacterial suspension in presence of catalase under the same conditions absorbed 14.4 μM oxygen.

Effects of exposure of resting Cl. sporogenes to air and to hydrogen peroxide

On exposing resting *Cl. sporogenes* to air, at 0°, for three of four hours a marked fall in the rate of anaerobic amino acid interaction takes place. Typical results are shown in Table XI (Expts. 1 and 2). This fall is reactivity is due to the presence of oxygen, as no diminution is experienced if the suspension of organisms is exposed to nitrogen for the same interval of time before addition of the amino acids (Table XI. Expt. 2). Moreover, the presence of the amino acids has no protective action. The toxic effect given by oxygen is given also by dilute hydrogen peroxide. Results shown in Table XI Expt. 3 make it clear that exposure of resting *Cl. sporogenes* to a concentration of hydrogen peroxide of less than 1/10,000 brings about an immediate drop in the rate of anaerobic amino acid interaction. It is evident, therefore, that both hydrogen peroxide and oxygen are toxic to the mechanisms underlying amino acid interaction in *Cl. sporogenes*. It is likely that oxygen is toxic *per se* as its presence induces toxicity when no consumption of oxygen by the bacterial preparation in absence of added substrates is noticeable and when, therefore, the production of hydrogen peroxide must be exceedingly minute.

TABLE XI

EFFECTS OF EXPOSURE OF *Cl. sporogenes* TO AIR AND HYDROGEN PEROXIDE ON

AMINO ACID INTERACTIONS

Warburg manometer vessels contained 1 ml suspension *Cl. sporogenes* (in 0.15 M KCl); 0.028 M NaHCO$_3$, Gas 93% N$_2$ + 7% CO$_2$. Total vol. 3.2 mg.

Expt.	Contents of vessel	Conditions of exposure of Cl. sporogenes	μM CO$_2$ formed	μM Glycine disappeared
1 Time 135′	L-Alanine (0.005 M) + Glycine (0.01 M)	Freshly prepared organism, used immediately	9.9	
	L-Alanine (0.005 M) + Glycine (0.01 M)	Organism exposed to air for 3 h at 0° before addition of amino acids	5.1	
	L-Alanine (0.005 M) + Glycine (0.01 M)	Organism exposed to air for 3 h at 0° in presence of alanine + glycine	4.3	
2 Time 90′	L-Alanine (0.02 M) + L-Proline (0.02 M)	Organism exposed to air for 4 h at 37° before addition of amino acids	13.4	
	L-Alanine (0.02 M) + L-Proline (0.02 M)	Organism exposed to 93% N$_2$+7% CO$_2$ for 4 h at 37° before addition of amino acids	35.6	
3 Time 135′	L-Alanine (0.005 M) + Glycine (0.01 M)	Freshly prepared organism used immediately after dilution with water, centrifuging and resuspension in 0.15 M KCl	14.5	27.5
	L-Alanine (0.005 M) + Glycine (0.01 M)	Freshly prepared organism treated with six times its vol. 1/10,000 hydrogen peroxide, centrifuged at once and resuspended in 0.15 M KCl	4.0	3.2

References p. 120.

Effects of pyruvate, α-ketoglutarate and thiol compounds on resting Cl. sporogenes after exposure to air or hydrogen peroxide

Exposure of resting *Cl. sporogenes* to air at 37° causes a fall in its ability to oxidise L-alanine (see Table XII) and the addition of pyruvate has but little stimulant effect. If, however, the exposure of *Cl. sporogenes* to air takes place in the presence of 0.01 M pyruvate or α-ketoglutarate, its subsequent ability to oxidase alanine is much increased and the stimulating action of the presence of pyruvate is again noticeable (Table XII).

TABLE XII

EFFECTS OF PYRUVATE AND α-KETOGLUTARATE ON ACTIVITY OF RESTING *Cl. sporogenes*

Warburg manometer vessels contained 1 ml suspension of *Cl. sporogenes* (in 0.15 M KCl) in 0.02 M phosphate buffer pH 7.3. Total vol. 3.2 ml. L-Alanine = 0.02 M. Pyruvate = 0.01 M.

Contents of vessel	Conditions of exposure of Cl. sporogenes	μM oxygen absorbed	μM NH₃ liberated
Alanine	Freshly prepared organism used immediately.	10.7	15.0
Alanine	1 ml organism diluted with 2 ml water, exposed to air at 37° for 40', centrifuged and resuspended in 1 ml 0.15 M KCl	4.3	6.7
Alanine + Pyruvate	1 ml organism diluted with 2 ml water, exposed to air at 37° for 40', centrifuged and resuspended in 1 ml 0.15 M KCl	5.7	7.7
Alanine	1 ml organism diluted with 2 ml sodium pyruvate soln. (0.01 M) exposed to air at 37° for 40 min centrifuged and resuspended in 1 ml 0.15 M KCl	8.9	11.8
Alanine + Pyruvate	1 ml organism diluted with 2 ml sodium pyruvate soln. (0.01 M) exposed to air at 37° for 40' centrifuged and resuspended in 1 ml 0.15M KCl	16.6	20.5
Alanine	1 ml organism diluted with 2 ml sodium α-ketoglutarate soln. (0.01 M) exposed to air at 37° for 10', centrifuged and resuspended 1 ml 0.15 M KCl	7.7	11.6
Alanine + Pyruvate	1 ml organism diluted with 2 ml sodium αketoglutarate soln. (0.01 M) exposed to air at 37° for 10', centrifuged and resuspended in 1 ml 0.15 M KCl	14.0	13.8

This phenomenon may be explained as being due to a toxic effect of oxygen on the amino acid oxidase system, that is obtained even in the absence of the amino acid, when there is no perceptible absorption of oxygen. The protective effects of pyruvate and α-ketoglutarate may be due either to destruction of traces of hydrogen peroxide or to a reversible linkage with thiol groups important in the oxidation of alanine, thus preserving them from irreversible oxidation by oxygen (or hydrogen peroxide). The fact that thiol groups are involved in the aerobic oxidation of L-alanine by *Cl. sporogenes* is indicated by the inhibitory effect of phenyl arsenoxide thioglycollate (200 μg/vessel) which diminishes the rate of alanine oxidation by 81 %.

The considerable diminution of the rate of anaerobic amino acid (alanine-glycine, interaction brought about by exposure of resting *Cl. sporogenes* to air at 0° (Tables XI) XII) may be prevented by the presence of sodium thioglycollate. Typical results are shown in Table XIII. This result would be expected it thioglycollate prevents access of oxygen to the organism by its preferential oxidation.

References p. 120.

TABLE XIII

EFFECTS OF THIOL COMPOUNDS ON LOSS OF ACTIVITY OF *Cl. sporogenes* DUE TO EXPOSURE
TO AIR OR HYDROGEN PEROXIDE

Warburg manometer vessels contained 1 ml *Cl. sporogenes* suspension (in 0.15 M KCL), 0.028 M NaHCO$_3$. Gas 93% N$_2$ + 7% CO$_2$. L-Alanine 0.005 M. Glycine 0.01 M. Time 135'. Temp. 37°. Total vol. 3.2 ml. Alanine tipped from side tube.

Expt.	Contents of vessel	Conditions of exposure of Cl. sporogenes	μM CO$_2$ evolved	μM Glycine disappeared
1	Alanine + Glycine + Thioglycollate (0.012 M)	Freshly prepared organism used immediately	12.5	25.5
	Alanine + Glycine	Freshly prepared organism used immediately	11.0	24.0
	Alanine + Glycine	Organism exposed to air at 0° for 3 h before addition of amino acids	1.0	<1.0
	Alanine + Glycine	Organism exposed to air at 0° for 3 h in presence of 0.12 M thioglycollate before addition of amino acids	10.5	17.2
2	Alanine + Glycine	Freshly prepared organism used immeditately	10.5	20.2
	Alanine + Glycine + Glutathione (0.005 M)	1 ml organism diluted with 40 vols. 0.15 M KCl, centrifuged and resuspended in 1 ml 0.15 M KCl	11.6	21.3
	Alanine + Glycine + Glutathione (0.005 M)	1 ml organism diluted with 40 vols. 1/50,000 H$_2$O$_2$, centrifuged at once, resuspended in 1 ml 0.15 M KCl	9.8	19.2
	Alanine + Glycine	1 ml organism diluted with 40 vols. 1/50,000 H$_2$O$_2$, centrifuged at once, resuspended in 1 ml 0.15 M KCl	3.7	3.7
	Alanine + Glycine + Thioglycollate (0.005 M)	1 ml organism diluted with 40 vols. 1/50,000 H$_2$O$_2$, centrifuged at once, resuspended in 1 ml 0.15 M KCl	10.0	17.6

Exposure of *Cl. sporogenes* to 1/50,000 hydrogen peroxide causes a large drop in the rate of anaerobic amino acid interaction. If an organism, exposed in this way, is washed free of hydrogen peroxide, and is now treated with amino acids in presence of glutathione or thioglycollate, almost complete recovery of the rate of amino acid interaction takes place. These results show that the toxic effects of dilute hydrogen peroxide, and presumably of oxygen, are reversed by subsequent exposure to thiol compounds, and lead to the conclusion that the compounds affected by oxygen or hydrogen peroxide have themselves a thiol constitution, and are possibly either thiol-enzymes or thiol co-enzymes.

Effects of organic arsenoxides on activities of Cl. sporogenes

The conclusion reached above that thiol compounds play a highly significant role in the activities of *Cl. sporogenes* is borne out by the extraordinary sensitivity of these organisms to the presence of arsenoxides. As shown by GORDON AND QUASTEL[24], phenyl-arsenoxide or mapharside (*m*-amino-*p*-hydroxy-phenylarsenoxide) is extremely reactive with thiol enzymes (see also SINGER[25]). The presence of these substances, at low concentrations, greatly reduces anaerobic amino acid interactions, a concentration of 8 μg/ml mapharside bringing about over 50% inhibition. Typical results are shown in Table XIV.

The amino acid reductase is much more vulnerable to attack by arsenoxide than the

References p. 120.

amino acid oxidase. This is indicated by the relatively high resistance of alanine oxidation to the presence of 8 μg/ml mapharside (Table XIV). Hydrogen uptake by the organisms in the presence of proline at this concentration of mapharside is completely suppressed.

TABLE XIV

EFFECTS OF ORGANIC ARSENOXIDES ON THE ACTIVITIES OF RESTING *Cl. sporogenes*

Warburg manometer vessels contained 1 ml *Cl. sporogenes* suspension (in 0.15 M KCl). Buffer either 0.028 M NaHCO$_3$ or 0.02 M phosphate (pH 7.3) as indicated. L-Alanine = 0.02 M. L-Proline = 0.02 M. Gas = 93% N$_2$ + 7% CO$_2$ or Air or Hydrogen as indicated. Total vol. 3.2 ml. Temp. + 37°. Time 90′.

Expt.	Contents of vessel	Arsenoxide present	Buffer	$\mu M\ H_2$ absorbed	$\mu M\ CO_2$ evolved	μO_2 consumed
1	Alanine + Proline	Nil	Bicarb-N$_2$/CO$_2$	—	38.0	—
	Alanine + Proline	25 μg Mapharside	Bicarb-N$_2$/CO$_2$	—	15.5	—
	Alanine	Nil	Phosp.-Air	—	—	6.6
	Alanine	25 μg Mapharside	Phosph.-Air	—	—	6.6
	Proline	Nil	Phosp.-Hydrogen	6.1	—	—
	Proline	25 μg Mapharside	Phosph.-Hydrogen	0.0	—	—
2	Alanine + Proline	Nil	Bicarb-N$_2$/CO$_2$	—	30.5	
	Alanine + Proline	12.5 μg Phenyl-arsenoxide-thio-glycollate	Bicarb-N$_2$/CO$_2$		27.5	
	Alanine + Proline	25 μg Phenyl-arsenoxide-thio-glycollate	Bicarb-N$_2$/CO$_2$		19.5	
	Alanine + Proline	50 μg Phenyl-arsenoxide-thio-glycollate	Bicarb-N$_2$/CO$_2$		8.2	
	Analine + Proline	100 μg Phenyl-arsenoxide-thio-glycollate	Bicarb-N$_2$/CO$_2$		1.7	
	Alanine + Proline	200 μg Phenyl-arsenoxide-thio-glycollate	Bicarb-N$_2$/CO$_2$		0.0	

The results indicate that the amino acid reductase of *Cl. sporogenes* is a highly vulnerable thiol system and appears to be the one most affected by the presence of oxygen, hydrogen peroxide, or organic arsenoxides.

The toxicity of organic arsenoxides to *Cl. sporogenes* is reversible (see also GORDON AND QUASTEL[24]), the addition of glutathione (0.3%) to an organism, that has been exposed for 30 minutes to phenylarsenoxide with a resultant drop of 84% in the rate of alanine-proline interaction, causing almost complete (over 80%) recovery of activity.

That the toxic action of the organic arsenoxide is due to the trivalent arsenic atom is shown by the entire lack of toxic activity of the corresponding pentavalent arsenic acids.

DISCUSSION

The results described in this preliminary survey of anaerobic amino acid interactions in *Cl. sporogenes* indicate that these interactions take place with diphosphopyridine nucleotide (DPN) playing an intermediate role as hydrogen carrier. Ferricyanide together with the amino acid hydrogen acceptors, and molecular hydrogen together with the amino acid hydrogen donators, compete for the DPN carrier system. Pyruvate has been

References p. 120.

established as an intermediate in the alanine-proline interaction by the fact that lactate is formed when animal lactic dehydrogenase is added to the system. Amino acid interactions, taking place anaerobically, bring about the disappearance of sulfanilamide, presumably by acetylation, when the appropriate enzyme in a pigeon liver extract is added to the system. The results would indicate that the following sequence of reactions takes place anaerobically in *Cl. sporogenes*:

$$\text{Amino Acid} + \text{DPN} + \text{H}_2\text{O} = \alpha\text{-Ketoacid} + \text{NH}_3 + \text{DPNH}_2$$
$$\text{Pyruvate} + \text{CoA} + \text{DPN} = \text{Acetyl-CoA} + \text{CO}_2 + \text{DPNH}_2$$
$$\text{Amino Acid} + \text{DPNH}_2 = \text{Reduced amino acid} + \text{DPN}$$

The course of metabolic events of *Cl. sporogenes* in the presence of oxygen indicates the high sensitivity of enzymatic mechanisms in these organisms to oxygen and hydrogen peroxide. Although pyruvate undergoes but little breakdown aerobically in presence of *Cl. sporogenes*, its presence has a large accelerative effect on the oxidation of L-alanine. This seems to be due to the fact that the added pyruvate prevents (by non-enzymic interaction) the accumulation of hydrogen peroxide which is highly toxic to the enzymes activating amino acids in *Cl. sporogenes*. A similar protective effect is shown by α-ketoglutarate.

Exposure of the organisms to air or hydrogen peroxide causes a large fall in the rate of amino acid interaction. That the toxic action of oxygen and of hydrogen peroxide (in low concentrations) is largely reversible may be shown by the resuscitating effect of the addition of thiol compounds to organisms that have been exposed to air or hydrogen peroxide on the speed of their anaerobic amino acid interactions. These effects of the additions of thiol compounds on the metabolism of *Cl. sporogenes* doubtless account for the original observation of QUASTEL AND STEPHENSON[26] that oxygenated cultures of these organisms exhibit little or no retardation in their rates of growth in media containing thiol compounds. It is suggested that the amino acid activating enzymes of *Cl. sporogenes* are thiol systems, highly sensitive to oxygen and hydrogen peroxide which convert the structures into –S–S–forms that are reduced to the active-SH condition by the addition of thiol compounds. The amino acid reductases are particularly sensitive thiol systems.

The amino acid activating enzymes are inhibited (reversibly) by low concentrations of organic arsenoxides, the amino acid reductases showing the highest sensitivities.

SUMMARY

1. Amino acid hydrogen donators compete with each other, and amino acid hydrogen acceptors also compete with each other, in anaerobic amino acid interactions in *Cl. sporogenes*.

2. The competition of these substances is due to the fact that diphosphopyridine nucleotide acts as a common hydrogen carrier between the amino acid hydrogen donators and the amino acid hydrogen acceptors.

3. Molecular hydrogen absorption by amino acid hydrogen acceptors is greatly suppressed by the presence of amino acid hydrogen donators in *Cl. sporogenes*.

4. Ferricyanide acts as a hydrogen acceptor, competing with amino acid hydrogen acceptors, in *Cl. sporogenes*.

5. Pyruvate is established as an intermediate in anaerobic alanine-proline interaction in *Cl. sporogenes*, by its diversion to lactate in presence of lactic dehydrogenase of animal tissues.

6. Anaerobic amino acid interactions, as well as pyruvate-amino acid interaction, give rise to sulfanilamide acetylation in extracts of *Cl. sporogenes*, when an extract of pigeon liver is added.

References p. 120.

7. Aerobic alanine oxidation by *Cl. sporogenes* is greatly accelerated by the presence of pyruvate or α-ketoglutarate, which acts in this way by non-enzymic interaction with hydrogen peroxide (formed during alanine oxidation).

8. Exposure of *Cl. sporogenes* to air, oxygen or hydrogen peroxide, exert highly toxic effects on amino acid oxidations or anaerobic interactions. These may be prevented by the presence of pyruvate or of thiol compounds.

9. The toxic effects of air or oxygen or dilute hydrogen peroxide on the enzymatic mechanisms of *Cl. sporogenes* may be reversed by subsequent additions of thiol compounds. It is suggested that the amino acid activating enzymes are thiol systems, which are converted to the inert–S–S–form by oxygen or dilute hydrogen peroxide. This inert form may be converted to the active –SH form by treatment with thiol compounds.

10. The amino acid activating enzymes, particularly the amino acid reductases, are highly sensitive to organic arsenoxides which exert large inhibitory effects on amino acid interactions in *Cl. sporogenes*.

RÉSUMÉ

1. Les aminoacides donateurs d'hydrogène, de même que les aminoacides accepteurs d'hydrogène, entrent en compétition les uns avec les autres au cours du métabolisme des aminoacides chez *Cl. sporogenes*.

2. La compétition entre ces substances est due au fait que le diphosphopyridine nucléotide constitue un transporteur d'hydrogène commun entre les amino acides donateurs d'hydrogène et les amino acides accepteurs d'hydrogène.

3. L'absorption d'hydrogène moléculaire par les amino acides accepteurs d'hydrogène est fortement inhibée, chez *Cl. sporogenes*, par la présence d'amino acides donateurs d'hydrogène.

4. Chez *Cl. sporogenes*, le ferricyanure joue le rôle d'un accepteur d'hydrogène, qui peut entrer en compétition avec les amino acides accepteurs d'hydrogène.

5. Le pyruvate sert d'intermédiaire dans l'interaction alanineproline, chez *Cl. sporogenes* en anaérobiose, ainsi que le montre sa transformation en lactate en présence de la déshydrogénase lactique des tissus animaux.

6. En anaérobiose les interactions entre amino acides, de même que l'interaction pyruvate-amino acide, donnent lieu, dans des extraits de *Cl. sporogenes*, à l'acétylation de la sulfanylamide, après addition d'un extrait de foie de pigeon.

7. L'oxydation aérobie de l'alanine par *Cl. sporogenes* est fortement accélérée par la présence de pyruvate ou d'α-cétoglutarate, qui intervient par une interaction non enzymatique avec l'eau oxygénée (produite par l'oxydation de l'alanine).

8. L'exposition de *Cl. sporogenes* à l'air, l'oxygène ou l'eau oxygénée, a des effets nettement toxiques sur les oxydations ou les interactions anaérobies des amino acides. Ces effets peuvent être supprimés par la présence de pyruvate ou de composés sulfhydrylés.

9. Les effets toxiques de l'air, de l'oxygène ou de l'eau oxygénée diluée sur les mécanismes enzymatiques de *Cl. sporogenes* peuvent être suspendus par l'addition ultérieure de composés sulfhydrylés. Il se peut que les enzymes activant les amino acides soient des enzymes à groupements thiols, qui passent sous la forme –S–S–inactive, sous l'action de l'oxygène de l'eau oxygénée diluée. Cette forme inactive peut être convertie en forme –SH active par traitement avec un composé sulfhydrylé.

10. Les enzymes activant les amino acides, particulièrement les réductases, sont très sensibles aux arsenoxydes organiques qui inhibent fortement les interactions des amino acides chez *Cl. sporogenes*.

ZUSAMMENFASSUNG

1. Bei anaerobischen Aminosäurereaktionen in *Cl. sporogenes* konkurrieren Aminosäurewasserstoffdonatoren und ebenfalls Aminosäurewasserstoffacceptoren miteinander.

2. Der Wettstreit dieser Substanzen ist der Tatsache zuzuschreiben, dass Diphosphopyridinnucleotid als ein gewöhnlicher Wasserstoffübertäger zwischen den Aminosäurewasserstoffdonatoren und den Aminosäurewasserstoffacceptoren wirkt.

3. Die molekulare Wasserstoffabsorption von Aminosäurewasserstoffacceptoren ist in Gegenwart von Aminosäurewasserstoffdonatoren in *Cl. sporogenes* sehr unterdrückt.

4. Ferricyanide wirken in *Cl. sporogenes* als Wasserstoffacceptoren, die mit den Aminosäurewasserstoffacceptoren konkurrieren.

5. Brenztraubensaures Salz wurde durch Überführung in Lactat bei Gegenwart der Milchsäuredehydrogenase tierischer Gewebe als ein Zwischenglied in der anaerobischen Alanin-Prolinreaktion in *Cl. sporogenes* festgestellt.

6. Anaerobische Aminosäurereaktionen, ebenso wie die Brenztraubensaures Salz-Aminosäurereaktion, geben, wenn ein Extrakt von Taubenleber hinzugefügt wird, Anlass zur Sulfanilamidacetylierung in Extrakten von *Cl. sporogenes*.

References p. 120.

7. Die aerobische Alaninoxydation in *Cl. sporogenes* wird sehr beschleunigt durch die Anwesenheit von brenztraubensauren und α-ketoglutarsauren Salzen, die auf diese Weise durch die nichtenzymatische Reaktion mit den während der Alaninoxydation gebildeten Hydrogenperoxyd wirken.

8. Das Aussetzen von *Cl. sporogenes* an Luft, Sauerstoff oder Hydrogenperoxyd übt eine höchst toxische Wirkung auf die Aminosäureoxydation oder die anaerobischen Reaktionen aus. Die kann durch die Gegenwart von brenztraubensaurem Salz oder Thiolverbindungen verhindert werden.

9. Der toxische Effekt von Luft oder Sauerstoff oder verdünnten Hydrogenperoxyd auf den Enzymmechanismus von *Cl. sporogenes* kann durch die nachfolgende Zugabe von Thiolverbindungen umgekehrt werden. Es wird vermutet, dass die aminosäureaktivierenden Enzyme Thiolenzyme sind, die durch Sauerstoff oder Hydrogenperoxyd in die inerte–S–S–Form umgewandelt werden. Diese inerte Form kann durch Behandlung mit Thiolverbindungen in die aktive SH-Form zurückverwandelt werden.

10. Die aminosäureaktivierenden Enzyme, besonders die Aminosäurereduktasen, sind höchst empfindlich für organische Arsenoxyde, die einen stark hemmenden Effekt auf die Aminosäurereaktionen in *Cl. sporogenes* aüsüben.

REFERENCES

[1] J. H. QUASTEL, M. STEPHENSON AND M. D. WHETHAM, *Biochem. J.*, 19 (1925) 304.
[2] J. H. QUASTEL AND M. STEPHENSON, *Biochem. J.*, 19 (1925) 660.
[3] J. H. QUASTEL, *Biochem. J.*, 19 (1925) 64.
[4] L. H. STICKLAND, *Biochem. J.*, 28 (1934) 746.
[5] L. H. STICKLAND, *Biochem. J.*, 29 (1935) 889, 288.
[6] W. KOCHOLATY AND J. C. HOOGERHEIDE, *Biochem. J.*, 32 (1938) 437.
[7] J. C. HOOGERHEIDE AND W. KOCHOLATY, *Biochem. J.*, 32 (1938) 949.
[8] B. NISMAN, *Compt. rend.*, 229 (1949) 633.
[9] A. J. ROSENBERG AND B. NISMAN, *Biochem. Biophys. Acta*, 3 (1949) 348.
[10] B. NISMAN AND G. VINET, *Ann. inst. Pasteur*, 77 (1949) 277.
[11] B. NISMAN AND G. VINET, *Compt. rend.*, 229 (1949) 675.
[12] B. NISMAN AND G. VINET, *Ann. inst. Pasteur*, 78 (1950) 115.
[13] B. NISMAN AND J. BERTRAND, *Compt. rend.*, 230 (1950) 248.
[14] B. NISMAN AND J. MAGER, *Nature*, 169 (1952) 243.
[15] D. E. HUGHES, *Brit. J. Exptl. Path.*, 32 (1951) 97.
[16] B. M. BRAGANCA, J. H. QUASTEL AND R. SCHUCHER, *Arch. Biochem. Biophys.*, 41 (1952) 478.
[17] M. JOWETT AND J. H. QUASTEL, *Biochem. J.*, 31 (1937) 275.
[18] J. B. BARKER AND W. H. SUMMERSON, *J. Biol. Chem.*, 138 (1941) 535.
[19] W. W. UMBREIT, R. H. BURRIS AND J. E. STAUFFER, *Manometric Technique and Tissue Metabolism*, Burgess Publishing Co. Minneapolis 1949, p. 192.
[20] A. C. BRATTON AND E. K. MARSHALL, *J. Biol. Chem.*, 128 (1939) 544.
[21] J. H. QUASTEL AND A. H. M. WHEATLEY, *Biochem.*, *J.*, 32 (1938) 936.
[22] B. NISMAN AND J. MAGER, *Nature*, 169 (1952) 243.
[23] P. J. G. MANN AND J. H. QUASTEL, *Biochem. J.*, 40 (1946) 139.
[24] J. J. GORDON AND J. H. QUASTEL, *Biochem. J.*, 42 (1948) 337.
[25] T. P. SINGER, *J. Biol. Chem.*, 174 (1948) 11.
[26] J. H. QUASTEL AND M. STEPHENSON, *Biochem. J.*, 20 (1926) 1125.
[27] D. D. WOODS, *Biochem. J.*, 30 (1936) 1934.

Received March 30th, 1953

HEAT OF HYDROLYSIS OF TRIMETAPHOSPHATE*

by

OTTO MEYERHOF**, ROMAS SHATAS*** AND ANN KAPLAN

*Department of Physiological Chemistry, School of Medicine,
University of Pennsylvania, Philadelphia, Pa. (U.S.A.)†*

INTRODUCTION

Although the occurrence of metaphosphate in yeast was discovered some sixty years ago by LIEBERMANN[1] and later by KOSSEL[2] more extensive investigations about its biochemical significance have been undertaken only in the past fifteen years. In 1928, KITASATO demonstrated the presence of metaphosphatase in enzyme extracts[3]. In 1936, MACFARLANE found metaphosphate in a nucleic acid preparation of yeast[4] and later MANN isolated metaphosphate from *Aspergillus niger*[5]. The same year JEENER AND BRACHET observed that by a preceding period of starvation, the absorption of ortho-phosphate by yeast was greatly enhanced[6]. Simultaneously, a basophilic substance was synthetized which was identified as metaphosphate by WIAME[7], and SCHMIDT, HECHT AND THANNHAUSER[8]. WIAME demonstrated employing a staining technique based on the metachromatic reaction[9] that a substance called volution, closely related with the processes of cell division, contained metaphosphate[10]. Later, LINDEGREN suggested the hypothesis that the "high energy" bond of metaphosphate could be used by the cell to synthetize nucleoproteins during the mitosis[11]. However, the role of metaphosphate in catabolism is far from completely understood[12, 13].

The clarification of energetic relations has contributed much to the rapid progress in the elucidation of phosphorus metabolism in the past. Likewise, knowledge of these relations would be of great help in devising a scheme to incorporate both the synthesis and the catabolic utilization of metaphosphate into the general picture of phosphorus metabolism[14]. These reasons induced us to study quantitatively the P-O-P bond energy of metaphosphate§.

Several different experimental approaches are possible to obtain the thermodynamic data necessary to calculate the change in free energy. The first one is based upon the determination of the equilibrium constant, K, in accordance with the equation

$$- \Delta F = RT \ln K.$$

* This paper is based on investigations supported by grants from The American Cancer Society (recommended by the Committee on Growth of the National Research Council) and the U.S. Public Health Service.

** Deceased: October 6, 1951.

*** Physicist, Bartol Research Foundation of The Franklin Institute, Swarthmore, Pennsylvania.

† One of the authors (R. S.) wishes to express his gratitude to The Bartol Research Foundation of The Franklin Institute for allowing him to use the facilities of the Foundation during the writing of this paper.

§ Due to the discontinuance of the laboratory of the principal investigator (OTTO MEYERHOF) after his death, the experiments on other condensates of orthophosphoric acid were interrupted.

References p. 127.

However, if ΔF is large, small amounts of trimetaphosphate have to be determined in the presence of relatively concentrated orthophosphate. No quantitatively reliable analytical procedure to perform this task has yet been found.

The second approach makes use of the thermodynamic equation of an isothermal process:

$$\Delta F = \Delta H - T\Delta S$$

ΔH, the change in enthalpy, can be calculated in principle from heats of combustion, solution and dissociation or, if the temperature dependency of the equilibrium constant is known, from van 't Hoff's equation

$$\frac{d\ln K}{dT} = \frac{\Delta H}{RT^2}$$

However, a direct calorimetric determination of the heat of reaction is the most reliable method in evaluation of ΔH. Therefore, we have undertaken a series of measurements of the heat evolved by the enzymic hydrolysis of trimetaphosphate.

EXPERIMENTAL

The calorimeter

The calorimetric measurements were carried out with an isothermal constant-flow calorimeter similar to that first described by OHLMEYER[15]. By the use of electronic circuits, his original arrangement has been adapted for a semi-automatic operation, with a simultaneous improvement in stability and dependability*.

Materials and preparations

The trisodium trimetaphosphate used was a sample from Calgon Inc. (Pittsburgh, Pa.) of better than 95% purity.

Trimetaphosphatase was prepared from baker's yeast as follows: a mixture of 6 g yeast, 0.5 ml 5% $NaHCO_3$, 2.5 ml 0.1 M glutathione (pH 7) and 16 ml water was vibrated for 75 min in a Raytheon magnetostrictive oscillator at 9 kc/s. The preparation was kept cold by a circulating water system, the temperature at the outlet being 8–10°. The vibrated mixture was centrifuged at 27,000 g for 5 min in a refrigerated centrifuge**. About 17.5 ml of supernatant resulted from each batch of vibrated yeast.

Solid ammonium sulfate was added to the supernatant to bring the concentration up to 30% and centrifuged at 27,000 g. The precipitate was discarded, with loss of some activity but much inert protein. The concentration of ammonium sulfate was raised to 60%, the solution centrifuged at 27,000 g, the supernatant discarded, and the precipitate (resulting from 17.5 ml of the original supernatant) dissolved in 1 ml 0.1 M sodium maleate at pH 7.0. Here the total volume was about 2.5 ml. This was dialyzed overnight against glass-distilled water buffered with 0.01 M maleate pH 7 with three changes of fluid. The enzyme solution was stored in the frozen state.

These partial purification were usually made with 35 ml of yeast supernatant yielding 4–5 ml enzyme solution. The Q_p of the preparation was 400***. Glass distilled water was used in all solutions.

Analytical methods

The purity of trimetaphosphate was assayed by the method of JONES[16]. Within the limits of accuracy of this method, no contamination by other phosphates was found. The metachromatic reaction[9] was also used to identify hexametaphosphate. The trimetaphosphate was not hydrolysed at all by crystalline pyrophosphatase†. If not mentioned explicitly, the assay was as follows: a mixture containing 0.2 ml 0.1 M trimetaphosphate at pH 7.0, 0.4–0.5 ml 0.1 M buffer pH 7, 0.2–0.1 ml enzyme and 0.2 ml of either the solution specified in the tables or 0.01 M $MgSO_4$ was incubated at 33° C for ten minutes. The reaction was stopped by the addition of 1 ml 5% trichloracetic acid and the supernatant analyzed for orthophosphate by the method of FISKE AND SUBBA ROW as modified by LOHMANN AND JENDRASSIK[17].

The nucleic acid/protein ration and the protein content during the purification of enzyme was determined in a Beckmann spectrophotometer** by the method of WARBURG AND CHRISTIAN[18].

---

* Details will be published in *The Journal of The Franklin Institute.*
** Loaned by The American Philosophical Society.
*** $Q_p = \mu l\ H_3PO_4$ formed per 1 mg dry substance in 1 h at 33° C.
† We wish to thank Dr M. KUNITZ for a generous sample of crystalline pyrophosphatase.

References p. 127.

Studies on the enzyme

The optimum hydrogen ion concentration of enzymic hydrolysis of trimetaphosphate was investigated between pH 4.25 and 9 and found to occur at a pH of approximately 7. This observation agrees with findings of SCHÄFFNER AND KRUMEY using enzyme extracts from dried yeast[19] and NEUBERG AND FISCHER who prepared the enzyme from *Aspergillus oryzae*[20]. However, both authors used tripolyphosphate as substrate. On the contrary, metaphosphatase prepared from Aspergillus niger showed a pH optimum of approximately 4 [5,21], except for some mutant strains, enzyme extracts of which attained maximum activity at pH 6[22].

The activation of the enzyme by some divalent metallic ions in $2 \cdot 10^{-3}$ M concentration at pH 7 is summarized in Table I. BAMANN AND HEUMÜLLER found that the

TABLE I

ACTIVATION OF ENZYME BY DIVALENT KATIONS

Ion ($2 \cdot 10^{-3}$ M final concentration)	Relative Activity
Mg⁺⁺	6.6
Mn⁺⁺	4.2
Co⁺⁺	3.4
Zn⁺⁺	2.3
Ni⁺⁺	1.1
None	1
Fe⁺⁺	0.6
Cu⁺⁺	0.5

enzyme prepared from liver was activated ten times more by Mn⁺⁺[23]. As our findings show, the enzyme of yeast is almost equally well activated either by Mn⁺⁺ or Mg⁺⁺.

The action of various inhibitors as azide, arsenate, KCN, NaF and glutathione is given in Table II.

TABLE II

INHIBITION OF ENZYME BY VARIOUS INHIBITORS

Inhibitor	Final Concentration	Average loss of activity in percent
Azide	$M/300$	0
	$M/100$	30
Arsenate	$M/3000$	4
	$M/300$	15
KCN	$M/500$	0
	$M/100$	50
Glutathione	$M/100$	17
NaF	$M/100$	53

The results indicate that at this level of purity, the enzyme is appreciably inhibited only by fluoride and cyanide.

The activity of the enzyme with trimetaphosphate, hexametaphosphate and pyrophosphate in equimolar concentrations as substrate at pH 7 is recorded in Table III.

This nonspecificity of pyro- and metaphosphatase preparations of yeast even after a thousandfold purification was discussed recently by HOFFMAN-OSTENHOF[24].

References p. 127.

The heat inactivation of the enzyme was studied by preincubation at 33° C and pH 7. A loss of activity up to 40 percent was observed after 3 h; however, the activity was completely preserved in a 50% solution of glycerol. A similar stabilization by glycerol was previously described by MEYERHOF AND OHLMEYER in the case of adenosine triphosphatase[25].

TABLE III

ACTIVITY OF ENZYME TOWARDS DIFFERENT PHOSPHATES
UNDER SIMILAR EXPERIMENTAL CONDITIONS

Substrate	Relative Activity
Pyrophosphate	2
Trimetaphosphate	1
Hexametaphosphate	0.3

We did not find any evidence that the enzymic cleavage of trimetaphosphate passes through an intermediate step of pyrophosphate. By addition of crystalline pyrophosphatase the rate of hydrolysis did not increase (Table IV).

Even if our enzyme contained pyrophosphatase, the Q_p of the added crystalline pyrophosphatase was more than 50,000 times higher.

TABLE IV

THE RATE OF ENZYMIC HYDROLYSIS OF TRIMETAPHOSPHATE
WITH AND WITHOUT ADDITION OF CRYSTALLINE PYROPHOSPHATASE

Enzyme	Orthophosphate formed in 10 min in micromoles
Metaphosphatase	6.4
Metaphosphatase and cryst. pyrophosphatase	6.2
Metaphosphatase; cryst. pyrophosphatase added after 5 min. incubation	6.4

Unlike the pyrophosphatase[26], the trimetaphosphatase is not inhibited by substrate concentration as high as 0.2 M as shown in Table V.

TABLE V

RATE OF ENZYMIC HYDROLYSIS OF TRIMETAPHOSPHATE AS FUNCTION OF SUBSTRATE CONCENTRATION

Molarity of trimetaphosphate	Orthophosphate formed μM
0.01 M	0.77
0.02 M	1.2
0.05 M	1.6
0.1 M	2.5
0.2 M	2.9

If the duration of incubation did not exceed 1 h, the kinetics of enzymic hydrolysis followed closely that of a reaction of first order (Fig. 1). After 3 h the rate of hydrolysis

References p. 127.

decreased to 60 % of the value expected for a reaction of the first order: however, this discrepancy was explained quantitatively by the inactivation of the enzyme.

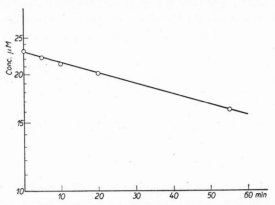

Fig. 1. Kinetics of enzymic hydrolysis of trimetaphosphate in semilogarithmic coordinates. Ordinate, substrate concentration, abscissa, duration of hydrolysis.

Calorimetric measurements

By an appropriate excess of buffer the constancy of hydrogen ion concentration of the assay mixture was maintained while trimetaphosphate was hydrolysed to ortho-phosphate. If the acidity of reactants and reaction products is different, the measured heat effect includes heat evolved by the neutralization of excess acidity by the buffer, which can be computed easily from the constants and enthalpies of dissociation[27].

However, thus far no reliable data were available concerning the trimetaphosphoric acid. On the other hand, by use of a buffer with a low enthalpy of dissociation, the numerical value of measured heat effect will differ only by a small corrective term from the change in enthalpy of that reaction. Therefore, we choose maleate (pK = 6.6, ΔH_{d2} = 380 cal/mole)[28] as a buffer.

In the purification of the enzyme employed in the heat measurements, we were interested primarily in achieving a low ratio of nucleic acids to protein. The necessity of a low nucleic acid content is based on the fact that their heat of neutralization is considerable. Thus, nucleic acids if present in the reaction mixture in an appreciable concentration may participate in the neutralization of excess acidity and contribute to the heat effect of reaction in an uncontrollable manner.

TABLE VI

HEAT OF HYDROLYSIS OF TRIMETAPHOSPHATE

Temperature, 33 °C; reaction mixture, 0.01 M (NaPO$_3$)$_3$, 0.02 M MgSO$_4$, 0.03 M sodium maleate buffer, pH 6.95

Run No.	Total Volume ml	Enzyme ml	I^2R mW	Q_H-Q'_H	Duration of measurement sec	Heat evolved mcal	Turnover μmoles	Heat of Hydrolysis cal/mole
1	31.5	0.5	4.19	0.254	3820	969.8	49.35	19.650
2	31.6	0.6	4.225	0.154	1613	252.3	13.7	18.420
3	30.6	0.6	3.515	0.068	4993	286	15.4	18.540
4	30.5	0.5	6.74	0.075	4986	602	29.2	20.630
							Average	19.310
							Standard deviation:	± 900

References p. 127.

The procedure of measurement was described in an earlier paper[29]. The concentration of nucleic acids in the heat assay was less than $M/5000$. At the end of the measurement, the reaction was stopped by addition of 4 ml of 40% trichloroacetic acid to the reaction mixture and aliquots taken out for the determination of orthophosphate formed. No measurable heat was evolved when the enzyme was blown in, in the absence of substrate.

The value of measured heat effect given in Table VI refers to all three P–O–P bonds of trimetaphosphate. A rough estimate of the heat of neutralization yields 700 cal/mole[*]. After subtracting this figure from the measured heat effect, we find $\Delta H = -18,600$ cal/mole as an approximate value for the change in enthalpy. Thus, the hydrolysis of each P-O-P bond of trimetaphosphate is accompanied by a decrease in enthalpy of approximately —6,000 cal/mole at a neutral pH. Our value is two times higher than the result listed with an older measurement of acid hydrolysis of an unidentified metaphosphate by GIRAN[30].

DISCUSSION

The knowledge of the change in enthalpy does not directly answer the question concerning the change in free energy; however, its magnitude can be evaluated if some additional data are available. In a previous paper we estimated the entropy factor, $T\Delta S$, of pyrophosphate hydrolysis at 1,000 cal/mole[30]. When trimetaphosphate is hydrolyzed, we may expect three times as large an increase in entropy because three P–O–P bonds are broken. Secondly, according to the BOLTZMANN's relation between probability and entropy, breaking down the trimetaphosphate contributes an additional increase in enthalpy because the formation of its ring structure is less probable than that of the single P–O–P bond of pyrophosphate. In the third place, even if we assume that at pH 7 the trimetaphosphoric acid is completely dissociated, an increase in acidity with the formation of orthophosphate would still occur, thus decreasing the over-all change in free energy. These reasons enable us to estimate the decrease in free energy accompanying the hydrolysis of trimetaphosphate at not less than 21,000 cal/mole. Thus, the P–O–P bond of trimetaphosphate should be regarded as a "high-energy" bond of intermediate range. It is very likely that other metaphosphates have similar bond energies. However, a definite proof can be supplied only by suitable measurements.

SUMMARY

An enzyme extract of yeast has been prepared which hydrolyzed inorganic trimetaphosphate to orthophosphate. The highest rate of enzymic hydrolysis has been observed at pH 7. Among divalent kations magnesium and manganese have been found to be the best activators. Fluoride, cyanide, and, to a lesser degree, azide inhibited the enzyme. By the addition of glycerol the activity of the enzyme at 33° C was much better preserved as compared to a water solution. The heat effect of enzymic hydrolysis of trimetaphosphate, 19,300 ± 900 cal/mole, was measured with the isothermal constant-flow calorimeter of OHLMEYER; an estimate of the decrease in enthalpy yielded 18,600 cal/mole for the ionization states of reactants and products at pH 7 and 33° C; likewise, the decrease in free energy was estimated at more than 21,000 cal/mole. Thus, the "high energy" content of the P-O-P bond of trimetaphosphate has been demonstrated.

RÉSUMÉ

Nous avons preparé un extrait des enzymes de levure capable de former l'orthophosphate en hydrolysant le trimétaphosphate inorganique. Le maximum de l'activité de l'enzyme a été observé avec un pH de 7. Nous avons obtenu l'activation la plus forte de l'enzyme par le Mg et le Mn de tous

---

[*] Assuming a complete dissociation of trimetaphosphoric acid at a neutral pH, the heat of neutralization of the partial second dissociation of orthophosphoric acid ($pK_2 = 6.8$) at pH 7 is
$$3 \times \frac{[H^+]}{[H^+] + K_2} \times 380 \text{ or } 700 \text{ cal per mole of trimetaphosphoric acid hydrolysed.}$$

References p. 127.

les cations métalliques divalents. L'enzyme a été inhibi par le fluoride, le cyanide et moins forte par l'azide. L'inactivation de l'enzyme autrement rapide dans une solution aqueuse à 33° C a été réduit considérablement par l'addition de glycerol. En utilisant le calorimètre isotherme OHLMEYER au flux de chaleur constant, nous avons determiné la tonalité thermique de l'hydrolyse fermentative de trimetaphosphate comme 19,300 ± 900 cal/mole. Pour l'état de l'ionization des participants et des produits de l'hydrolyse à un pH 7 et à une temperature de 33° C le changement de l'enthalpie a été estimé à —18,600 cal/mole et ce de l'enthalpie libre au moins à —21,000 cal/mole. Par ce, nous avons démontré la richesse d'énergie de la liaison P–O–P de trimetaphosphate.

ZUSAMMENFASSUNG

Ein das inorganische Trimetaphosphat zu Orthophosphat hydrolisierender Fermentauszug wurde aus der Hefe gewonnen; sein pH Optimum betrug 7. Von allen untersuchten metallischen Kationen aktivierten Magnesium und Mangan das Ferment am stärksten. Das Ferment wurde durch Fluorid, Cyanid und in einem geringeren Ausmass durch Azid gehemmt. Die Zugabe von Glycerol unterdrückte die sonst bei 33° C in einer wässerigen Lösung rasch einsetzende Inaktivierung. Mit dem isothermen, einen konstanten Wärmefluss aufweisenden Kalorimeter nach OHLMEYER haben wir die bei der fermentativen Hydrolyse des Trimetaphosphate entwickelte Wärme zu 19,300 ± 900 cal/Mol gemessen. Für den Ionisationszustand der Reaktionsteilnehmer und Produkte bei pH 7 und 33° C wurde die Änderung der Enthalpie zu —18,600 cal/Mol und die der freien Enthalpie zu mindestens —21,000 cal/Mol geschätzt. Dadurch haben wir die "Energiereichheit" der P–O–P Bindung des Trimetaphosphates gezeigt.

REFERENCES

[1] L. LIEBERMANN, (Pflügers) Arch. ges. Physiol., 43 (1888) 97; 47 (1890) 155.
[2] A. KOSSEL, Arch. Anat. u. Physiol., Physiol. Abt., (1893) 160.
[3] T. KITASATO, Biochem. Z., 197 (1928) 257; 201 (1928) 206.
[4] M. G. MACFARLANE, Biochem. J., 30 (1936) 1369.
[5] T. MANN, Biochem. J., 38 (1944) 345.
[6] R. JEENER AND J. BRACHET, Enzymologia, 11 (1944) 222.
[7] J. M. WIAME, Bull. soc. chim. biol., 28 (1946) 552.
[8] G. SCHMIDT, L. HECHT AND S. J. THANNHAUSER, J. Biol. Chem., 166 (1946) 775.
[9] J. M. WIAME, J. Am. Chem. Soc., 69 (1947) 3146.
[10] J. M. WIAME, Fed. Proc. Am. Soc. Expt. Biol., 6 (1947) 302.
[11] C. C. LINDEGREN, Proc. Natl. Acad. Sci. (U.S.), 34 (1948) 187.
[12] J. M. WIAME, J. Biol. Chem., 178 (1949) 919.
[13] G. SCHMIDT, L. HECHT AND S. J. THANNHAUSER, J. Biol. Chem., 178 (1949) 733.
[14] O. MEYERHOF in W. D. MCELROY AND B. GLASS, ed., Phosphorus Metabolism, Vol. 1, Johns-Hopkins Press, Baltimore, Md., 1951.
[15] P. OHLMEYER, Z. physiol. Chem., 282 (1945) 38; Z. Naturforsch., 1 (1946) 30.
[16] L. T. JONES, Ind. Eng. Chem. Anal. Ed., 14 (1942) 536.
[17] K. LOHMANN AND L. JENDRASSIK, Biochem. Z., 178 (1926) 419.
[18] O. WARBURG AND W. CHRISTIAN, Biochem. Z., 310 (1941) 384.
[19] A. SCHÄFFNER AND F. KRUMEY, Z. Physiol. Chem., 255 (1938) 145.
[20] C. NEUBERG AND A. H. FISCHER, Enzymologia, 2 (1937) 241.
[21] B. INGELMAN AND H. MALMGREN, Acta Chem. Scand., 1 (1947) 422.
[22] P. S. KRISHNAN AND V. BAJAJ, Arch. Biochem. Biophys., 42 (1953) 175.
[23] E. BAMANN AND E. HEUMÜLLER, Naturwissenschaften, 28 (1940) 535.
[24] O. HOFFMAN–OSTENHOF, Abstr. of papers, 12th Intern. Congr. Pure Appl. Chem. (1951), p. 119.
[25] O. MEYERHOF AND P. OHLMEYER, J. Biol. Chem., 195 (1952) 11.
[26] K. BAILEY AND E. C. WEBB, Biochem. J., 38 (1944) 394.
[27] O. MEYERHOF AND R. SHATAS, Arch. Biochem. Biophys., 40 (1952) 253.
[28] LANDOLT–BÖRNSTEIN, 5th Ed. (1923).
[29] P. OHLMEYER AND R. SHATAS, Arch. Biochem. Biophys., 36 (1952) 411.
[30] H. GIRAN, Compt. rend., 135 (1902) 1333.

Received March 31st, 1953

THE SERIES ELASTIC COMPONENT IN MUSCLE*

by

DELBERT E. PHILPOTT AND ALBERT SZENT-GYÖRGYI

The Institute for Muscle Research,
Marine Biological Laboratory, Woods Hole, Massachusetts (U.S.A.)

The rubber-like elasticity of resting muscle fibers indicates the presence of folded fibrous material which can be straightened out by stretching. The contractility of the same fibers suggests the presence of fibrous proteins which can shorten and develop tension by their folding. The more a protein filament would be folded, the less tension it could develop by its further folding. Since it is the primary function of muscle to develop tension, it now becomes difficult to see why this tension should be developed by fibers which would already be folded in the resting state. The question arises as to whether or not extensibility and contractility are not due to different fibrous elements arranged in series. In resting muscle the one responsible for contraction would be straight, while the other, responsible for extensibility, could be in the folded state.

LEVIN AND WYMAN, working in A. V. HILLS' laboratory a quarter of a century ago, obtained length-tension diagrams which indicated that two different elements, a viscous-elastic and a purely elastic element shunted in series, were responsible for the behaviour of cross striated muscle. Recently A. V. HILL returned to the study of this problem and showed that muscle contained, at the site of the contractile matter, a "series elastic component" which was evidently identical with LEVIN AND WYMAN's viscous-elastic material. He called it "tendon", indicating by the quotation marks that it may be anything, the tendon, or even the contractile matter itself. In Germany, REICHEL devoted attention to this series elastic component which he expected to find in molecular dimensions.

The purpose of the present paper is to identify the series elastic component by means of the electron microscope. Essentially, the technique consisted of fixing muscle at different degrees of extension or contraction, treating it with an electron stain, embedding, sectioning, and studying the sections by means of the electron microscope. We were led to conclude that the protofibrils, running continuously along the muscle fiber, are built up alternately of contractile and purely elastic material. This segmentation lies in histological dimensions. Each sarcoma has in its middle on either side of the H-band (which contains the M membrane) such elastic material, which in the unextended state has the same density as the contractile matter. The part of the A-band which contains contractile matter thus cannot be distinguished in this state from the part which contains the elastic matter. If, however, the elastic portion is stretched, by

* This research was sponsored by Armour and Company, Chicago, Illinois, the American Heart Association, the Association for the Aid of Crippled Children, and the Muscular Dystrophy Associations.

References p. 133.

stretching the whole resting muscle fiber or by the contraction of the contractile elements, then its density decreases making it clearly distinguishable from that part of the A-band proper which contains the contractile elements.

METHOD

The technique employed consisted of tying strips of psoas muscle from freshly killed rabbits to applicator sticks at the desired length. Then quickly immersing these preparations for an hour into 10% formalin at 0° C, leaving them over night in unbuffered osmic acid, dehydrating with *iso*propyl alcohol, embedding in 2/3 butyl and 1/3 methyl methacrylate, sectioning them (following essentially NEWMAN, BORYSKO AND SWERDLOW's technique) and studying the sections by the RCA EMU electron microscope without removing the plastics. Besides the *iso*propyl alcohol and the mixture of two plastics, there was one other deviation from the Bureau of Standards method –the glass knife introduced by LATTA AND HARTMAN provided the cutting edge for sectioning.

Contraction of the muscle was produced by dipping it into hexane at −20° C, freezing it at rest-length, and then allowing it to thaw, whereupon it contracted energetically to the desired length. The muscle was then fixed by tying it to the applicator stick at the desired final length prior to placing it in the fixative.

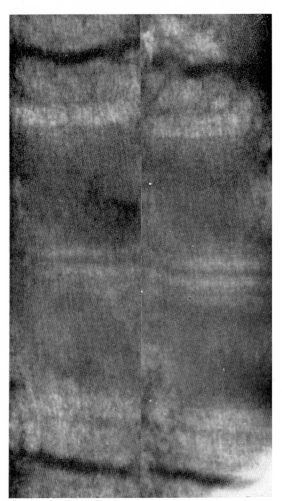

Fig. 1. Explanation in text.

OBSERVATIONS

We want to illustrate our findings by the Figs. 1–4. Fig. 1 shows the muscle at its equilibrium length to which it contracts elastically if cut out. This equilibrium length is about 20% shorter than the rest-length at which the muscle is suspended in the animal. At the equilibrium length no tension exists and thus we can expect to find the elastic elements completely unextended.

The two narrow dark lines towards the top and the bottom in Fig. 1 are Z membranes, lying two microns apart. The broad and lighter segments adjoining these membranes are the I-bands. The broad darker segment towards the middle of the sarcomer is what is usually called the A-band. In the middle of the sarcomer there is a fainter dark line, the M membrane, delineated on either side by the lighter, less dense, and narrow H-band. The space between the H-band and the I-band is filled with material of uniform density.

The muscle can be stretched elastically from its equilibrium length to its rest-length

References p. 133.

8*

with relatively little force. Consequently, at rest-length the muscle has a definite, though relatively low, elastic tension. Fig. 2 shows the muscle in this condition. The dark line in the middle is a Z membrane. The short dark lines in the left top corner and the right bottom corner are also Z membranes. The figure shows the M membrane and the closely adjoining H-bands unchanged. At the site of the latter (H-band) a new segment of

Fig. 2. Explanation in text.

relatively low density has appeared. Evidently part of the material adjoining the H-band has to some extent been stretched, and the stretching has decreased its density. This new band of low density we will call the "E-band". The width of the two E-bands corresponds to about 10% of the whole height of one sarcomer. The appearance of this band thus accounts for half of the gain in length from equilibrium to rest-length.

The resting muscle can be stretched reversibly from its rest-length by about 45%. Fig. 3 shows a muscle stretched by 40% from its rest-length. If we call rest-length

length 100, then this muscle has length 140. From equilibrium length 80 the muscle must be stretched by 75% to reach this length. As the picture shows, the E-band now distinguishes itself sharply by its low density from the A-band proper, having been stretched almost to the limit of its reversible extensibility. The additive width of the two E-bands is 20% of the whole height of the sarcomer. The appearance of the E-band

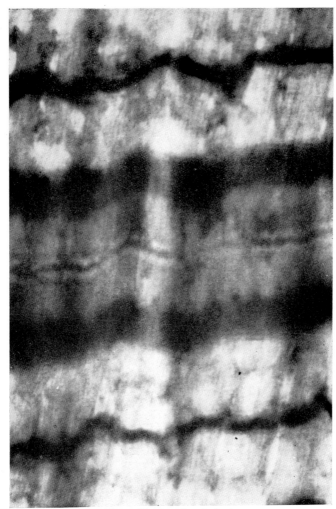

Fig. 3. Explanation in text.

thus again accounts grossly for half of the gain in length of the muscle fiber. The A-band proper, if anything, has become narrower. The rest of the gain in length is accounted for by the increase in the distance between the Z membrane and A-band.

It is easy to predict the changes which can be expected to take place in an isometric contraction: the E-band will appear. This is borne out by Fig. 4 which shows muscle of equilibrium length in isometric contraction and should be compared with Fig.1 which shows muscle of the same length at rest. This figure also shows the protofibrils running

References p. 133.

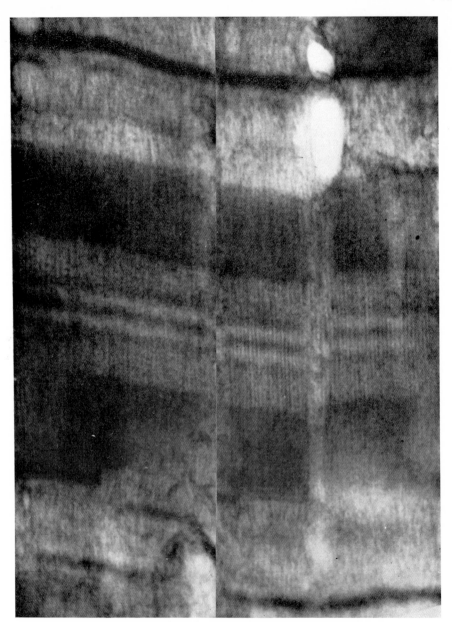

Fig. 4. Explanation in text.

continuously through the E and H-bands in direct continuation of the protofibrils of the A-band.

As Fig. 4 indicates, the extended elastic segments of the protofibrils have a different appearance than their contractile portions. While in these latter the outines are always found to be fairly vague, in the former the contours of the single protofibrils stand out sharply, reminding one of the wires in a piano. This difference is still stronger at higher degrees of extension which can be produced by stretching a contracted muscle. In such pictures the M membranes and the two adjoining narrower membrane-like densities are missing, suggesting that these formations, easily recognizable in resting muscle, consisted of the fully coiled elastic matter.

The chemical nature of the elastic material forming the elastic segment of the protofibrils is unknown. It is not impossible that the building material is BAILEY's tropomyosin, which has no contractility. Sections in which the protofibrils absorbed the electron stain to a marked degree suggest that the protofibrils, in their elastic segment, have a spiral structure with a periodicity of 80 A.

The importance of the elastic component in series for the physiology and pathology of muscle needs no emphasis. Its physiological implications have clearly been recognized by LEVIN AND WYMAN while the pathological importance, especially for heart dilation, has been emphasized by REICHEL.

HILL has set the limit of the elastic extensibility of the parallel elastic component to 10–15%. Our pictures suggest a wider limit. They also explain why the resting muscle shows a normal thermo-elastic behaviour on extension and why this behaviour never yielded a clue to the understanding of contraction; extensibility and contractility being the qualities of different structures.

SUMMARY

Electron microscopic pictures of the muscle show that the protofibrils of the cross striated muscle are built alternatingly of contractile and elastic segments. The division lies in histological dimensions. In its middle every sarcomer contains such an elastic segment.

RÉSUMÉ

La microscopie électronique du muscle strié montre que les protofibrilles sont formés de segments alternativement contractiles et élastiques. La division est située dans des dimensions histologiques. Il y a un segment élastique au milieu de chaque sarcomère.

ZUSAMMENFASSUNG

Aufnahmen des Muskels mit den Elektronenmikroskop zeigen, dass die Protofibrillen des quergestreifen Muskels abwechselnd aus kontraktilen und elastischen Segmenten aufgebaut sind. Die Unterteilung liegt in histologischen Dimensionen. In der Mitte jedes Sarkomers befindet sich ein elastisches Segment.

REFERENCES

K. BAILEY, *Nature*, 157 (1946) 368.
A. V. HILL, *Proc. Roy. Soc. B*, 137 (1950) 273; 130 (1951 325; 139 (1952) 464.
H. LATTA AND J. F. HARTMAN, *Proc. Soc. Exptl. Biol. Med.*, 74 (1950) 436.
A. LEVIN AND J. WYMAN, *Proc. Roy. Soc. B*, 101 (1927) 218.
S. B. NEWMAN, E. BORYSKO AND M. SWERDLOW, *J. Res. Natl. Bureau Stand.*, 43 (1949) 183.
H. REICHEL, *Verhandl. deut. Ges. Kreislaufforschg*, 16 (1950) 13.
H. REICHEL, *Verhandl. deut. Ges. Kreislaufforschg*, 16 (1950) 13; *Z. Biol.*, 104 (1951) 469; 105 (1952) 7, 73, 162.

Received April 3rd, 1953

ÜBER DEN WIRKUNGSMECHANISMUS DES DICUMAROLS UND VERWANDTER VERBINDUNGEN

von

CARL MARTIUS und DAGOBERT NITZ-LITZOW

Physiologisch-chemisches Institut der Universität, Tübingen (Deutschland)

Zu den am meisten untersuchten und am besten bekannten Stoffen mit Antivitamincharakter gehört das Dicumarol [3,3'-Methylen-bis-(4-Oxy-Kumarin)] das wegen seiner den Prothrombinspiegel des Blutes herabsetzenden Eigenschaften vielfache therapeutische Anwendung findet. Die Ansichten über die Wirkungsweise des Dicumarols gingen bisher auseinander[1]. Eine gewisse Ähnlichkeit der Strukturen des Dicumarols mit dem Vitamin K führte einerseits dazu, einen direkten Antagonismus beider Stoffe in einem an der Bildung des Prothrombins beteiligten Enzymsystem anzunehmen. Andere Beobachtungen schienen auf einen weniger spezifischen Wirkungsmechanismus hinzuweisen, der in einer allgemein toxischen Wirkung des Dicumarols gesehen wurde, die bekanntlich auch die therapeutische Anwendbarkeit dieses Stoffes beeinträchtigt. Nach den im Folgenden mitgeteilten Versuchen treffen im Grunde beide Erklärungen zu.

Im Verlaufe von Untersuchungen über den Mechanismus der Atmungskettenphosphorylierung (oxydativen Phosphorylierung) in isolierten Lebermitochondrien konnten wir feststellen, dass Dicumarol in sehr niedrigen Konzentrationen (10^{-5} M und darunter) die oxydativen Phosphorylierungsprocesse hemmt ohne die Atmung wesentlich zu beeinflussen. Es wirkt also in ähnlicher Weise "entkoppelnd" wie Dinitrophenol oder Thyroxin[4]. Die Untersuchung weiterer Stoffe mit Antivitamin-K-Charakter sowie von Verbindungen der Oxynaphthochinonreihe, die nach WENDEL[2] sowie BALL und Mitarbeitern[3] starke Atmungsgifte darstellen, führt uns schliesslich dazu, die Beziehungen des Vitamin K zur Prothrombinbildung als sekundärer Art aufzufassen und diesem Wirkstoff eine viel allgemeinere Bedeutung für den Zellstoffwechsel zuzuweisen.

METHODIK

Das Ausmass der Atmungskettenphosphorylierung wurde in unseren Versuchen durch Bestimmung des P/O-Quotienten isolierter Mitochondrien aus Rattenlebern nach den bekannten Methoden gemessen. Die Mitochondrien wurden mittels isotonischer Rohrzuckerlösung isoliert. Leider stand uns für diese Versuche nur ein Tiermaterial sehr unterschiedlicher Qualität zur Verfügung, woraus sich die z.T. ziemlich beträchtlichen Unterschiede in den P/O-Quotienten der Kontrollen erklären, die nicht etwa auf Verschiedenheiten in der Durchführung der Versuche beruhen. Selbstverständlich wurden Kontroll- und Versuchsansätze stets mit dem gleichen Material und unter identischen Bedingungen durchgeführt.

Als Versuchslösung diente eine Mischung von je 1 Teil KCl 0.75 M, MgCl$_2$ 0.2 M, β-Oxybuttersaures Na 0.3 M, KF 0.4 M, DPN 0.02 M; je 2.5 Teilen ATP und AMP 0.006 M; 3 Teilen Cytochrom c 10^{-4} M und 4 Teilen Phosphatpuffer pH 7.4 0.1 M. Die Versuche wurden teilweise in Warburg-

Literatur S. 140.

trögen der üblichen Grösse (15 ml), teilweise in solchen mit nur 5 ml Inhalt ausgeführt, was bei der Beurteilung der Atmungs- und Phosphorylierungswerte zu berücksichtigen ist. Für einen 5 ml Trog wurden 0.7 ml dieser Mischung, und 0.2 ml Mitochondriensuspension in das Hauptgefäss, 0.3 ml der Lösung eines Hexokinasepräparates, das auch die Glucose und noch etwas Phosphat enthielt, in das Seitengefäss gegeben. Bezüglich weiterer Einzelheiten verweisen wir auf die Angaben einer Publikation von MARTIUS UND HESS[4].

Die verschiedenen Präparate von symmetrischen Dicumarolen[6], das Methylen-bis-(4,6-dioxo-2-methyl-dihydropyran)[7], 4-Oxykumarin[5], 3-Methyl-1,4-naphthochinon, sowie das 2-Oxy-3-(2'-methyloktyl)-1,4-naphthochinon)[8] im Folgenden stets als SN 5949 vgl.[3] bezeichnet) wurden von uns nach Angaben der Literatur synthetisch hergestellt und waren schmelzpunktsrein. Phthiocol war uns von der deutschen Hoffmann-LaRoche A.G. freundlicherweise zur Verfügung gestellt worden. Für ein Präparat von 3-Naphthyl-4-oxy-kumarin danken wir Herrn Prof. Dr. MENTZER, Lyon ganz besonders. Für die Herstellung von Stammlösungen dieser Stoffe, die vor jedem Versuch frisch bereitet wurden, wurde eine gewogene Menge mit Hilfe von wenig 0.1 N NaOH in Lösung gebracht und auf ein bestimmtes Volumen aufgefüllt. Alle nachfolgend gemachten Konzentrationsangaben beziehen sich stets auf die Endkonzentration im kompletten Versuchsansatz.

ERGEBNISSE

Wie die Tabelle I zeigt bewirkt der Zusatz von Dicumarol zum Versuchsmedium atmender und phosphorylierender Mitochondriensuspensionen schon in einer Konzentration von 10^{-5} molar und darunter eine erhebliche Hemmung der oxydativen Phosphorylierung. Die Atmung wird meist nur geringfügig oder gar nicht gehemmt, so dass eine echte "Entkopplung" von Atmung und Phosphorylierung resultiert. Als Mittelwert von 10 gleichartigen Versuchen mit Dicumarol der Konzentration von $10^{-5}\,M$ ergab sich eine 63%ige Hemmung der Phosphorylierung während die Atmung im Mittel nur um ca 10% gehemmt wurde.

TABELLE I

Exp. Nr.	Dicumarol	O_2 μ-Atome	P μ-Atome	P/O	Hemmung der Phosphorylierung	Atmung
78	—	4.9	6.7	1.3	—	—
	10^{-6}	4.3	5.7	1.3	—	(12%)
	$3.3 \cdot 10^{-6}$	5.0	5.4	1.1	15%	0
	10^{-5}	4.85	0.74	0.15	88%	0
79	—	1.65	3.0	1.8	—	—
	10^{-6}	1.64	2.85	1.7	0	0
	$3.3 \cdot 10^{-6}$	1.5	2.1	1.3	27%	9%
	10^{-5}	1.3	1.3	1.0	45%	21%
60	—	5.25	10.35	2.0	—	—
	10^{-5}	5.38	2.58	0.6	70%	17%
72	—	7.6	11.3	1.5	—	—
	10^{-5}	7.2	2.8	0.4	73%	5%
100	—	2.67	4.7	1.8	—	—
	10^{-5}	2.5	1.9	0.7	62%	6%
104	—	2.0	3.4	1.7	—	—
	10^{-5}	1.84	0.34	0.7	60%	8%
64	—	4.69	8.82	1.9	—	—
	$2 \cdot 10^{-5}$	4.27	2.57	0.6	68%	9%

Die Werte in dieser und den folgenden Tabellen sind stets Mittelwerte aus 2 oder 3 Parallelbestimmungen.

Literatur S. 140.

9

Zur Prüfung der Frage, ob zwischen der Hemmung der Prothrombinbildung durch Dicumarol und diesem Entkopplungseffekt eine Beziehung besteht, erschien es uns wichtig, auch das Verhalten anderer Stoffe im Phosphorylierungstest zu prüfen, deren Wirkung als Antikoagulantia *in vivo* bereits von anderen Autoren untersucht worden ist. Aus der grossen Zahl von Stoffen, die von LINK auf ihre Antivitamin-K-Eigenschaften am Kaninchen untersucht und mit Dicumarol verglichen worden sind, wählten wir einige Vertreter aus und prüften ausserdem noch zwei weitere von anderen Autoren geprüfte Stoffe. Wie Tabelle II zeigt, wirken alle *in vivo* wirksamen Stoffe auch im Phosphorylierungstest als Inhibitoren.

TABELLE II

Exp. Nr.	Substanz Konzentration	O μ-Atome	P	P/O	Hemmung der Atmung	Phosphorylierung	Antikoagulationsindex Dicumarol = 100
83	4-Oxykumarin						0,12
	—	2.8	5.2	1.8	—	—	
	$3.3 \cdot 10^{-5}$	3.1	5.6	1.8	0	0	
	10^{-4}	2.63	4.74	1.8	0	0	
	$3.3 \cdot 10^{-4}$	2.9	5.5	1.8	0	0	
102	Äthyliden 3.3'-bis-(4-Oxy kumarin)						24
	—	1.67	3.7	2.2	—	—	
	10^{-5}	1.26	2.4	1.9	23%	15%	
	$3 \cdot 10^{-5}$	0.92	1.34	1.4	40%	36%	
100	3.3'-Propyliden-bis-(4-oxykumarin)						32
	—	2.67	4.7	1.8	—	—	
	10^{-5}	2.57	4.7	1.8	0	0	
	$3 \cdot 10^{-5}$	2.9	4.6	1.6	0	11%	
105		2.5	4.7	1.9	—	—	
	—						
	$4.8 \cdot 10^{-5}$	1.48	0.44	0.3	40%	84%	
	$7 \cdot 10^{-5}$	1.2	0	0	52%	100%	
72	3.3' Butyliden-bis-						8.6
	—	7,6	11.3	1.5	—	—	
	10^{-5}	7.9	13.3	1.68	0	0	
73	—	5.2	10.0	1.9	—	—	
	$1.3 \cdot 10^{-4}$	5.3	0	0	0	100%	
77	3.3'-Benzyliden-bis-(4-oxykumarin)						0.4
	—	5.4	8.5	1.6	—	—	
	10^{-5}	5.8	6.7	1.1	0	30%	
	10^{-4}	4.2	0	0	22%	100%	
81	3.3'-Carboxymethylen-bis-(4-oxykumarin)						0.2
	—	5.9	11.3	1.9	—	—	
	10^{-5}	5.8	11.0	1.9	0	0	
	$3.3 \cdot 10^{-5}$	6.6	8.9	1.3	0	32%	
	10^{-4}	4.7	0	0	24%	100%	
104	3-Naphthyl-4-kumarin						("sehr wirksam")[11]
	—	2.0	3.4	1.7	—	—	
	10^{-5}	2.3	3.3	1.45	0	15%	
	$3 \cdot 10^{-5}$	2.15	2.5	1.2	0	30%	
60	Methylen-bis-(4.6-di-oxo-2-methyl-dihydropyran)						("unwirksam")[10]
	—	5.25	10.35	2.0	—	,	
	10^{-5}	5.17	11.0	2.1	0	0	
62	—	5.9	9.2	1.56	—	—	
	10^{-5}	6.2	9.4	1.52	0	0	

Literatur S. 140.

Wie ein Vergleich mit den Antikoagulationsindexziffern von LINK zeigt, besteht in erster Annäherung Parallelität zwischen Wirksamkeit im Blutgerinnungstest und im Entkopplungsversuch. Mehr als eine annähernde Übereinstimmung des Verhaltens in beiden Testen konnte auch nicht erwartet werden. Dafür ist einmal die Zahl unserer Versuche zu gering. Vor allem aber ist zu bedenken, dass im Gerinnungstest ganz andere Bedingungen vorliegen als in den Versuchen *in vitro* insbesondere, dass bei den *per os* zugeführten Stoffen ausser der spezifischen Antivitamin K-Wirkung auch noch die Resorption, Ausscheidung und Zerstörung derselben zu berücksichtigen ist. Bei den im Gerinnungstest wenig wirksamen Stoffen, die in grösseren Mengen *per os* zugeführt werden müssen, gelangt offenbar nur ein kleiner Teil zur Wirkung während *in vitro* stets die volle zugegebene Menge auch an den Ort der Wirkung gelangt.

Nach der Aufdeckung dieser Zusammenhänge war es von Interesse, die Einwirkung einer anderen Klasse von Stoffen auf die oxydative Phosphorylierung zu untersuchen, die ebenfalls in ihrer Struktur dem Vitamin K nahe stehen, nämlich der substituierten 2-Oxy-1,4-naphthochinone. Eine grosse Zahl derartiger Naphthochinonderivative ist von FIESER und Mitarbeitern[8] synthetisiert worden, nachdem man entdeckt hatte, dass sich unter ihnen wirksame Malariaheilmittel befinden. Wie WENDEL[2] und nach ihm BALL[3] feststellten, befinden sich unter den Angehörigen dieser Stoffklasse äusserst wirksame Atmungsgifte. Wir haben neben dem als Atmungsinhibitor kaum wirksamen Phthiocol den überaus wirksamen Stoff SN 5949 (2-Oxy-3-(2-methyl-octyl)-1,4-naphthochinon) und ausserdem noch 2-Methyl-1,4-naphthochinon in ihrem Verhalten gegenüber Atmung und Phosphorylierung von Lebermitochondrien geprüft.

TABELLE III

Exp. Nr.	SN 5949	O_2 μ-Atome	P	P/O	Hemmung der Phosphorylierung	Atmung
93	—	4.48	6.78	1.5	—	—
	10^{-7}	4.43	5.7	1.3	(13%)	0
	10^{-6}	4.29	5.5	1.3	(13%)	0
	10^{-5}	0.83	0.23	0.3	80%	83%
95	—	9.0	15.0	1.6	—	—
	$6 \cdot 10^{-6}$	1.7	0	0	100%	80%
	10^{-5}	0.4	0	0	100%	95%
97	—	6.65	10.65	1.6	—	—
	$1.76 \cdot 10^{-6}$	6.0	9.0	1.5	8%	10%
	$3.0 \cdot 10^{-6}$	3.76	3.9	0.9	44%	43%
	$4.8 \cdot 10^{-6}$	1.7	0	0	100%	75%
98	—	5.9	9.0	1.5	—	—
	$1.76 \cdot 10^{-6}$	5.9	6.9	1.1	27%	0
	$3.0 \cdot 10^{-6}$	2.79	2.0	0.7	53%	54%
	$4.8 \cdot 10^{-6}$	2.3	0	0	100%	61%
	Phthiocol					
85	—	5.6	15.0	2.7	—	—
	10^{-4}	6.4	10.7	1.7	40%	0
86	—	6.7	11.0	1.6	—	—
	10^{-5}	6.6	10.0	1.6	0	0
	10^{-4}	6.2	7.5	1.2	20%	7%
	2-Methyl-1.4-naphthochinon					
89	—	2.2	4.2	1.9	—	—
	10^{-4}	3.0	2.5	0.8	60%	0
	$5 \cdot 10^{-4}$	1.8	0	0	100%	20%
90	—	2.05	3.4	1.7	—	—
	10^{-6}	1.9	2.4	1.3	25%	0
	10^{-5}	1.9	2.0	1.0	40%	0

Wie Tabelle III zeigt, erweist sich in diesem System der Stoff SN 5949 als äusserst wirksamer Atmungshemmstoff, während in den Versuchen von BALL[3] die Atmung von Leberschnitten wesentlich weniger stark beeinflusst wurde. Wir möchten diesen Unterschied nicht darauf zurückführen, dass die Permeabilität der Leberzellen für diesen Stoff zu gering ist, wie BALL annimmt, sondern eher, dass durch Bindung an Leberproteine (SH-Gruppen?) eine Inaktivierung eintritt. Wie die Versuche der Tabelle III weiter zeigen, geht völlig parallel mit der Hemmung der Atmung eine Hemmung der oxydativen Phosphorylierung. Dass letztere nicht einfach eine Folge der Hemmung der Atmung ist, geht daraus hervor, dass eine Erniedrigung des P/O Quotienten auch bei solch niedrigen Konzentrationen des Inhibitors zu beobachten ist, bei denen nur eine geringe oder gar keine Beeinflussung der Atmung stattfindet. Es ist in diesem Zusammenhange von besonderem Interesse, dass auch eine Wirkung von Substanzen dieser Stoffklasse auf die Blutgerinnung bereits beobachtet worden ist, speziell auch des Stoffes SN 5949[15]. Die Wirkung der beiden anderen von uns noch geprüften Stoffe, Phthiocol und Methylnaphthochinon, auf die Atmung von Mitochondrien ist demgegenüber sehr gering. Grösser ist die Hemmung der oxydativen Phosphorylierung, besonders durch das Methylnaphthochinon.

DISKUSSION

Wie die vorstehend beschriebenen Versuchen zeigen, vermag eine grosse Zahl von Stoffen, die dem natürlichen Vitamin K_1 strukturell ähnlich gebaut sind, auch eine gleichartige hemmende Wirkung auf die Atmungskettenphosphorylierung auszuüben. Für den Eintritt dieser Hemmwirkung sind offenbar zwei ganz verschiedenen Strukturelemente von Bedeutung: Erstens das Vorhandensein eines zweikernigen, kondensierten aromatischen Ringsystemes mit mindestens einer phenolischen OH-Gruppe in der 1 bzw. 4-Stellung, und zweitens eine Seitenkette in der 3-Stellung, deren Form und Grösse in ziemlich weiten Grenzen variieren kann. Kombination einer (Oxy-) Naphthochinongruppe, die für sich allein bereits phosphorylierungshemmende Wirkung aufweist, mit einer Seitenkette geeigneter Form und Grösse führt zu Stoffen mit starker Wirkung auf Phosphorylierung *und* Atmung.

Geht man von der Annahme aus, dass sich die Wirkung aller dieser Inhibitoren durch einen Antagonismus mit einem Wirkstoff von der Konstitution des Vitamin K zurückführen lässt, gelangt man zu einer einheitlichen Erklärung beider Effekte. Man hätte demnach anzunehmen, dass das Vitamin K sowohl Glied der Atmungskette wie auch eines Systemes phosphorylierender Enzyme ist; mit anderen Worten, wir hätten in ihm ein Kopplungsglied zwischen Atmung und Phosphorylierung zu sehen. Während Stoffe vom Dicumaroltyp nur auf die weniger strukturspezifische dafür aber empfindlichere Phosphorylierungsfunktion

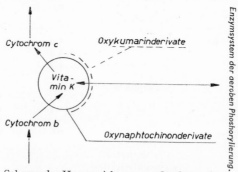

Schema der Hemmwirkung von Oxykumarin -und Oxynaphthochinonderivaten.

einwirken, erfolgt durch Stoffe vom Typ des SN 5949 eine Ausschaltung beider Funktionen. Eine solche Hypothese erscheint nun tatsächlich geeignet, eine ganze Reihe bekannter Beobachtungen zu erklären.

Literatur S. 140.

Die Existenz eines bisher noch unbekannten Gliedes der Atmungskette, zwischen Cytochrom b und c stehend, ist aus verschiedenen Beobachtungen gefolgert worden[12,13]. Was über die Eigenschaften und Beeinflussbarkeit dieses Stoffes bisher bekannt ist, scheint uns durchaus mit der Annahme vereinbar, dass es sich dabei um Vitamin K bzw. um einen Komplex mit diesem Vitamin als Wirkungsgruppe handelt.

In der Tatsache, dass Vitamin K als antihämorrhagisches Vitamin wirkt, erblicken wir keinen Widerspruch gegen eine solche Hypothese. Dass sich die Funktion dieses Vitamines auf die Beteiligung an einem Prothrombin bildenden Enzymsystem beschränken soll, erscheint doch wohl äusserst unwahrscheinlich in Anbetracht des Faktums, dass dieses Vitamin verbreitet in Bakterien und Pflanzen vorkommt, wo eine solche Rolle überhaupt völlig sinnlos wäre. Das Vorkommen des Vitamins in den Chloroplasten deutet doch gradezu auf eine Beteiligung an Processen der oxydativen Phosphorylierung hin. Damit erhebt sich nun die Frage, ob das Vitamin K überhaupt unmittelbar mit dem System der Prothrombin bildenden Enzyme verknüpft ist. Wenn diese Frage wohl bis auf weiteres noch als offen betrachtet werden muss, neigen wir doch der Auffassung zu, das man in der Hemmung der Prothrombinbildung bei Mangel an Vitamin K oder Darreichung von Dicumarol nur ein erstes, sehr empfindliches Zeichen für eine verschlechterte Atmungskettenphosphorylierung in den Leberzellen zu sehen hat. Damit wäre auch den Vertretern der Theorie Recht gegeben, die die Dicumarolwirkung nur als Folge einer allgemeinen Intoxikation betrachten. Die Störung der Prothrombinbildung durch andere leberschädigende Stoffe, die in erster Linie stets auch die Atmungskettenphosphorylierung schädigen dürften, ebenso wie die bei Thyreotoxikose[14] angegebene Verzögerung der Blutgerinnung fügt sich zwanglos diesem Bilde ein.

Wenn bisher nur allgemein von Vitamin K gesprochen wurde, haben wir damit bewusst die Frage nach der chemischen Natur des im Tierkörper wirkenden Stoffes umgangen. Es wäre möglich, dass es sich dabei um das bekannte Vitamin K_1 (α-Phyllochinon) handelt. Gewisse Beobachtungen, die experimentell weiter verfolgt werden sollen, lassen es uns allerdings nicht als unwahrscheinlich erscheinen, dass im Tierkörper ein vom Phyllochinon verschiedener, jedoch strukturell ähnlicher Wirkstoff vorkommt. Für viel weniger wahrscheinlich halten wir es dagegen, dass im Tierkörper 2-Methyl-1,4-naphthochinon als solches wirksam ist.

Der Deutschen Forschungsgemeinschaft sprechen wir für die finanzielle Unterstützung dieser Arbeit unseren verbindlichsten Dank aus.

ZUSAMMENFASSUNG

Es wurde gezeigt, dass Dicumarol [3,3′-Methylen-bis(4-oxykumarin)] und verwandte Verbindungen die oxydative Phosphorylierung in Rattenleber-Mitochondrien hemmen. Die Bedeutung dieser Befunde für die Theorie der Vitamin K-Wirkung wird diskutiert.

SUMMARY

It has been demonstrated that the rate of aerobic phosphorylation in rat liver mitochondria is depressed by dicumarol 3,3′methylen-bis-(4-hydroxycoumarin) and related substances. The significance of these findings for the theory of the mode of action of vitamin K is discussed.

RÉSUMÉ

Il fut démontré que la phosphorylation aérobie des mitochondries de foie (rat) est inhibée par le dicumarol et des substances semblables. La signification de ces résultats pour la théorie du mode d'action de la vitamine K est discutée.

Literatur S. 140.

LITERATUR

[1] H. Dam in *Vitamins and Hormones*, VI, pag. 27 (1948).
[2] W. B. Wendel, *Federation Proc.*, 5 (1946) 406.
[3] E. G. Ball, C. B. Anfinsen and O. Cooper, *J. Biol. Chem.*, 168, (1947) 257.
[4] C. Martius und B. Hess, erscheint in *Z. physiol. Chem.*
[5] M. A. Stahmann, I. Wolf and K. P. Link, *J. Am. Chem. Soc.*, 65 (1943) 2285.
[6] W. R. Sullivan, Ch. F. Huebner, M. A. Stahmann and K. P. Link, *J. Am. Chem. Soc.*, 65 (1943) 2288.
[7] W. Dickman und F. Breest, *Ber.*, 37 (1904) 3391.
[8] L. F. Fieser und Mitarbeiter, *J. Am. Chem. Soc.*, 70 (1948) 3174.
[9] K. P. Link und Mitarbeiter, *J. Biol. Chem.*, 153 (1944) 5.
[10] K. F. Jansen und K. A. Jensen, *Z. physiol. Chem.*, 277 (1942) 66.
[11] Vortrag von Mentzer auf einer Tagung in Tübingen, Februar 1952.
[12] F. B. Straub, *Z. physiol. Chem.*, 272 (1942) 218.
[13] E. C. Slater, *Biochem. J.*, 46, (1950) 484.
[14] E. Zunz et G. S. de la Guesta, *C. r. Soc. Biol.*, Paris, 112 (1933) 1547.
[15] C. C. Smith, *Proc. Soc. Exptl Biol. Med.*, 64 (1947) 45.

Eingegangen den 4. April 1953

ACETYL COENZYME A SYNTHESIS THROUGH PYROPHOSPHORYL SPLIT OF ADENOSINE TRIPHOSPHATE

by

MARY ELLEN JONES[*], SIMON BLACK[**], RUTH M. FLYNN, AND FRITZ LIPMANN

Biochemical Research Laboratory, Massachusetts General Hospital,
Department of Biological Chemistry, Harvard Medical School, Boston, Massachusetts (U.S.A.)

Two different enzymic pathways exist for the activation of acetate. One pathway is initiated by phosphorylation of acetate[1]:

$$\text{acetate} + \text{ATP} \rightleftharpoons \text{acetyl phosphate} + \text{ADP}[***] \tag{1}$$

followed by acetyl transfer through transacetylase[2,3] to coenzyme A (CoA):

$$\text{acetyl phosphate} + \text{CoA} \rightleftharpoons \text{acetyl CoA} + \text{phosphate} \tag{2}$$

This relatively well understood mechanism is present in most micro-organisms[4,5], but not in animal tissues[6]. In tissues, yeast and probably also in some micro-organisms, another enzymic pathway leads through a complex reaction between ATP, CoA and acetate to acetyl CoA[7,8]. Inorganic pyrophosphate was recently found to be a product of this reaction[9,10]. It appears that a pyrophosphate split of ATP is involved in this energy transfer, which is formulated as follows:

$$\text{ATP} + \text{CoA} + \text{acetate} \rightleftharpoons \text{acetyl CoA} + \text{AMP} + \text{pyrophosphate} \tag{3}$$

Earlier experiments seemed to support a primary reaction between ATP and CoA, yielding presumably CoA-pyrophosphate. A more exhaustive study, however, has left us undecided with regard to the finer mechanism of reaction[3], which we assume to represent a double transfer system of some kind[§]. Some details of our experiments on this problem are presented here.

ENZYME PREPARATIONS AND ASSAY SYSTEM

Pigeon liver enzyme was prepared as described by KAPLAN AND LIPMANN[11] and by CHOU AND LIPMANN[12].

In most experiments yeast enzyme was used. Most brands of commercial Bakers' yeast were found to be suitable; the best preparations were obtained with "National" brand yeast.

The system extracts well from quick-frozen yeast; 1 part of yeast is mixed with 1 part of ether and 1.5 parts of dry ice, and stirred well. After 30 minutes the liquid is poured off, the yeast spread out in a thin layer on a cloth, and air is blown over it by a fan under a well-ventilated hood. An additional 1.5 parts of dry ice are mixed with the yeast and ventilation continued until practically all the ether is removed. The preparation is then generally stored in a deep freeze. On thawing, the yeast

---

[*] Fellow of the Atomic Energy Commission.
[**] Present address: National Institute for Arthritic and Metabolic Diseases, National Institutes of Health, Bethesda 14, Maryland.
[***] The following abbreviations have been used: ATP, adenosine triphosphate; ADP, adenosine diphosphate; AMP, adenosine monophosphate; CoA, coenzyme A; PP, inorganic pyrophosphate; and P_i, orthophosphate.
[§] Cf. addendum at end of paper (p. 147).

References p. 149.

autolyzes rather quickly. To promote this further, 33 ml of M dipotassium phosphate are mixed with 1,000 g of yeast and the mixture stirred overnight in the cold room at o–5°. The yeast autolysate is centrifuged in a cold centrifuge. The supernatant solution does not store well and it is desirable to carry it immediately through the first ammonium sulfate fractionation step.

Sonic preparations. One part of fresh Bakers' yeast is mixed to a paste with 1 part of 0.1 M cold dipotassium phosphate and exposed to vibration in a 10 kilocycle magnetostrictive oscillator (Raytheon Manufacturing Company) for 40 minutes. The mixture is centrifuged in the cold in a Servall centrifuge at top speed (12,000 r.p.m.) for 30 minutes. The supernatant solution, amounting to slightly more than half the original volume, may be frozen and kept for a considerable length of time in the deep freeze.

This extract has the same specific activity as fraction 1 in Table I but is only half as concentrated. It behaves on fractionation like the ether extract and, after fractionation step 3, the two preparations become very similar in all respects.

Protamine precipitation. The slightly turbid supernatant solution is treated with protamine. The precipitate, containing very little active material, is discarded. For every mg of nucleic acid, 0.5 mg of protamine is added, using a 2% protamine sulfate solution. The protamine precipitate is centrifuged at o° in a cooled centrifuge.

The nucleic acid content is determined turbidimetrically in the following manner: to 0.05 ml of the solution to be analyzed are added 4.5 ml of 0.05 M phosphate buffer, pH 6.1, and 0.5 ml of 2% protamine sulfate solution. The tubes are mixed and the turbidity is measured on a Klett colorimeter using filter No. 54. The reading is compared with a standard curve prepared with 0.1 to 0.6 mg of yeast nucleate adjusted to pH 6.

First ammonium sulfate precipitation. To 1,000 ml of clear supernatant solution (pH about 6), 350 g of solid ammonium sulfate are added (55% saturation). The active material is precipitated and centrifuged off; the supernatant solution is discarded. The precipitate is dissolved with 66 ml of 0.05 M potassium bicarbonate solution. The resulting solution is 20% saturated with ammonium sulfate.

Second ammonium sulfate precipitation. Enough saturated ammonium sulfate solution is added to bring the above enzyme preparation from 20% to 35% saturation with respect to ammonium sulfate. The precipitate is discarded and the supernatant solution is brought to 45% saturation with saturated ammonium sulfate solution. The precipitate is dissolved in 0.05 M bicarbonate solution and is generally used in this form without further treatment. The enzyme is stable in ammonium sulfate for a considerable length of time when stored in the deep freeze, while dialyzed enzyme preparations are much less stable even when frozen. Therefore, in most cases, dialysis is omitted. However, for certain experiments, it is desirable to remove the ammonium sulfate. For this purpose, the solution may be dialyzed with agitation at o° against a solution of 0.05 M potassium bicarbonate in 0.5% potassium chloride for 2 to 3 hours. Typical results of the above fractionation procedure are illustrated in Table I.

TABLE I

ACTIVITY OF VARIOUS YEAST FRACTIONS

Fraction	Description	Volume ml	Units per ml	Protein per ml[*] mg	Specific activity units per mg protein	Total units	Recovery %
1	Original extract	1020	66	66	1.0	67,400	100
2	Protamine supernate	1000	66	33	2.0	66,000	98
3	Ammonium sulfate precipitate 0–55%	132	495	97	5.1	65,200	97
4	Ammonium sulfate precipitate 35–45%	32	1063	95	11.2	34,000	51

[*] Turbidimetric[2].

Assay system; enzyme units. In general, enzyme activity was determined by the hydroxamic acid method as described by Chou[12]. Chou observed that, for the assay of the isolated ATP-CoA-acetate donor system, contained in the 40% acetone precipitate from pigeon liver extract (A-40 fraction), high concentrations of hydroxylamine were necessary. He also found that, in the pigeon liver fraction precipitating between 40% and 60% acetone (A-60 fraction) which contained the acceptor enzyme for aromatic amines, there was present another enzyme which catalyzed the reaction of acetyl CoA with hydroxylamine. The presence of the latter enzyme was demonstrated by the fact that, if the A-40 and A-60 fractions were combined, hydroxamic acid formation was maximal at low concentrations of hydroxylamine. The cruder yeast preparations seem also to contain an enzyme which catalyzes the hydroxylamine reaction. As shown in Chou's experiments, the effect of the hydroxylamine acceptor enzyme is minimized by the use of higher concentrations of hydroxylamine [12]. The hydroxamic acid assay has occasionally been checked using a procedure which measures arylamine acetylation, namely: by combining the A-60 fraction of CHOU with the yeast enzyme. The combined assay has the advantage of greater sensitivity. As shown in Fig. 1b, it is linear over a wider concentration range than is the hydroxamic acid assay (Fig. 1a) which, at higher enzyme concentration, becomes less reliable.

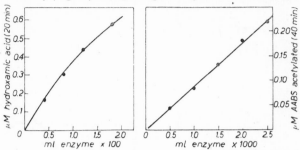

Fig. 1a. 1b. Comparison of hydroxamic acid and mixed enzyme assay.

The combined assay system was worked out by BESSMAN[13], who will report on this procedure separately. This assay is similar to the CoA assay described by HANDSCHUMACHER *et al*[14], using however, instead of their aminoazobenzene, aminoazobenzene sulfonate as acetyl acceptor. This compound has the advantage of greater solubility.

Hydroxamic acid assay[15]. One ml assay mixture contains: 25 units CoA, 10 μM ATP*, 10 μM potassium acetate, 100 μM potassium phosphate buffer, 200 μM hydroxylamine, (neutralized with KOH to pH 7.4), 50 μM KF, 10 μM MgCl$_2$, and 10 μM glutathione. The tubes are incubated at 37° for 20 minutes, at which time are added 1.5 ml of a ferric chloride reagent which contains 10% FeCl$_3$ and 3.3% trichloroacetic acid in 0.66 N HCl. The acethydroxamate formed is measured in the Klett-Summerson colorimeter with a No. 54 filter using 1 ml of H$_2$O and 1.5 ml of the FeCl$_3$ reagent to set the zero point. In all cases a blank tube which contains no CoA is incubated along with the. tube containing CoA. The blank reading is subtracted from the reading obtained when CoA is present With increasing purification the blank reading becomes negligible. One unit enzyme activity is defined as that amount of enzyme which gives a reading of 100 (0.4 μM of hydroxamic acid) under these conditions.

Mixed assay. One ml of assay mixture contains: 100 μM potassium phosphate, 50 μM KF, 10 μM potassium acetate, 25 units CoA, 10 μM ATP, 10 units A-60 enzyme[13], 10 μM glutathione, 10 μM MgCl$_2$, and 0.6 μM aminoazobenzene sulfonate. The pH of the phosphate-acetate-fluoride mixture is set at 7.4. The tubes are incubated 40 minutes at 37°. At this time 0.2 ml of the incubation mixture is added to 3.0 ml of 10% TCA in 50% ethanol and centrifuged. The amount of dye acetylated is measured by the reduction in colour observed in the Klett-Summerson colorimeter with a No. 50 filter. The zero time reading is about 290. The colour difference should be less than 150 Klett units.

THE COMPONENTS OF THE ENZYMIC SYSTEM

CHOU had already found that magnesium was a component of the ATP-acetate reaction[12]. Magnesium dependence is shown in Fig. 2. It may be mentioned here that we routinely used all salts in the form of potassium salts in view of the general experience that this type of reaction seems to go better in a potassium-containing medium. We have, however, not studied the effect of monovalent ions in detail.

In Fig. 3, a pH-activity curve is shown, indicating an optimum between 7.2 and 7.8.

CoA reduction. When hydroxylamine was used to trap the acetyl CoA formed, glutathione was used to reduce the coenzyme. In stoichiometric balance experiments hydrogen sulfide was generally used except when a sulfhydryl balance was desirable. In this instance the CoA was reduced with potassium borohydride (Metal Hydrides, Inc.)

---

* The ATP used was purchased as the disodium salt from the Pabst Brewing Company. For a majority of the experiments, the CoA preparations were prepared from *Streptomyces fradiae* cultures by Dr. J. D. GREGORY. These products were 65 to 80% pure. For some of the experiments, the CoA was purchased from the Pabst Brewing Company. This product is about 75% pure.

References p. 149.

in the following manner: for each μM of CoA (310 units = 1 μM), 75 μM of KBH_4 in 0.002 M KOH and 10 μM of tris(hydroxymethyl)aminomethane buffer, pH 9, were added. The vessel was incubated for 15 minutes at 37°, at which time the contents were

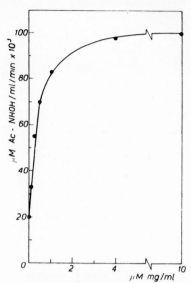

Fig. 2. Effect of magnesium concentration of the rate of acetate-ATP-CoA reaction. Each tube contained, in 1 ml. of reaction mixture: 25 units COA; 10 μM ATP; 10 μM potassium acetate; 200 μM tris (hydroxymethyl) - aminomethane buffer, pH 7.5; 50 μM KF; 10 μM glutathione; and 200 μM NH_2OH, neutralized to pH 7.4 with KOH; 0.01 ml (10 units) of yeast fraction 4 and $MgCl_2$ as indicated. Final pH was 7.4–7.2. The tubes were incubated at 37°, and 0.2 ml. samples were taken at 13, 30, and 60 minutes to determine the rate of the reaction.

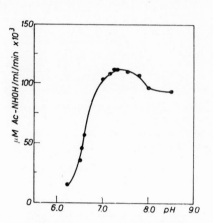

Fig. 3. Effect of pH on the rate of acetate-ATP-CoA reaction. Each vessel contained, in 1 ml reaction mixture: 25 units CoA; 10 μM ATP; 10 μM potassium acetate; 50 μM KF; 10 μM $MgCl_2$; 10 μM glutathione; 200 μM NH_2OH (pH adjusted with KOH to that of buffer); 50 μM each tris (hydroxymethyl)aminomethane and potassium phosphate buffer adjusted to the desired pH; and 0.01 ml (10 units) of yeast fraction 4. The tubes were incubated at 37°, and 0.2 ml samples were taken at 20, 40, and 60 minutes to determine the rate of the reaction.

neutralized with HCl to pH 7.2 and the volume adjusted with water to give a CoA solution of the desired concentration. Although solutions store fairly well on freezing, we have routinely prepared fresh solutions each day.

CoA concentration. It is a characteristic of the hydroxamic acid system that relatively high concentrations of CoA and hydroxylamine[12] are required for saturation. Under our conditions, as shown in Fig. 4, the maximum activity is approached at about 100 units of CoA. Since the reaction between acetyl mercapto CoA and hydroxylamine is non-enzymatic, this relatively high saturation concentration is not surprising.

The effect of inorganic phosphate. The addition of 50 to 100 μM of phosphate per ml generally increases the rate of the hydroxamic acid reaction considerably. For this reason phosphate was included in our assay system. Phosphate, however, is not indispensable. The mechanism of the phosphate effect is not clear.

References p. 149.

Identification of the reaction products. CHOU had frequently observed that the amount of phosphate liberated was far below the amount of hydroxamic acid formed. Recently these studies were resumed, particularly in view of LYNEN's identification of acetyl CoA as the mercaptoester of CoA[16]. Various observations then indicated that inorganic pyrophosphate rather than orthophosphate was being liberated. It was found that the liberation of inorganic phosphate could be almost completely suppressed by the addition of fluoride. Under these conditions the easily hydrolyzable phosphate did not change, but a substance appeared which gave, with the Fiske-Subbarow molybdate reagent, a slowly developing colour similar to that observed earlier by SACKS AND DAVENPORT with inorganic pyrophosphate[17]. In Table II an experiment is presented with CoA as acetyl acceptor. If fluoride is added, approximately equivalent amounts of pyrophosphate appear, as determined by the manganese precipitation method of KORNBERG[18] and also by a colorimetric method utilizing the above-mentioned colour increase with the molybdate reagent.

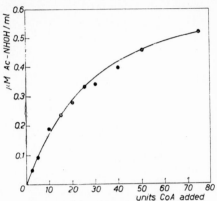

Fig. 4. CoA-concentration curve. Each tube contained, in 1 ml: 25 units CoA; 10 μM ATP; 10 μM potassium acetate; 50 μM KF; 100 μM potassium phosphate buffer (pH 7.4); 200 μM hydroxylamine neutralized with KOH to pH 7.4; 10 μM glutathione; 0.02 ml (1 unit) of yeast fraction 1. Tubes were incubated at 37° for 20 minutes at which time 1.5 ml of the 10% FeCl$_3$ reagent were added.

This colour reaction has been developed into the convenient colorimetric method for determination of inorganic pyrophosphate, which will be described elsewhere.

TABLE II

EFFECT OF FLUORIDE ON PYROPHOSPHATE FORMATION

Fluoride added μM per ml	CoA* added μM per ml	Acetyl CoA μM per ml	PP μM per ml	Pi μM per ml
0	0	0	0	7.4
0	2.9	2.72	0	13.2
50	0	0	0	1.75
50	2.9	2.88	3.10** 3.16***	2.10

* 1 μM CoA = 310 units.
** Determined by colour increase.
*** Determined by Mn precipitation method.
   Each vessel contained in 1 ml: 12 μM ATP; 10 μM potassium acetate; 10 μM MgCl$_2$; 20 μM H$_2$S; 200 μM tris(hydroxymethyl) aminomethane buffer, pH 7.5 and 0.02 ml (20 units) of yeast enzyme fraction 4. Vessels were incubated at 37° for 30 minutes.

Without fluoride the excess of inorganic phosphate over the CoA-free blank corresponds to about twice the amount of acetyl CoA formed. As shown by KUNITZ[19], fluoride inhibits strongly the pyrophosphatase which is present in our yeast fractions. For this reason the presence of fluoride is necessary to preserve the pyrophosphate formed.

References p. 149.

In the experiment shown in Table III a determination of adenosine-5-phosphate (AMP) with the KALCKAR-SCHMIDT[20] procedure is included and, in addition, the acetylation of CoA is followed by determining the disappearance of SH-CoA[21] as well as the formation of acetyl-S-CoA. A similar balance with pigeon liver extract is presented in Table IV.

TABLE III
BALANCE FOR ACETYLATION OF COA

Free SH	Acetyl CoA*	PP**	AMP
— 2.29	+ 1.66	+ 1.53	+ 2.28***

* Hydroxamic acid method.

** No sulfur bound PP could be demonstrated on treatment of the deproteinized samples with mercuric acetate.

*** Corrected for AMP formed in absence of CoA due to ATP-ase.

Concentration of factors per ml of reaction mixture: 0.1 ml (100 units) of yeast fraction 4; 5 μM Pabst CoA, reduced with potassium borohydride; 5 μM ATP; 20 μM potassium acetate; 10 μM MgCl$_2$; 50 μM KF; 100 μM tris (hydroxymethyl)aminomethane buffer, pH 7.5. The tubes were incubated at 37° for 15 minutes.

TABLE IV
CATALYTIC BALANCE WITH CRUDE PIGEON LIVER EXTRACT

CoA added units	Time of incubation minutes	Hydroxamic acid μM	AMP μM	P–P μM
	0	0	0	0.3
0	30	1.87	—	—
	120	4.25	6.9	1.85
	0	0	0	0
325	30	5.67	—	—
	120	16.6	16.3	16.2
				12.2*

* Assay by pyrophosphatase.

Each vessel contained, in a total volume of 3.2 ml: 47 μM ATP, of which 17 were added at 0 minutes and 30 μM at 30 minutes; 170 μM KF; 460 μM tris (hydroxymethyl)aminomethane buffer, pH 8.2; 75 μM MgCl$_2$; 870 μM NH$_2$OH, pH 6.5; 80 μM glutathione; 250 μM K acetate; and 0.96 ml crude pigeon liver enzyme. Vessels were incubated at 30° for 120 minutes.

TABLE V
CONVERSION OF ACETYL COA, PYROPHOSPHATE,
AND ADENOSINE-5-PHOSPHATE TO ADENOSINE TRIPHOSPHATE

	ATP μM	AMP μM	Acetyl phosphate μM
Complete system	+ 6.5	— 7.7	— 5.0*
Replace pyrophosphate with orthophosphate	+ 0.3	— 0.5	0
Omit CoA	+ 0	— 0.2	— 0.7

Each vessel contained: 25 μM lithium acetyl phosphate; 0.25 μM CoA; 100 μM potassium pyrophosphate; 10 μM potassium adenylate; 10 μM MgCl$_2$; 10 μM cysteine; and 50 μM KF; 0.1 ml transacetylase, *Clostridium kluyveri*; 0.3 ml yeast enzyme preparation. The pH was 7.1. The vessels were incubated for 30 minutes at 37°.

* These values are corrected for spontaneous breakdown of acetyl phosphate.

References p. 149.

Reversibility. The conversion of the energy-rich bond of acetyl CoA into the energy-rich pyrophosphoryl bond of ATP was demonstrated by using acetyl phosphate and phosphotransacetylase as acetyl feeder system with catalytic amounts of CoA. The experiment of Table V shows that the addition of pyrophosphate and AMP is necessary for this reaction.

Furthermore, the reversibility of the reaction can be shown spectrophotometrically using the mercaptoester absorption at 232 μM as described by STADTMAN[22] for determination of acetyl CoA. As shown in Fig. 5, on mixing the enzyme, ATP, CoA and acetate, the absorption reaches steady values in about 10 minutes. If at this time pyrophosphate is added, a rather rapid decrease of the acetyl CoA absorption is observed, the degree of which depends on the pyrophosphate concentration. The reason for the slow secondary decline in the absorption of acetyl CoA with higher pyrophosphate concentration is not understood at the present time.

Attempts to clarify the finer mechanism of the reaction. In a previous report experiments were presented which seemed to indicate a primary reaction between pyrophosphate and acetyl CoA and were interpreted as an indication of the formation of a CoA-pyrophosphate. However, it has been difficult to reproduce these experiments with more highly purified acetyl CoA preparations. It is now suspected that the disappearance of acetyl CoA under these conditions may be explained through contamination with small amounts of AMP. If large amounts of pyrophosphate are added, very little AMP is needed for the reverse reaction. At-

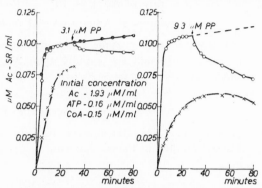

Fig. 5. Reversibility of ATP-CoA-acetate reaction by addition of pyrophosphate. Each cell contained, per ml: 0.15 μM CoA-SH (reduced with potassium borohydride); 0.16 μM ATP; 1.93 μM potassium acetate; 35 μM KF; 2 μM MgCl$_2$; 40 μM tris (hydroxymethyl) aminomethane buffer, pH 7.5; and 0.001 ml (1 unit) of yeast enzyme fraction 4.
Left Figure: Solid circles = control cell to which no pyrophosphate is added. Open circles = cell which contains the same reactants as the control tube except that 3.1 μM potassium pyrophosphate buffer, pH 7.5, are added at the time indicated by the arrow. Crosses = cells which contain the same reactants as the control cell except that 3.1 μM potassium pyrophosphate buffer, pH 7.5, are added at the start.
Right Figure: Curves as above except that 9.3 μM of the pyrophosphate buffer, pH 7.5, were added to the open circle and cross curves rather than 3.1 μM.

tempts also were made to obtain a reaction between ATP and CoA. Frequently in such experiments a small disappearance of ATP may be observed without addition of acetate. However, it was found very difficult to exclude a contamination with small amounts of acetate, to which this system is quite sensitive.

We conclude, therefore, that a separate reaction either between ATP and CoA or between acetyl CoA and pyrophosphate has not been proven convincingly. Furthermore, attempts to divide the system into two enzyme fractions have not given encouraging results (see also Addendum).

Addendum (added in proof)

Further information on the finer mechanism was recently obtained by JONES,

LIPMANN, HILZ AND LYNEN[23] through the use of isotopes. The isotope experiments are interpreted to indicate enzyme-bound intermediaries. ATP (Ad·P $\sim$ PP) equilibrates rapidly through yeast enzyme with inorganic ^{32}P-pyrophosphate in the absence of other components of the system. This seems to implicate an enzyme-adenosine monophosphate (Ad·P) compound:

$$\text{Enzyme} + \text{Ad·P} \sim \text{PP} \rightleftharpoons \text{Enzyme} \sim \text{P·Ad} + \text{PP} \qquad (4)$$

A subsequent replacement of Ad·P in enzyme $\sim$ P·Ad by CoA is indicated by a reduction of the rate of Ad·P $\sim$ PP $\rightleftharpoons$ PP-exchange through the addition of CoA:

$$\text{Enzyme} \sim \text{P·Ad} + \text{CoA·SH} \rightleftharpoons \text{Enzyme} \sim \text{S·CoA} + \text{Ad·P} \qquad (5)$$

Finally, the same enzyme was found to equilibrate acetyl CoA with free acetate rather easily, although less rapidly than Ad·P $\sim$ PP and pyrophosphate. Such an exchange indicates enzyme $\sim$ S·CoA to react eventually with acetate to yield the final product, acetyl $\sim$ S·CoA:

$$\text{Enzyme} \sim \text{S·CoA} + \text{acetate} \rightleftharpoons \text{Enzyme} + \text{acetyl} \sim \text{S·CoA} \qquad (6)$$

It is felt that this interpretation furnishes a reasonably good approximation to the final understanding of the mechanism.

SUMMARY

The formation of acetyl CoA by interaction of ATP, CoA and acetate has been studied with yeast and pigeon liver preparations.

Pyrophosphate and AMP have been found to be the products of the reaction, with the formulation as follows:

$$\text{ATP} + \text{CoA} + \text{acetate} \rightleftharpoons \text{acetyl CoA} + \text{AMP} + \text{pyrophosphate}$$

Magnesium is a component of the enzyme system.

The reaction is reversible as shown by the conversion of acetyl CoA, pyrophosphate and AMP, to ATP and free CoA. The reversion specifically requires pyrophosphate.

Enrichment of the yeast enzyme is described.

RÉSUMÉ

Les auteurs ont étudié la formation d'acétyl CoA par interaction entre l'ATP, le CoA et l'acétate chez des levures et dans des préparations de foie de pigeon.

La réaction conduit au pyrophosphate et à l'AMP. Elle peut se formuler ainsi:

$$\text{ATP} + \text{CoA} + \text{acétate} \rightleftharpoons \text{acétyl CoA} + \text{AMP} + \text{pyrophosphate}$$

Le magnesium est un constituant du système enzymatique.

La réaction est réversible ainsi que le montre la transformation de l'acétyl CoA, du pyrophosphate et de l'AMP en ATP et CoA libre. Le renversement de la réaction exige spécifiquement du pyrophosphate.

Une purification partielle de l'enzyme de la levure est décrite.

ZUSAMMENFASSUNG

Die Bildung des Acetyl-CoA bei der Reaktion mit ATP, CoA und Acetat wurde mit Hefe und Taubenleberpräparaten untersucht.

Es wurde gefunden, dass Pyrophosphat und AMP die Produkte der Reaktion sind, die sich wie folgt formulieren lässt:

$$\text{ATP} + \text{CoA} + \text{Acetat} \rightleftharpoons \text{Acetyl CoA} + \text{AMP} + \text{Pyrophosphat}$$

Magnesium ist ein Bestandteil des Enzymsystems.

Die Reaktion is reversibel, wie durch die Umwandlung von Acetyl-CoA, Pyrophosphat und AMP in ATP und freies CoA gezeigt wurde. Die Umkehr erfordert die Gegenwart von Pyrophosphat.

Die Anreicherung von Hefeenzym wird beschrieben.

References p. 149.

REFERENCES

[1] F. LIPMANN, *J. Biol. Chem.*, 144 (1944) 55.

[2] E. R. STADTMAN, G. D. NOVELLI AND F. LIPMANN, *J. Biol. Chem.*, 191 (1951) 365.

[3] E. R. STADTMAN AND H. A. BARKER, *J. Biol. Chem.*, 180 (1949) 1117.

[4] H. J. KOEPSELL, M. J. JOHNSON AND J. S. MEEK, *J. Biol. Chem.*, 154 (1944) 535.

[5] M. F. UTTER AND C. H. WERKMAN, *Arch. Biochem.*, 2 (1943) 491.

[6] F. LIPMANN, Harvey Lectures, Series XLIV, 1948–1949 (1950) 99.

[7] D. NACHMANSOHN AND A. L. MACHADO, *J. Neurophysiol*, 6 (1943) 397.

[8] F. LIPMANN, *J. Biol. Chem.*, 160 (1945) 173.

[9] F. LIPMANN, M. E. JONES, S. BLACK AND R. M. FLYNN, *J. Am. Chem. Soc.*, 74 (1952) 2384.

[10] F. LIPMANN, M. E. JONES AND S. BLACK, *Sympos. sur le Cycle Tricarboxylique*, IInd Congrès Internatl. de Biochimie, Paris (1952) 55.

[11] N. O. KAPLAN AND F. LIPMANN, *J. Biol. Chem.*, 174 (1948) 37.

[12] T. C. CHOU AND F. LIPMANN, *J. Biol. Chem.*, 196 (1952) 89.

[13] S. BESSMAN, in preparation.

[14] R. E. HANDSCHUMACHER, G. G. MUELLER AND F. M. STRONG, *J. Biol. Chem.*, 189 (1951) 335.

[15] F. LIPMANN AND L. C. TUTTLE, *J. Biol. Chem.*, 159 (1945) 21.

[16] F. LYNEN, E. REICHERT AND L. RUEFF, *Ann. Chem.*, 574 (1951) 1.

[17] H. A. DAVENPORT AND J. SACKS, *J. Biol. Chem.*, 81 (1929) 469.

[18] A. KORNBERG, *J. Biol. Chem.*, 182 (1950) 779.

[19] M. KUNITZ, *J. Gen. Physiol.*, 35 (1952) 423.

[20] H. M. KALCKAR, *J. Biol. Chem.*, 167 (1947) 445.

[21] R. R. GRUNERT AND P. H. PHILLIPS, *Arch. Biochem. Biophys.*, 30 (1951) 217.

[22] E. R. STADTMAN, Abstr. of Papers, 122nd Meet. of ACS, Sept. (1952) 32C.

[23] M. E. JONES, F. LIPMANN, H. HILZ AND F. LYNEN, *J. Am. Chem. Soc.*, (1953), in press.

Received April 6th, 1953

MUSKELKONTRAKTION, ZELLMOTILITÄT UND ATP

von

HANS H. WEBER

Physiologisches Institut der Universität, Tübingen (Deutschland)

I

Es war die Fragestellung und es waren die sensationellen Ergebnisse Otto Warburgs, die die Physiologie fortschreiten liessen von der Betrachtung der Gesamtbilanz des Betriebsstoffwechsels zur Untersuchung des Mechanismus der einzelnen energieliefernden Reaktionen. Warburgs Werk verdanken wir—zum Teil unmittelbar, zum Teil mittelbar—die Kenntnis, Reindarstellung und oft auch Kristallisation der zahlreichen Enzyme, die in langen Ketten Gärung und Oxydation der Betriebsstoffe von Stufe zu Stufe katalysieren[1,2].

Die Kenntnis dieser Reaktionsketten aber klärt gleichzeitig ein 2. sehr allgemeines Grundproblem der Biologie: Den Mechanismus, durch den die Energie von Gärung und Atmung mit dem bekannten hohen Nutzeffekt verwendet werden kann. Denn die Zerlegung dieser Vorgänge in Einzelschritte gestattet es, die Schritte, durch die nennenswerte Energiebeträge gewonnen werden, so mit Phosphorylierungs- oder Umphosphorylierungsreaktionen zu verbinden, dass dabei energiereiche Phosphatbindungen entstehen. So werden 60–70% des Energiegewinnes der einzelnen Abbaustufe festgelegt und durch weitere Umphosphorylierungen auf Adenosintriphosphat (ATP) übertragen[3,4,5,6]. Weil schliesslich jeder Energiegewinn der Stoffwechselvorgänge mit seinem Hauptteil in den Phosphatbindungen des ATP festgelegt wird, wird allgemein angenommen, dass ATP der unmittelbare Energielieferant für die chemische, osmotische und mechanische Arbeit sei. Diese Annahme ist für viele Vorgänge chemischer Arbeitsleistung bewiesen. Denn da die energieliefernden Abbauvorgänge weitgehend reversibel sind, ist ATP nicht nur der Energiespeicher der Abbauvorgänge, sondern auch der Energielieferant für die entsprechenden Aufbauvorgänge. Das gleiche ist aber auch für eine Reihe andersartiger Synthesen erwiesen[4,6].

Die Koppelung der Abbauvorgänge mit Phosphorylierungen lässt schliesslich ein 3. biologisches Grundproblem in neuem Licht erscheinen: Das Problem der Anpassung des Stoffwechsels an den Bedarf, die Steigerung des Stoffwechsels bei dem Übergang der Gewebe von Ruhe zu Erregung. Der hierbei auftretende Mehrbedarf an Energie wird im allgemeinen dem Kohlehydratspeicher entnommen. Die Kohlehydrate (KH) aber können nur in Gestalt ganz bestimmter Phosphorsäureester abgebaut werden, die nur durch ATP-Spaltung entstehen. Da so die ATP-Spaltung den K.H.-Abbau reguliert, wird die Frage nach der Anpassung des Stoffwechsels—zum mindesten des KH-Stoffwechsels—zu der Frage vereinfacht. Aas welchem Grund wächst die Spaltungsrate des ATP beim Übergang von Ruhe zur Erregung so stark an?

Es wird im folgenden gezeigt, dass die Annahme, ATP sei die unmittelbare Energie-

Literatur S. 161/162.

quelle der mechanischen Arbeit, offenbar für alle Arten von Muskelarbeit und für gewisse Bewegungen wachsender und sich vermehrender Zellen gilt (vgl. II, III, IV). Es wird ferner über Befunde berichtet, die eine gewisse Antwort auf die Frage geben, warum die Spaltungsrate des ATP im Augenblick der Erregung so stark ansteigt (VIII). Schliesslich ergibt sich dabei, warum der Muskel für seinen explosiven Energiebedarf angewiesen ist auf Guanidinophosphate als zusätzlichen Speicher sofort greifbarer Energie und nicht einfach einen entsprechenden höheren Gehalt an ATP besitzt (vgl. VII, VIII).

II

Werden Wasser-Glycerin-extrahierte Fibroblastenkulturen der verschiedensten Zellarten* (Zellmodelle) oder extrahierte Fasern oder Streifen aus glatten oder quergestreiften Muskeln (sogenannte Fasermodelle) in ATP-Lösungen physiologischer Konzentration gebracht, so kontrahieren sich die Fasermodelle (Tab. 1) wie die Zellmodelle (Fig. 1). Befinden sich die Fibroblasten gerade im Beginn der Anaphase der Zellteilung, so wandern unter ATP die Chromosomensätze des Zellmodells genau so auseinander, wie sie es getan hätten, wenn die Zelle am Leben geblieben wäre[14].

Wird dafür gesorgt, dass die Präparate die Warburg'sche Grenzschichtdicke** nicht überschreiten, so verkürzen sich alle Modelle um 75–85 % ihrer Ausgangslänge, falls sie unbelastet sind (Tab. 1). Dieser Betrag der maximalen Verkürzung ist physiologisch für glatte Muskeln und für Fibroblasten, die aus dem Zustand der Ruhe in den Zustand der Kernteilung übergehen. Dieser Betrag ist unphysiologisch für Skelettmuskelfasern, die sich im allgemeinen nur um 30–50 % verkürzen. Doch sind auch lebende Skelettmuskelfasern zu der gleichen hohen maximalen Verkürzung imstande, wenn sie in den sogenannten Δ-state gebracht werden[16].

Werden die Fasermodelle an der Verkürzung verhindert, so entwickeln sie Spannung. Die Spannung ist maximal, wenn das Fasermodell unverkürzt ist. Sie hat dann etwa die

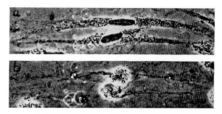

Fig. 1. Die ATP-Kontraktion der Zellmodelle aus Sclera-Fibroblasten. (Nach HOFFMANN-BERLING UND WEBER. unveröffentlich). 32 Tage mit 45%iger Glycerinlösung der Ionenstärke 0.15 μ extrahiert. Phasenkontrastmikroskop; Vergrösserung 600 fach. a. Ohne ATP. b. Mit 2.5·10⁻³ M ATP nach 10 min. bei 37° C. Die Modelle haben sich zu Kugeln zusammengezogen. Die feinen Spuren der ursprünglichen Zellform beruhen anscheinend auf Membranresten, die bei der stürmischen Kontraktion im Fibrin-Nährboden hängen geblieben sind. pH 7.0, Ionenstärke 0.13 μ, MgCl$_2$ 0.004 M, Cystein 0.004 M.

gleiche Grösse wie die isometrische Maximalspannung des lebenden Muskels, aus dem das Fasermodell jeweils hergestellt ist (Tab. 1). Infolgedessen differieren die Maximalspannungen sehr stark: von 4–5 kg/cm² bei Modellen aus dem Kaninchenpsoas oder dem glatten gelben Anteil des Adductor der Anodonta bis zu 600 g/cm² für die glatte Längsmuskulatur des Rinderrectums (Tab. 1). Mit zunehmender Verkürzung fällt die maximale Spannung aller Modelle etwa geradlinig auf Null.

---

* Amnion, Leber, Milz, Sclera, Muskel, Osteoblasten, Subcutangewebe, verschiedene Tumoren u.s.w.[7].

** Die Grenzschichtdicke für ATP wird bisher für alle Modelle aus der Diffusionskonstanten des ATP berechnet, die für das Fasermodell aus Kaninchenpsoas experimentell bestimmt ist[15], und aus den verschiedenen Spaltungsraten der einzelnen Muskelmodelle[11].

Literatur S. 161/162.

Die maximale Spannung wird also—im Gegensatz zur maximalen Verkürzung—beim Übergang vom Muskel zum Modell nicht nivelliert. Doch beweist das nicht, dass die maximale Spannung durch die Eigenschaften des kontraktilen Proteins selbst—des Aktomyosin—bestimmt ist. Denn geordnete Fäden aus dem gereinigten Aktomyosin des Kaninchenpsoas zerreissen sich selbst, sowie ihre isometrische Spannung auf 200–300 g/cm² angewachsen ist (Tab. I).

TABELLE I

MAXIMALE SPANNUNG UND VERKÜRZUNG VON ZELLMODELLEN UND MODELLEN AUS
QUERGESTREIFTEN UND GLATTEN MUSKELN

Modelle aus	Maximale Spannung in kg/cm²	Maximale Verkürzung in % der Anfangslänge
Fibroblasten		
Sclera	—	~ 80[14]
Amnion	—	~ 80[14]
Muskel	—	~ 80[14]
Skelettmuskel: Fasermodell		
Kaninchen	4[8]	> 85[8,12,10]
Frosch	1[9]	~ 70[10]
Fadenmodell		
Kaninchen	0.3[13]	~ 70[13]
Glatte Muskeln		
Anodonta: Adductor posterior		
gelber Teil	5[11]	> 80[11]
weisser Teil	2[11]	> 80[11]
Retractor pedis	—	> 70[11]
Rectum vom Rind (Längsmuskel)	0.6[11]	~ 80[11]

III

Die Spannung von Muskeln und Modellen hängt von der Temperatur ab. Diese Abhängigkeit ist klein für die aufgezwungene Spannung der schwach gedehnten lebenden Muskeln oder Modelle ohne ATP[28], sie ist viel grösser für die aktive Maximalspannung der Muskeln oder Modelle in Kontraktion (Fig. 2). Das Ausmass—in Ruhe sogar die Richtung — der Temperaturabhängigkeit ist für verschiedene Muskelarten sehr verschieden, aber für Muskel und Modell der gleichen Art immer ungefähr gleich. Da das — soweit untersucht — sogar für das Fadenmodell aus reinem Aktomyosin gilt (Fig. 2), mag die Tempera-

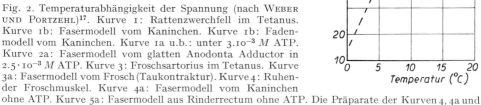

Fig. 2. Temperaturabhängigkeit der Spannung (nach WEBER UND PORTZEHL)[17]. Kurve 1: Rattenzwerchfell im Tetanus. Kurve 1b: Fasermodell vom Kaninchen. Kurve 1b: Fadenmodell vom Kaninchen. Kurve 1a u.b.: unter 3.10⁻³ M ATP. Kurve 2a: Fasermodell vom glatten Anodonta Adductor in 2.5·10⁻³ M ATP. Kurve 3: Froschsartorius im Tetanus. Kurve 3a: Fasermodell vom Frosch (Taukontraktur). Kurve 4: Ruhender Froschmuskel. Kurve 4a: Fasermodell vom Kaninchen ohne ATP. Kurve 5a: Fasermodell aus Rinderrectum ohne ATP. Die Präparate der Kurven 4, 4a und 5a sind mechanisch gespannt.

Literatur S. 161/162.

turabhängigkeit der Spannung durch das kontraktile Protein selbst bestimmt sein.

Wird den aktiven Muskelmodellen freie Verkürzung erlaubt, so nimmt mit fallender Temperatur statt der Spannung die maximale Verkürzung ab. Das gleiche gilt für die Zellmodelle unter ATP aus Fibroblasten, deren Spannung nicht gemessen werden kann[14].

IV

Werden lebende Muskeln oder Modelle in isometrischer Kontraktion so losgelassen, dass sie sich um 5–10% ihrer Ruhelänge frei verkürzen können (quick release), so sinkt die Spannung nicht einfach auf den isometrischen Maximalwert der neuen Länge, sondern sie bricht vollständig zusammen und entwickelt sich anschliessend bei der neuen Länge von neuem. Dies gilt für glatte und quergestreifte Muskeln, ihre Faser- und Fadenmodelle (Fig. 3). Das Quick-Release-Phänomen ist sonst nie beobachtet worden — z.B. bei keiner Form der elastischen Verkürzung. Es ist für die Reaktion kontraktiler Proteine mit ATP ebenso charakteristisch wie die Kontraktion selbst.

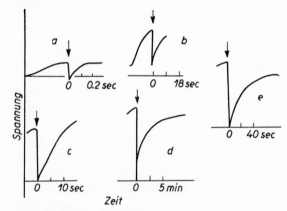

Fig. 3. Spannungsentwicklung nach einem "quick release". a. Froschmuskel (GASSER UND HILL[19]), ↓ release ∼ 10%; b. Wandmuskulatur von Holothuria (HILL[20]), ↓ release ∼ 4%; c. Fasermodell aus Kaninchenpsoas (A. WEBER[8]), ↓ release ∼ 5%; d. Fasermodell vom Rinderrectum (G. UND M. ULBRECHT[11]), ↓ release ∼ 10%; e. Fadenmodell aus Kaninchen-Aktomyosin (PORTZEHL[13]). ↓ release ∼ 3%.

Der unkontrahierte Warmblütermuskel und sein unkontrahiertes Modell haben die gleiche Eigen-, Form- und Gesamtdoppelbrechung. Bei isotonischer Kontraktion nimmt ausserdem die Gesamtdoppelbrechung von Muskel und Modell um den gleichen Betrag ab[21, 21a]. Es darf infolgedessen angenommen werden, dass auch die Abnahme der Eigen- und der Formdoppelbrechung — beide sind bisher nur bei der Modellkontraktion getrennt bestimmt — für Muskel und Modell identisch ist[21, 21a]. Die Analyse dieser Doppelbrechungsänderungen ergibt, dass die achsenparallele Lage der submikroskopischen Eiweissfilamente während Kontraktion und Verkürzung unverändert bleibt, und dass nur die Länge der Filamente abnimmt[21]. Dasselbe zeigt die electronenmikroskopische Aufnahme kontrahierter Fibrillen aus intakten Muskelfasern und aus Modellen — wenigstens für den Teil der Eiweissfilamente, der elektronenmikroskopisch auflösbar ist[22, 23, 24]. Ausserdem zeigen elektronenmikroskopische und Phasenkontrastaufnahmen von Modellen und Muskeln, dass eine Substanzverschiebung aus der A-Bande in die I-Bande während der Kontraktion stattfindet[22, 23, 24, 25, 26]. Da die von A nach I

Literatur S. 161/162.

wandernde Substanz selbst elektronenmikroskopisch nicht mehr auflösbar ist, ergibt sich aus der Gesamtheit der optischen Beobachtungen nur, dass der Fundamentalprozess der Kontraktion sich an molekularen Einheiten vollzieht und dass er kompliziert ist. Wesentlich aber ist, dass er bis in die molecularen Dimensionen hinein für die vitale und die Modellkontraktion gleich ist.

Auch die Bewegungen der Zellen und der Zellmodelle mögen auf demselben molekularen Vorgang beruhen. Denn ebenso wie die Viskosität von Aktomyosinlösungen aus Muskeln auf ATP-Zusatz steil abfällt und nach der Spaltung des ATP langsam auf den alten Wert zurückkehrt, fällt auch die Viskosität von Extrakten aus dem sehr beweglichen Plasmodium des Myxomyceten Physarum polycephalum auf ATP-Zusatz steil ab und kehrt langsam zur Norm zurück[26a].

V

Wenn lebende Muskeln oder Modelle mit merklicher Geschwindigkeit ATP spalten, kontrahierten sie sich. Die durchsichtigen Bedingungen des Modellversuches zeigen, dass für alle Modelle ATP die kontraktionserzeugende Substanz ist. Die vollständige Übereinstimmung der Kontraktionsphase von Modell- und Vitalkontraktion in allen Einzelzügen beweist aber, dass das gleiche auch für die Kontraktionsphase aller Arten von lebenden Muskeln gilt. Die Ähnlichkeit im Verhalten der Zell- und Muskelmodelle spricht ferner dafür, dass auch gewisse Zellbewegungen auf der gleichen oder einer ähnlichen Wechselwirkung zwischen kontraktilem Protein und ATP beruhen.

Wenn Muskel oder Muskelmodelle kein ATP enthalten, sind sie "starr". Es ist dabei gleichgültig, auf welche Weise die ATP-Verarmung des lebenden Muskels herbeigeführt ist. "Starre" Muskeln und Modelle können nur um wenige Prozent gedehnt werden, ohne dass die Struktur irreversibel geschädigt oder zerrissen wird[8, 27]. Der statische* Dehnungswiderstand ist dabei hoch und beträgt 5–10 $kg \cdot cm^{-2} \cdot L \cdot \varDelta L^{-1}$ oder mehr[32, 33].

Während der "Kontraktion" können Muskel und Modelle stark gedehnt werden ohne zu zerreissen, und der statische* Dehnungswiderstand ist nur wenig grösser als die jeweilige aktive Spannung[21, 28].

Wenn die Muskeln oder Modelle eine physiologische Konzentration an ATP enthalten (je nach der Muskelart $3–8 \cdot 10^{-3} M$ ATP) — ohne das ATP gleichzeitig zu spalten, sinkt der statische* Dehnungswiderstand weiter ab auf 0.04–0.5 $kg \cdot cm^{-2} \cdot L \cdot \varDelta L^{-1}$ — je nach dem Dehnungszustand[34, 35, 36]. Dieser Zustand ist der Ruhezustand.

Er kann bei den Modellen nur durch besondere Massnahmen hergestellt werden: 1. durch Vergiftung der ATP-Spaltung mit SH-Komplexbildern wie Salyrgan[32]; 2. auf physiologischem Wege durch Komplettierung des Aktomyosinsystems mit Hilfe des MARSH[29]-BENDALL[30]-Faktors (M-B-Faktor)** zu einem System, das ebenfalls ATP unter normalen Umständen nicht spaltet[31]. Da durch Zusatz von Salyrgan oder M-B-Faktor ohne ATP der Dehnungswiderstand der starren Modelle nicht erniedrigt wird, muss die "Weichheit" des "Ruhezustandes" auf dem ATP beruhen (vgl. ferner Fig. 4b). ATP ist ein Weichmacher, solange es nur gebunden wird, Es ist Kontraktionssubstanz, sobald es vom Aktomyosingel gespalten wird. Als Kontraktionssubstanz kann es nur durch

---

* Der "statische" Widerstand wird bei sehr langsamer (theoretisch "unendlich" langsamer) Dehnung erhalten. Der "dynamische" Widerstand bei schneller Dehnung ist viel höher.
** Der M-B-Faktor wird aus frischem Muskelbrei extrahiert.

Literatur S. 161/162.

Inosintriphosphat (ITP) vertreten werden[37, 38], als Weichmacher dagegen anscheinend durch alle anorganischen und organischen Polyphosphate[32].

VI

Da die Erschlaffung nichts anderes ist als der Übergang aus dem kontrahierten in den Ruhezustand, ist zu fordern, dass der Zusatz von Salyrgan oder M-B-Faktor zu ATP-haltigen, im Kontraktionszustand befindlichen Modellen Erschlaffung bewirkt. Und das ist auch so (Fig. 4a, b). Wird die Blockierung der ATP-Spaltung wieder aufgehoben — für Salyrgan durch Cystein und für den M-B-Faktor durch Coffein* oder Calcium-Ionen — so kontrahieren sich die Modelle wieder von neuem. Dieses Spiel lässt sich beliebig fortsetzen. Aus Kontraktionsphase und Erschlaffungsphase wird der Arbeitszyklus. Energielieferant ist die ATP-Spaltung.

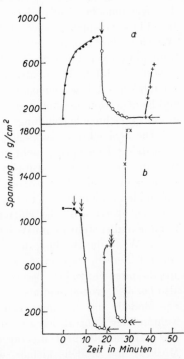

Dass in diesem Arbeitszyklus die ATP-Energie während der Kontraktionsphase aufgenommen wird, und dass die Erschlaffungsphase der thermodynamisch freiwillige Teil des Zyklus ist, geht schon aus dem bisher Gesagten hervor. Es lässt sich mit Sicherheit dadurch beweisen, dass es gelingt, die Erschlaffung der Modelle nicht nur durch Zugabe eines Inhibitors zu bewirken, sondern auch durch nichts anderes als die Entfernung des ATP. Man muss nur verhindern, dass das Modell dabei starr wird: Wird ein Modell abwechselnd in ATP-haltige und ATP-freie Bäder getaucht, die aber immer $1.5 \cdot 10^{-2} M$ Pyrophosphat als Weichmacher enthalten, so kontrahieren sich die Modelle beim Auftreten des ATP und erschlaffen bei seinem Verschwinden wieder (Fig. 5).

Fig. 4. Erschlaffung durch Unterdrückung der ATP-Spaltung. a. Mit Salyrgan (PORTZEHL[32]). .–.–.– Kontraktion durch $1.7 \cdot 10^{-3} M$ ATP, ↓ $10^{-4} M$ Salyrgan ← $2 \cdot 10^{-2} M$ Cystein (Fasermodell). b. Mit M-B-Faktor (HASSELBACH unveröffentlicht); ATP aus dem kontrahierten Fasermodell ausgewaschen, ↓ M-B-Faktor zugefügt, ↓↓ von neuen ATP zugefügt ($5 \cdot 10^{-3} M$) ← Coffein hinzugefügt, ↓↓ Badwechsel M-B-Faktor + $5 \cdot 10^{-3} M$ ATP (ohne Coffein). ← $8 \cdot 10^{-3} M$ CaCl$_2$ hinzugefügt.

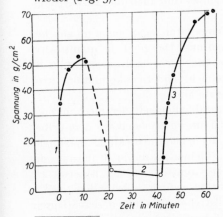

Fig. 5. Kontraktion und Erschlaffung bei Dauergegenwart von $1.5 \cdot 10^{-2} M$ Pyrophosphat. (Nach PORTZEHL[32]) 1 Kontraktion mit $1.6 \cdot 10^{-3} M$ ATP, 2 Erschlaffung durch Entfernung des ATP, 3 Kontraktion durch neue ATP-Gabe ($4 \cdot 10^{-3} M$). Fadenmodell.

---

* Auch die Coffein-Kontraktur des lebenden Muskels beruht wahrscheinlich auf der Inaktivierung des M-B-faktor. Sie wäre damit in Wirklichkeit eine ATP-Kontraktur.

Literatur S. 161/162.

VII

Es ist somit sicher, dass die Spaltungsenergie des ATP während der Kontraktions-phase auf das kontraktile System übertragen wird. Es ist aber nicht sicher, dass die Übertragung genau in dem Zeitpunkt erfolgt, in dem das einzelne ATP-Molekül de-phosphoryliert wird. Die Übertragung könnte auf Grund der bisher berichteten Tat-sachen nämlich auch in dem Augenblick erfolgen, in dem das einzelne ATP-Molekül vom Aktomyosin in einer besonderen Weise gebunden wird. Doch wäre dies nur unter drei- im übrigen völlig unbewiesenen — Voraussetzungen möglich: 1. Das ATP müsste als "Weichmacher" an andere Gruppen des Aktomyosin gebunden sein und nicht an die ATPase-Gruppen des kontraktilen Proteins. 2. Bei dem Übergang des ATP aus der "Weichmacherbindung" in die "ATPase-Bindung" müsste ein Energiebetrag für die Kontraktion verfügbar werden, der fast so gross ist wie die Spaltungsenergie des ATP (12000 cal. Mol^{-1}). Die Spaltungsenergie selbst würde dann nur noch dazu dienen, das entstehende ADP wieder vom Aktomyosin abzulösen. 3. Alle Inhibitoren von Spaltung und Kontraktion müssten dadurch wirken, dass sie das ATP aus der "ATPase-Bindung" in die "Weichmacherbindung" abdrängen.

Die beobachtete Koppelung zwischen ATP-Spaltung und ATP-Kontraktion wäre nach dieser Konzeption mehr zufällig: Sie würde nur darauf beruhen, dass die ATP-Bindung an bestimmte Gruppen des kontraktilen Proteins nicht nur zur Kontraktion, sondern auch zur ATP-Spaltung führt. Könnte die Bindung an die fraglichen Gruppen stattfinden, aber trotzdem die Spaltung verhindert werden, so erhielte man den "idealen Sperrtonus" des glatten Muskels. Diese Konzeption wirkt etwas gezwungen. Vor allem aber steht sie im Widerspruch zu folgenden Beobachtungen:

1. Wenn die Bindung des ATP an die ATPase-Gruppen des kontraktilen Proteins einen hohen Energiebetrag freimachen soll, müsste diese Bindung auf Grund der annähernden Gültigkeit des BERTHELOT'schen Prinzips auch exotherm sein. Sie sollte also bei 0° C grösser sein als bei 20° C. Infolgedessen müsste die maximale Verkürzung der Modelle mit fallender Temperatur zunehmen. In Wirklichkeit vermindert sich während der Kontraktion aller die maximale Verkürzung aller Zell- und Muskelmodelle (vgl. III), sobald die Temperatur fällt. Ausser der Arbeit wird auch die Leistung aller Muskeln und Modelle kleiner, weil mit fallender Temperatur auch die Verkürzungs-geschwindigkeit sinkt.

Die mechanische Leistung sinkt mit fallender Temperatur sogar genau im gleichen Umfang wie die Energielieferung durch die ATP-Spaltung. Das zeigt die quantitative Untersuchung. Also ist für die mechanische Arbeitsleistung nicht die Konzentration des ATP in einer besonderen spezifischen Bindung massgeblich, sondern es kommt unmittel-bar und ausschliesslich auf die Grösse der Spaltungsrate an.

Eine quantitative Untersuchung der Temperaturabhängigkeit der mechanischen Leistung kann besonders exakt durchgeführt werden am Fasermodell aus dem gelben Adductor von Anodonta[38]. Dieses Modell zerreisst auch bei Entwicklung maximaler Spannung nicht. Seine Spaltungsrate ist etwa 6 mal kleiner als die Spaltungsrate des Modells aus Skelettmuskeln, d.h. die WARBURG'sche Grenzschichtdicke ist etwa 2½ mal grösser. Sie kann infolgedessen leicht unterschritten werden — besonders, weil es ohne weiteres möglich ist, aus diesem Muskel Modellstreifen zu isolieren, deren Durch-messer kleiner ist als 30 μ. Dann zeigt sich, dass die Verkürzungsgeschwindigkeit mit fallender Temperatur, steigendem Verkürzungsgrad und steigender relativer Be-

Literatur S. 161/162.

lastung abnimmt. Sie ist für das unbelastete Fasermodell in der Ausgangslänge bei 20° C = 22% dieser Ausgangslänge pro Sekunde und bei 0° C = 7%. Das Maximum der mechanischen Leistung wird erreicht, wenn die relative Belastung 1/5 der Maximalspannung beträgt. Dann berechnet sich die maximale Leistung von 1 g des Fasermodells in Ausgangslänge zu annähernd 60 g cm · sec.$^{-1}$, bei 20° C und zu nicht ganz 9 g cm.sec.$^{-1}$ bei 0° C. D.h. die maximale mechanische Leistung wächst zwischen 0 und 20° C auf etwa das 7-fache. Und ebenso wächst die Spaltungsrate auf das 7-fache: $1.9 \cdot 10^{-7}$ Mol pro Gramm-Modell und Sek. bei 20° und $0.28 \cdot 10^{-7}$ Mol pro Gramm-Modell und Sekunde bei 0° C. Die Spaltungsrate ist an einer Suspension maximal kontrahierter Modellfasern gemessen. Wird angenommen, die Spaltungsrate sei während des Verkürzungsvorgangs ebenso gross wie im maximal verkürzten Zustand, so würde sich für 0° wie für 20° C der gleiche hohe mechanische Nutzeffekt der ATP-Spaltungsenergie von 60–70% ergeben. Es ist aber möglich, dass die Spaltungsrate während des Verkürzungsvorganges höher ist als im verkürzten Zustand. Denn der lebende Muskel mobilisiert während des Verkürzungsvorganges mehr Energie als bei isometrischer Kontraktion (die sogenannte "Extraenergie" von A. V. HILL oder der sogenannte "FENN-Effect"). Es ist noch nicht gelungen festzustellen, ob das für die Modelle auch gilt. Falls es so ist, wäre der Nutzeffekt niedriger und würde sich den üblichen Werten des lebenden Muskels — zwischen 30 und 50% — mehr nähern. Doch ist auf jeden Fall bemerkenswert, wie gut das Modell die Spaltungsenergie des ATP ausnutzt.

2. Wenn Modelle mit steigender ATP-Konzentration durchtränkt werden, muss nach dem Massenwirkungsgesetz der Anteil des ATP, der in "ATPase-Bindung" gebunden ist, ebenfalls steigen, bis die ATPase-Gruppen des Aktomyosin gesättigt sind und weiterhin konstant bleiben. Die Spaltungsrate aber braucht sich nicht so zu verhalten, und sie verhält sich tatsächlich nicht so. Wie bei vielen Fermenten gibt es auch beim Aktomyosin eine "Eigenhemmung" durch das Substrat. Oberhalb einer bestimmten ATP-Konzentration fällt die ATP-Spaltung wieder ab. Dieser Abfall beginnt im allgemeinen bei Konzentrationen $\sim 10^{-2}$ M ATP[17, 21]. Im einzelnen variiert der Beginn des Abfalls etwas mit der Art des Muskels, der Ionenstärke und der Temperatur[17, 21].

In jedem Fall ist aber dieser "überoptimale" Abfall der Spaltung begleitet von einem entsprechenden Abfall der Kontraktion. Dies gilt ebenso für Zellmodelle aus Fibroblasten wie für die Modelle glatter und quergestreifter Muskelfasern[17, 21] (Fig. 6a und 7).

Auch dies Verhalten zeigt, dass die ATP-Kontraktion auf der ATP-Spaltung und nicht auf einer Spezialbindung des ATP beruht. Ausserdem bedeutet es, dass lebende Zellen keine höhere ATP-Konzentration enthalten dürfen als $\sim 10^{-2}$ M: Sie könnten sonst ihr eigenes ATP infolge der "überoptimalen Eigenhemmung" nicht mehr benutzen. Hiermit ist geklärt, warum Gewebe mit explosivem Energiebedarf — wie die Muskeln — einen 2. sofort angreifbaren Energiespeicher in Gestalt der Guanodinophosphate besitzen müssen, um die Zeit bis zur Restitution des ATP durch den K-H-Stoffwechsel zu überbrücken.

VIII

Der Umfang der ATP-Spaltung bedingt den Umfang der Arbeitsleistung und der Restitutionsvorgänge. Und was bestimmt nun den Umfang der ATP-Spaltung? Für den Muskel läuft diese Frage auf 2 Fragen hinaus: 1. nach dem Mechanismus, durch den

Literatur S. 161/162.

die Polarisationsänderungen der erregten Membran mit der ATP-Spaltung verknüpft sind. Dies gilt für die Lieferung der sogenannten "Aktivierungsenergie" bei isometrischer Kontraktion (A. V. HILL). Die 2. Frage betrifft die Auslösung der Produktion von *"Extra-Energie"*[39], wenn dem Muskel Verkürzung erlaubt ist. Wie weit analoge Fragen für die Zellmotilität zu stellen sind, ist noch unbekannt.

Nur für die Beantwortung der 1. Frage stehen gewisse experimentelle Tatsachen zur Verfügung. Der Beginn der Kontraktion des lebenden Muskels ist offenbar immer mit einer Depolarisation oder Umpolarisation der Membran verknüpft[40,41,42]. Die Aktivierung der kontraktilen Substanz beginnt beim Froschmuskel etwa 1 mill. sec. später und ist etwa 30–40 mill. sec. später vollständig[41]. Allein durch Diffusion kann in dieser kurzen Zeit kein Stoff von der Membran bis zur innersten Fibrille einer Faser gelangen[45], die etwa 100 μ dick ist. Infolgedessen wird die Koppelung zwischen der Fibrillenaktivierung und den Membranvorgängen einer elektrisch beschleunigten Ionenwanderung zugeschrieben — und zwar der Wanderung des Calcium-Ions[41]. Die Argumente sind

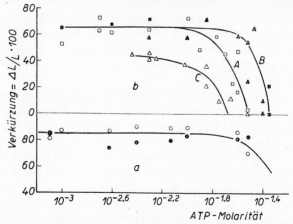

Fig. 6. Abhängigkeit der Kontraktion von der Extraktionsdauer der Zell- und Fasermodelle, der ATP-Konzentration und der Gegenwart von Calcium. a. Modell aus Sclera-Fibroblasten (Nach HOFFMANN-BERLING UND WEBER[14]). □ - □ - □ - (Kurve A) = 2 bis 10 Tage extrahierte Modelle ohne Ca++; ■ - ■ - ■ (Kurve B) = ebenso mit $5 \cdot 10^{-3} M$ Ca++; △ - △ - △ (Kurve C) = eine Stunde extrahierte Modelle ohne Ca++; ▲ - ▲ - ▲ (Kurve B) = ebenso mit $5 \cdot 10^{-3} M$ Ca++. — Ionenstärke = 0.15 μ, mit ATP-Konzentrationen $> 10^{-2} M$ steigend bis $\sim$ 0.3 μ. b. Fasermodell aus Fibrillen des Kaninchenmuskels (Nach PORTZEHL unveröffentlicht). Extraktionsdauer 7 bis 10 Tage. O - O - O ohne Ca++ ·—·—·— mit $5 \cdot 10^{-3} M$ Ca++. — Ionenstärke 0.13 μ mit ATP-Konzentrationen $> 10^{-2} M$ steigend bis 0.25 μ.

recht lückenhaft. Darum ist es wesentlich zu wissen, wie weit die ATP-Spaltung und die ATP-Kontraktion ionenempfindlich und insbesondere Calcium-empfindlich sind. Wir finden:

Werden Muskelfasern oder Fibroblastenkulturen mehrere Tage oder Wochen mit Wasser und Glycerin extrahiert, so ist die ATP-Spaltung und ATP-Kontraktion gegen kleine Änderungen des physiologischen Ionenbestandes ausserordentlich unempfindlich. Nur vollständige Entfernung des Mg++ durch gute Enthärter vermag die Kontraktion zu unterdrücken[17]. Dagegen beeinflusst die Höhe des Ca++-Spiegels — weit über die physiologischen Grenzen hinaus — die ATP-Kontraktion nicht (Fig. 6a, b).

Werden dagegen Zell- oder Fasermodelle nur wenige Stunden extrahiert, so kontrahieren sie sich bei Gegenwart physiologischer ATP- und Mg^{++}-Konzentration nicht mehr (Fasermodelle[44]) oder sehr unvollständig (Zellmodelle, Abb. 6a). Sie kontrahieren sich dagegen sofort wieder vollständig, sowie physiologische Konzentrationen an Calcium ($\sim 10^{-3} M$) hinzugesetzt werden (Fig. 6a und 4b).

Der Unterschied in der ATP- und Calcium-Empfindlichkeit kurz und lang extrahierter Modelle kann für alle Muskelmodelle auf das Vorhandensein (kurze Extraktion) oder aber das Fehlen (lange Extraktion) des von MARSH[29] and BENDALL[30] entdeckten Prinzips (M-B-Faktor) erklärt werden.

Der M-B-Faktor ist ein mit $0.15 M$ KCl-Lösung extrahierbarer und nicht dialysabler Stoff mit einem Teilchengewicht $> 10^{-4}$, der noch nicht rein dargestellt werden konnte[31]. BENDALL hielt ihn zunächst für einen Inhibitor, der in seiner Wirkung dem Salyrgan vergleichbar wäre[30]. Diese Ansicht ist nicht richtig.

Denn der M-B-Faktor blockiert die Reaktion zwischen Aktomyosin und ATP nicht, sondern er sensibilisiert sie! Wird nämlich das Fasermodell aus einem beliebigen Muskel mit einer Lösung des Faktors durchtränkt, so werden zwar in ATP-Lösungen physiologischer Konzentration Spaltung und Spannung unterdrückt, aber nicht in Lösungen, deren ATP-Konzentration 10 mal kleiner ist ($< 10^{-3} M$). Der Faktor hemmt die physiologische ATP-Verwendung nicht dadurch, dass er mit dem ATP konkurriert, sondern dadurch, dass er den Bereich der "ATP-Eigenhemmung", den "überoptimalen" Bereich der ATP-Konzentration auf physiologische ATP-Konzentrationen ausdehnt (Fig. 7a und b). Der gehemmte Bereich reicht infolgedessen umso tiefer herab, je höher die Faktorkonzentration ist und auch je höher die Ionenstärke und die Mg-Konzentration sind (Fig. 7b). Denn Erhöhung der Ionenstärke und der Mg^{++}-Konzentration lassen ebenfalls — auch schon ohne Faktor — den Bereich der ATP-Eigenhemmung mit niedrigeren ATP-Konzentrationen beginnen als vorher (Fig. 7b).

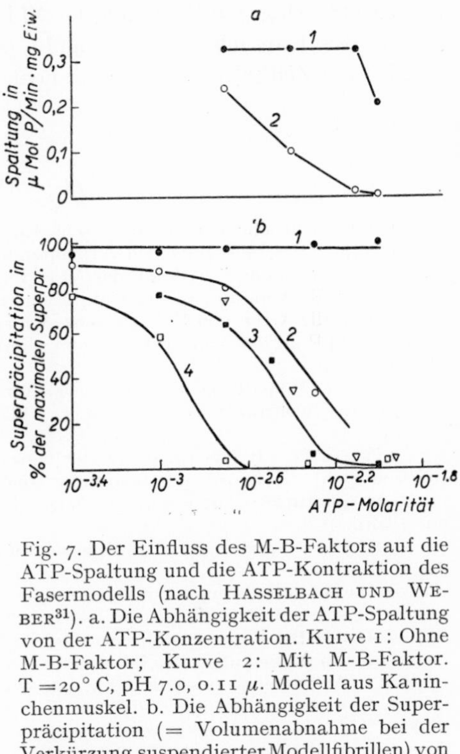

Mit Faktorlösung gesättigte Fasermodelle aller Muskelarten spalten und kontrahieren wieder völlig normal, wenn ihnen 7.10^{-4} M Ca^{++} hinzugefügt wird[31]. Bereits mit 1.10^{-4} M Ca^{++} wird die Ca^{++}-wirkung merklich[31]. Dass so geringe Verschiebungen der Ca^{++}-Ionen-Konzentration genügen, um den Kom-

Fig. 7. Der Einfluss des M-B-Faktors auf die ATP-Spaltung und die ATP-Kontraktion des Fasermodells (nach HASSELBACH UND WEBER[31]). a. Die Abhängigkeit der ATP-Spaltung von der ATP-Konzentration. Kurve 1: Ohne M-B-Faktor; Kurve 2: Mit M-B-Faktor. T $=20°$ C, pH 7.0, 0.11 μ. Modell aus Kaninchenmuskel. b. Die Abhängigkeit der Superpräcipitation (= Volumenabnahme bei der Verkürzung suspendierter Modellfibrillen) von der ATP-Konzentration. Kurve 1: Ohne M-B-Faktor, Ionenstärke = 0.14 μ, Kurve 2: Ebenso, Ionenstärke = 0.25 μ, Kurve 3: Mit M-B-Faktor, Ionenstärke = 0.14 μ, Kurve 4: Ebenso. Ionenstärke = 0.25 μ. △ △ △ Spaltung zur Superpräcipitation der Kurve 3 in Prozenten der Maximalspaltung. T = 20° C, pH 7.0.

plex aus Aktomyosin und M-B-Faktor zwischen Ruhe und Aktivität hin und·her pendeln zu lassen, stützt die Ansicht, dass Ca^{++}-Verschiebungen den Polarisationszustand der Membran mit dem Funktionszustand des kontraktilen Proteins verbinden.

Literatur S. 161/162.

Wir haben gesehen (VII), dass die physiologische ATP-Konzentration nicht höher sein darf, als sie ist, weil dann das ATP im Erregungszustand infolge der "ATP-Eigenhemmung" nicht mehr verwendbar wäre. Wir sehen jetzt, dass sie auch nicht niedriger sein darf. Sonst wäre die ATP-Spaltung auch in Ruhe nicht zu unterdrücken. Der M-B-Faktor kann den Bereich der ATP-Eigenhemmung nicht beliebig weit nach unten ausdehnen. Die Berechtigung dieses Gedankenganges wird dadurch bewiesen, dass die Muskeln, kurz bevor sie starr werden, meist in Kontraktur übergehen. Ehe der "Weichmacher ATP" erschöpft ist (Starre), sinkt die Konzentration der Kontraktionssubstanz ATP soweit ab, dass ihre Spaltung auch durch den *M-B*-Faktor nicht mehr verhindert werden kann (Kontraktur).

Es ist vielleicht nicht uninteressant, dass der M-B-Faktor aus Kaninchenmuskeln nicht nur auf Aktomyosinmodelle aus Kaninchenmuskeln sondern auch auf Modelle aus Froschmuskeln, ja sogar auf Fasermodelle aus dem glatten Adductor von Anodonta voll wirkt[31]. Dagegen lässt sich die ATP-Kontraktion der Zellmodelle durch den M-B-Faktor des Kaninchenmuskels nicht beeinflussen[14]. Die Herstellung eines analogen Faktors aus Zellkulturen ist bisher noch nicht gelungen[14].

ZUSAMMENFASSUNG

1. Die natürliche, beinahe plastische Konsistenz von Muskeln und Zellen, die eine notwendige Voraussetzung der Bewegung sich vermehrender Zellen und sich kontrahierender Muskeln ist, beruht auf der "Weichmacher" wirkung des ATP. Für die Bewegungen der Zellen wie für die Kontraktion aller glatten Muskeln und aller Skeletmuskeln ist ATP darüber hinaus die Verkürzungssubstanz.

2. Für alle Arten von Muskeln lässt sich zeigen, dass die "Weichmacherwirkung" auf einer Bindung des ATP an das kontraktile Protein und die Kontraktion auf einer ATP-Spaltung durch das Protein beruht.

3. Die ATP-Spaltung setzt die Energie für die Kontraktion frei und überträgt sie auf das Protein während der Kontraktionsphase. Die Erschlaffungsphase beginnt, sobald die ATP-Spaltung aufhört.

4. Versuche mit Fasermodellen der verschiedenen Muskelarten zeigen, dass während der Kontraktion nicht die Grösse der Spannung sondern der mechanischen Leistung die Rate der ATP-Spaltung quantitativ entspricht. Sie zeigen ferner, dass die Spaltungsenergie dabei sehr gut ausgenutzt wird.

5. Die ATP-Spaltung wird im Ruhezustand des lebenden Muskels unterdrückt durch die Wirkung des M-B-Faktors.

6. Die ATP-Spaltung findet statt, wenn der M-B-Faktor inaktiviert wird—durch Calcium Ionen (physiologischer Mechanismus) oder durch Coffein.

7. Der M-B-Faktor sensibilisiert das Aktomyosin für die "Eigenhemmung" der ATP-Spaltung. Diese setzt in Abwesenheit des Faktors ein, wenn die ATP Konzentration 10^{-2} M überschreitet, und beginnt in Anwesenheit des Faktors bereits, wenn die ATP Konzentration grösser ist als 10^{-3} M.

8. So wird es verständlich, dass die ATP Konzentration der lebenden Muskeln zwischen 10^{-3} M und 10^{-2} M liegt: Wäre sie grösser, so könnte der Muskel sein eigenes ATP auch dann nicht spalten, wenn der M-B-Faktor – etwa während der Erregung – durch Calciumionen inaktiviert ist. Wäre dagegen die physiologische ATP Konzentration niedriger als 10^{-3} molar, so könnte die ATP-Spaltung auch durch einen aktivierten M-B-Faktor nicht mehr verhindert werden.

9. Der M-B-Faktor aus Kaninchenmuskel wirkt auch auf Froschmuskeln und den glatten Adduktor von Anodonta. Dagegen verhindert er die ATP-Kontraktion der Zellmodelle aus Fibroblasten nicht.

SUMMARY

1. The great plasticity of muscles and cells necessary for the motility of multiplying cells and contracting muscles is produced by the "plasticising" effect of ATP. In addition, ATP is the shortening agent for the contractions of multiplying cells as well as of all smooth and skeletal muscles.

2. It can be shown for all kinds of muscles that the "plasticising" effect is produced by the binding of ATP to the contractile protein and that the contraction is initiated by the splitting of ATP.

Literatur S. 161/162.

3. The energy of ATP-splitting is liberated and transferred to the contractile protein during the phase of contraction. Relaxation sets in as soon as the splitting of ATP ceases.

4. Experiments with fibre models of various kinds of muscles prove that not the tension but the power is proportional to the rate of ATP splitting. Furthermore they indicate that the energy of splitting is used with a good efficiency.

5. In resting living muscles the splitting of ATP is suppressed by the M-B-factor.

6. ATP is split when the M-B-factor is inactivated by calcium ions (physiological effect) or by caffein.

7. The M-B-factor sensitises the effect of substrate inhibition on the ATPase activity of actomyosin. The overoptimal concentration of ATP is shifted from 10^{-2} M ATP in the absence of the factor to 10^{-3} M in the presence of the factor.

8. Thus it appears obvious why the ATP concentration of living muscles ranges between 10^{-3} to 10^{-2} M ATP. If the concentration would be higher the muscle would not be able to split its own ATP even when the M-B-factor was inhibited by calcium ions during excitation. On the other hand, if the physiological concentration would be lower than 10^{-3} M, the splitting of ATP could not be prevented at all by the M-B-factor.

9. The M-B-factor of rabbit muscle is effective with frog muscles and the smooth adductor of Anodonta. But it does not inhibit the ATP contraction of the models prepared from fibroblasts.

RÉSUMÉ

1. La grande plasticité des muscles et des cellules, nécessaire à la motilité des cellules qui se multiplient et des muscles qui se contractent, est due à l'"effet plastifiant" de l'ATP. En outre, l'ATP provoque le racourcissement nécessaire à la contraction des cellules en voie de multiplication, et celui de tous les muscles lisses ou squelettiques.

2. Dans tous les muscles, l'"effet plastifiant" est dû à la fixation de l'ATP sur la protéine contractile et la contraction est provoquée par la décomposition de l'ATP.

3. L'énergie produite par la décomposition de l'ATP est transmise à la protéine contractile pendant la phase de contraction. Le relâchement a lieu aussitôt que cesse la décomposition d'ATP.

4. Des expériences sur des modèles fibreux de diverses catégories de muscles montrent que ce n'est pas la tension mais la puissance qui est proportionnelle à la vitesse de la libération de l'ATP. En outre, elles indiquent que l'énergie libérée est utilisée avec un bon rendement.

5. Dans des muscles vivants au repos, la décomposition de l'ATP est supprimée par le facteur M-B.

6. L'ATP est décomposé quand le facteur M-B est inactivé par les ions calcium (conditions physiologiques) ou par la caféine.

7. Le facteur M-B rend l'activité ATP-asique de l'actomyosine plus sensible à l'inhibition par le substrat. La concentration optimum en ATP passe de 10^{-2} M en l'absence de facteur à 10^{-3} M en présence de facteur.

8. C'est pourquoi la concentration en ATP des muscles vivants oscille entre 10^{-3} et 10^{-2} M. Si la concentration était plus élevée, le muscle ne pourrait pas décomposer son propre ATP même après inhibition du facteur M-B par les ions calcium pendant l'excitation. Si, au contraire, la concentration physiologique était inférieure à 10^{-3} M, le facteur M-B ne pourrait plus du tout empêcher la décomposition de l'ATP.

9. Le facteur M-B du muscle de lapin est actif sur les muscles de grenouilles et sur le muscle adducteur lisse d'Anodonte. Mais il n'inhibe pas la contraction par l'ATP de modèles préparés à l'aide de fibroblastes.

LITERATUR

[1] O. WARBURG, *Wasserstoffübertragende Fermente*. W. Saenger, Berlin 1948.
   O. WARBURG UND W. CHRISTIAN, *Biochem. Z.* 310 (1941) 384 und 314 (1943) 399.
[2] O. WARBURG, *Schwermetalle als Wirkungsgruppen von Fermenten*, W. Saenger, Berlin 1946.
[3] N. O. KAPLAN, *The Enzymes. Chemistry and Mechanism of Action*. Edited by JAMES B. SUMNER AND KARL MYRBÄCK. Acad. Press. Inc., New York, 1951.
[4] OCHOA, *J. Biol. Chem.* 151 (1943) 493.
[5] F. LIPMANN, *Adv. Enzymol.* 1 (1941) 99.
[6] K. FELIX, *Naturwissensch.*, 40 (1953) 44.
[7] H. HOFFMANN–BERLING, *Biochim. Biophys. Acta*, 10 (1953) 628.
[8] A. WEBER, *Biochim. Biophys. Acta*, 7 (1951) 214.
[9] K. BRECHT UND O. EPPLE, *Pflüg. Arch.* 255 (1952) 315.
[10] A. SZENT GYÖRGYI, *Chemistry of Muscular Contraction*, 2nd Ed., Acad. Press Inc., New York, 1951.
[11] G. UND M. ULBRECHT, *Z. Naturforschg.*, 7b (1952) 434.

[12] L. VARGA, *Hung. Acta. Physiol.*, 1 (1946) 1.
[13] H. PORTZEHL, *Z. Naturforschg.*, 6b (1951) 355.
[14] H. HOFFMANN-BERLING U. H. H. WEBER, *Biochim. Biophys. Acta*, 10 (1953) 629.
[15] W. HASSELBACH, *Z. Naturforschg.*, 7b (1952) 334.
[16] R. W. RAMSEY U. S. W. STREET, *J. Cell. Comp. Physiol.*, 15 (1940) 11.
[17] H. H. WEBER UND H. PORTZEHL, *Progr. Biophys.*, (1953) im Druck.
[18] G. ULBRECHT, *Z. Biol.*, 103 (1950) 278.
[19] H. GASSER UND A. V. HILL, *Proc. Roy. Soc. B.*, 96 (1924) 398.
[20] A. V. HILL, *Proc. Roy. Soc. B.*, 100 (1926) 108.
[21] H. H. WEBER UND H. PORTZEHL, *Erg. Physiol.*, 47 (1952) 369.
[21a] G. STRÖBEL, *Z. Naturforschg.*, 7b (1952) 102.
[22] M. H. DRAPER UND A. J. HODGE, *Austral. J. Exptl. Biol. Med. Science*, 27 (1949) 465.
[23] C. E. HALL, M. A. JAKUS UND F. O. SCHMITT, *Biol. Bull.*, 90 (1946) 32.
[24] C. A. ASHLEY, K. R. PORTER, D. E. PHILPOTT UND G. M. HAAS, *J. Exptl. Med.*, 94 (1951) 9.
[25] J. HANSON, *Nature*, 169 (1952) 530.
[26] S. V. PERRY, *Biochim. Biophys. Acta*, 8 (1952) 483.
[26a] A. G. LOEWY, *J. Cell. Comp. Physiol.*, 40 (1952) 127.
[27] A. SZENT GYÖRGYI, *Biol. Bull.*, 96 (1949) 140.
[28] H. REICHEL, *Erg. Physiol.*, 47 (1952) 469.
[29] B. B. MARSH, *Biochim. Biophys. Acta*, 9 (1952) 247.
[30] J. R. BENDALL, *Proc. Roy. Soc. B*, 139 (1952) 523 und unveröffentlichte Versuche.
[31] W. HASSELBACH UND H. H. WEBER, *Biochim. Biophys. Acta*, 11 (1953) 157.
[32] H. PORTZEHL, *Z. Naturforschg.*, 7b (1952) 1.
[33] E. C. BATE–SMITH UND J. R. BENDALL, *J. Physiol.*, 106 (1947) 177 und 110 (1949) 47.
[34] A. V. HILL, *Proc. Roy. Soc. B*, 136 (1949) 420.
[35] E. WÖHLISCH UND H. G. CLAMANN, *Pflüg. Arch.*, 237 (1936) 590.
[36] F. BUCHTHAL, *Det. Kgl. Dansk. Videnskab. Selskab. Biol. Med.*, 17 (1942) Nr. 2.
[37] S. SPICER UND W. J. BOWEN, *J. Biol. Chem.* 188 (1951) 741.
[38] G. UND M. ULBRECHT, *Biochim. Biophys. Acta*, 11 (1953) 138.
[39] A. V. HILL, *Rev. Canad. Biol.*, 10 (1951) 103.
[40] S. W. KUFFLER, *Ann. N.Y. Acad. Sciences*, 47 (1947) 767 und *J. Neurophysiol.*, 9 (1946) 367.
[41] A. SANDOW, *Yale J. Biol. Med.*, 25 (1952) 176.
[42] A. FLECKENSTEIN, E. WAGNER UND K. H. GÖGEL, *Pflüg. Arch.*, 253 (1950) 38.
[43] A. V. HILL, *Proc. Roy. Soc. B.*, 137 (1950) 40.
[44] E. BOZLER, *Am. J. Physiol.*, 167 (1951) 276.

Eingegangen den 10. April 1953

ENZYMIC STUDIES ON ASCITIC TUMORS AND THEIR HOST'S BLOOD PLASMAS

by

ARTHUR L. SCHADE

*Laboratory of Infectious Diseases, National Microbiological Institute
National Institutes of Health, Public Health Service, U.S. Department of Health,
Education, and Welfare, Bethesda, Md. (U.S.A.)*

INTRODUCTION

OTTO WARBURG, adding to his monumental contributions to the metabolism of tumors[1-3], has continued to direct attention to the high anaerobic metabolic activity of cancer tissues as "indeed the biochemical key to the cancer problem"[4]. In recent investigations of the metabolism of ascites tumor cells[5], WARBURG found that Ehrlich carcinoma ascitic cells possess very high anaerobic $(Q\,N_2/CO_2)$ and aerobic $(Q\,O_2/CO_2)$ glycolytic capacities, of the order of 45 to 55 and 35 to 45 respectively, when analyzed in their own ascitic fluid fresh from the host peritoneal cavity. Since it was shown that both the sugar and oxygen supplies to the tumor cells *in vivo* are relatively small in contrast to their metabolic capacities, WARBURG emphasizes the efficiency of these cells not only to remain alive in the host body but to flourish on the apparently restricted available energy. Further, the interesting observation was made that the aldolase concentration of the ascitic fluid increased several fold when Ehrlich carcinoma ascitic cell suspensions were incubated under anaerobic conditions *in vitro*. The occurrence of relatively high amounts of aldolase in the fresh ascitic fluid as found by WARBURG[5] and others[6] reflects, he believes, the essentially anaerobic conditions under which the tumor cells exist in the peritoneal cavity of the host.

For the past two years we have investigated the metabolism of the dba mouse thymoma[7]. The anaerobic glycolytic Q values for this tumor, in ascitic fluid as well as in Krebs-Ringer carbonate media, ranged from 33 to the unusually high value of 83; — in general, the older the tumor the higher the Q value. The aerobic glycolytic Q values ranged from 8 to 25 and were likewise dependent on tumor age. Stimulated by WARBURG's work on the aldolase concentration of both fresh and anaerobically incubated Ehrlich carcinoma ascitic fluids, we examined thymoma ascitic cell suspensions under similar conditions and extended the observations to include, in addition to aldolase, isomerase and α-glycerophosphate dehydrogenase concentrations in the ascitic fluids from tumors of different ages and in the blood plasmas of the hosts. Comparative investigations were made on the Ehrlich ascites carcinoma in strain C albino mice. Some studies restricted to the aldolase pattern of the Krebs-2 ascites carcinoma in the same host strain were also made. The results of these experiments are presented in this paper.

References p. 171.

EXPERIMENTAL

Materials

The dba mouse ascites thymoma was obtained through the generosity of Dr. T. Hauschka of the Institute for Cancer Research, Philadelphia, Pennsylvania and maintained by serial passage as ascites in dba mice. The Ehrlich ascites carcinoma and the Krebs-2 ascites carcinoma were kindly provided by Dr. V. Evans and Dr. Dean Burk, respectively, of the National Cancer Institute, Bethesda, Maryland and were maintained as ascites in strain C albino mice.

Crystalline aldolase was prepared from rabbit muscle by the method of Warburg and Chris-tian[8]. Crystalline phosphoglyceraldehyde dehydrogenase (oxidizing enzyme) was made from rabbit muscle by the method of Cori, Slein and Cori[9]. Partially purified isomerase containing a trace of a-glycerophosphate dehydrogenase but free of aldolase and phosphoglyceraldehyde dehydrogenase was prepared from rabbit muscle by the method of Meyerhof and Beck[10].

Monomagnesium fructose-1,6-diphosphate (HDP) was purchased from the Schwarz Laboratories, New York, N.Y.; the dioxane addition compound of 1-bromide 3-phosphoglyceraldehyde from the Concord Laboratories, Cambridge, Massachusetts; and the diphosphopyridine nucleotide (DPN), 95% purity, from Nutritional Biochemicals, Cleveland, Ohio. Reduced DPN was prepared by the method given in "Biochemical Preparations"[11].

Methods

The aldolase assay method employed was essentially that described by Warburg and Chris-tian[8]. Each test was run in a cuvette containing: 0.75 ml HDP, pH 7.4 (50 mg/ml); 0.3 ml glycine (20 mg/ml); 0.3 ml Na arsenate (54 mg/ml); 0.15 ml DPN, pH 7.4 (10 mg/ml); 1.2 ml cysteine·HCl, pH 7.4 (7 mg/ml); and 0.01 ml crystalline muscle oxidizing enzyme (25 mg/ml). Five minutes incuba-tion time was allowed for activation of the muscle oxidizing enzyme by the cysteine before addition of the sample to be assayed. The amount of sample used, 0.1 or 0.2 ml, effected a ΔE 1 cm/340 mμ of 0.050 to 0.500 in 10 minutes at room temperature (*ca.* 25° C). The aldolase activity of the sample is given by $W = \Delta \ln I/I^0$/hour, corrected for dilution. Since E 1 cm/340 mμ as obtained in the Beckman spectro-photometer is based on logarithms to the base 10, the readings are multiplied by the factor 2.3 to convert to natural logarithms. One ml of a fluid with a W of 1 is considered to contain one aldolase unit capable of splitting 0.08 μ moles HDP per hour.

Isomerase determination followed, in general, the method described by Warburg and Chris-tian[8]. A 0.03 ml sample to be assayed, or a dilution thereof, was incubated at room temperature with 2 ml of a solution of the dioxane addition compound of phosphoglyceraldehyde-1-Br, containing 5 mg of the compound in 7 ml of 0.01 M phosphate buffer with a final pH of 7.5. After 10 minutes the reac-tion was stopped by the addition of 0.15 ml of N HCl and the mixture allowed to stand for five minutes to destroy the isomerase. The amount of phosphoglyceraldehyde remaining unconverted was determined enzymatically. 1.0 ml of 0.1 M pyrophosphate buffer, pH 7.5; 0.2 ml DPN (10 mg/ml); 0.3 ml Na arsenate (54 mg/ml); 0.5 ml H$_2$O; and 1.0 ml of the neutralized isomerase test reaction mix-ture were put into a cuvette. After the E 1 cm/340 mμ of this mixture was noted, 0.05 ml of an oxidizing enzyme solution, pH 7.4, (10 mg enzyme plus 300 γ cysteine·HCl, per ml) were added and the reaction allowed to go to completion at room temperature (8–10 minutes). A 2 ml aliquot of the original phos-phoglyceraldehyde solution plus 0.03 ml of water in place of the sample for test was assayed in a similar manner to give the amount of substrate originally present. We arbitrarily designate the per-centage of phosphoglyceraldehyde converted to dihydroxyacetone phosphate multiplied by 100 as the isomerase unitage of the sample assayed. Amounts or dilutions of the sample were chosen which converted 20 to 50% of the total phosphoglyceraldehyde in ten minutes. All results are expressed as isomerase units in 0.03 ml of the original sample. On this basis, 0.03 ml of a blood plasma or ascitic fluid with an isomerase activity of unity would convert 0.07 μ moles of phosphoglyceraldehyde to dihydroxyacetone phosphate in 10 minutes.

a-Glycerophosphate dehydrogenase was determined by the decrease in light absorption (Δ log I_0/I) after 3½ minutes at 340 mμ for 1 cm light path at 25° C of 3.1 ml of a solution containing, in addition to the test sample, 200 γ of reduced DPN, 30 mg of HDP, 1200 units of crystalline aldolase and 50,000 units of isomerase. In carrying out the test, all reagents with the exception of the HDP were brought to a volume of 2.7 ml in 0.01 M phosphate buffer, pH 7.5, in a cuvette and read in a Beckman spectrophotometer at 340 mμ. Then, 0.4 ml of HDP solution (30 mg HDP) at pH 7.5 were added and, after 3½ minutes, a reading was again taken. By the use of large amounts of HDP, aldolase, and isomerase, a non-limiting concentration of dihydroxyacetone phosphate was assured as a substrate for reduction to a-glycerophosphate by the reduced DPN under the influence of the dehydrogenase in the added test sample. The $-\Delta E$ 1 cm/340 mμ in 3½ minutes was directly proportional to the volume of test solution added provided the ΔE was not greater than 0.150. For convenience of graphical re-presentation, all a-glycerophosphate dehydrogenase activities are expressed on the basis of the ΔE per 10 minutes per ml of biological fluid.

References p. 171.

For the studies reported here, twenty to thirty mice of the dba or the Calbino strain were inoculated intraperitoneally with 0.2 ml of a 6- or 7-day old appropriate ascites tumor cell suspension. At time of inoculation, usually four mice were sacrificed and bled. The pooled plasma was analyzed for the enzymes aldolase, isomerase, and α-glycerophosphate dehydrogenase. After five days, in the case of the Ehrlich carcinoma, and six days for the thymoma, 4 to 6 animals were killed and bled. The ascitic cell suspensions were removed from the peritoneal cavities and pooled after addition of 0.1 mg of heparin per ml of suspension. Aliquots of the ascitic cell suspension were put into two ordinary Warburg respirometer vessels, gassed with 95% N_2 plus 5% CO_2 in one case and with 95% O_2 plus 5% CO_2 in the other, and shaken gently for one and a half hours at 37° C to keep the cells from sedimenting. The suspensions were then centrifuged at 500 g for 10 minutes at room temperature in a horizontal centrifuge. The cell-free ascitic fluids were analyzed and the results compared with those obtained with the ascitic fluid from an aliquot of the same cell suspension centrifuged immediately after removal from the animals.

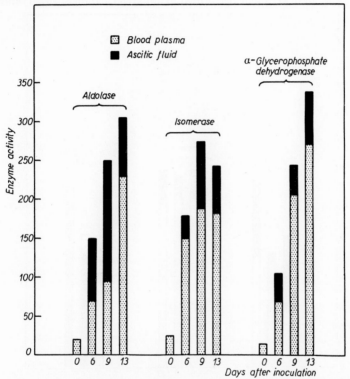

Fig. 1. dba Ascites thymoma. Aldolase, isomerase, and α-glycerophosphate dehydrogenase concentrations in blood plasma of normal dba mice, and in blood plasma and ascitic fluid of dba mice 6, 9, and 13 days after intraperitoneal inoculation with dba ascites thymoma.

RESULTS

A summary of results from a typical experiment with the ascites thymoma in dba mice is given in Fig. 1 which illustrates a comparison of the enzyme activity levels for aldolase, isomerase and α-glycerophosphate dehydrogenase in the blood plasma and fresh ascitic fluid of animals sacrificed 6, 9, and 13 days after tumor inoculation. With this tumor, under the cultural conditions employed, the fifth or sixth day after inoculation was the earliest that the tumor had sufficiently developed (0.5 to 1.0 ml) to permit rapid and convenient accumulation of adequate ascitic cell suspension for the tests reported. By 13 days, 4 to 7 ml of tumor material per animal were available and the host was

References p. 171.

often moribund. From Fig. 1 it is evident that the concentrations of the three enzymes in the blood plasmas of the tumorous mice were increased over the normal controls. Aldolase and α-glycerophosphate dehydrogenase concentrations rose steeply to 13 and 20 times, respectively, the normal values with increasing age of the tumor while the isomerase remained essentially constant over the observed tumor growth period of 6 to 13 days at the 6 to 7 fold elevated level. The ascitic fluids obtained from ascitic tumor cell suspensions 6, 9, and 13 days after inoculation into the hosts all showed enzyme levels significantly greater than those found in the companion blood plasmas.

Fig. 2 summarizes typical data obtained with the Ehrlich ascites carcinoma in strain C albino mice from an experiment performed in a manner parallel to that employed with

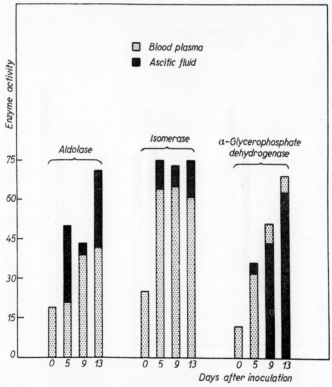

Fig. 2. Ehrlich ascites carcinoma. Aldolase, isomerase, and α-glycerophosphate dehydrogenase concentrations in blood plasma of normal strain C albino mice, and in blood plasma and ascitic fluid of strain C albino mice 5, 9, and 13 days after intraperitoneal inoculation with Ehrlich ascites carcinoma.

the dba thymoma and described above. Under our conditions, the Ehrlich ascites carcinoma developed at such a rate that 0.5 to 1.0 ml of ascitic cell suspension was conveniently available one day earlier than with the dba thymoma. Death of the hosts of both tumors, however, ensued after the same lapse of time, 13 to 14 days on the average. As is seen from Fig. 2, the level of the several enzymes in the blood plasmas of the tumor bearing mice compared to that of the normal was sharply elevated in a way qualitatively similar to that found with the dba thymoma. Quantitatively the rise was much less, being only 2 to 3 fold for aldolase and isomerase and 6 fold for the α-glycerophosphate dehydrogenase. With the exception of the concentration of the dehydrogenase in the

References p. 171.

ascitic fluids of the 9- and 13-day old tumors, the levels of activity of all three enzymes in the ascitic fluids were greater than those of the assiociated plasmas. Repeated experiments with the Ehrlich ascites carcinoma showed the α-glycerophosphate dehydrogenase concentrations in both the ascitic fluid and the blood plasma to be comparable or slightly in favour of the blood plasma while the other two enzymes were always in greater concentrations in the ascitic fluids.

After aliquots of the several ascitic cell suspensions of both the dba thymoma and the Ehrlich ascites carcinoma were incubated in nitrogen and in oxygen for 90 minutes,

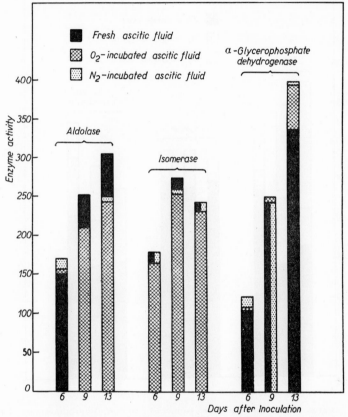

Fig. 3. dba ascites thymoma. Aldolase, isomerase, and α-glycerophosphate dehydrogenase concentrations in fresh ascitic fluid and in ascitic fluid incubated in N_2 and in O_2, of dba mice 6, 9, and 13 days after intraperitoneal inoculation with dba ascites thymoma.

the cells were centrifuged off and the enzyme levels of the ascitic fluids were determined. The results obtained were then compared with the values earlier established for the aldolase, isomerase, and α-glycerophosphate dehydrogenase activity of the fresh ascitic fluids.

Fig. 3 presents the data recorded for the dba thymoma. With this tumor there was no significant increase in the aldolase or isomerase activity of the ascitic fluids as a result of the anaerobic incubation of the ascitic cell suspensions. The incubation in oxygen effected a slight decrease in aldolase activity of the fluids from older tumor cell suspensions while it appeared to affect little, if at all, their isomerase activity. Only with respect to the α-glycerophosphate dehydrogenase was there a suggestion that incubation in nitrogen, under our conditions, led to an increase in the activity of this enzyme in the ascitic fluids. However, since comparable increases in activity were observed in those fluids from cell suspensions incubated in oxygen, the small enzymatic activity rise (*ca.* 17%) was not attributable to anaerobiosis.

Fig. 4 summarizes the data obtained with the Ehrlich ascites carcinoma maintained n nitrogen and oxygen atmospheres. The results contrast strikingly with those ob-

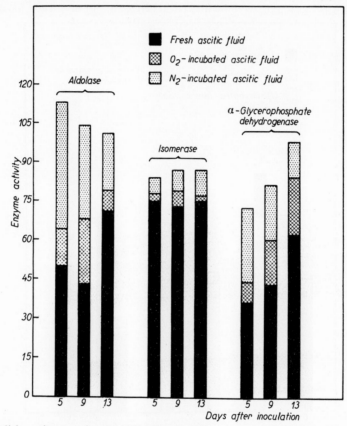

Fig. 4. Ehrlich ascites carcinoma. Aldolase, isomerase, and α-glycerophosphate dehydrogenase concentrations in fresh ascitic fluid and in ascitic fluid incubated in N_2 and in O_2, of strain C albino mice 5, 9, and 13 days after intraperitoneal inoculation with Ehrlich ascites carcinoma.

served for the dba thymoma. Here, with the Ehrlich carcinoma, incubation of the ascites cell suspensions in nitrogen led to large increases in the aldolase concentration of the ascitic fluids as already reported by WARBURG AND HIEPLER[5]. Comparable increases were observed in the α-glycerophosphate dehydrogenase concentrations, while definite, though smaller, rises in the isomerase levels also occurred. Incubation in oxygen resulted in some rise in the concentration of all three enzymes in the ascitic fluids but of less magnitude. In all our experiments with the Ehrlich ascites tumor, anaerobic incubation of the cell suspensions always led to increase in these enzymic activities of the ascitic fluid while aerobic incubation resulted in slight reduction, in no change, or in some increase in activity.

References p. 171.

The difference in response to anaerobic incubation of the Ehrlich ascites carcinoma and of the dba ascites thymoma might be ascribed in part to the differences in cell volume per ml of the cell suspensions of the two tumors. The cell volume of the Ehrlich tumor cell suspension generally comprised 35 to 25% of the total while that of the dba tumor cell suspension varied from 30 to 15% of the combined cell and ascitic fluid volume. The higher percentages were associated with the younger tumors (5- to 6-day old). However, when we brought the cell volume of a 10-day old thymoma cell suspension up to that of a 10-day old Ehrlich tumor suspension (295 mm³ cells/ml suspension) and incubated both suspensions anaerobically for one and one-half hours, we observed only an 18% increase in aldolase activity of the thymoma ascitic fluid compared to a 327% increase in that of the Ehrlich carcinoma. The corresponding values for the a-glycerophosphate dehydrogenase were 40% and 265% increase in activity of the treated samples over that of the freshly drawn ascitic fluids. It is of interest to note that the per cent increases of both enzyme concentrations following anaerobic incubation of the Ehrlich ascites carcinoma were unusually high. Our evidence suggests that this fact is due to the preliminary centrifugation of the cell suspensions (500 g) carried out with both tumors followed by resuspension in their respective ascitic fluids to increase the thymoma cell concentration to its proper value and to have a fitting control in the Ehrlich carcinoma. Worthy of further note is the fact that the percentage rise in enzyme concentration in the incubated ascitic fluid of the Ehrlich tumor was disproportionately dependent upon the per cent cell volume. For example, in the experiment just cited, when we reduced the Ehrlich tumor cell volume from 295 to 148 mm³ per ml of cell suspension, the percentage increase in aldolase activity of the incubated ascitic fluid over that of the fresh fluid was only 67% rather than the 327% increase of the 2 fold more concentrated cell suspension in the same ascitic fluid. The percentage increase values of the a-glycero phosphate dehydrogenase concentrations were likewise disproportionately lower, namely, 56%, in comparison with the 265% of the 2 times concentrated cell suspension.

In an attempt to determine the relative concentrations of aldolase and of a-glycerophosphate dehydrogenase in the cells of both the Ehrlich carcinoma and the dba thymoma with respect to their ascitic fluids, we prepared homogenates of cells of both tumors before and after incubation in nitrogen. For this purpose glass homogenizers, cooled in an ice bath, were used and the cells were extracted by two (for Ehrlich carcinoma) and four (for dba thymoma) repeated homogenizations with physiological saline. The results showed that, volume for volume, the cells of both tumors contained essentially equivalent concentrations of the two enzymes. In the case of the Ehrlich ascites carcinoma, the concentration of aldolase in one ml of packed fresh cells was approximately 116 times the concentration found in one ml of ascitic fluid while one ml of packed fresh thymoma cells contained roughly 25 times the concentration of aldolase found in one ml of the fluid. The corresponding values for a-glycerophosphate dehydrogenase concentrations were 45 for the Ehrlich tumor cells and 18 for the thymoma tumor cells. In the course of extraction of the nitrogen incubated cells it was noted that with respect to both enzymes of the dba thymoma, 85 to 90% of the total in the cells was extracted into the saline solution after two homogenizations, the first accounting for 60% of the total, while four treatments were required of the fresh cells to give comparable (85–90%) yields, the first homogenization of the four yielding only 25 to 30% of the total. With the nitrogen incubated Ehrlich tumor cells, almost all of the aldolase and a-glycerophosphate dehydrogenase was extracted in the first homogenization while the fresh cells still contained some activity following the second homogenization.

Aldolase levels were determined in the ascitic fluids of Krebs-2 ascites carcinoma cell suspensions as they were removed fresh from the hosts and after the suspensions were incubated in nitrogen and in oxygen. The results showed that the Krebs-2 tumor, with respect to both the absolute levels of aldolase in the ascitic fluid and the heightened levels in the anaerobically incubated aliquots, was similar to the Ehrlich ascites carcinoma. The response of this tumor cell suspension to aerobic incubation also led to the same conclusion.

DISCUSSION

The increase in concentration of aldolase, isomerase, and α-glycerophosphate dehydrogenase in the blood plasmas of both the albino C and dba strains of mice bearing the Ehrlich carcinoma and thymoma ascitic tumors respectively is apparently a reflection of the generally higher concentrations of these enzymes in the ascitic fluids associated with the tumors growing as discrete cell suspensions in the peritoneal cavity of the hosts. That the tumor cells serve, at least in part if not entirely, as the source of these enzymes appears probable since, as shown most readily with the Ehrlich and Krebs-2 carcinoma, short time anaerobic *in vitro* incubation of the tumor cell suspensions led to greatly increased enzyme concentrations in the ascitic fluids. As WARBURG has pointed out[5], the *in vivo* conditions during the development of the Ehrlich ascites tumor are essentially anaerobic as a consequence of the very high metabolic capacity of the tumor and the relatively restricted supply of oxygen.

Although the intracellular concentrations of these enzymes are many times those found in the ascitic fluids and although the anaerobic conditions apparently obtaining within the peritoneum are conducive to loss of some of these enzymes from the cells to the ascitic fluid, it is improbable that their relatively high concentration in the fluid is solely the result of passive loss from the tumor cells. We are led to consider the fact that the dba thymoma, despite its relative refractivity to loss of these enzymes from its cells to the ascitic fluid under *in vitro* anaerobic conditions, did show enzyme concentrations in the ascitic fluid of the dba mouse 3 to 4 times as high as the Ehrlich ascites carcinoma in the strain C albino mouse. That this observation derives from the behaviour of the tumor rather than reflects a particular host response was demonstrated by our injecting the Ehrlich ascites carcinoma into the dba strain mouse. The enzyme levels in the blood plasma samples as well as in the ascitic fluids of the dba mice after appropriate intervals following inoculation were similar to those of the Ehrlich tumor in the strain C albino host.

ACKNOWLEDGEMENTS

It is a pleasure gratefully to acknowledge the ever valuable collaboration of my colleague, Dr. HILTON LEVY, in this investigation. To Mr. ROBERT REINHART and Mr. LEROY SNELLBAKER I am indebted for their most helpful technical assistance.

SUMMARY

OTTO WARBURG's finding that the aldolase concentration in the ascitic fluid of the Ehrlich ascites carcinoma increases significantly upon anaerobic *in vitro* incubation was confirmed. dba thymoma ascitic cell suspensions from dba mice were investigated under similar conditions and the ob-

References p. 171.

servations extended to include, in addition to aldolase, both isomerase and α-glycerophosphate dehydrogenase concentrations in the ascitic fluids from tumors of different ages and in the blood plasmas of the hosts. Comparative studies were made on the Ehrlich ascites carcinoma in strain C albino mice.

RÉSUMÉ

Ainsi que l'avait déjà montré OTTO WARBURG, la concentration en aldolase du liquide des ascites provoquées par le sarcome d'Ehrlich augmente nettement après incubation anaérobie *in vitro*. Les auteurs ont examiné dans des conditions analogues des suspensions de cellules ascitiques de tumeurs du thymus de souris dba et déterminé, outre la concentration en aldolase, les concentrations en isomérase et en α-glycérophosphate déshydrogénase dans les liquides ascitiques de tumeurs de différents âges et dans le plasma sanguin des hôtes. Des études comparatives ont été faites sur les ascites du sarcome d'Ehrlich chez des souris albinos de souche C.

ZUSAMMENFASSUNG

OTTO WARBURGS Entdeckung, dass die Aldolasekonzentration in der Ascitenflüssigkeit des Ehrlich'schen Ascitescarcinoms bei anaerobischer Inkubation *in vitro* bedeutend ansteigt wurde bekräftigt. Dba-thymomaascitenzellsuspensionen aus Dba-Mäusen wurden unter ähnlichen Bedingungen untersucht und die Beobachtungen, in Anlehnung an Aldose, auf die Isomerase- und α-Glycerophosphatdehydrogenasekonzentration in der Ascitenflüssigkeit von Tumoren verschiedenen Alters und in dem Blutplasma des Wirtes ausgedehnt. Vergleichende Untersuchungen wurden am Ehrlich'schen Ascitencarcinom in Albinomäusen des Stammes C unternommen.

REFERENCES

[1] O. WARBURG, *Stoffwechsel der Tumoren*, Verlag Springer, Berlin, 1926.
[2] O. WARBURG AND W. CHRISTIAN, *Biochem. Z.*, 314 (1943) 399.
[3] O. WARBURG, *Math.-naturw. Abh. d. Deutsch. Akad. d. Wissensch. z.*, Berlin, (1947) Nr. 3.
[4] O. WARBURG, personal communication, Dec. 1952.
[5] O. WARBURG AND E. HIEPLER, *Z. Naturforsch.*, 7b (1952) 193.
[6] E. KUN, P. TALALAY AND H. G. WILLIAMS-ASHMAN, *Cancer Research*, 11 (1951) 855.
[7] H. B. LEVY, H. DAVIDSON, R. REINHART AND A. L. SCHADE. *Cancer Research*, in press.
[8] O. WARBURG AND W. CHRISTIAN, *Biochem. Z.*, 314 (1943) 149.
[9] G. CORI, M. SLEIN AND C. CORI, *J. Biol. Chem.*, 159 (1945) 565.
[10] O. MEYERHOF AND L. BECK, *J. Biol. Chem.*, 156 (1944) 109.
[11] H. E. CARTER, *Biochemical Preparations*, Vol. 2, John Wiley & Sons, New York 1952.

Received April 13th, 1953

SOME REACTIONS OF ADENOSINE AND INOSINE PHOSPHATES IN ANIMAL TISSUES*

by

H. A. KREBS AND R. HEMS

*Medical Research Council Unit for Research in Cell Metabolism,
Department of Biochemistry, The University of Sheffield (England)*

The starting point of the present investigations was the observation that inosine triphosphate (ITP), on addition to respiring pigeon breast muscle suspensions, becomes radioactive when $^{32}PO_4$ is present. Such suspensions readily synthesise adenosine triphosphate (ATP) from adenosine diphosphate (ADP) and inorganic orthophosphate, and the formation of isotopic ITP raised the question whether inosine diphosphate (IDP) can replace ADP in the enzyme system forming the triphosphate. The experiments reported in this paper show that this is not the case. ITP does not arise by synthesis from IDP and inorganic phosphate but by transfer of isotopic phosphate from ATP to IDP.

MATERIALS AND METHODS

The ATP preparations were the same as those used in previous work from this laboratory (EGGLESTON AND HEMS[1]; KREBS, RUFFO, JOHNSON, EGGLESTON AND HEMS[2]. ITP was prepared according to KLEINZELLER[3]. Both preparations contained some diphosphates; the quantities of these are given in the Tables as the zero values. Radioactive ATP, containing ^{32}P in the two terminal phosphate groups of ATP, was prepared according to HEMS AND BARTLEY[4].

The quantities of the various adenosine and inosine phosphates in the enzyme solution were determined paper chromatographically by a modification of the method of EGGLESTON AND HEMS[1]. The original method separates the three adenosine phosphates from other phosphates, including ITP, the R_F value of the latter being lower than that of ATP. But the R_F value of IDP and ATP, and of IMP and ADP, are about the same in the solvents used by EGGLESTON AND HEMS[1]. The following modification satisfactorily separates the three inosine and adenosine phosphates. At a first ascending stage the inorganic orthophosphate, having the highest R_F value, is separated from all other phosphates and the paper containing it is cut off. The chromatography is then continued in the opposite direction with a different solvent. The new procedure is quicker than the earlier one. It can handle larger amounts of material and is less affected by the presence of salts and by variations of temperature. The relative R_F values of the adenosine and inosine phosphates are as follows: AMP, 1.0; ADP, 0.80; ATP, 0.66; IMP, 0.53; IDP, 0.39; ITP, 0.26.

Whatman No. 1 filter papers (20 × 60 cm) are washed in aqueous ethylenediamine tetra-acetic acid by the method described by EGGLESTON AND HEMS[1] and, after drying, the papers are folded along a line 18 cm from one end, dividing the paper into two parts, a longer one subsequently called A and a shorter one B.

Solutions to be analysed and standard marker solutions, including $KH_2{}^{32}PO_4$, are placed in 5 μl quantities at intervals of about 3 cm on a line 3 cm from the fold on B. The spots are dried in a current of warm air from a hair drier, at a temperature not higher than 30°. By placing up to ten 5 μl quantities of solution on one spot with an "Agla" micrometer syringe, between 2 and 10 μg total P are accumulated on each spot.

The paper required has to be longer than the commercially available size** and an extension piece, with a pad, is made as follows: an (unwashed) paper (20 × 40 cm) is folded over half its length to form a pad 2 cm wide and this is attached to the end of B with a stapling machine, whilst the other end of

---

* This work was aided by a grant from the Rockefeller Foundation.
** 100 ft lengths of this paper have now become commercially available.

References p. 180.

the extension is fastened to A with two paper clips (see diagram). The end of A is then folded to provide a flap of about 2 cm to be attached to the lid of the glass tank. The exact measurements depend on the distance between the lid and the surface of the solvent. About 1.5 cm of the papers should be immersed in the solvent at the bottom of the tank.

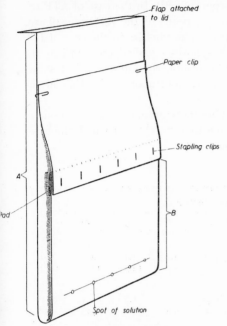

Fig. 1. Folding of filter paper for chromatographic analysis.

Glass tanks for ascending and descending chromatography are of the shape described by EGGLESTON AND HEMS[1]; for descending chromatography they are fitted with a framework of glass rods which carries two glass troughs 28 cm long and holding 70–80 ml of solvent[5].

Two solvents are used. The first consists of 90 ml *iso*propyl ether/60 ml 90% (w/v) formic acid (HANES AND ISHERWOOD[6]); the second of 100 ml *iso*butyric acid, 60 ml N ammonia, 1.6 ml 0.1 M ethylene diamine tetraacetic acid. This is a modification of the solvent described by ZETTERSTRÖM AND LJUNGGREN[7].

The papers are developed first for 3–4 hrs by ascending chromatography in the first solvent. They are then removed from the tank and, whilst still fastened to the lid, dried in a current of cold air. This takes about 30 min. When dry the papers are detached from the lid, and the paper clips are removed so that the whole length of the paper can be spread out flat. The position of the orthophosphate is then located by scanning with a radiation monitor (Alpha Beta Type 1021 B; Messrs McMichael Radio Ltd., Slough, Bucks). When ^{32}P is not present in the experimental solution it is added as a marker to make location of the orthophosphate possible without chemical treatment of the paper. The nucleotides are located by their U.V. absorption with a "Hanovia Chromatolite" (Hanovia Ltd., 3 Victoria St., London, S.W.1). The paper carrying the orthophosphate is cut off from the remainder of the chromatogram and kept for the analysis of orthophosphate. The nucleotides stay near the starting line, and sufficient paper is left to form a "wick" for the descending chromatography with the second solvent. The direction of flow of this solvent is opposite to that of the first. After 16–18 h the papers are removed and dried by heating for 20 min at 80°. The positions of the nucleotides are located with the U.V. light and ringed in pencil. The identity of the spots is confirmed by spraying with the acid molybdate according to HANES AND ISHERWOOD[6].

The spots are cut out, wet-ashed and analysed for phosphorus and radioactivity as described by EGGLESTON AND HEMS[1].

Enzyme material deproteinised with trichloroacetic acid is suitable for the above procedure. Samples of deproteinised solutions which could not be analysed immediately were stored at —14°.

RESULTS

Reactivity of ATP and ITP-phosphorus in pigeon breast muscle

Pigeon breast muscle was minced in a Lapatie mill and disintegrated in a stainless steel "homogeniser" of the Potter-Elvehjem type with 21.5 volumes of the medium used by KREBS *et al.*[2], all operations being carried out with ice-cooled containers and reagents. Of this suspension 3 ml, together with 1 ml additional solution containing substrates and cofactors, were shaken in Warburg manometers at 20°. The gas space contained O_2. The final concentration of the substrate (α-ketoglutarate) was 0.02 M, of ATP about 0.0006 M, of ITP 0.0008 M. Inorganic phosphate containing ^{32}P was added from a side arm at zero time. Enzymic activities were stopped by the addition of 0.5 ml 30% trichloroacetic acid. The phosphate fractions were separated by paper chromatographic analysis of the filtrate.

References p. 180.

The results of an experiment are summarised in Table I. During the first 20 mins the concentrations of inorganic phosphate, ATP and ITP remained fairly constant. A small rise in the concentration of ITP was probably due to the presence of IDP in the starting material. Both ATP and ITP rapidly incorporated ^{32}P. In the case of ATP the rate of incorporation slowed down when the specific activity of the ATP phosphorus equalled two-thirds of the specific activity of inorganic phosphorus. In the case of ITP the rate fell when the specific activity of ITP phosphorus equalled one-third of the specific activity of inorganic phosphates. The last horizontal column of Table I shows that the specific activity of ATP phosphorus was throughout about twice that of the specific activity of the ITP phosphorus.

The results of this experiment show that two phosphate groups of ATP and one of ITP readily interchange with inorganic phosphate and that the rates at which the three different phosphate groups concerned react are about equal.

TABLE I

INCORPORATION OF INORGANIC PHOSPHATE INTO ATP AND ITP IN PIGEON BREAST MUSCLE SUSPENSIONS
(For experimental conditions see text)

Period of incubation (mins)	0	3	6	9	20	60
Inorganic phosphate						
amount (μg/40 μl)	4.31	4.26	4.23	4.17	4.59	6.61
specific activity (counts/min/μg P)	1962	1365	1336	1290	1106	1078
ATP-phosphorus						
amount (μg/40 μl)	1.32	1.44	1.49	1.20	1.37	0.16
specific activity (counts/min/μg P)	0	521	576	627	725	835
ITP-phosphorus						
amount (μg/40 μl)	2.04	2.65	2.68	2.11	2.14	0.78
specific activity (counts/min/μg P)	0	236	303	326	350	400
Ratio specific activity of ATP-phosphorus / specific activity of inorganic phosphate		0.382	0.431	0.485	0.655	0.777
Ratio specific activity of ITP-phosphorus / specific activity of inorganic phosphate		0.173	0.227	0.253	0.317	0.372
Ratio specific activity of ATP-phosphorus / specific activity of ITP phosphorus		2.21	1.90	1.92	2.07	2.09

Action of myokinase (adenylate phosphokinase) on ITP

It seemed feasible that an incorporation of ^{32}P into ITP was brought about by myokinase if IDP could replace ADP. Mixtures of ITP, IDP and IMP, and of ITP, IDP and AMP were added to myokinase, prepared from pigeon breast muscle according to KALCKAR[8]. Under the conditions used, as described by EGGLESTON AND HEMS[1], adenosine phosphates reached equilibrium concentrations in less than 45 mins. In contrast the concentrations of inosine phosphates did not change. Thus myokinase is not responsible for the reactions of ITP.

Hydrolysis of ITP by muscle tissue

The incorporation of ^{32}P into ITP requires probably two separate steps, the first being the fission of ITP into IDP, the second the reversal of this reaction. The first step was studied by investigating the decomposition of ITP in various enzyme preparations.

References p. 180.

TABLE II

HYDROLYSIS OF ITP AND ATP BY PIGEON BREAST MUSCLE SUSPENSIONS

(For experimental conditions see text. The initial value for inorganic P was mainly derived from the saline medium. No AMP was detectable among the products.)

		Quantity of P found (µg P for 40 µl deproteinised solution) after				
		0 min.	3 min.	6 min.	20 min.	60 min.
Substrate	ITP	2.76	1.88	1.38	0.77	0.25
ITP	IDP	1.34	1.97	2.30	2.62	2.60
and	IMP	∼0	∼0	∼0	0.31	0.45
IDP	inorg. ortho P	1.28	1.55	1.79	1.92	2.69
Substrate	ATP	2.35	1.81	1.47	0.59	0
ATP	ADP	1.83	0.57	0.41	0.22	0
and	IMP	∼0	0.78	1.02	1.49	1.74
ADP	inorg. ortho-P	1.48	2.14	2.37	3.67	4.42

Whilst it is well known that both ITP and ATP are hydrolysed by animal tissues (KLEINZELLER[3]; SPICER AND BOWEN[9]) it was thought desirable to obtain data on the relative rates of hydrolysis in the enzyme preparations used in the present work. Pigeon breast muscle was disintegrated in calcium-free saline as described before. The final suspension contained 1% tissue, $1.25 \cdot 10^{-3}$ M $MgCl_2$ and inosine and adenosine phosphates in the quantities stated under zero time in Table II. The solutions were incubated at 20° in Thunberg tubes in vacuo. The results are given in Table II. The rates of disappearance of ATP and ITP were of the same order; initially ITP reacted a little faster than ATP. The main product of the decomposition of ITP was IDP. No IMP was detectable in the early stages but small amounts appeared after 20 and 60 mins. The main end product of the decomposition of ATP was IMP. The yield of this substance and of the inorganic phosphate indicated a partial hydrolysis of IMP. ADP did not accumulate; the ADP initially present gradually decreased. No AMP appeared. Muscle tissue is known to possess at least two different enzymes capable of hydrolysing ATP – myosin-ATPase and a "soluble" ATPase. Myosin was prepared according to BAILEY[10] from pigeon breast muscle. 20 grams of muscle yielded 50 ml solution of myosin in 0.5 M KCl. The soluble ATPase was prepared from rat leg muscle according to KIELLEY AND MEYERHOF[11]. The details of the experimental conditions and the results of the experiments are given in Tables III and IV. Both enzymes behaved similarly: when the substrates were added separately they were both split. As measured by the liberation of inorganic phosphate the rate of hydrolysis of ITP was a little slower than that of ATP. But when added together the rates were not additive; on the contrary the formation of inorganic phosphate was slower in a mixture of ATP and ITP than with ATP alone. The observations may

TABLE III

HYDROLYSIS OF ATP AND ITP BY MYOSIN

Each test tube contained 1 ml myosin solution, 0.1 ml 0.11 M $CaCl_2$, 0.5 ml 0.5 M triethanolamine buffer of pH 7.4, substrate as indicated below, water to 5.0 ml, 25°. Inorganic P determined according to LOWRY AND LOPEZ[19]. Substrate (1 ml each 0.01 M): I: ATP; II: ITP; III: ATP and ITP

Time (mins)	µg inorganic P formed in 0.1 ml solution I	II	III
20	2.18	1.53	1.69
40	4.40	2.52	3.10

be taken to indicate that the two nucleotide triphosphates are hydrolysed by the same enzymes and that they competitively inhibit the decomposition.

TABLE IV

HYDROLYSIS OF ATP AND ITP BY SOLUBLE ATPase

Each test tube contained 1 ml enzyme solution, 0.15 ml 0.1 M MgCl$_2$, 0.2 ml 0.5 M triethanolamine buffer pH 7.4, and substrate as indicated below. Water to 5.5 ml. 30°. Inorganic P determined according to LOWRY AND LOPEZ[19]. Substrate (1 ml each 0.01 M) I: ATP; II: ITP; III: ATP and ITP.

Time (mins)	μg inorganic P formed in 0.1 ml solutions		
	I	II	III
5	1.6	0.5	1.2
15	3.3	2.5	2.8
30	4.6	3.2	4.4
45	5.7	3.3	5.2

Anaerobic transfer of phosphate from ATP to ITP

The synthesis of ITP from IDP and inorganic phosphate could be a direct reversal of the hydrolysis; if this were the case ITP should become radioactive when incubated with $^{32}PO_4$ anaerobically in the presence of ITPases. Experiments however show that this is not the case. Alternatively, inorganic phosphate might first be incorporated into ATP, *e.g.* by oxidative phosphorylation, and the radioactivity of ITP could then arise by transfer of ATP phosphorus to IDP. The following experiment is evidence in support of this mechanism. Pigeon breast muscle was disintegrated as described before and suspended in 73 ml saline medium and 1 ml 0.1 M MgCl$_2$; 1.6 ml of this suspension was incubated at 22° anaerobically with 0.2 ml isotopic ATP (about 0.0055 M, ^{32}P in β-and γ-phosphate) and 0.2 ml non-isotopic ITP (0.009 M). Nine parallel tubes were set up and the incubation was stopped at various intervals by the addition of 0.2 ml 30% (w/v) trichloroacetic acid. The results of the analyses are shown in Table V. The amounts of ATP gradually fell and reached zero value after about 10 min. The specific activity of the ATP phosphorus remained virtually constant, indicating that no ATP was synthesized. There was some initial radioactivity in the ITP phosphorus and inorganic phosphorus which was due to the presence of these substances in the sample of radioactive ATP. The amounts of ITP decreased slowly only as long as appreciable quantities of ATP were present, *i.e.* during the first 6 min. Afterwards it decreased rapidly. The specific

TABLE V

ANAEROBIC TRANSFER OF PHOSPHATE FROM ATP TO ITP IN PIGEON BREAST MUSCLE SUSPENSIONS
(For experimental conditions see text)

Time (mins)	ATP phosphorus		ITP phosphorus		Inorganic P amounts (μg in 40 μl solution)
	amounts (μg in 40 μl solution)	specific activity (cts min. μg P)	amounts (μg in 40 μl solution)	specific activity (cts min. μg P)	
0	1.56	889	2.46	63	1.52
2	1.19	900	2.57	163	1.95
4	0.86	919	2.32	246	2.27
6	0.54	827	2.35	241	2.76
9	0.19		2.12	316	2.94
12	0		1.64	303	3.12
20	0		0.61	318	3.52
40	0		0.21		4.30
60	0		0.17		4.05

activity of the ITP phosphorus rose rapidly even during the first 6 min when its concentration hardly changed. The specific activity reached a maximum when all ATP had broken down and then remained constant. These findings can be explained by the assumption that both ATP and ITP are hydrolysed by the muscle preparation and that the IDP formed is rephosphorylated by ATP; in other words that the muscle suspension contains an enzyme capable of transferring a phosphate group of ATP to IDP.

To test whether this transfer is brought about by one of the known enzymes a similar experiment was carried out where the myosin ATPase of BAILEY[10] replaced the pigeon breast muscle suspension. The incubated solution contained β-γ-labelled ATP, non-isotopic ITP and IDP, 0.002 M $CaCl_2$, 0.02 M triethanolamine buffer pH 7.4, and 2 ml myosin in a total volume of 10 ml. Both ATP and ITP were hydrolysed but there was no change in the specific activity of the two substances. The enzyme preparation used therefore did not transfer ATP phosphorus. Another experiment with the soluble ATPase of KIELLEY AND MEYERHOF[11], where $CaCl_2$ was replaced by $MgCl_2$, also failed to indicate a transfer.

On the other hand a dialysed crude extract of rat intestinal mucosa effected a rapid transfer of radiophosphorus from ATP to ITP. When added separately to extracts the two substrates were hydrolysed at about the same rate (70 micrograms P formed per mg dry/wt per h at 38° and pH 8.7). As expected[9,12] all three phosphate groups were split off.

The phosphate transfer is shown in the following experiment. The mucosa was scraped off the rat ileum and disintegrated with 10 volumes of water. The suspension was filtered through glass wool and the filtrate was dialysed against water for 1 h to reduce the concentration of inorganic phosphate. 2 ml dialysed enzyme solution, 2 ml β-γ-labelled ATP (containing some ADP; ATP + ADP phosphorus about 0.01 M), 2 ml non-isotopic ITP (containing some IDP; ITP + IDP phosphorus about 0.01 M), 0.4 ml 0.2 M triethanolamine buffer pH 7.4 and 3.6 ml water were incubated at 30°. At intervals 1 ml samples were removed and deproteinised with 0.1 ml 30% trichloroacetic acid. The results of the analyses are shown in Table VI. The concentration of ATP progressively decreased and unlike in previous experiments the specific activity of ATP phosphorus also fell. The concentration of ITP changed little in the earlier stages of incubation, but as before decreased more rapidly when the concentration of ATP had fallen to a low value. The specific activity of ITP rose rapidly as long as ATP was present. The concentration and radioactivity of inorganic phosphate rose as expected. There was also an increase in the quantities of IMP and AMP, but this was less than expected on the assumption that these substances were the only end products. No transfer occurred under the same conditions when ITP was replaced by IMP or glucose.

The results can be explained by the assumption that in addition to the hydrolysis of the pyrophosphates a reversible transfer of phosphorus takes place between ATP and ITP. The fall of the specific activity of ATP indicates that ATP must be formed during the incubation. Under the given conditions the transfer of phosphate of ITP to ADP is the only feasible mechanism of ATP formation.

Crude extracts of the intestine are known to contain relatively large amounts of alkaline phosphatases and the preceding experiment was therefore repeated with a commercial preparation (Armour Laboratories) of purified calf intestinal phosphatase. This was prepared according to SCHMIDT AND THANNHAUSER[12] and is stated to contain 15 units/mg. Both ATP and ITP were hydrolysed but the rate of decomposition was slow compared with that of the hydrolysis of glycerophosphate[12]. At 30° at pH 7.4, 170 μg P were released from ATP per mg dry/wt per hr. No transfer of phosphate took place.

TABLE VI

TRANSFER OF PHOSPHATE FROM ATP TO ITP IN RAT INTESTINAL MUCOSA

(The data refer to quantities found in 25 μl of deproteinised solution. For experimental details see text.)

Time (mins)	ATP amount (µgP/25 µl)	ATP specific activity (cts/min/µgP)	ITP amount (µgP/25 µl)	ITP specific activity (cts/min/µgP)	inorg. P amount (µgP/25 µl)	inorg. P specific activity (cts/min/µgP)	ADP (µgP/25 µl)	IDP (µg P/25 µl)	AMP (µg P/25 µl)	IMP (µgP/25 µl)
0	2.64	3790	2.57	148	1.00	1110	1.82	2.17	0.35	0.74
5	2.29	3210	2.58	425	1.26	1290				
10	2.05	3090	2.27	667	1.44	1595				
15	2.01	2780	2.35	789	1.60	1468				
20	1.94	2480	2.16	868	1.64	1800				
30	1.76	2420	2.04	959	2.03	1620				
40	1.52	2450	1.61	1085	2.48	1865	1.86	2.15	0.50	1.14
50	0.87	2303	1.09	891	4.36	1848	1.68	2.00	0.74	1.29
120	0.33	2285	0.47	815	5.77	1810	1.35	1.91	1.04	1.36

DISCUSSION

The observation that ITP becomes radioactive when added together with radio-active ATP to striated muscle or intestinal mucosa could be accounted for by the anaerobic reaction

$$ATP + IDP \longrightarrow ADP + ITP. \tag{1}$$

The simultaneous fall of the specific activity of ATP phosphorus in suspensions of intestinal mucosa suggests that the reaction is reversible. The incorporation of radio-active inorganic phosphate could be explained by oxidative phosphorylation leading to radioactive ATP, followed by reaction (1).

The nature of the enzymes which may catalyse reaction (1) is unsettled. The reaction is not catalysed by myokinase, which transfers phosphate groups from ATP to AMP, and from one ADP molecule to another. As several hydrolytic enzymes, including phosphatases (AXELROD[12a]; MEYERHOF AND GREEN[13]), are known to transfer specific radicals either to water (in which case they hydrolyse) or to other hydroxy compounds (in which case they transfer) it is conceivable that the transfer of phosphate is brought about by one of the hydrolytic ATPase. But three of these which were tested – the myosin ATPase, the soluble ATPase of KIELLEY AND MEYERHOF and purified alkaline phosphatase fail to catalyse reaction (1).

GREEN AND MEYERHOF[14] noted that crude preparations of semen phosphatase transfer phosphate from ATP to glycerol but that purification of the enzyme reduces the ability to transfer ATP phosphorus. At the same time transfer from acetyl phosphate and p-nitrophenyl phosphate was not affected by purification. The authors deduced the presence of a phosphokinase specific for ATP. If ATPases play a role in the transfer reaction described in this paper they must be supplemented by a phosphokinase. It is also possible that a phosphokinase alone catalyses a phosphate transfer between ATP and ITP.

The analogy of reaction (1) with the interaction between ATP and creatine raises the question whether ITP, like creatine phosphate, is a storage form of phosphate bond energy. The methods described in this paper have been used by OLIVER[15] to measure the concentration of inosine phosphates in various animal tissues, but no appreciable quantity (*i.e.* less than 0.1 μg P per g tissue) was found in frog muscle if the metabolic activities of the tissue were stopped by treatment with dry ice within seconds after removal from the animal (see also LOHMANN[16]).

Experiments of WAJZER AND NEKHOROCHEFF[17] and of WEIL-MALHERBE[18] suggest that animal tissues can convert IMP into ATP. It is feasible that reaction (1) is a step in this synthesis.

SUMMARY

1. A paper chromatographic procedure for the separation of the 5- mono-, di-, and tri-phosphates of adenosine and inosine is described.

2. The terminal phosphate group of added ITP becomes radioactive at about the same rate as the two terminal phosphate groups of added ATP when respiring suspensions of pigeon breast muscle are incubated with $^{32}PO_4$.

3. ITP also becomes radioactive when incubated anaerobically with suspensions of muscle or intestinal mucosa containing ^{32}P labelled ATP.

4. Purified myokinase, myosin ATPase, or soluble ATPase do not transfer phosphate from ATP to inosine phosphates. The two latter enzymes hydrolyse both ATP and ITP, but when the two substrates are added together the rate of hydrolysis is lower than the sum of the rates of reaction found when the substrates are added singly.

References p. 180.

5. The observations are in accordance with the assumption that animal tissues contain a specific phospho-kinase which catalyses the reaction ATP + IDP ⇌ ADP + ITP.

RÉSUMÉ

1. Les 5- mono-, di- et triphosphates d'adénosine et d'inosine peuvent être séparés par chromatographie sur papier.

2. Quand on ajoute de l'ITP à des suspensions de muscle thoracique de pigeon incubé avec $^{32}PO_4$, son groupe phosphate terminal devient radioactif (il en est de même pour les deux groupes terminaux de l'ATP).

3. L'ITP devient également radioactif quand on l'incube en anaérobiose avec des suspensions de muscle ou de mucus intestinal renfermant de l'ATP marqué par ^{32}P.

4. La myokinase purifiée, la myosine ATP-ase ou l'ATP-ase soluble ne transfèrent pas de phosphate de l'ATP aux phosphates d'inosine. Ces deux derniers enzymes hydrolysent à la fois ATP et ITP, mais si ces deux substrates sont ajoutés ensemble, la vitesse d'hydrolyse est plus faible que la somme des vitesses trouvées quand les substrats sont ajoutés séparément.

5. Ces observations sont en accord avec l'hypothèse selon laquelle les tissus animaux contiendraient une phosphokinase spécifique catalysant la réaction ATP + IDP ⇌ ADP + ITP.

ZUSAMMENFASSUNG

1. Es wird ein papierchromatographisches Verfahren zur Trennung der 5-Mono-, Di- und Triphosphates von Adenosin und Inosin beschrieben.

2. Die entständige Phosphatgruppe von hinzugefügter ITP wird (in ungefähr dem gleichen Masse wie bei den endständigen Phosphatgruppen von hinzugefügter ATP) radioaktiv, wenn respirierende Suspensionen von Taubenbrustmuskeln in Gegenwart von $^{32}PO_4$ bebrütet werden.

3. ITP wird ebenfalls radioaktiv, wenn es anaerob mit Suspensionen von Muskel- oder Darmschleimhaut bebrütet wird, die mit ^{32}P markierte ATP enthalten.

4. Gereinigte Myokinase, Myosin-ATP-ase oder lösliche ATP-ase übertragen kein Phosphat von ATP auf Inosinphosphate. Die beiden letzteren Enzyme hydrolysieren sowohl ATP wie ITP, aber wenn die beiden Substrate zusammen hinzugefügt werden, ist die Hydrolysengeschwindigkeit geringer als die Summe der Reaktionsgeschwindigkeiten, die man findet, wenn die beiden Substrate einzeln hinzugefügt werden.

5. Die Beobachtungen sind in Übereinstimmung mit der Annahme, dass tierische Gewebe eine spezifische Phosphokinase enthalten, die die Reaktion ATP + IDP ⇌ ADP + ITP katalysiert.

REFERENCES

[1] L. V. EGGLESTON AND R. HEMS, *Biochem. J.*, 52 (1952) 156.
[2] H. A. KREBS, A. RUFFO, M. JOHNSON, L. V. EGGLESTON AND R. HEMS, *Biochem. J.*, 54 (1953) 107.
[3] A. KLEINZELLER, *Biochem. J.*, 36 (1942) 729.
[4] R. HEMS AND W. BARTLEY, *Biochem. J.*, (1953) In press.
[5] R. J. BLOCK, R. LESTRANGE AND G. ZWEIG, *Paper Chromatography, Academic Press Inc.*, New York (1952).
[6] C. S. HANES AND F. A. ISHERWOOD, *Nature*, 164 (1949) 1107.
[7] R. ZETTERSTRÖM AND M. LJUNGGREN, *Acta Chem. Scand.*, 5 (1951) 291.
[8] H. M. KALCKAR, *J. Biol. Chem.* 148 (1943) 127.
[9] S. S. SPICER AND W. J. BOWEN, *J. Biol. Chem.*, 188 (1951) 741.
[10] K. BAILEY, *Biochem. J.*, 36 (1942) 121.
[11] W. W. KIELLEY AND O. MEYERHOF, *J. Biol. Chem.*, 176 (1948) 591.
[12] G. SCHMIDT AND S. J. THANNHAUSER, *J. Biol. Chem.*, 149 (1943) 369.
[12a] B. AXELROD, *J. Biol. Chem.*, 172 (1948) 1.
[13] O. MEYERHOF AND H. GREEN, *J. Biol. Chem.*, 183 (1950) 377.
[14] H. GREEN AND O. MEYERHOF, *J. Biol. Chem.*, 197 (1952) 347.
[15] I. T. OLIVER, unpublished.
[16] K. LOHMANN, *Biochem. Z.*, 254 (1932) 381.
[17] J. WAJZER AND J. NEKHOROCHEFF, *Compt. rend. soc. biol.*, 144 (1950) 807 and *Abstr. II Int. Biochem. Congr.*, (1952) 207.
[18] H. WEIL-MALHERBE, *Communic. to Biochem. Soc.*, (27.3.1953).
[19] O. H. LOWRY AND J. A. LOPEZ, *J. Biol. Chem.*, 162 (1946) 421.

Received April 17th, 1953

ON THE COMPOSITION OF THE SOLUBLE NITROGEN FRACTION IN THE PEA PLANT AND ALDER

by

ARTTURI I. VIRTANEN AND J. K. MIETTINEN

Biochemical Institute, Helsinki (Finland)

Development of new methods of analysis, especially paper chromatography, in the recent years has made it possible to study in greater detail than before the soluble nitrogen compounds of plants. This "non-protein" nitrogen fraction has drawn particular attention because it is obviously the source of protein synthesis and also contains decomposition products of proteins and amino acids. So far especially the amino acid composition of the soluble nitrogen fraction has been examined with certain plants. Among the investigators working in this field should be mentioned in particular DENT, STEWARD and collaborators[1, 2, 3, 4] HUNT[5], SYNGE[6], HULME AND ARTHINGTON[7]. STEWARD AND THOMPSON[3] have reviewed the literature up to the end of 1949.

The investigations so far have many-sidedly revealed which amino acids are in general found free in higher plants. The amino acids present generally in proteins, *e.g.* aspartic and glutamic acids and their amides, alanine, valine, leucines, phenylalanine, tyrosine, serine, threonine, proline, lysine, arginine, have been found as common free amino acids in higher plants. Certain new amino acids, unknown in proteins, have been detected by chromatographic methods free in higher plants. STEWARD *et al.*[2] identified and isolated γ-amino butyric acid (γ-AB) first from potato and later it has been found to be a common amino acid in plants. Piperidine-2-carboxylic acid has been isolated from *Trifolium repens* (MORRISON[8, 9]), from seeds of bean[10], from apple[7], and growing pea[11]. γ-Methylene glutamine, a new amide, has been isolated from *Arachis hypogaea* (DONE AND FOWDEN[12, 13]). In this laboratory homoserine has recently been isolated from growing pea (MIETTINEN *et al.*[11]).

The occurrence of some unusual amino acids in high concentration in certain plants

In this laboratory the composition of the soluble nitrogen fraction especially in different tissues of leguminous plants and alder has been studied during the last two years. These plants receive their nitrogen nutrition from the atmosphere by the action of their root nodules. However, they are also able to grow on the nitrogen compounds taken up by their roots. It is therefore of great interest to examine how the composition of the soluble nitrogen fraction is affected by the nature of the nitrogen nutrition. We shall revert to this question in another connection. The leguminous plants are also the protein-richest of all plants, hence, the powerful protein synthesis taking place in them is enough to arouse special interest in their soluble nitrogen fraction.

The composition of the soluble nitrogen fraction differs to a surprising extent in alder (*Alnus glutinosa* and *incana*) and pea (*Pisum sativum*). In pea the amount of

References p. 187.

amides is high, asparagine is usually found 5 times more than glutamine. In no parts of alder have these amides been found. On the other hand, we[14, 15] have found L(+)-citrulline more than any other free amino acid in the root nodules as well as in other parts of alder, whereas it has never been found in any parts of pea including the nodules, and to date it has never been found in any higher plants except the water-melon (WADA[16]). The amount of citrulline in the root nodules of alder is in summer about 0.2 % of the dry weight. After the leaves had fallen in October the amount was already about 0.9 % of the dry weight in *A. incana*. The citrulline content of *A. glutinosa* nodules was nearly 2 % of the dry weight in January. Citrulline must therefore be regarded as a nitrogen store which is rapidly used in the spring when growth begins but which is continuously found, although to a lesser extent, during the growth period. There are only traces of arginine and ornithine in the nodules, whereas they as well as citrulline are abundant in the parts of the roots nearest to nodules. It is remarkable that we[17] have not been able to find any arginase effect in the nodules, roots and leaves of alder, accordingly, the decomposition of arginine to ornithine and urea does not seem likely in alder. In its action citrulline may be in some way comparable with glutamine and asparagine, which are abundantly found in legumes, and also may act as store and carrier of nitrogen. Because citrulline is also found in alder, which has grown with combined nitrogen without nodules, its formation is not linked to the molecular nitrogen fixation.

In pea plants we have recently found, as mentioned above, considerable quantities of homoserine which is not found in alder. After its existence had been indicated paper chromatographically homoserine was isolated from pea plants as follows[11].

Protein-free extract was boiled under a reflux condenser for 3 hours with 1 N HCl for decomposition of amides, polysaccharides etc. after which the coloured impurities were removed by active carbon. The amino acids were divided into groups by alkaline ion exchange resin Dowex-2. The group of neutral amino acids was further fractioned with Dowex-50 resin according to STEIN AND MOORE[18] by using elution analysis with hydrochloric acid.

A part of the homoserine could be eluted by the acid cycle coming through before alanine, another part remaining firmly bound in the column evidently as the basic lactone form. This part was recovered only by displacement with ammonia.

At the moment it is unknown why some amino acids, *e.g.*, citrulline and homoserine, which are not known as common protein components, may occur in some plants even in surprisingly large quantities, in others again not at all. Other examples are γ-methylene-glutamine in *Arachis hypogaea*[12,13] and hydroxyproline in *Santalum album*[19]. The common occurrence of free γ-aminobutyric acid in plants is evidently due to its formation as a decarboxylation product of glutamic acid. Its possible role in the metabolism of plants is unknown. Citrulline is an intermediate product in the synthesis of arginine. Whether it has some other role is unknown. Homoserine acts as a precursor in the synthesis of methionine and threonine. In addition, canavanine is a derivative of homoserine. It is possible that amino acids, which are absent from the proteins but present in the soluble nitrogen fraction, function in the biosynthesis of alkaloids and other substances.

Effect of light on the occurrence of free amino acids

By using the paper chromatographic semiquantitative method we have followed the amount of free amino acids in pea at different ages (after 12, 30, 43, and 61 days).

References p. 187.

These results will be discussed in another paper. We have also paid special attention to changes taking place in the soluble nitrogen fraction when keeping the plants in the dark. In two days great increase occurred in the soluble nitrogen fraction of all tissues of growing pea, as appears from the results in Table I.

TABLE I

NITROGEN SOLUBLE IN 70% BY WT. ETHANOL
(μg N per 100 mg. dry wt.) Peas in full bloom, 43 days old

	Soluble N		N of all determined[*] free amino acids, in total	
	in normal light	after 2 days in the dark	in normal light	after 2 days in the dark
Leaves	320	720	98	309
Stems	290	430	162	248
Roots	376	450	117	184
Nodules	1170	1600	—	—

[*] Several amino acids could not be determined quantitatively.

As the assimilation of carbon dioxide ceases in the dark, the decomposition processes set in and the breakdown of proteins and deamination of amino acids are detectable. In connection with them the synthesis of amino acids through transamination, reductive amination of keto-acids etc. will possibly affect the soluble N-fraction in another way than in plants grown in light when free amino acids are continuously removed through the protein synthesis. It is therefore interesting to follow the changes in the soluble nitrogen fraction caused by the darkness. Our experiments so far have been carried out with pea plants growing in sand without combined nitrogen, solely with atmospheric nitrogen fixed in their root nodules. Parallel experiments with nitrate or ammonium nitrogen have not yet been made. Since the red nitrogen-fixing nodules of pea lose their activity in the dark[20] at breaking of the porphin ring of leghemoglobin through oxidation[21, 22], the pea plants in these experiments have no longer received any nitrogen nutrition.

The darkening affected the proportions of free amino acids in pea plants in the following manner. As a rule the concentration of those amino acids, which normally are either absent or present only in minute amounts in free state, rose most. Thus, arginine and lysine appeared, and the quantities of leucine, *iso*leucine, phenylalanine, and valine rose to approximately 5–10-fold. Some free histidine was also found in the leaves of darkened plants, normally it is completely absent from the plants. Glycine, threonine, tyrosine, and methionine, which have not been found free in the leaves of pea growing in light, became distinctly detectable during the darkening and their concentration rose in the nodules. The amount of free aspartic acid increased during the darkness to about 20-fold in the leaves; in the roots it remained unchanged but in the nodules decreased. Similar changes occurred in glutamic acid but its increase in the leaves was only about 3-fold. Amides and γ-AB were affected in approximately the same way.

Such amino acids as occur liberally in free state in normal plants, *e.g.* alanine and serine, increased only in approximately the same proportion as soluble nitrogen. Darkening did not essentially affect the amount of homoserine.

The interpretation of the obtained results is difficult because many different reactions affect the mutual relations of amino acids during the darkness. The general im-

References p. 187.

pression is that the increase of free amino acids during the darkness is due chiefly to protein breakdown. It may also be possible that the synthesis of amino acids continues still in the dark although the synthesis of peptides and proteins is inhibited, whereby just such amino acids are concentrated that normally are used for the protein synthesis as they are formed.

The amino acid composition of the "peptide" fraction

The nitrogen of the free amino acids constitute about 30–70% of the soluble nitrogen of pea at different ages. Thus, the soluble nitrogen fraction contains besides free amino acids a number of other nitrogen compounds, *e.g.* purines, pyrimidines, free bases and also compounds from which amino acids are liberated by hydrolysis. These last mentioned compounds, in particular, have been subjects of our interest.

In the acid hydrolysis of the ethanol extract especially of young pea plants we were able to demonstrate for certain a heavy increase of glutamic acid. Likewise threonine, glycine, lysine, and proline were increased. The amount of certain amino acids, as serine, alanine and valine, was decreased by hydrolysis in some samples. Since in the total hydrolysis (6 N HCl for 20 h at 108° C in closed tube) only serine and threonine are decomposed to any greater extent in the absence of carbohydrates, the decrease of alanine, valine, and some other amino acids in the ethanol extract must be due to the reactions between amino acids and carbohydrates and even other non-nitrogen compounds present in the extract. Copious formation of brown decomposition products in the hydrolysis (10–20% of the total N of the extract was found in the brown precipitate) indicates that such reactions really take place.

In order to obtain more information of the compounds from which amino acids are liberated by hydrolysis we have tried to isolate the fraction in question. By using ion-exchange resin Amberlite IR-105 (H+) of the sulphonic acid type, we obtained from the ethanol extract of pea a fraction which contained no free amino acids. The nitrogen of this fraction amounted to 10–30 % of the nitrogen of the extract. On hydrolysis of the "peptide" fraction the same amino acids were formed as are generally met in free state in the pea extract with a voluminous brown precipitate, containing ca. 20 % of the nitrogen of this fraction. *Abundant* formation of glutamic acid, aspartic acid, alanine, valine, leucine, *iso*leucine, *moderate* of glycine, serine, threonine, proline, homoserine, lysine, *slight* of tyrosine, phenylalanine, γ-AB, β-alanine, and two unknown compounds and *traces* of α-AB and arginine occurred in total hydrolysis of the fraction.

On dialysis of the fraction 98.5% of its nitrogen passed through the dialysis membrane. The amino acid composition of the "non-dialysable" did not essentially differ from that of the "dialysable". About 30% of the nitrogen of the dialysate was absorbed in the active carbon. All of the bound tyrosine and a major part of the bound β-alanine were retained by the carbon but otherwise the adsorbed fraction did not differ essentially from the unadsorbed one. About half of the adsorbed nitrogen compounds corresponding to 11 % of the nitrogen of the peptide fraction, could be displaced again from the carbon by phenol, the rest remaining irreversibly adsorbed.

In order to ascertain whether the amino acids bound in the "peptide" fraction are linked together by peptide bonds or whether they are attached to sugars or appear as acyl-amino acids etc., a hydrolysis was carried out on the dialysed fraction in three different ways: a. 1 N HCl 1 h 100° C, b. 1 N HCl 3 h 100° C, and c. total hydrolysis 6 N HCl 24 h 108° C.

References p. 187.

Fig. 1 A–D shows paper chromatograms of these hydrolysates. As can be seen from them no amino acids were liberated by 1 h hydrolysis. In the chromatogram of the 3 h hydrolysate wide indefinite spots were formed, thus amino acids, possibly liberated to a small extent, were difficult to identify. Perhaps some homoserine, serine, glycine, glutamic acid, proline, and aspartic acid were liberated. Not until in the total hydrolysis

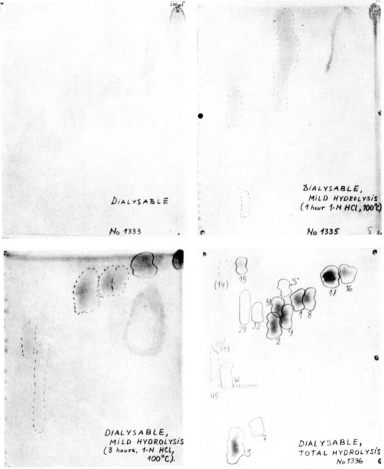

Fig. 1. Dialysable "peptides", not hydrolysed and the same after mild and strong hydrolysis. For solvents and technique see[11] or [15]. 1 = gly, 2 = ala, 3 = val, 7 = tyr, 8 = ser, 9 = thr, 11 = pro, 14 = arg, 15 = lys, 16 = asp. ac., 17 = glu. ac., 29 = γ-AB, 32 = β-ala, 45 = ethanolamine, 51 = homoserine, "S" and "W" = unknown spots.

were all the amino acids liberated and the unclear spots disappeared. The results of the hydrolysis suggest that at least a major part of the amino acids have been bound by difficultly hydrolyzable bonds. Our experiments on the hydrolysis of acetyl glucosamine have shown that acetyl group is split off from it as soon as within 1 h hydrolysis with 1 N HCl. Thus no acetylamino acids should be present in our "peptide" fraction.

An interesting question is the manner of combination in the "peptide" fraction of such amino acids as homoserine, γ-AB, and β-alanine, which are liberated in the acid

References p. 187.

hydrolysis of the fraction but have hitherto not been met in proteins. It has been shown by GOTTSCHALK AND PARTRIDGE[23] that in the reaction between α-amino acids and reducing sugars the reactivity of the amino group increases as its distance from the carboxyl group increases. β- and γ-amino acids are, therefore, more inclined than α-amino acids to complex-formation with sugars. In fact we have demonstrated paper chromatographically by using ammoniacal silver nitrate[24] and CHAPMAN-MCFARLANE[25] reagents that the "peptide" fraction contains strongly reducing compounds resembling those formed by sugars and amino compounds.

The nature of compounds in this fraction is still obscure. No fractionation of the "peptide" fraction with electric current was obtained at pH 7 in silica-jelly ionophoresis by the method of CONSDEN et al.[26]. Since it was also found that the "peptides" are not bound to the cation exchange resin Amberlite IR-105 (H+) it is evident that their end-amino groups are blocked.

When examining the soluble nitrogen compounds of rye grass SYNGE[6] came to investigate the nature of nitrogen compounds in many respects similar to those contained in our "peptide" fraction. He discussed the nature of these nitrogen compounds, considering it possible that they are compounds of amino acids and sugars, acyl amino acids, or cyclopeptides. According to our findings the presence of acyl amino acids is unlikely in our fraction. The chemical nature of the compounds contained in the "peptide" fraction isolated by us is under more detailed study.*

SUMMARY

Great differences have been observed in the composition of the free amino acids of alder and pea. Citrulline is the predominating free amino acid in alder, whereas it is completely absent from pea. On the other hand, amides, which are quantitatively dominant in the soluble nitrogen fraction of pea, are absent from the alder. Homoserine, which earlier has not been detected in higher plants, has been identified and isolated from pea in crystalline form. Special attention has been paid to the soluble fraction of pea containing bound amino acids. This fraction has been isolated free from free amino acids. On total hydrolysis, but not on mild hydrolysis, this "peptide" fraction yields the same amino acids as are met in free state in the pea plant, among them e.g. γ-amino butyric acid, β-alanine, and homoserine. The chemical nature of the nitrogen compounds in this fraction has been discussed.

RÉSUMÉ

La composition en acides aminés libres de l'aune est très différente de celle du pois. Chez l'aune, la citrulline est l'acide aminé libre le plus abondant, alors qu'elle est absente chez le pois. Au contraire, les amides, qui dominent quantitativement dans la fraction soluble de l'azote du pois, sont absentes chez l'aune. L'homosérine, qui n'avait pas été trouvée jusqu'à présent chez des plantes supérieures, a été identifiée et isolée sous forme cristalline à partir du pois. Nous avons étudié particulièrement la fraction soluble du pois qui renferme des acides aminés liés. Cette fraction a été isolée et débarrassée des acides aminés libres. Après hydrolyse totale, mais non après hydrolyse ménagée, la fraction "peptidique" renferme les acides aminés qu'on trouve à l'état libre chez le pois, parmi lesquels par exemple l'acide γ-aminobutyrique, la β-alanine et l'homosérine. La nature chimique des composés azotés de cette fraction est envisagée.

---

* *Addition to the proof.* Evidence has been found that this fraction contains compounds of amino acids with sugars. Through the influence of proteolytic enzymes (pepsine + trypsine) no amino acids were split from the original nor mildly HCl-hydrolyzed "peptide"-fraction. Thus, there is no proof for peptide bonds so far.

References p. 187.

ZUSAMMENFASSUNG

Bedeutende Unterschiede zwischen der Erle und der wachsenden Erbse bezüglich des Gehalts an freien Aminosäuren sind festgestellt worden. L-(+)-Citrullin ist die Aminosäure, welche sich in der Erle reichlichst findet, wogegen es in der Erbse gar nicht gefunden wird. Die Amide, welche in der löslichen Fraktion der Erbse quantitativ im Vordergrund sind, fehlen dagegen aus der Erle. Eine früher in höheren Pflanzen unbekannte Aminosäure, das Homoserin, wurde aus der Erbse kristallinisch isoliert. Homoserin kommt in bedeutenden Mengen in allen Teilen der Erbsenpflanze vor. Eine besondere Aufmerksamkeit ist auf die lösliche, gebundene Aminosäuren enthaltende Fraktion der Erbse gerichtet worden, die frei von freien Aminosäuren isoliert wurde. Aus dieser "Peptid"-fraktion werden durch Totalhydrolyse, nicht aber durch eine schwache Hydrolyse, dieselben Aminosäuren, die in Erbse frei vorhanden sind, gebildet, unter diesen u.a. α-Aminobuttersäure, β-Alanin und Homoserin. Die chemische Natur der Stickstoffverbindungen dieser Fraktion ist diskutiert worden.

REFERENCES

[1] C. E. DENT, W. STEPKA AND F. C. STEWARD, Nature, 160 (1947) 682.
[2] F. C. STEWARD, J. F. THOMPSON AND C. E. DENT, Science, 110 (1949) 439.
[3] F. C. STEWARD AND J. F. THOMPSON, Ann. Rev. Plant Physiol., 1 (1950) 233.
[4] F. C. STEWARD, J. F. THOMPSON, F. K. MILLAR, M. D. THOMAS AND R. H. HENDRIKS, Plant Physiol., 26 (1951) 123.
[5] G. E. HUNT, Am. J. Botany, 38 (1951) 452.
[6] R. L. M. SYNGE, Biochem. J., 49 (1951) 642.
[7] A. C. HULME AND W. ARTHINGTON, Nature, 170 (1952) 659.
[8] R. I. MORRISON, Biochem. J., 50 (1952) XIV.
[9] R. I. MORRISON, Biochem. J., 53 (1953) 474.
[10] R. M. ZACHARIAS, J. F. THOMPSON AND F. C. STEWARD, J. Am. Chem. Soc., 74 (1952) 2949.
[11] J. K. MIETTINEN, S. KARI, T. MOISIO, M. ALFTHAN AND A. I. VIRTANEN, Suomen Kemistilehti B, 26 (1953) 26.
[12] J. DONE AND L. FOWDEN, Biochem. J., 49 (1951) XX.
[13] J. DONE AND L. FOWDEN, Biochem. J., 51 (1952) 451.
[14] A. I. VIRTANEN AND J. K. MIETTINEN, Nature, 170 (1952) 283.
[15] J. K. MIETTINEN AND A. I. VIRTANEN, Physiol. Plantarum, 5 (1952) 540.
[16] M. WADA, Biochem. Z., 224 (1930) 420.
[17] J. K. MIETTINEN AND A. I. VIRTANEN, Acta Chem. Scand., 7 (1953) 289.
[18] W. H. STEIN AND S. MOORE, Cold Spring Harbor Symposia Quant. Biol., 14 (1949) 188.
[19] K. V. GIRI, K. S. GOPALKRISHNAN, A. N. RADHAKRISHNAN AND C. S. VAIDYANATHAN, Nature, 170 (1952) 579.
[20] A. I. VIRTANEN, Nature, 155 (1945) 747.
[21] A. I. VIRTANEN AND T. LAINE, Nature, 157 (1946) 25.
[22] J. K. MIETTINEN AND A. I. VIRTANEN, Acta Chem. Scand., 3 (1949) 17.
[23] A. GOTTSCHALK AND S. M. PARTRIDGE, Nature, 165 (1950) 684.
[24] S. M. PARTRIDGE, Nature, 158 (1946) 270.
[25] R. A. CHAPMAN AND W. D. MCFARLANE, Can. J. Research, 23B, (1945) 91.
[26] R. CONSDEN, A. H. GORDON AND A. J. P. MARTIN, Biochem. J., 40 (1946) 33.

Received April 14th, 1953

THE ENZYMIC OXIDATION OF d- AND l-β-HYDROXYBUTYRATE[*]

by

ALBERT L. LEHNINGER[**] AND GUY D. GREVILLE

*Department of Physiological Chemistry, Johns Hopkins School of Medicine, Baltimore, Md., (U.S.A.)
and the Department of Biochemistry, The University, Cambridge (England)*

Ever since the isolation of l-β-hydroxybutyric acid[***] from the urine of diabetics was first reported by MAGNUS-LEVY[4], this substance has been regarded as an intermediate in the metabolism of fatty acids although its exact role is still obscure. The only known enzyme attacking it, the l-specific DPN-linked β-hydroxybutyric dehydrogenase[5], converts it into acetoacetate, which is now known to be oxidized to completion in various tissues via the tricarboxylic acid cycle.

Although the l-isomer has been commonly regarded as the "naturally occurring" form, some evidence exists that the d-isomer undergoes biological utilization. In 1902 MCKENZIE demonstrated that the d-isomer is metabolized by the intact dog and apparently at a greater rate than the l-isomer, a finding which was confirmed by DAKIN[7]. Furthermore, FRIEDMANN demonstrated in 1931 that fermenting yeast reduces acetoacetate to dextrorotatory β-hydroxybutyrate[8]. More recently it has been found that both isomers of the racemic compound undergo oxidation in suspensions of particulate elements (mitochondria) from liver and kidney[9, 10]. We have made similar observations, some of which indicated that the two isomers have somewhat different pathways of oxidation in liver preparations. In this communication we wish to present data obtained employing the pure stereoisomers of β-hydroxybutyric acid which delineate the different enzymic pathways taken by the two forms. From these findings it appears probable that the d-isomer is also of "natural occurrence" and that it plays a role in ketone body and fatty acid metabolism.

EXPERIMENTAL DETAILS

Resolution of dl-β-hydroxybutyric acid. dl-β-hydroxybutyric acid, prepared from the sodium salt (British Drug Houses), was converted into the calcium-zinc double salt[11] which was recrystallized. Resolution of the purified acid regenerated from the double salt was based on the method of CLARKE[12],

[*] This work was supported in part by grants from the Nutrition Foundation, Inc., and from the National Institutes of Health, U.S. Public Health Service.

[**] A.L.L. was a Fellow of the John Simon Guggenheim Foundation and a Research Scholar under the Fulbright Act in the Department of Biochemistry, University of Cambridge, when this investigation was initiated and he wishes to express his gratitude to Prof. F. G. YOUNG, F.R.S., for the hospitality of his laboratory.

[***] Throughout this paper the designation l-β-hydroxybutyric acid (l-BOH) refers to levorotatory β-hydroxybutyric acid and d-β-hydroxybutyric (d-BOH) refers to the dextrorotatory form in accordance with long usage in the case of this particular compound in the biochemical literature. However, it should be pointed out that the configurational relationships of the β-hydroxybutyric acids to the lactic acids have been definitely established[1, 2, 3]. Thus levorotatory BOH is of the D-series and should be designated as D(—)β-hydroxybutyric acid and the dextrorotatory form as L(+)β-hydroxybutyric acid.

References p. 202.

itself an improvement of that of McKenzie[6]. The quinine salt, after one recrystallization from acetone at 2° and five at about 16°, yielded d-acid with the $[a]_D$ shown in Table I, c being determined by titration with NaOH with exclusion of CO_2. The mother liquors from the first five recrystallizations of the quinine dl-salt were evaporated *in vacuo*, and the resulting residue recrystallized three times from water at 0–2°, the crystals being filtered in the cold room and washed. This material then yielded l-acid with the $[a]_D$ shown in Table I, c being determined as before; $[a]_D$ was independent of concentration, in agreement with Magnus-Levy[1], and decreased by approx. 0.10 per 1° rise of temperature. Allowing for temperature, the specific rotations of the d- and l-acids compared favorably with the greatest values reported in the literature. The acids were converted into sodium salts, which were recrystallized from absolute ethanol-dry ether. The specific rotations (Table I) were determined with samples dried to constant weight over P_2O_5 (0.1 mm, room temperature).

TABLE I

SPECIFIC ROTATIONS IN WATER OF d- AND l-β-HYDROXYBUTYRIC ACIDS AND THEIR SODIUM SALTS

	l	c	t	$[a]_D$
d-Acid	2	6.0	15°	+ 25.2
l-Acid	2.2	6.1	10°	−25.8
	2.2	6.1	15°	−25.3
	2.2	6.1	20°	−24.8
	2.2	6.1	25°	−24.4
	4	2.4	10°	−26.0
	4	2.4	15°	−25.3
	4	2.4	20°	−24.8
	4	2.4	25°	−24.4
d-Salt	2	8.4	17°	+ 14.2*
	2	8.4	20°	+ 14.4*
l-Salt	2	8.5	19°	−14.4

* After correction for 1.1% of moisture in dried salt.

Previous values for $[a]_D$: d-Acid, + 24.3 (10°; c, 2.2) (McKenzie[6]), l-Acid, −24.2 (21°; c, 1.4 – 11.0) (Magnus-Levy[4]), − 24.8 (20°; c, 3.3) (McKenzie[6]), −24.5 (25°; c, 5) (Levene and Haller[15]), l-Salt, −14.3 (18–20°; c, 2.4–12.6) (Magnus-Levy[4],) −14.5 (15°; c, 8.5), −14.3 (17°, c, 3.4), −13.8 (17°, c, 1.4) (McKenzie[6]), −14.5 (15°) (Lenoël[16]).

As β-hydroxybutyric acid can form anhydro-derivatives[6,13,14] a sample of the l-acid was heated with a measured excess of aqueous NaOH on a boiling water bath for 30 min and back-titrated (phenolphthalein) with HCl. The alkali neutralized exceeded that required for direct titration of the l-acid at room temperature by only 0.2%. A similar rest revealed no alkali-labile anhydro-compound in the sodium salt of the d-acid.

Enzyme preparations. The easily sedimented particulate elements, consisting largely of mitochondria and nuclei, were obtained from homogenates of rat liver and kidney in two volumes of 0.14 M KCl – 0.01 M phosphate, pH 7.5, by centrifugation as previously described in detail[17]. The residues were washed twice with cold KCl-phosphate and finally suspended in cold KCl-phosphate. Such preparations were used for the experiments described in Tables II–IV.

For the preparation of mitochondrial extracts acetone-dried powders of mitochondria formed the starting material. Two types of preparation were employed. The mitochondrial fraction was obtained from homogenates of rat liver in 8.5% sucrose as described by Schneider[18], washed three times with cold 0.15 M KCl in the refrigerated centrifuge, and then suspended in about twenty volumes of acetone at—15° C with stirring. The suspension in cold acetone was repeated 4 times, separating the solid material each time by means of the centrifuge. The final residue was freed of acetone in vacuo, yielding a white powder which was stored at—15° C in a desiccator. Since this procedure was relatively laborious and required the use of large volumes of homogenate to obtain any significant amounts of the dry powder, the procedure was abridged in the following method.

The livers of 12 albino rats (147 g wet weight) were homogenized for exactly thirty seconds in a Waring blender with 600 ml of cold 0.15 M KCl. The homogenate was strained through gauze and centrifuged at 1500 g for 15 minutes in the cold. The supernatant was decanted and the residue resuspended in 600 ml fresh cold 0.15 M KCl and again centrifuged. This washing was repeated once more. To the final washed liver residues (largely mitochondria and nuclei) was added 600 ml of acetone at—15° C and the mixture well dispersed. The solid material was washed twice more with acetone, then freed of acetone *in vacuo*, yielding 9.1 g of a fluffy white powder. This was stable for at least 6 weeks in a desiccator at—15° C.

References p. 202.

To prepare extracts the powder was triturated with 10 parts by weight of cold 0.02 M NaHCO$_3$ for 20'–30' in an ice bath and centrifuged in the cold at 20,000 g for 20 minutes. The clear, reddish supernatant was then exhaustively dialyzed for 4–6 hours in thin cellulose tubing (diameter 0.75 cm), with constant efficient stirring, against several changes of cold 0.02 M NaHCO$_3$. The clear dialyzed extract was again centrifuged at 20,000 g for 20 minutes and the supernatant was then stored in the frozen state at—15°C in which form it was stable for at least 4 weeks. Extracts prepared in this manner from KCl-washed particulate material (*i.e.*, the second procedure above) contained little or no β-hydroxybutyric dehydrogenase, whereas those from mitochondria prepared from sucrose appeared to contain considerable activity.

Analytical methods. Manometric experiments were carried out employing standard equipment and techniques. Air was used as the gas phase in all the manometric experiments reported. Times quoted in protocols of such experiments were measured from the entry of the vessel into the bath. Taps were closed at five minutes. Oxygen uptakes were corrected for the 5 minute equilibration period by extrapolation.

Pyruvic acid was used as the lithium salt, other organic acids as K or Na salts. Most of the Coenzyme A used in this work was obtained from Pabst Laboratories, Inc., Milwaukee, Wisconsin and was about 80% pure. The DPN used was 85–90% pure (Sigma Chemical Co., St. Louis).

Hydroxamic acid formation was measured by a micro modification of the method of LIPMANN AND TUTTLE[19]. Isolation of hydroxamic acids and their paper chromatography were carried out by the methods described by STADTMAN AND BARKER[20]. Whatman No. 43 paper was used most successfully with the butanol-water system.

Citric acid was determined in trichloracetic acid filtrates by the method of SPECK, MOULDER AND EVANS[21]. It was found desirable to use a standard batch of ethylene glycol in order to obtain standards of consistent optical density. Colour was allowed to develop for 25 minutes at 20° and read at 457 mμ, at which the absorption was found to be maximal, in the Unicam D. G. Spectrophotometer. Micro-determinations of citric acid were performed by the method of NATELSON, LUGOVOY AND PINCUS[22].

Acetoacetate was determined by the method described by BARKULIS AND LEHNINGER[23]. With British specimens of HCl it was necessary to extract the 2 N HCl solution of 2,4-dinitrophenyl-hydrazine several times with CCl$_4$ to remove an otherwise very troublesome chromogen.

EXPERIMENTAL RESULTS

Previous work[24] has shown that β-hydroxybutyrate (BOH) is oxidized to aceto-acetate by well-washed preparations of rat liver mitochondria according to the equation

$$l\text{-}\beta\text{-hydroxybutyrate} + [\text{O}] \longrightarrow \text{acetoacetate} + \text{H}_2\text{O} \tag{1}$$

presumably by the l-specific DPN-linked β-hydroxybutyric dehydrogenase[5]. Aceto-acetate is apparently inert and accumulates quantitatively in such systems[24,25]. Although oxygen uptake data with rabbit kidney "cyclophorase" preparations indicate that both isomers of the dl-BOH used as substrate undergo oxidation[9,10], no report has been made of separate tests of the two pure isomers.

In Table II are shown typical data we have collected on the oxidation of the pure optical isomers of β-hydroxybutyrate under various conditions by rat liver and kidney mitochondrial preparations. It is seen from experiments 1, 2, and 3, Table II, that, as expected, the l-isomer is oxidized to acetoacetate in the absence of fumarate by liver preparations, the oxygen uptake and acetoacetate formation agreeing fairly well with the stoichiometry expressed by equation (1). Under the same conditions, the d-isomer is not attacked and no acetoacetate is formed, indicating that the l-specific β-hydroxy-butyric dehydrogenase is involved in the oxidation of the l-isomer under these particular conditions.

On the other hand, in the presence of fumarate the d-isomer does undergo oxidation by liver mitochondria as indicated by extra oxygen uptake and the accumulation of extra citrate in large amounts, comparable to the amounts which accumulate when pyruvate is oxidized in the presence of fumarate under the same conditions. It would appear then that the d-isomer undergoes oxidation in the presence of an oxalacetate

References p. 202.

precursor by a mechanism involving citrate formation, presumably the tricarboxylic acid cycle, but no oxidation of d-BOH takes place in the absence of fumarate.

The data in Table II also show that the l-isomer gives rise to acetoacetate in the presence of fumarate as well as in its absence, although in some experiments there is a

TABLE II

FORMATION OF ACETOACETATE AND CITRATE FROM d- AND l-β-HYDROXYBUTYRATE BY INTACT PARTICULATE PREPARATIONS OF LIVER AND KIDNEY

All vessels in Experiments 1, 2 and 3 contained 0.005 M $MgCl_2$, 0.001 M ATP, 0.014 M phosphate buffer pH 7.5, 0.06 M KCl and liver particles from 0.45 g fresh liver in a total volume of 3.0 ml. In Experiment 4 the vessels contained 0.005 M $MgCl_2$, 0.001 M ATP, 0.033 M phosphate buffer pH 7.5, 0.045 M KCl, and particles from 0.30 g fresh rat kidney, in 3.0 ml total volume. Where added, final concentrations of l-BOH, d-BOH and fumarate were 0.01 M. Experiment 1, 22°, 70 minutes; Experiment 2, 25°, 60 minutes; Experiment 3, 25°, 44 minutes; Experiment 4, 30°, 70 minutes.

Expt.	Organ	β-Hydroxybutyrate	Fumarate added	O_2 uptake microatoms	Acetoacetate formation micromoles	Citrate formation micromoles
1	Liver	None	None	2.0	0.1	0.00
		l-BOH	None	21.2	16.1	0.00
		d-BOH	None	3.6	1.2	0.05
		None	0.01 M	38.0	0.0	0.65
		l-BOH	0.01 M	42.9	9.0	2.65
		d-BOH	0.01 M	44.9	0.9	5.90
2	Liver	None	None	1.0	0.0	0.0
		l-BOH	None	16.4	15.0	0.2
		d-BOH	None	1.8	1.2	0.1
		Acetoacetate	None	1.2	—	0.2
		None	0.01 M	26.4	0.6	0.9
		l-BOH	0.01 M	38.9	14.2	1.5
		d-BOH	0.01 M	39.9	0.4	7.2
		Acetoacetate	0.01 M	25.6	—	1.9
3	Liver	None	None	2.8	0.1	0.4
		l-BOH	None	12.3	9.7	0.6
		d-BOH	None	2.9	0.4	0.8
		None	0.01 M	26.4	0.4	1.3
		l-BOH	0.01 M	34.8	9.1	2.0
		d-BOH	0.01 M	37.4	0.1	6.0
4	Kidney	None	0.01 M	40.7	—	0.50
		l-BOH	0.01 M	48.8	—	3.85
		d-BOH	0.01 M	50.1	—	4.55

significant decrease in acetoacetate formation in the presence of fumarate. Since previous work with such enzyme preparations has indicated that acetoacetate is essentially inert and accumulates quantitatively[24, 25], formation of citrate from l-BOH would not be expected if the β-hydroxybutyric dehydrogenase represents the only mechanism of oxidative attack on l-BOH. However, in many of our experiments (see especially Expt. 1, Table II) some extra citrate was actually formed from l-BOH although this extra citrate formation from l-BOH never approached the amounts formed from d-BOH. The reasons for the rather unexpected formation of small amounts of citrate from l-BOH under these particular conditions are not entirely clear but will be discussed later in this

References p. 202.

report. The important facts concerning citrate formation from the isomers of BOH in the liver systems are that d-BOH readily undergoes oxidation via the tricarboxylic acid cycle, as evidenced by extra oxygen uptake and extra citrate formation, whereas l-BOH forms considerably less or no citrate under the same circumstances and is largely oxidized to acetoacetate.

Tests with washed kidney preparations (expt. 4, Table I) showed that *both* isomers cause extra oxygen uptake in the presence of fumarate and both form extra citrate, indicating that both isomers are oxidized via the tricarboxylic acid cycle, and at approximately equal rates. Such kidney preparations are known to oxidize acetoacetate via the cycle quite readily[9], in contradistinction to liver mitochondrial preparations. Differences in mechanism of oxidation of the two isomers of β-hydroxybutyrate are thus apparent only in the liver preparations, because of the very limited ability of these to utilize free acetoacetate.

Other experiments showed that the citrate formation from d-β-hydroxybutyrate in both liver and kidney mitochondrial systems is almost completely inhibited by low concentrations (0.0005 M) of sodium fluoride, although such amounts of fluoride do not interfere with citrate formation from pyruvate (see Table III). Fluoride is known to inhibit fatty acid oxidation[26, 27], suggesting that there is a locus of fluoride inhibition in

TABLE III

EFFECT OF FLUORIDE ON CITRATE FORMATION FROM d-BOH.

Each vessel contained 0.005 M MgCl$_2$, 0.001 M ATP, 0.014 M phosphate buffer pH 7.5, 0.06 M KCl, 0.01 M fumarate and washed particles from 0.45 g (wet wt.) rat liver. Total volume 3.0 ml. Pyruvate (0.01 M final), d-BOH (0.01 M), and fluoride (0.002 M) were added as indicated. Temperature, 22°. Time, 65 minutes.

Substrate	Fluoride (0.002 M)	Oxygen uptake microatoms	Citrate formed micromoles
None	—	33.7	0.90
None	+	28.4	0.90
d-BOH	—	44.0	4.90
d-BOH	+	31.1	1.35
pyruvate	—	42.9	7.25
pyruvate	+	45.3	6.60

citrate formation which may be common to the oxidation pathways taken by d-BOH and the saturated fatty acids. CHELDELIN AND BEINERT have observed that 0.033 M fluoride prevents utilization of dl-BOH beyond the acetoacetate stage in rabbit liver mitochondrial systems[28].

Although the d-isomer formed little acetoacetate under any circumstances in the experiments with liver particle systems described above, acetoacetate formation from d-BOH was found to occur if relatively small concentrations of a tricarboxylic acid cycle intermediate were present in the system. With low concentrations of fumarate (1–5·10^{-4} M), d-BOH gives rise to significant amounts of acetoacetate, although these never approached the yield expected from the extra oxygen uptake if equation (1) also represented the oxidation of d-BOH (See Table IV). It is also seen that with increasingly higher concentrations of fumarate, acetoacetate no longer appears as product. It may be concluded that the formation of acetoacetate from d-BOH depends on "priming" or "sparking" by low concentrations of cycle intermediates. The l-isomer, on the other hand, requires no "sparking" to be oxidized to acetoacetate.

References p. 202.

The necessity for "sparking" (which is also required for oxidation of saturated fatty acids[26]) may thus be taken as an indication that oxidative phosphorylation processes may be involved in "activating" the d-isomer of β-hydroxybutyric in some manner so that it can undergo oxidation to acetoacetate and possibly also citrate. It may be concluded from the foregoing experiments that both the d- and l-isomers of β-hydroxybutyric acid undergo biological oxidation via the tricarboxylic acid cycle in kidney preparations, but that the initial stages of oxidation of the two isomers are quite different in liver mitochondrial preparations.

Dialyzed aqueous extracts of acetone-dried rat liver mitochondrial preparations were found to catalyze the reduction of diphosphopyridine nucleotide (DPN+) at the expense of d- and l-BOH under appropriate experimental conditions. Study of these extracts permitted delineation of the essentially different mechanisms involved. The course of these reactions was followed by measuring changes in optical density at 340 mμ, caused by appearance or disappearance of the reduced form of the nucleotide, by the now widely used spectrophotometric technique originated by Prof. OTTO WARBURG.

TABLE IV

"SPARKING" OF OXIDATION OF d-β-HYDROXYBUTYRATE

All vessels contained 0.005 M MgCl$_2$, 0.001 M ATP, 0.014 M phosphate buffer pH 7.5, 0.06 M KCl and washed particles from 0.45 g rat liver. Total volume 3.0 ml. Concentration of d-BOH where added was 0.01 M. Fumarate was added in concentrations shown. In experiment I, Temperature 22° C, time 65 minutes. In experiment II, temperature 20° C, time 75 minutes.

Expt.	Substrate	Fumarate concentration	O_2 uptake microatoms	Acetoacetate formation micromoles
I	d-BOH	none	3.9	1.3
	none	$1 \cdot 10^{-4}$ M	4.7	0.1
	d-BOH	$1 \cdot 10^{-4}$ M	13.4	2.6
	none	$5 \cdot 10^{-4}$ M	13.7	0.0
	d-BOH	$5 \cdot 10^{-4}$ M	39.0	4.0
II	none	none	1.8	0.3
	d-BOH	none	2.6	0.7
	none	$2 \cdot 10^{-4}$ M	7.2	0.2
	d-BOH	$2 \cdot 10^{-4}$ M	19.4	3.4
	none	$6 \cdot 10^{-4}$ M	14.3	0.3
	d-BOH	$6 \cdot 10^{-4}$ M	34.7	5.6
	none	$2 \cdot 10^{-3}$ M	19.6	0.3
	d-BOH	$2 \cdot 10^{-3}$ M	44.2	1.9
	none	0.01 M	19.1	0.3
	d-BOH	0.01 M	48.7	0.2

Such extracts contain the already known[5], DPN-linked l-specific β-hydroxybutyric dehydrogenase, as is shown by the data in Table V. There is virtually no reduction of DPN+ in the absence of added substrate or with d-BOH as substrate. It is seen that this reaction requires only extract, l-BOH, DPN+ and cysteine (β-hydroxybutyric dehydrogenase is known to be dependent on –SH groups[5, 29]) and addition of ATP, Mg++ and CoA does not affect the reaction. It is concluded that the oxidation of l-BOH in these extracts occurs by the reaction

$$l\text{-}\beta\text{-hydroxybutyrate} + DPN^+ \rightleftharpoons \text{acetoacetate} + DPNH + H^+ \tag{2}$$

In similar experiments it was found that acetoacetate is reduced by DPNH, as would be expected, since reaction (2) is known to be readily reversible.

References p. 202.

Since the already described experiments with intact mitochondria showed that the "sparking" or "priming" phenomenon was necessary to initiate oxidation of the *d*-isomer, but not the *l*-isomer, it appeared that this "sparking" process might involve ATP and Coenzyme A. Recently it has been demonstrated that the enzymic oxidation

TABLE V

REDUCTION OF DPN⁺ BY *l*- AND *d*-BOH IN EXTRACTS OF MITOCHONDRIA

Basic test system contained 0.10 ml of dialyzed extract of acetone-dried mitochondria (prepared by sucrose method; see "Experimental Details") 0.1 M KCl, 0.05 M tris (hydroxymethyl)aminomethane-HCl ("tris") buffer pH 8.0, 0.001 M DPN⁺, 0.01 M cysteine, and 0.025 M *d*-BOH or *l*-BOH as shown. Where added, ATP was 0.002 M, CoA was 0.0005 M, and MgCl₂ was 0.005 M. The volume of all systems was 1.0 ml, made up with H₂O. Temp. 20°, time 20 minutes. Optical path, 1.0 cm. The test systems were exposed to air during the reaction periods.

Substrate	ATP	CoA	MgCl₂	$\Delta \log Io/I$
None	—	—	—	0.024
l-BOH	—	—	—	0.196
d-BOH	—	—	—	0.021
l-BOH (cysteine omitted)	—	—	—	0.074
l-BOH	+	+	+	0.187
d-BOH	+	+	+	0.324
d-BOH	+	—	+	0.111
d-BOH	—	+	+	0.019
d-BOH	+	+	—	0.186
None	+	+	+	0.020

of butyrate, a process which also requires "sparking", only occurs after the Coenzyme A derivative of butyric acid has been formed[26, 30]. The interpretation has been made that the "sparking" phenomenon actually represents the enzymic formation of the CoA derivative. By analogy it was reasoned that the "sparking" of *d*-BOH oxidation likewise involves CoA and ATP. Experiments soon revealed that the addition of ATP, CoA, and Mg⁺⁺ to the extracts described above enabled them to cause the reduction of DPN⁺ by *d*-BOH at a high rate but such additions did not stimulate the reduction of DPN⁺ by *l*-BOH. It is seen from Table V that all three components (ATP, CoA, and Mg⁺⁺) were necessary to demonstrate maximal reduction of DPN⁺ by *d*-BOH. There was very little blank reduction of DPN⁺ in the presence of the three supplements. In the presence of the additions the reduction of DPN⁺ by *d*-BOH occurs at a linear rate for a period of at least 30–40 minutes under the conditions studied. These clear extracts of mitochondria therefore contain the enzymes catalyzing the reactions by which the *d*- and *l*-forms of β-hydroxybutyrate undergo at least the first stages of biological oxidation and it is clearly evident that the oxidation of *d*-BOH proceeds by a mechanism somewhat different from that involved in the oxidation of *l*-BOH.

By varying the manner of preparation of the extracts described above (see Experimental Details) or by fractionation procedures still under study, it was found possible to obtain extracts having very little or no demonstrable activity in the reduction of DPN⁺ by *l*-BOH, in the presence or absence of ATP, CoA, and Mg⁺⁺, but which showed high activity toward *d*-BOH in the presence of ATP, CoA, and Mg. Typical data obtained from such extracts are shown in Table VI. It is seen that the rate of reduction of DPN by *l*-BOH (in the absence or presence of ATP, CoA, and Mg^{++}) is, at the most, less than 5% of the rate of reduction of DPN^+ by *d*-BOH under the conditions employed.

TABLE VI

REDUCTION OF DPN^+ BY *d*-BOH IN EXTRACTS ESSENTIALLY FREE OF *l*-BOH DEHYDROGENASE

Test conditions exactly as in Table IV, with the exception that the extracts used were prepared from acetone-powdered KCl-washed liver residue (see "Experimental Details"). 0.10 ml of each extract in total volume of 1.0 ml, as in Table IV.

Extract	Substrate	ATP	CoA	$MgCl_2$	$\Delta \log I_0/I$
3-C-3	*d*-BOH	+	+	+	0.670
	none	+	+	+	0.015
	d-BOH	—	+	+	0.005
	d-BOH	+	—	+	0.062
	d-BOH	+	+	—	0.149
	l-BOH	+	+	+	0.040
	l-BOH	—	—	—	0.052
3-C-7	*d*-BOH	+	+	+	0.472
	none	+	+	+	0.020
	d-BOH	—	+	+	0.020
	d-BOH	+	—	+	0.122
	d-BOH	+	+	—	0.187
	l-BOH	+	+	+	0.024
	l-BOH	—	—	—	0.027

The experiments in Table VI are not consistent with the view that the *l*-β-hydroxy-butyric dehydrogenase is involved in the oxidation of the *d*-isomer, following an enzymic racemization. Such a hypothesis would require that the rate of oxidation of *d*-BOH could not exceed the maximal rate of oxidation of *l*-BOH, measured under identical conditions. It is evident from the data that the rate of oxidation of the *d*-isomer is at least twenty-fold greater than the rate of oxidation of the *l*-isomer. It may be concluded that the *l*-specific dehydrogenase is not involved in the oxidation of the *d*-isomer observed.

As a working hypothesis it was proposed that *d*-BOH reduces DPN^+ in these extracts through a sequence of two reactions:

$$d\text{-}\beta\text{-hydroxybutyrate} + CoA \xrightarrow{\text{ATP}} d\text{-}\beta\text{-hydroxybutyryl-CoA} \qquad (3)$$

$$d\text{-}\beta\text{-hydroxybutyryl-CoA} + DPN^+ \rightleftharpoons \text{acetoacetyl-CoA} + DPNH + H^+ \qquad (4)$$

Such a mechanism would account for the requirement of ATP and CoA in the reduction of DPN^+ by *d*-BOH. Experimental evidence supporting this mechanism follows.

That the *d*-isomer undergoes reaction (3) was indicated by the finding that the hydroxamic acid derivative of BOH is formed when *d*-BOH is incubated with the extracts in the presence of ATP, CoA, Mg^{++}, and hydroxylamine as trapping agent (Table VII). It is seen from the data that the formation of the hydroxamic acid derivative is absolutely dependent on the presence of ATP and CoA and is maximal in the presence of Mg^{++}. The hydroxamic acid derivative formed from *d*-BOH was established as that of β-hydroxybutyric acid by paper chromatography. The hydroxamic acid formed in the test system was separated and chromatographed on paper by the procedure outlined by STADTMAN AND BARKER[20]. The R_F of the hydroxamic acid derivative on Whatman No. 43 paper, using a butanol-water system, was found to be 0.35. An authentic specimen of β-hydroxybutyrohydroxamic acid, prepared from the pure ethyl ester, showed an

References p. 202.

R_F under the same conditions of 0.35. No other hydroxamic acid spots were detected on such papergrams of the reaction products. From the now very extensive evidence that this ATP- and CoA-dependent trapping reaction indicates the formation of acyl-CoA conjugates, it may be concluded that the β-hydroxybutyryl-CoA complex is in fact formed in these extracts.

Although the chromatographic method identified the hydroxamic derivative as that of β-hydroxybutyric acid it was of course uncertain whether this was present as the CoA complex of the d- or the l-isomer. Additional evidence was collected however which leaves very little doubt that the d-isomer is present in this complex although the direct measurement of the rotation of pure β-hydroxybutyryl CoA has not been made. The first point of evidence bearing on this problem is that l-BOH, which does not undergo significant oxidation by DPN$^+$ in the extracts used in experiments of Table VI does nevertheless also form a hydroxamic acid derivative under the same circumstances as d-BOH (see Table VII). This formation is also absolutely dependent on ATP and CoA but

TABLE VII

HYDROXAMIC ACID FORMATION FROM d- AND l-BOH

System contained 0.3 ml extract (3-C-7), 0.1 M KCl, 0.01 M cysteine, 0.05 M "tris" buffer pH 8.0, 0.5 M hydroxylamine (brought to pH 8.0), 0.025 M d- or l-BOH, 0.005 M ATP. 0.005 M MgCl$_2$, and 0.001 M CoA. Total volume, 1.0 ml. Time, 60 minutes; temp. 22° C.

Substrate	System	Hydroxamic acid formed micromoles
d-BOH	Complete	0.62
None	Complete	0.02
d-BOH	Omit ATP	0.02
d-BOH	Omit CoA	0.04
d-BOH	Omit Mg^{++}	0.27
l-BOH	Complete	0.54
None	Complete	0.02
l-BOH	Omit ATP	0.00
l-BOH	Omit CoA	0.07
l-BOH	Omit Mg^{++}	0.31

has been found to proceed at a slightly lower rate than that from the d-isomer (the difference in rate may not be significant). Furthermore, by paper chromatography it was established that this hydroxamic acid moves at the same rate as that formed from d-BOH on Whatman No. 43 paper using the butanol-water system. It would appear therefore that reaction (3) is not very specific stereochemically and that both isomers form CoA derivatives in the presence of enzyme, ATP and CoA. However it must be pointed out again that only the d-isomer causes reduction of DPN$^+$ in the oxidation test system. It would appear then that although the l-β-hydroxybutyryl-CoA complex is also formed, it does not cause reduction of DPN$^+$ in these extracts. The dehydrogenase catalyzing reaction (4) is therefore probably specific for the d-β-hydroxybutyryl-CoA. Such experiments also indicate that the l-β-hydroxybutyryl-CoA does not undergo enzymic racemization in these extracts at any significant rate.

Other points of evidence may be summarized. Both crotonate and vinyl acetate, when substituted for d-BOH in the complete test system, cause reduction of DPN$^+$ at about the same rate as does d-BOH. In each case there is an absolute requirement

References p. 202.

for ATP and CoA. It would appear that each of these acids must also form CoA derivatives prior to dehydrogenation. This question was tested by means of the hydroxylamine trapping reaction and both substrates were found to form amounts of hydroxamic acid approximately equivalent to the formation from d-BOH. These enzymically formed hydroxamic derivatives were isolated and chromatographed on paper, by the procedures used for the BOH derivatives, with the following results: product formed from crotonate, $R_F = 0.70$, authentic crotonylhydroxamic acid, $R_F = 0.70$, product formed from vinyl acetate, $R_F = 0.74$, authentic vinylacetylhydroxamic acid $R_F = 0.74$. It is evident, then, that both crotonate and vinyl acetate yield their corresponding CoA derivatives in the trapping reaction. Since both cause reduction of DPN$^+$ it appears unlikely that l-BOH as such or as the CoA derivative can be an intermediate in the oxidation of crotonyl-CoA or vinylacetyl-CoA, which presumably would first require hydration to β-hydroxybutyryl-CoA. These data indicate that the trapping reaction does in fact trap the corresponding CoA derivative in each case and that apparently no significant conversion of one of these acids to another, either as such or as the CoA derivative takes place in the presence of hydroxylamine in the concentrations used (0.5 M). Furthermore no evidence could be found that either d- or l-BOH undergo enzymic dehydration to form either vinyl acetate or crotonate, in the *absence* of ATP, CoA, and DPN$^+$ in these extracts. As a sensitive test, d- or l-BOH were incubated with the extract and then the medium, after acidification, was extracted with ether; the extracted material was examined in the ultraviolet region for the characteristic absorptions of the unsaturated acids. No conversion of free l-BOH or d-BOH to crotonate or vinyl acetate was detectable.

These findings, taken together, therefore indicate quite strongly that the CoA derivative formed from d-BOH is probably the d-β-hydroxybutyryl-CoA. Direct proof could only come from direct polarimetric analysis of a relatively large quantity of the highly purified reaction product, an experimental development that is extremely unlikely in the near future because of the relatively large amount of material required and the relatively low specific rotation expected, or perhaps by use of a highly purified sample of the l-specific β-hydroxybutyric dehydrogenase as an enzymic test of the optical properties of free β-hydroxybutyrate liberated from the enzymically formed CoA derivatives by alkaline hydrolysis. This dehydrogenase has unfortunately never been purified to any significant extent.

Very significant complementary evidence for the findings described in this paper is the report of LYNEN *et al.*[31] which recently appeared as our work was being completed. These investigators isolated from sheep liver in apparently pure form a dehydrogenase catalyzing the following reaction:

$$\text{Acetoacetyl-CoA} + \text{DPNH} + \text{H}^+ \rightleftharpoons \beta\text{-hydroxybutyryl-CoA} + \text{DPN}^+ \qquad (5)$$

The reaction was followed in the forward direction as written by measuring the disappearance of DPNH in the presence of enzymically formed acetoacetyl-CoA or, alternatively, in the presence of synthetic S-acetoacetyl-N-acetyl-cysteamine, a "model" of acetoacetyl-CoA. β-hydroxybutyryl-CoA was identified as the reduction product by the hydroxylamine reaction and paper chromatography of the hydroxamic acid. The reaction was found to be reversible and approximations of the equilibrium constant were made. The enzyme did not act on free acetoacetate or free β-hydroxybutyrate. The authors did not discuss the question of the stereochemical configuration or the rotation of the β-hydroxybutyryl-CoA formed. Their findings however furnished strong support-

References p. 202.

ing evidence for the reaction sequence postulated in this paper. This dehydrogenase is probably identical with that reported here and it appears quite probable from our work therefore that the β-hydroxybutyryl-CoA participating in the reaction catalyzed contains the d-isomer.

That acetoacetyl-CoA is the probable oxidation product of d-BOH in the extracts we have studied was indicated by the finding that on the addition of oxalacetate to a system composed of mitochondrial extract, ATP, excess CoA, Mg^{++}, d-BOH, and DPN$^+$, citrate was formed. Omission of any component caused complete or almost complete loss of the capacity to form citrate. Citrate was not formed from free acetoacetate under the same circumstances. See Table VIII. The formation of citrate from acetoacetyl-CoA occurs in two steps by already well-known reactions[32, 33]:

$$\text{Acetoacetyl-CoA} + \text{CoA} \rightleftharpoons 2 \text{ acetyl-CoA} \tag{6}$$

$$\text{Acetyl-CoA} + \text{oxalacetate} \rightleftharpoons \text{citrate} + \text{CoA} \tag{7}$$

Since the "condensing enzyme" catalyzing reaction (7) requires acetyl-CoA, either acetyl-CoA or a precursor of it must be formed in the oxidation of d-BOH. It is of course

TABLE VIII

FORMATION OF CITRATE FROM d-BOH

Systems contained 0.4 ml extract (3-C-7), 0.1 M KCl, 0.05 M "tris" buffer pH 8.0, 0.01 M cysteine, 0.025 M d-BOH or acetoacetate, 0.01 M oxalacetate, 0.005 M ATP, 0.005 M MgCl$_2$, and 0.001 M CoA. Total volume, 2.0 ml. Time, 60 minutes; temp. 22° C.

Substrate	System	Citrate formed micromoles
None	Complete	0.12
d-BOH	Complete	1.27
d-BOH	CoA omitted	0.16
d-BOH	ATP omitted	0.17
d-BOH	oxalacetate omitted	0.02
Acetoacetate	Complete	0.20
Acetoacetate	ATP omitted	0.18

most likely that acetoacetyl-CoA is formed directly by dehydrogenation of d-β-hydroxy-butyryl-CoA and is split to acetyl-CoA by reaction (6). The fact that "free" acetoacetate does not form citrate excludes it as a direct intermediate and also excludes the presence in the extracts used of the enzyme catalyzing the reaction

$$\text{Acetoacetate} + \text{CoA} \xrightarrow{\text{ATP}} \text{acetoacetyl-CoA} \tag{8}$$

Other properties of the d-BOH dehydrogenase system were examined. It was found, using extracts containing no detectable l-β-hydroxybutyric dehydrogenase activity, that higher β-hydroxy acids caused the reduction of DPN$^+$ at about the same rate as did d-BOH, namely dl-β-hydroxyoctanoate and dl-β-hydroxynonanoate. The optical isomers of these acids were not available for direct test, but it appeared probable that only the d-isomers underwent dehydrogenation since both ATP and CoA were absolute require-ments for the reduction of DPN$^+$. Triphosphopyridine nucleotide was not detectably reduced when it was substituted for DPN$^+$ in the d-BOH system.

The reduction of DPN$^+$ by d-BOH in the presence of ATP, CoA, and Mg^{++} was not inhibited by 0.005 M NaF and inhibited only 22% by 0.02 M NaF. The presence of orthophosphate did not increase the inhibition. It is therefore probable that reactions

References p. 202.

(3) and (4) are not the fluoride-sensitive points in the conversion of d-BOH to citrate observed in intact respiring mitochondria. It is of some interest in this connection that DRYSDALE AND LARDY[34] found no inhibitory effects of fluoride on the oxidation of (presumably) butyryl-CoA to acetoacetyl-CoA although the oxidation of fatty acids in intact mitochondria is inhibited by fluoride ($cf.$[26, 27, 28]).

The reduction of DPN+ by d-BOH was strongly inhibited by pyrophosphate (85% by 0.005 M pyrophosphate) but not by orthophosphate at concentrations up to 0.03 M. This finding would be expected, on the basis of mass action effects, if the activation reaction (3) is written in detail as follows:

$$\text{ATP} + \text{CoA} + \text{RCOOH} \rightleftharpoons \text{R—C—S—CoA} + \text{pyrophosphate} + \text{adenylate} \qquad (9)$$
$$\overset{\|}{\text{O}}$$

The activation of fatty acids apparently proceeds according to this general equation[35, 36].

There was no striking experimental evidence of a competitive antagonism between d- and l-BOH in the d-BOH reaction; the addition of 0.01 M l-BOH to a system acting on 0.01 M d-BOH had no detectable effect on the rate of reduction of DPN+. Much higher molar ratios of l-BOH to d-BOH were not tested. It should be pointed out, however, that without knowledge of which reaction is rate-limiting in the sequence of reactions (3) and (4) it cannot necessarily be concluded that competitive antagonism between d- and l-BOH or their CoA derivatives does not take place in either of the reactions in this sequence.

The reduction of DPN+ by d-BOH in the presence of ATP and CoA was not severely inhibited by hydroxylamine except at very high concentrations of the latter. For most effective trapping as the hydroxamic acid it was necessary to use 0.5 M hydroxylamine. In the presence of this concentration of hydroxylamine slight reduction of DPN+ could still be observed. This finding is consistent with the relatively low inhibitory effects of hydroxalamine on the fatty acid oxidase system in extracts of *C. Kluyveri*[37] and in mitochondrial extracts[34]. It appears probable that the ability of hydroxylamine to react non-enzymically with various acyl-CoA derivatives varies considerably. Acetyl-CoA is known to be trapped effectively at much lower hydroxylamine concentrations than the CoA derivatives of higher fatty acids ($cf.$ 38).

Some evidence was obtained that the dehydrogenation reaction (4) is reversible. When the extract is supplemented with excess acetate, ATP, CoA, Mg++, and DPNH, the DPNH is slowly reoxidized as indicated by disappearance of the characteristic absorption at 340 mμ. The reaction requires the presence of acetate, ATP, CoA, and Mg++. The reoxidation of DPNH presumably occurs by the intervention of the following known reactions:

$$\text{Acetate} + \text{CoA} \xrightarrow{\text{ATP}} \text{Acetyl-CoA} \qquad (10)$$

$$2 \text{ Acetyl-CoA} \rightleftharpoons \text{Acetoacetyl-CoA} + \text{CoA} \qquad (6)$$

$$\text{Acetoacetyl-CoA} + \text{DPNH} + \text{H}^+ \rightleftharpoons \beta\text{-hydroxybutyryl-CoA} + \text{DPN}^+ \qquad (5)$$

This experimental approach resembles that employed by LYNEN *et al.*[31].

It has been established that reaction (10) occurs in these extracts, by means of the hydroxylamine trapping reaction. Reaction (6), known to be reversible[32], is responsible for formation of acetyl-CoA from acetoacetyl-CoA in the citrate synthesis experiments just described and in citrate synthesis from fatty acids in mitochondrial extracts described by others[34]. Although the reoxidation of DPNH by acetate in the system described

References p. 202.

would be expected if reaction (5) is reversible, the data reported are probably not suffi-cient to establish reversibility of reaction beyond any doubt (4). However with the appearance of the work of LYNEN et al.[31], further work on this question appeared re-dundant.

DISCUSSION

The work reported in this communication demonstrates that d-β-hydroxybutyrate undergoes biological oxidation, and clarifies the mechanisms involved. It also indicates that d-β-hydroxybutyrate, and possibly higher d-β-hydroxy acids may be normal meta-bolic intermediates. This suggestion derives from the very probable reversibility of reaction (4) for which evidence has been presented by us and by LYNEN and his colleagues. It appears quite probable on the basis of current knowledge, that the oxidation of fatty acids follows the pattern:

$$RCH_2CH_2CH_2COOH + CoA \xrightarrow{ATP} RCH_2CH_2CH_2COCoA \qquad (11)$$

$$RCH_2CH_2CH_2COCoA \longrightarrow RCH_2CH = CHCOCoA + 2\,\varepsilon \qquad (12)$$

$$RCH_2CH = CHCOCoA + H_2O \longrightarrow RCH_2\underset{\underset{OH}{|}}{C}HCH_2\overset{\overset{O}{\parallel}}{C}CoA \qquad (13)$$

$$RCH_2\underset{\underset{O}{\parallel}}{C}HOHCH_2\overset{\overset{}{}}{C}CoA + DPN^+ \longrightarrow RCH_2\underset{\underset{O}{\parallel}}{C}CH_2COCoA + DPNH + H^+ \qquad (14)$$

followed by "thioclastic" cleavage[25] of the β-keto acid-CoA derivative to yield acetyl-CoA and a shortened fatty acid CoA derivative. Our work suggests that the β-hydroxy-acid participating as the CoA complex in these reactions may be in the dextrorotatory form.

It may be pointed out that longer chain dextrorotatory β-hydroxy acids have re-cently been isolated as hydrolysis products of certain complex lipids of micro-organisms[40].

The two different and specific mechanisms for dehydrogenation of the two isomers described in this report, taken together with the enzymic reactions of acetoacetate summarized by STERN et al.[32], also provide an enzymic mechanism for biological race-mization of β-hydroxybutyrate. This mechanism may be outlined briefly as follows: d-BOH, as its CoA derivative, may be oxidized to acetoacetyl-CoA, as already described. A deacylase exists, capable of hydrolyzing the latter, with the formation of free aceto-acetate, which may then be reduced reversibly to l-BOH by the l-β-hydroxybutyric dehydrogenase. The reverse transformation may take place by intervention of the enzyme catalyzing the formation of acetoacetyl-CoA at the expense of ATP. Although this en-zyme apparently has only limited activity in the liver, it is quite active in other tissues[32]. It appears possible that the general reaction pattern involved here may underlie other instances of biological racemization which are dependent on the "sparking" phenom-enon[41, 42]. Preliminary experiments by one of us (A.L.L.) suggest such a pattern to be involved in the enzymic oxidation of the stereoisomers of lactic acid.

In the work on intact mitochondria reported here it was observed that l-BOH gave rise to small but significant amounts of citrate. Although the liver appears not to attack free acetoacetate readily[24, 25, 39], it is possible that the citrate formed from l-BOH derives from acetoacetate, the major oxidation product of l-BOH. On the other hand, it is conceivable that l-β-hydroxybutyryl-CoA, which has been shown to be formed by mitochondrial extracts, may undergo dehydrogenation by an l-specific β-hydroxy-butyryl-CoA dehydrogenase. Although the mitochondrial extracts we have studied do not contain such an enzyme, it is possible it exists in intact mitochondria but is inactivated in the preparation of the extracts used.

SUMMARY

Both dextrorotatory and levorotatory forms of β-hydroxybutyric acid are oxidized aerobically by suspensions of rat liver and kidney particles (mitochondria). However the data clearly indicate that the initial stages of oxidation of the two isomers are quite different in liver, although ultimately both isomers are oxidized via the tricarboxylic acid cycle.

The enzymic mechanisms involved in the primary dehydrogenation of the two isomers were examined in clear extracts of acetone-dried mitochondria. It was found that the l-isomer causes the reduction of DPN$^+$, presumably by action of the already known l-specific DPN-linked β-hydroxy-butyric dehydrogenase, which of course does not attack the d-isomer. The d-isomer also causes reduction of DPN$^+$ but only if the extracts are supplemented with ATP, Coenzyme A, and Mg^{++}. Evidence is presented that d-BOH is capable of forming a CoA derivative at the expense of ATP:

$$d\text{-}\beta\text{-hydroxybutyrate} + \text{CoA} \xrightleftharpoons{\text{ATP}} d\text{-}\beta\text{-hydroxybutyryl-CoA} \qquad (1)$$

The extracts contain a dehydrogenase catalyzing reversibly the reduction of DPN$^+$ by d-β-hydroxy-butyryl-CoA

$$d\text{-}\beta\text{-hydroxybutyryl-CoA} + \text{DPN}^+ \rightleftharpoons \text{acetoacetyl-CoA} + \text{DPNH} + \text{H}^+. \qquad (2)$$

Reaction (1) is not stereochemically specific; both isomers form a CoA derivative. However the dehydrogenase catalyzing reaction (2) appears to be specific for d-β-hydroxybutyryl-CoA.

The metabolic significance of the pathways taken by the two isomers of β-hydroxybutyrate are briefly discussed.

RÉSUMÉ

Les formes lévogyres et dextrogyres de l'acide β-hydroxybutyrique sont toutes les deux oxydées en aérobiose par des suspensions de particules (mitochondries) du foie et du rein du rat. Cependant les résultats obtenus montrent clairement que les stades initiaux de l'oxydation des deux isomères sont complètement différents dans le foie, quoique en fin de compte les deux isomères soient oxydés par l'intermédiaire du cycle tricarboxylique.

Nous avons examiné les réactions enzymatiques qui interviennent dans la déshydrogénation initiale des deux isomères dans des extraits limpides de mitochondries séchées à l'acétone.

L'isomère L provoque la réduction du DPN$^+$, sans doute sous l'action de la déshydrogénase l-spécifique liée au DPN et déjà connue. Cette déshydrogénase n'agit naturellement pas sur l'isomère d-. L'isomère d provoque également la réduction du DPN$^+$, mais seulement dans le cas ou les extraits sont additionnés d'ATP, de coenzyme A, et de Mg^{++}. Nous fournissons la preuve que l'acide β-hydroxy-butyrique d'est capable de former un dérivé du CoA aux dépens de l'ATP:

$$d\text{-}\beta\text{-hydroxybutyrate} + \text{CoA} \xrightleftharpoons{\text{ATP}} d\text{-}\beta\text{-hydroxybutyryl-CoA} \qquad (1)$$

Les extraits renferment une déshydrogénase qui catalyse réversiblement la réduction du DPN$^+$ par le d-β-hydroxybutyryl-CoA.

$$d\text{-}\beta\text{-hydroxybutyryl-CoA} + \text{DPN}^+ \rightleftharpoons \text{acetoacetyl-CoA} + \text{DPNH} + \text{H}^+ \qquad (2)$$

La réaction (1) n'a pas de spécificité stéréochimique; les deux isomères forment un dérivé du CoA. Cependant la déshydrogénase qui catalyse la réaction (2) parait spécifique du d-β-hydroxybutyryl CoA.

Nous discutons brièvement la signification métabolique des chemins suivis par les deux β-hydroxybutyrates isomères.

ZUSAMMENFASSUNG

Sowohl die rechtsdrehende wie die linksdrehende Form von β-Oxybuttersäure wird aerobisch von Suspensionen von Rattenleber- und -nierenteilchen (Mitochondrien) oxydiert. Die Daten zeigen jedoch klar, dass die Anfangsstufen der Oxydation der beiden Isomeren in der Leber ganz verschieden sind, obwohl schliesslich beide Isomere über den Tricarbonsäurecyclus oxydiert werden.

Der Enzymmechanismus, der bei der primären Dehydrogenierung der zwei Isomieren eine Rolle spielt, wurde in den klaren Extrakten von mit Aceton getrockneten Mitochondrien geprüft. Es wurde gefunden, dass das l-Isomer die Reduktion von DPN$^+$ verursacht, vermutlich durch die Wirkung der schon bekannten l-spezifischen, mit DPN verbundenen β-Oxybuttersäuredehydrogenase, die natürlich das d-Isomer nicht angreift. Das d-Isomer verursacht ebenfalls die Reduktion der DPN$^+$, aber nur, wenn die Extrakte mit ATP, Coenzym A und Mg^{++} ergänzt werden. Es wird augenscheinlich dargelegt, dass die d-BOH zur Bildung eines CoA-Derivates auf Kosten der ATP fähig ist:

$$d\text{-}\beta\text{-Oxybuttersaures Salz} + \text{CoA} \xrightleftharpoons{\text{ATP}} d\text{-}\beta\text{-Oxybutyryl-CoA} \tag{1}$$

Die Extrakte enthalten eine Dehydrogenase, die die Reduktion der DPN$^+$ mit d-β-Oxybutyryl-CoA reversible katalysiert.

$$d\text{-}\beta\text{-Oxybutyryl-CoA} = \text{DPN}^+ \rightleftharpoons \text{Acetoacetyl-CoA} + \text{DPNH} + \text{H}^+ \tag{2}$$

Reaktion (1) ist nicht stereochemisch spezifisch; beide Isomere bilden ein CoA-Derivat. Jedoch erscheint die durch Dehydrogenase katalysierte Reaktion spezifisch für d-β-Oxybutyryl-CoA zu sein. Die Bedeutung des von den beiden Isomeren der β-Oxybuttersäure eingeschlagenen Reaktionweges für den Stoffwechsel wird kurz besprochen.

REFERENCES

[1] P. KARRER AND W. KLARER, *Helv. Chim. Acta*, 8 (1925) 393.
[2] P. A. LEVENE AND H. L. HALLER, *J. Biol. Chem.*, 67 (1926) 329.
[3] R. U. LEMIEUX AND J. GIGUERE, *Can. J. Chem.*, 29 (1951) 678.
[4] A. MAGNUS-LEVY, *Arch. exptl. Path. Pharmakol.*, 45 (1901) 389.
[5] D. E. GREEN, J. G. DEWAN AND L. F. LELOIR, *Biochem. J.*, 31 (1937) 934.
[6] A. McKENZIE, *J. Chem. Soc.*, 81 (1902) 1402.
[7] H. D. DAKIN, *J. Biol. Chem.*, 8 (1910) 97.
[8] E. FRIEDMANN, *Biochem. Z.*, 243 (1931) 125.
[9] A. L. GRAFFLIN AND D. E. GREEN, *J. Biol. Chem.*, 176 (1948) 95.
[10] H. A. LARDY AND G. FELDOTT, *Ann. N.Y. Acad. Sci.*, 54 (1951) 645.
[11] P. A. SHAFFER AND W. M. MARRIOTT, *J. Biol. Chem.*, 16 (1913–1914) 265.
[12] H. T. CLARKE, private communication.
[13] M. GEHRKE AND H. H. WILLRATH, *Z. physik. Chem.*, A142 (1929) 301.
[14] D. PRESSMAN AND H. J. LUCAS, *J. Am. Chem. Soc.*, 61 (1939) 2271.
[15] P. A. LEVENE AND H. L. HALLER, *J. Biol. Chem.*, 65 (1925) 49.
[16] C. P. LENOËL, *Bull. soc. chim. biol.*, 31 (1949) 1562.
[17] A. L. LEHNINGER AND E. P. KENNEDY, *J. Biol. Chem.*, 174 (1948) 883.
[18] W. C. SCHNEIDER, *J. Biol. Chem.*, 176 (1948) 259.
[19] F. LIPMANN AND L. C. TUTTLE, *J. Biol. Chem.*, 159 (1945) 21.
[20] E. R. STADTMAN AND H. A. BARKER, *J. Biol. Chem.*, 184 (1950) 769.
[21] J. F. SPECK, J. W. MOULDER AND E. A. EVANS, *J. Biol. Chem.*, 164 (1946) 119.
[22] S. NATELSON, J. K. LUGUVOY AND J. B. PINCUS, *J. Biol. Chem.*, 170 (1947) 597.
[23] S. S. BARKULIS AND A. L. LEHNINGER, *J. Biol. Chem.*, 190 (1951) 339.
[24] A. L. LEHNINGER AND S. W. SMITH, *J. Biol. Chem.*, 181 (1949) 415.
[25] A. L. LEHNINGER, *J. Biol. Chem.*, 164 (1946) 291.
[26] E. P. KENNEDY AND A. L. LEHNINGER, *Phosphorus Metabolism*, II, (1952) 253.
[27] R. B. JOHNSON AND H. A. LARDY, *J. Biol. Chem.*, 184 (1950) 235.
[28] V. H. CHELDELIN AND H. BEINERT, *Biochim. Biophys. Acta*, 9 (1952) 661.
[29] T. P. SINGER AND E. S. G. BARRON, *J. Biol. Chem.*, 157 (1945) 241.
[30] H. R. MAHLER, *Phosphorus Metabolism*, II (1952) 286.
[31] F. LYNEN, L. WESSELY, O. WIELAND AND L. RUEFF, *Angew Chem.*, 64 (1952) 687.
[32] J. R. STERN, M. J. COON AND A. DEL CAMPILLO, *Nature*, 171 (1953) 28.
[33] J. R. STERN, B. SHAPIRO, E. R. STADTMAN AND S. OCHOA, *J. Biol. Chem.*, 193 (1951) 703.
[34] G. R. DRYSDALE AND H. A. LARDY, *Phosphorus Metabolism*, II (1952) 281.
[35] F. LIPMANN, S. BLACK, M. E. JONES AND R. M. FLYNN, *Abstracts, 122nd Meeting, American Chemical Society*, September, 1952.
[36] S. WAKIL AND H. R. MAHLER, *Federation Proc.*, 12 (1953) 285.
[37] E. R. KENNEDY AND H. A. BARKER, *J. Biol. Chem.*, 191 (1951) 419.
[38] F. LIPMANN AND L. C. TUTTLE, *Biochim. Biophys. Acta*, 4 (1950) 301.
[39] S. WEINHOUSE, R. MILLINGTON AND M. E. VOLK, *J. Biol. Chem.*, 185 (1950) 191.
[40] R. LEMIEUX, *Can. J. Chem.*, 29 (1951) 415.
[41] F. M. HUENNEKENS, H. R. MAHLER AND J. NORDMANN, *Arch. Biochem. Biophys.*, 30 (1951) 66.
[42] H. R. MAHLER, A. TOMISEK AND F. M. HUENNEKENS, *Exptl. Cell. Research*, 4 (1953) 208.

Received April 17th, 1953

DEGRADATION OF ALDOSES BY MEANS OF THEIR DISULFONES

by

D. L. MacDONALD AND HERMANN O. L. FISCHER

Department of Biochemistry, University of California, Berkeley (U.S.A.)

The most elegant method to shorten the carbon chain of a sugar with regard to mildness of conditions and good yields is no doubt the splitting of the chain by lead tetra-acetate or periodic acid. Since both reagents however require as point of attack a pair of free hydroxyls on adjacent carbon atoms with the rest of the hydroxyls blocked by an easily removable substituent, it is not always easy to obtain a suitable starting material.

Good examples for this procedure are a series of reactions[1] leading from D-glucose, via D-sorbitol and 1,3-2,4-diethylidene D-sorbitol to diethylidene L-xylose which upon hydrolysis yields L-xylose, or the preparation of the same pentose[2] by oxidation of 2,4-benzylidene D-sorbitol with lead tetra-acetate and subsequent hydrolysis.

More generally applicable for the degradation of an aldose to the next lower sugar are the classical methods by WEERMANN, RUFF AND WOHL.

WEERMANN[3] degrades the amide of the easily prepared aldonic acid *e.g.* D-gluconic acid amide by means of sodium hypochlorite to D-arabinose. Since NaOCl also oxidizes the newly formed arabinose the yield leaves much to be desired.

A similar disadvantage is inherent in the well-known method of RUFF[4]. Here the aldonic acid is oxidized with hydrogen peroxide in the presence of ferric acetate. This method more recently has received much study and, in 1950, FLETCHER, DIEHL AND HUDSON[5] reported considerable improvements in the preparation of D-arabinose from calcium D-gluconate and D-lyxose from calcium D-galactonate. Ion-exchange resins, not available at the time of earlier work, were successfully used to remove gross quantities of organic and inorganic materials, thus greatly enhancing the yield of the pentose.

The well-known WOHL degradation[6] uses as starting material the sugar oximes and involves the removal of the cyanide group from the acetylated nitrile which can be formed from the oxime by acetylation with acetic anhydride and sodium acetate. Many papers are concerned with determining optimal conditions[7] for the degradation of the *acetylated* nitriles, but a later paper by WOHL AND WOLLENBERG[8] has found little attention. These authors demonstrate that the degradation of *free* gluconic acid nitrile by water at 100° yields pure crystalline D-arabinose in a yield of 84 per cent.

An interesting new method of sugar degradation, starting like the WOHL method from the oxime of aldoses, has recently been published by WEYGAND AND LÖWENFELD[9]. These authors react the oxime of an aldo sugar with 2,4-dinitrofluorobenzene, and the next lower aldose is formed along with 2,4-dinitrophenol and HCN.

Recently, a novel method of sugar degradation has been described[10] which utilizes the sugar *mercaptals* as the starting point for the conversion of a hexose into the corres-

References p. 206.

ponding pentose. The procedure involved acetylation of the hexose mercaptal, followed by oxidation by means of monoperphthalic acid in ether, to produce an acetylated disulfone. Treatment of this disulfone with hydrazine hydrate in methanol, followed by splitting the anticipated hydrazone with benzaldehyde, gave a solution from which the crystalline pentose could be isolated in good yield by deionization and concentration *in vacuo*.

The present paper reports on an improvement of this degradation scheme, in which the operations are simpler and much shorter, and the yield of pentose is equally as good as that previously obtained. One change was in the use of perpropionic acid rather than monoperphthalic acid. In the case of the latter oxidant, the phthalic acid formed is difficult to remove unless the oxidation product is soluble in chloroform, in which case, use can be made of the sparing solubility of phthalic acid in this solvent. The previously used *acetylated* sulfones were soluble in chloroform and thus their purification involved no difficulty. In the present communication, the unacetylated mercaptals were oxidized, and consequently another oxidant had to be chosen and perpropionic acid proved highly satisfactory. Perpropionic acid was used rather than peracetic acid, for there is much less danger attending the distillation of the former reagent.

When a hexose diethyl mercaptal such as that from D-mannose (I) was dissolved

$$
\begin{array}{ccc}
\text{HC—(SC}_2\text{H}_5)_2 & \text{HC—(SO}_2\text{C}_2\text{H}_5)_2 & \text{CH}_2(\text{SO}_2\text{C}_2\text{H}_5)_2 \\
| & | & \text{III} \\
\text{HO—C—H} & \text{HO—C—H} & \\
| & | & \text{HC}=\text{O} \\
\text{HO—C—H} & \text{HO—C—H} & | \\
| \quad \xrightarrow{\text{Perpropionic Acid}} & | \quad \xrightarrow{\text{Dilute NH}_4\text{OH}} & \text{HOCH} \\
\text{H—C—OH} & \text{H—C—OH} & | \\
| & | & \text{H—C—OH} \\
\text{H—C—OH} & \text{H—C—OH} & | \\
| & | & \text{H C—OH} \\
\text{CH}_2\text{OH} & \text{CH}_2\text{OH} & | \\
\text{I} & \text{II} & \text{CH}_2\text{OH} \\
& & \text{IV}
\end{array}
$$

in hot dioxane, and the solution cooled, but not sufficiently to cause crystallization of the mercaptal, the addition of perpropionic acid resulted in a rapid oxidation. Within a few minutes, the resulting disulfone (II) crystallized in yields of about 90 per cent. The exact nature of the oxidation product has not been worked out as yet, but two components were usually present in the crystalline mixture, as evidenced by paper chromatography. This complexity did not affect the subsequent steps, however. The air-dried product was slurried in water, and a drop of aqueous ammonia was added. The mixture undergoes a rapid change, with dissolution of the sugar derivative and concomitant precipitation of bis (ethanesulfonyl) methane (III), which can be removed by chloroform extraction. Concentration of the aqueous layer *in vacuo* gives crystalline D-arabinose (IV) in yields of 80–83%, having a rotation of —102 to —103°. The accepted specific rotation of D-arabinose et equilibrium in water is —104.5°.

Thus, the free, unacetylated sugar disulfone has to be treated at room temperature only with very dilute aqueous ammonia to cause complete splitting into bis-(ethanesulfonyl)-methane and the next lower sugar. In the case of the acetylated disulfones, hydrazine or hydroxylamine was required for the degradation, and thus our experiences are comparable to those of WOHL AND WOLLENBERG in that in each case the *un*acetylated compounds were found to degrade much more readily than the acetylated ones. It is

References p. 206.

hoped therefore that the method can be perfected so as to permit the degradation of the hexuronic acids to the corresponding penturonic acids. The physical and chemical properties of the latter having been ascertained, a search for these interesting compounds in nature might be successful.

The present authors wish to gratefully acknowledge that they were prompted to reinvestigate the degradation of the *un*acetylated sugar disulfones by observations made in our laboratory by Prof. ELVIN A. KABAT*. He was able to prepare the hitherto unobtainable disulfone derived from D,L-glyceraldehyde[11] by treating D,L-glyceraldehyde diethyl mercaptal with perpropionic acid in an anhydrous medium. This disulfone when treated with cold aqueous ammonia readily decomposed into bis (ethanesulfonyl)-methane and, most probably, glycolic aldehyde, but the latter compound has not yet been identified. Dr KABAT and the present authors plan to report about this at a later date.

EXPERIMENTAL

D-arabinose from D-mannose diethyl mercaptal

Two g of D-mannose diethyl mercaptal[12] were dissolved by warming in 40 ml of purified dioxane[13], the solution was cooled somewhat and distilled perpropionic acid[14] was added (15% excess over the required four moles). The solution became quite warm and within a few minutes the crystalline disulfone began to precipitate from solution. After 5 minutes, the mixture was placed in ice for a further ½ hour, then filtered and washed with cold dioxane to yield 2.20 g (90%) of the disulfone.

The crude disulfone was mixed with 40 ml of water and to the slurry there was added one drop of concentrated aqueous ammonia. Within a minute the precipitation of bis (ethanesulfonyl) methane was observable. After ½ hour at room temperature, the mixture was extracted four times with 20-ml portions of chloroform, and the aqueous layer was concentrated at reduced pressure (bath temperature below 55°). Final concentration in a vacuum over at 40° C, was followed by addition of methanol and crystallization at +4° C. In a typical experiment there was obtained 0.87 g of D-arabinose (83% based on the mercaptal) having $[a]_D^{25} = -102.8°$ (equilibrium, C, 4, water).

The chloroform extracts were dried (sodium sulfate) and concentrated at reduced pressure to give 1.09 g (78%) of bis (ethanesulfonyl) methane, which melted at 101–103° after recrystallization from water. A mixed melting point with authentic bis (ethanesulfonyl) methane was undepressed.

SUMMARY

A simple procedure is described for the degradation of hexoses to pentoses in excellent yields. The method involves oxidation of the hexose mercaptal to the disulfone, followed by treatment with very dilute aqueous ammonia, to give the pentose and bis(ethanesulfonyl)methane.

RÉSUMÉ

Une méthode simple pour la dégradation de hexoses aux pentoses à haut rapport est decrite. Ladite méthode utilise l'oxidation du mercaptal de l'hexose au disulfone, suivi par traitement avec une solution d'ammoniac aqueuse tres diluée, donnant le pentose et le bis(ethanesulfonile)methane.

ZUSAMMENFASSUNG

Es wird eine einfache Methode beschrieben, um Hexosen zu Pentosen in gute Ausbeute abzubauen. Zuerst wird das Merkaptal der Hexose zu dem entsprechenden Disulphon oxydiert. Das Disulphon zerfällt bei der Behandlung mit sehr verdünntem wässrigen Ammoniak in die nächstniedrige Pentose und Bis(ethansulphonyl)methane.

* On sabbatical leave in Berkeley from Columbia University, winter 1952–53.

References p. 206.

REFERENCES

[1] H. APPEL, *J. Chem. Soc.*, (1935) 425.
[2] L. v. VARGHA, *Ber.*, 68 (1935) 18, 1377.
[3] R. A. WEERMANN, *Rec. trav. chim.*, 37 (1917) 16.
[4] O. RUFF, *Ber.*, 31 (1898) 1573; 32 (1899) 550, 3672; 34 (1901) 1362; O. RUFF AND G. OLLENDORFF, *Ber.*, 33 (1900) 1798.
[5] *J. Am. Chem. Soc.*, 73 (1950) 4546.
[6] A. WOHL, *Ber.*, 26 (1893) 730; A. WOHL AND E. LIST, *Ber.*, 30 (1897) 3101; A. WOHL, *Ber.*, 32 (1899) 3666.
[7] G. ZEMPLÉN AND D. KISS, *Ber.*, 60 (1927) 165; V. DEULOFEU, *J. Chem. Soc.* (1930) 2602; R. C. HOCKETT, V. DEULOFEU, A. L. SEDOFF AMD J. R. MENDIVE, *J. Am. Chem. Soc.*, 60 (1938) 278.
[8] A. WOHL AND O. WOLLENBERG, *Ann.*, 500 (1932) 281.
[9] *Ber.*, 83 (1950) 559.
[10] D. L. MACDONALD AND H. O. L. FISCHER, *J. Am. Chem. Soc.*, 74 (1952) 2087.
[11] E. ROTHSTEIN, *J. Chem. Soc.*, (1940) 1560.
[12] E. FISCHER, *Ber.*, 27 (1894) 673.
[13] L. F. FIESER, *Experiments in Organic Chemistry*, 2nd Edition, Heath and Co., New York, N.Y., 1941, p. 368.
[14] J. D'ANS AND W. FREY, *Ber.*, 45 (1912) 1845.

Received April 20th, 1953

CO$_2$ TURNOVER IN THE FERMENTATION OF 3, 4, 5 AND 6 CARBON COMPOUNDS BY THE PROPIONIC ACID BACTERIA*

by

HARLAND G. WOOD AND F. W. LEAVER**

*Department of Biochemistry, Western Reserve University School of Medicine,
Cleveland, Ohio (U.S.A.)*

The principal products of fermentation of glucose, glycerol, and lactate by the propionic acid bacteria are propionate, acetate, succinate, and carbon dioxide. The following schematic diagram represents the most generally accepted mechanism by which these substrates are fermented.

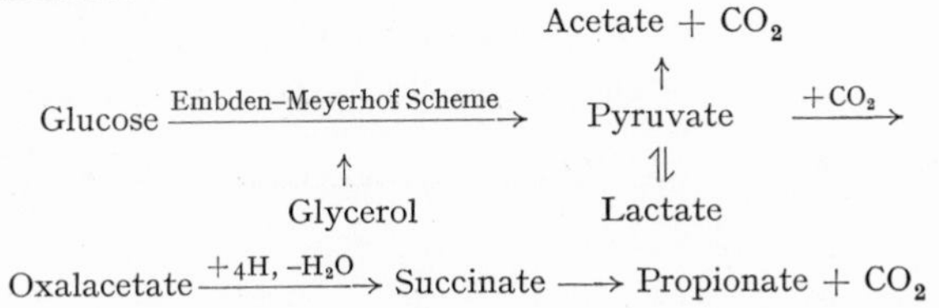

$$\text{Acetate} + \text{CO}_2$$
$$\uparrow$$
$$\text{Glucose} \xrightarrow{\text{Embden–Meyerhof Scheme}} \text{Pyruvate} \xrightarrow{+\text{CO}_2}$$
$$\uparrow \qquad\qquad \updownarrow$$
$$\text{Glycerol} \qquad\qquad \text{Lactate}$$
$$\text{Oxalacetate} \xrightarrow{+4\text{H},\ -\text{H}_2\text{O}} \text{Succinate} \longrightarrow \text{Propionate} + \text{CO}_2$$

Fig. 1

The evidence for this mechanism of dissimilation of glucose and glycerol rests mainly upon the following observations:

First, several of the intermediate compounds of the Meyerhof scheme have been isolated from the fermentations of glucose and glycerol[1,2,3], and have been shown to be utilized. Second, it has been shown that oxalacetate can be converted to succinic acid[4], and that succinic acid is decarboxylated to propionic acid and CO$_2$[5,6,7]. Third, ^{13}CO$_2$ was incorporated into the carboxyl carbons of succinate and propionate and the dilution of the final ^{13}CO$_2$ by ^{12}CO$_2$ arising from the substrate was of the proper magnitude to be explained by the above scheme[8].

However, several workers have pointed out that the scheme is not a complete explanation of the fermentation mechanism. WERKMAN et al.[9] have suggested that in addition to the Meyerhof scheme there is a second mechanism of glucose fermentation which is not fluoride sensitive. The scheme of Fig. 1 also is not entirely adequate because it indicates that the molar quantity of CO$_2$ should be equal to or less than the acetate, whereas in some fermentations the CO$_2$ is much greater than the acetate[10]. To account for this it has been proposed that the C$_2$ compound is in some way converted to succinate possibly by direct condensation[2,11] or via the Krebs cycle[12].

* Supported in part by grants from the Atomic Energy Commission and the Prentiss Foundation of Western Reserve University. The isotopes used in this investigation were received on allocation from the Atomic Energy Commission.

** Postdoctoral Fellow, National Institutes of Health. Present address: Department of Biochemistry, University of Pennsylvania School of Veterinary Medicine, Philadelphia, Pennsylvania.

References p. 221/222.

The propionic acid bacteria ferment 3, 4, 5, and 6 carbon polyalcohols and therefore present an unique opportunity to compare the fermentation of compounds of different length. Our present knowledge of the fermentation is based almost entirely on results from either 3 or 6 carbon substrates. It was considered possible that the fermentations of 4 and 5 carbon substrates might involve production or utilization of CO_2 to form 3 or 6 carbon compounds which then might be fermented by the usual mechanisms. If so, such a mechanism might be revealed either by an increased CO_2 turnover and increased fixation of CO_2 or fixation into positions other than the carboxyl groups. This possibility has been investigated in the present study. This work and other investigations have been discussed recently by LEAVER AND WOOD[13].

PRODUCTS FROM 3, 4, 5, AND 6 CARBON SUBSTRATES

The products of the fermentation of 3 to 6 carbon substrates are shown in Tables I, II, and III. The fermentations shown in Tables I and II are taken from experiments which

TABLE I

THE FERMENTATION OF 3, 4, 5 AND 6 CARBON SUBSTRATES BY PROLIFERATING CELLS OF
P. pentosaceum, 49W

No.	Substrate	mM of substrate fermented 100/ml	CO_2	Succinate	Propionate	Acetate	Pyruvate	Non-reducing sugar*	Carbon recovery %	O/R
			mM of products per 100/mM of substrate fermented							
1	Glycerol	21.8	—23.2	25.3	65.8	2.60	—	1.13	97.8	1.07
2	Erythritol	12.1	—17.6	21.3	95.0	5.99	1.61	1.19	94.8	0.94
3	Adonitol	12.5	— 5.16	21.1	116.7	15.9	0.28	0.57	93.2	0.96
4	Mannitol	10.6	23.6	9.34	150.1	25.0			93.5	1.04
5	Arabinose	11.0	41.0	14.3	104.5	42.3	1.05	0.26	100.1	0.93
6	Galactose	10.2	57.0	18.6	129.0	30.2			96.5	1.03

* Calculated from reducing value after hydrolysis, on the basis of a 6 carbon sugar with a reducing value equivalent to glucose[43].
   250 ml of medium containing 2.0 per cent. substrate, 1.75 per cent. sodium bicarbonate and 0.4 per cent. yeast extract in 300 ml flask; N_2 gas. Incubated 25 days at 30° C. Procedures and methods, WOOD AND WERKMAN[24].

TABLE II

FERMENTATION OF 3, 4, 5 AND 6 CARBON SUBSTRATES BY WASHED CELLS OF *P. pentosaceum*, 49W

No.	Substrate	mM of substrate fermented 100/ml	CO_2	Succinate	Propionate	Acetate	Alcohol	Non-reducing sugar	Formic acid	Carbon recovery %	O/R
			mM of products per 100/mM of substrate								
7	Glycerol	20.7	—32.7	36.1	57.9	2.47	1.77	0.0	0.0	98.7	1.06
8	Erythritol	4.92	—12.5	27.7	90.7	11.1	0.0	0.81	5.81	100.8	1.15
9	Adonitol	12.3	—24.6	48.8	92.1	8.41	0.46	4.72	0.91	98.9	1.05
10	Mannitol	10.5	— 3.33	38.6	123.8	21.2	0.82	5.90	0.29	100.5	1.04
11	Arabinose	12.1	+35.5	24.4	86.3	18.1	0.71	8.59	0.21	96.4	1.08

   2 per cent. substrate, 1.75 per cent. sodium bicarbonate and 2.7 per cent. wet cells; 150 ml in 300 ml flask under N_2. Temperature 30° C, time 10 days. Procedures and methods as in WOOD AND WERKMAN[24]. The fermentations were set up under sterile conditions with bacteria from 6 days growth on glycerol 1.0 per cent., yeast extract 0.4 per cent., and K-phosphate buffer 0.1 M, pH 7.2.

References p. 221/222.

were done several years ago, those in Table III are from experiments using $^{14}CO_2$ and were set up under conditions suitable for measurement of CO_2 turnover. The fermentations in Table I were with proliferating cells but in all other fermentations resting cells were used. Arabinose was included as representative of a pentose and galactose of a hexose which had not been previously studied.

The most noteworthy aspect of the results shown in these tables is that no matter what the length of the carbon chain of the substrate the products are identical and the amounts are very similar. This point is shown more clearly in Table IV in which the results are expressed on the basis of 300 mM of fermented carbon, i.e., equivalent to 100 mM of 3-carbon compounds. The level of oxidation or reduction of the substrate, of course, has an effect on the amounts of products in an anaerobic fermentation. Thus glycerol and pyruvate yield a different ratio of products (Table III); the fermentation

TABLE III

FERMENTATION OF 3, 4 AND 5 CARBON SUBSTRATES BY WASHED CELLS OF *P. arabinosum*, 34W

		mM per 100/mM of fermented substrate							
No.	Substrate	CO$_2$	Succinate	Propionate	Acetate	Formate*	Alcohol**	Carbon recovery %	O/R
12	Pyruvate	63.0	4.7	46.9	41.7	9.3	—	105	93
13	Glycerol	—6.6	10.1	97.4	0.0	0.0	—	108	1.05
14	Erythritol	6.2	3.4	100.0	8.1	20.1	13.8	99.5	95
15	Adonitol	20.7	11.7	101.5	47.6	4.0	13.5	103	1.18

* Formate has not been reported as a product of the propionic acid fermentation but it was found in significant amount – especially from erythritol, see also Table II.
** The alcohol was not identified and the values are the volatile acid resulting from oxidation of the neutral distillate. WOOD AND WERKMAN[24] have identified propyl alcohol as a product of glycerol fermentation and the balances are calculated on the basis that the alcohol is propyl alcohol.

100 ml of mixture in a 1 liter flask under N$_2$ at 20 to 30 cm Hg; 0.1 M substrate, 0.3 M K-phosphate buffer at pH 7.0, 5% wet cells, NaH^{14}CO$_3$ 0.01 to 0.03 M (cf. Table VI). Temperature 30° C. Time 43 h except for glycerol 20 h. The bacteria were from 3 days growth on 0.3% glycerol, 0.05% i-erythritol, 0.05% d-mannitol, 0.05% d-adonitol, 0.5% yeast extract and 0.01 M K-phosphate buffer at pH 7.0. The inoculum for the above medium was grown on 0.3% i-erythritol, 0.05% d-mannitol, 0.05% d-adonitol, 0.005% glucose, 0.5% yeast and 0.01 M phosphate buffer at pH 7.0. Methods were as described in text.

of pyruvate results in more CO_2 and less of the reduced product propionate than the fermentation of glycerol. In general the more reduced the substrate the greater was the utilization of CO_2.

The fact that the products of the 3, 4, 5, and 6 carbon compounds are identical and the relative amounts are similar if differences in the oxidation and reduction level of the substrates are taken into consideration is a very interesting observation, and at present there is no adequate explanation of the results. If erythritol underwent a simple cleavage, it would be expected to give rise to $C_3 + C_1$ compound, or to C_2 compounds. Since only small amounts of C_1 and C_2 compounds were formed, it is obvious that either the initial reaction was not a simple cleavage or extensive secondary conversion of the cleavage products must have occurred. The fact that all substrates gave similar products raises the question of whether or not these substrates are converted to 6 or 3 carbon compounds. For erythritol the following two examples may serve as illustrations:

References p. 221/222.

$$C_4 \to 2\,C_2;\ 2\,C_4 + 2\,C_2 \longrightarrow 2\,C_6 \tag{1}$$

$$2\,C_6 \longrightarrow 4\,C_3 \longrightarrow \text{products of fermentation}$$

The overall reaction is $3\,C_4 \longrightarrow 2\,C_6 \longrightarrow 4\,C_3 \longrightarrow$ products

$$C_4 \longrightarrow 2\,C_2;\ 2\,C_4 \longrightarrow 2\,C_3 + 2\,C_1;\ 2\,C_2 + 2\,C_1 \longrightarrow 2\,C_3 \tag{2}$$

The overall reaction is $3\,C_4 \longrightarrow 4\,C_3 \longrightarrow$ products

If the C_1 in the second example were CO_2 it is evident that it could be distinguished from the first mechanism by determination of the CO_2 turnover.

TABLE IV

RESULTS OF TABLE II EXPRESSED ON THE BASIS OF 300 MM FERMENTED CARBON

No.	Substrate	CO_2	Succinate	Propionate	Acetate	Alcohol	NRC	Formate
7	Glycerol	−32.7	36.1	57.9	2.47	1.77	0.0	0.0
8	Erythritol	− 9.4	20.8	68.0	8.32	0.0	0.6	4.36
9	Adonitol	−14.8	29.3	55.3	5.05	0.28	2.83	0.55
10	Mannitol	− 1.66	19.3	61.7	10.60	0.41	2.95	0.15
11	Arabinose	+ 21.3	14.6	51.8	10.9	0.43	5.15	0.13

With adonital and arabinose a cleavage to C_3 and C_2 compounds may be involved. The fermentation of pentose by *Lactobacillus pentosus* as investigated by FRED et al.[14] and more recently by the tracer technique by GEST AND LAMPEN[15] and BERNSTEIN[16] is an example of such a cleavage. A similar cleavage has been investigated with *Lactobacillus arabinosum* by RAPPOPORT et al.[17]. If such a cleavage occurs in the propionic acid fermentation the C_2 compounds must have been used in further conversion since per 100 mM of adonital fermented there is far less than the expected 100 mM of C_2 compounds. From the investigations of AKABORI[18], HORECKER[19], and RACKER[20] it has become evident that erythrulose and sedoheptulose may be involved in the formation of a C_3 from the pentose. These studies indicate that the fermentation of pentose may involve a rather complicated series of reactions.

TURNOVER STUDIES WITH $^{14}CO_2$

Present concepts of CO_2 turnover by the propionic acid bacteria are largely based on the observations of WOOD et al.[8] who obtained the following results from a fermentation of glycerol expressed as atom per cent excess ^{13}C: Original $CO_2 = 3.55$, final $CO_2 = 2.53$, COOH of propionate $= 1.17$ and COOH of succinate $= 1.12$. The ^{13}C of the carboxyl groups of succinate and propionate though not equal to one-half that of the average of the CO_2 did approach the theoretical values as required for the scheme given in Fig. 1.

ERB[21] and WERKMAN AND WOOD[5] (p. 151) found that succinate was decarboxylated by the propionic acid bacteria at pH 5.2 and propionate and CO_2 were formed[5], but the reaction rate was slow. However, DELWICHE[6] and JOHNS[7] concluded from their studies with these bacteria that propionate is most likely formed by this mechanism. At acid pH the rate of decarboxylation of succinate was found to be comparable to the rate of propionate formation. BARBAN AND AJL[22] have investigated the reversibility of the decarboxylation of succinate using resting cells of propionic bacteria, $^{14}CO_2$, succinate, fumarate and malate. It was found that the succinate was labelled but not the fumarate or malate. In the presence of ^{14}C-propionate the succinate became labelled. The rate of the reaction was not studied so the quantitative significance is difficult to judge.

It was decided to reinvestigate CO_2 turnover and fixation to determine if the turnover was sufficient to account for the formation of all the propionate by decarboxylation of succinate. For this purpose, the fermentations were conducted under partial vacuum in flasks 5 to 10 times the volume of the reaction mixture. The flasks were fitted with ground glass joints and were shaken continuously to ensure equilibration between the liquid and gas phases. [14]CO_2-NaH[14]CO_3 of known specific activity and amount was introduced into the closed system and from the dilution of the [14]CO_2 the CO_2 turned over in the reaction was estimated.

Calculations and assumptions

BARKER et al.[23] have pointed out that the total carbon dioxide production (CO_2 total) must exceed the observed or net carbon dioxide production (CO_2 observed) by the amount used for synthetic reactions (CO_2 used) i.e.

$$CO_2 \text{ total} = CO_2 \text{ observed} + CO_2 \text{ used}$$

If the CO_2 observed is negative, the above equation still applies.

The following equation has been derived by BARKER et al.[23] for the purpose of calculation of the CO_2 used and thus the CO_2 total.

$$A = \log \frac{X_i}{X_f} \bigg/ \log \frac{V_f}{V_i} \tag{1}$$

Where: A is a proportionality factor ($A \times CO_2 \text{ observed} = CO_2 \text{ used}$)

$X_i =$ the total counts in the initial CO_2

$X_f =$ the total counts in the final CO_2

$V_i =$ the mM of initial CO_2

$V_f =$ the mM of final CO_2

The following assumptions are inherent in the derivation of the equation:

1. That A as defined above applies, i.e. the fermentation is uniform (stoichiometric) during the entire course of the reaction and that for every mole of CO_2 observed (net production or net utilization) there is a proportional amount of CO_2 used.

2. That there are no secondary conversions of the end products that cause a change in the ^{14}C concentration of the CO_2.

3. That the CO_2 inside and outside of the cell are in isotopic equilibrium at all times.

4. That the fermenting system does not differentiate between compounds containing ^{12}C and those containing [14]C.

The validity of each of these assumptions as applied to the propionic acid fermentation will be considered briefly.

The assumption that the fermentation is uniform may not be completely valid under some conditions. This has been shown by WOOD et al.[2, 24] in fermentations of glucose and glycerol with proliferating cells grown over a long period of time (0 to 30 days). The present fermentations were conducted for a relatively short period of time and though a thorough study was not made there was no indication of a gross variation of products in fermentations of short duration with resting cells.

References p. 221/222.

The assumption that there are no secondary conversions of the end products that cause a change in the ^{14}C concentration of the CO_2 has been investigated and it has been found not to be valid. Experiments testing this point are shown in Table V in which glycerol fermentations were conducted with ^{14}C-propionate added at the beginning of

TABLE V

METABOLISM OF ^{14}C-PROPIONATE DURING GLYCEROL FERMENTATION

No.	Labelled position	mM per 100/ml			Total counts			% of added ^{14}C in final CO_2	Distribution of ^{14}C in propionate		
		Initial propionate	Initial CO_2	Final CO_2	Initial propionate	Initial CO_2	Final CO_2		CH_3	cpm per μM CH_2	COOH
17	COOH	0.83	12.5	11.0	40,500	0	9,300	23.0	—	—	1.81**
18*	CH_3	3.23	12.5	10.8	12,150	0	0	0	0.486	0.375	0.00

* The distribution of ^{14}C in the succinate was 0.054 in the COOH and 0.540 in the CH_2 in cpm per μM. By total carbon the succinate contained 1.165 cpm per μM, the propionate 0.865 cpm per μM.
** The propionate was not degraded, all the ^{14}C has been assumed to be in the carboxyl group.
Fermentation No. 23 of Table VIII was set up simultaneously with these fermentations as a control for measurement of CO_2 turnover. The glycerol fermented and mM of products were very similar in the three fermentations.
The conditions of fermentation were the same as No. 20, 21, 22 of Table VIII except there was 60 ml of reaction mixture and in Fermentation 17 propionate-1-^{14}C (48.9 cpm per μM) and in Fermentation 18 propionate-3-^{14}C (3.65 cpm per μM) were added. Time was 40 h. Culture 34W. Procedures are given in the text.

the fermentation. It is seen in Fermentation 17 that 23.0% of the ^{14}C added as carboxyl labelled propionate was converted to CO_2. The methyl group of propionate was not oxidized to CO_2 but it is clear that the propionate was metabolized because the ^{14}C was 87% randomized in the α and β positions $(0.375 \times 2/0.486 + 0.375)$. The succinate from this fermentation was degraded and it was found to be labelled in the methylene positions with somewhat higher activity than the propionate. The results are thus in accord with the view that the randomization of α and β carbons of propionate via conversion to a C_4-dicarboxylic acid. The higher activity of the succinate than propionate is probably due to the incorporation of high activity propionate early in the fermentation and failure to equilibrate with low activity propionate late in the fermentation. In other experiments which will be published elsewhere it has been found by incubation of resting cells with propionate-3-^{14}C and succinate, that the isotope becomes completely randomized in the α and β carbons of propionate but the succinate only reaches 15% of the activity of the final propionate. This is interpreted as an indication that extracellular succinate may equilibrate with intracellular succinate slower than do the corresponding propionate "pools". The present results are very similar to results obtained independently by DELWICHE et al.[25]. They have found with an enzyme preparation from propionic acid bacteria that succinate-1,2-^{14}C is formed from propionate-2-^{14}C, $^{14}CO_2$ and unlabelled succinate, but the incorporation of ^{14}C from propionate is fifty to seventy times that from $^{14}CO_2$. Likewise the yield of propionate-1-^{14}C was twenty times that of $^{14}CO_2$ from succinate-1-^{14}C. ATP and CoA were required for the reaction. Likewise WHITELEY[26] has found with extracts of Micrococcus lactilyticus that ATP, CoA and cocarboxylase stimulate the decarboxylation of succinate. From the standpoint of the present discussion the important point is that the exchange of the carboxyl group of propionate with CO_2 is slower than is the randomization of the α and β carbons. It would appear that randomization via a C_4-dicarboxylic acid can occur without equivalent conversion of the

References p. 221/222.

carboxyl group to $^{14}CO_2$. Possibly the C_1 formed during the decarboxylation of the C_4-dicarboxylic acid remains linked with CoA and thus does not equilibrate with the CO_2. This problem will be discussed further in relation to the CO_2 turnover studies.

Although the assumption that there is no significant secondary conversions of the end products which will cause a change in the ^{14}C concentration of the CO_2 is not valid, for purposes of the present investigation the error is not serious. It is seen in Tables VIII and IX that the carboxyl groups of the propionate and succinate always contain less activity than the final $^{14}CO_2$. There is little or no net change in the amount of propionate or succinate under conditions in which the α and β carbons of propionate are randomized. Thus if the exchange of $^{14}CO_2$ with the carboxyls of propionate and succinate occurs by this conversion, it will introduce ^{14}C into the carboxyls and decrease the ^{14}C in the CO_2. Thus it will decrease x_f. It is apparent from Equation I that this will increase the value of A and thus the calculated $CO_{2\ used}$ and $CO_{2\ total}$ will be higher than that which would have been obtained if no secondary reactions were occuring. Since the principal conclusion made from the CO_2 turnover studies is that the $CO_{2\ total}$ or $CO_{2\ produced}$ is lower than predicted from generally accepted concepts of the fermentation, the error will not favour or invalidate these conclusions. It therefore seems justified to use the calculation with due realization of limited accuracy.

The validity of the assumption of equilibration of the CO_2 inside and outside of the cell has not been tested. If equilibrium is not attained, the calculated $CO_{2\ used}$ will be low since less $^{14}CO_2$ will be taken up by the cell and therefore the dilution of the $^{14}CO_2$ would be less than assumed for the calculation.

Nothing has been done to determine whether the cells distinguish between ^{12}C and ^{14}C, although this is known to occur in some reactions.

The above discussion serves to emphasize the difficulties that must be confronted in turnover studies. It is to be noted that the present conditions involving a unicellular organism in a homogeneous suspension in a controlled atmosphere in a closed system are more favourable for such studies than is possible in many investigations.

CO_2 turnover and fixation with 3, 4 and 5 carbon compounds. The calculated values for CO_2 utilization and production during fermentation of 3, 4, and 5 carbon compounds are shown in Table VI and the distribution of the fixed ^{14}C in the products in Table VII.

TABLE VI

CO₂ TURNOVER CALCULATED FROM $^{14}CO_2$ DILUTION

		mM 100/ml			cpm μM		mM/100 mM substrate		
No.	Substrate	Substrate fermented	Initial CO₂	Final CO₂	Initial CO₂	Final CO₂	Calculated CO₂ used (a)	CO₂ observed (b)	Calculated CO₂ produced (CO₂ total) (a + b)
12	Pyruvate	7.04	1.16	5.59	83.8	15.8	3.8	63.0	66.8
12	Glycerol	6.95	2.27	1.81	78.4	65.2	12.0	—6.6	5.4
14	Erythritol	4.33	2.31	2.58	83.8	53.7	18.6	6.2	24.8
15	Adonitol	7.45	2.27	3.81	78.4	23.8	26.8	20.7	47.5

(a) Calculated by Equation 1.
See Table III and Table VII for additional data on these fermentations.

The calculated values for $CO_{2\ produced}$ from glycerol, erythritol and adonitol were respectively 5.4, 24.8 and 47.5 mM per 100 mM of fermented substrate. It is seen in Table III that approximately 100 mM of propionate were produced per 100 mM sub-

References p. 221/222.

strate in each case. Thus only in the case of adonitol was there a production of $^{12}CO_2$ which approached 50 mM as predicted from the scheme of Fig. 1. However, this production of CO_2 may not be intimately related to the formation of propionate as such but rather be inherent in the fermentation of the 5 carbon substrate. The following example is presented only as an illustration:

$$3\,C_5 \longrightarrow 3\,C_3 + 3\,C_2;\ C_2 \longrightarrow 2\,C_1$$
$$2\,C_2 + 2\,C_1 \longrightarrow 2\,C_3$$

The overall reaction is $3\,C_5 \longrightarrow 5\,C_3 \longrightarrow$ products.

The $C_2 + C_1$ reaction might be an alpha carboxylation such as the reverse of the so-called phosphoroclastic reaction to yield pyruvate[27],[28],[29] or perhaps some modification of the beta fixation with formaldehyde of which the condensation with glycine to form serine serves as an example[30],[31]. The fact that the propionic acid bacteria utilize formaldehyde and incorporate it in all positions of propionate[32] and also produce formaldehyde[33],[34] from glucose and glycerol makes this latter hypothesis attractive.

Inspection of the data from the glycerol fermentation in Table VI indicates clearly the small CO_2 turnover with this substrate. 6.95 mM of glycerol were fermented and it was converted almost entirely to propionate. According to the scheme of Fig. 1, 6.95 mM of CO_2 would be produced and one-half would be of substrate origin, thus 3.5 mM of $^{12}CO_2$ would be produced. There were only 2.27 mM of $^{14}CO_2$ present in the pool so that direct dilution should have reduced the specific activity by more than half whereas it was actually reduced from 78.4 to 65.2 cpm/perμM or only 17%. It thus appears quite certain than the major part of the propionate was not formed in this case by decarboxylation of succinate with formation of free CO_2.

If the mechanism of propionate formation is by decarboxylation of succinate or a C_4-dicarboxylic acid it appears that a "C_1" other than CO_2 must be formed. Evidence pointing to this possiblity has already been presented in discussing the assumptions made in the calculation of turnover and the idea of a "C_1" not identical with CO_2 was suggested earlier by LEAVER AND WOOD[13]. Furthermore, there is good reason to reserve judgment on the mechanism of propionate formation because there is evidence that propionate can be formed by certain organisms without the occurrence of a C_4 dicarboxylic acid as an intermediate. CARDON AND BARKER[35] and JOHNS[36] have presented results with *Clostridium propionicum* that indicate there is a direct reduction of lactate to propionate, possibly via acrylate. Recently LEAVER[37] has provided additional evidence supporting this possibility in that the fermentation of lactate-3-^{14}C by *C. propionicum* led to almost quantitative formation of propionate-3-^{14}C. On the other hand with *P. arabinosum* the ^{14}C from lactate was almost completely randomized in the 2, 3 positions of the propionate, as would be expected if a symmetrical C_4-dicarboxylic acid were an intermediate. However, the finding that propionate may undergo secondary reactions in which the ^{14}C of propionate is randomized (Table V) makes it necessary to leave open the possibility that the propionate is in part at least, first formed by direct reduction of a C_3 compound and only by secondary reactions is randomized. It likewise is possible that formation of propionic acid by *C. propionicum* involves a C_4-dicarboxylic acid but it does not pass through a symmetrical form.

These observations indicate that: (1) there is a biological mechanism for formation of propionate by direct reduction, (2) in the propionic acid fermentation, the CO_2 turnover is too low to indicate that all the propionate is formed by decarboxylation of

References p. 221/222.

succinate to propionate and CO_2, (3) there is a mechanism for randomization of the 2 and 3 positions of propionate, and (4) there is evidence that a C_1 other than CO_2 may be formed in the conversion of succinate to propionate. It is apparent that further study is required before it is possible to determine whether or not propionate can be formed without involvement of a C_4-dicarboxylic acid.

The CO_2 turnover studies with erythritol and adonitol are of additional interest as related to the mechanism of fermentation of 4 and 5 carbon compounds. The results in Table VI indicate that extensive formation of exchangeable CO_2 is not a characteristic of these fermentations. Furthermore, judging from the distribution of the fixed $^{14}CO_2$, in the products, these fermentations do not involve CO_2 fixation mechanisms which differ from those occurring during dissimilation of C_6 and C_3 compounds. This is shown in Table VII in which the fixed $^{14}CO_2$ is confined almost entirely to carboxyl groups

TABLE VII

DISTRIBUTION OF FIXED $^{14}CO_2$ IN THE PRODUCTS OF FERMENTATION BY CULTURE 34W

No.	Substrate	Propionate			Succinate		Acetate cpm/μM
		Total cpm/μM	COOH cpm/μM C	α, β C cpm/μM C	Total cpm/μM	COOH cpm/μM C	
12	Pyruvate	2.04					0.14
14	Erythritol	9.75	9.70		16.8	8.38	
16	Erythritol	10.4	10.4	0.04	17.3		0.12
15	Adonitol	8.83	8.55	0.16	17.3	8.70	0.21
25	Glucose	12.0	12.0	0.06	19.8		0.111*

* The acetate was degraded and found to contain 0.058 cpm/μM in the carboxyl group and 0.053 cpm/μM in the methyl group. The counting was done on a flow counter and was at a level of 8 and 7 cts. above background. The background count was 24.

Fermentation 16 was similar to Fermentation 14, see Table III.
Fermentation 25 is described in Table IX.

just as found previously with C_3 and C_6 substrates. Thus the CO_2 turnover and CO_2 fixation studies provide no definite clues as to the mechanism of these interesting fermentations. Further speculation does not seem profitable at present although it is attractive to consider that C_1 compounds such as formaldehyde may play a role in these fermentations[13,32,34].

Conditions necessary for extensive CO_2 fixation in glycerol fermentations. It is apparent that the fixation of CO_2 as reported in the experiments of Table III was far less than in those presented in Table II. Different species of bacteria were used and it seemed possible that this was the cause of the variation. A further difference was the method of growing the cells. The cells used in Table III were cultivated by a special regime with polyhydric alcohols as substrates. This was done in order to obtain cells which were quite active on all four substrates, glycerol, erythritol, adonitol, and mannitol. On the other hand the cells used in Table II were grown on a glycerol-phosphate-yeast extract medium[38]. It has previously been found[38] that the ability to fix CO_2 is markedly influenced by the composition of the growth medium and by far the best results were obtained using the latter medium.

It seemed advisable to determine if fixation of $^{14}CO_2$ during glycerol fermentation similar to those previously reported[8,38] could again be obtained. A number of preliminary tests were run with bacteria grown on the glycerol-phosphate-yeast extract medium

References p. 221/222.

TABLE VIII
CO_2 TURNOVER AND FIXATION IN GLYCEROL FERMENTATIONS

No.	Culture*	mM per 100 ml			Products per 100 mM of glycerol fermented					cpm/μM			
		Glycerol fermented	Initial CO_2	Final CO_2	Volatile acid m. eq.	Non-volatile Acid m.g q.	CO_2 Fixed	Calculated CO_2 used	Calculated CO_2 produced (CO_2 total)***	Initial CO_2	Final CO_2	Propionate	Succinate
19	34 W	7.56	3.36	3.36	77.9	19.3	10.8	12.6	1.80	20.2	19.3	2.92	4.68
20	19	7.34	12.50	10.40	76.8	58.0	31.4	42.4	11.0	25.2	23.6	6.60	13.40
21	19	9.33	12.50	10.43**	68.3	44.4	22.2**	52.5	30.3	25.2	19.7	9.85	15.80
22	49 W	9.87	12.50	11.11	68.9	31.0	14.1	29.2	15.1	25.2	22.2	—	—
23	34 W	8.98	12.50	11.00	76.6	28.8	16.7	48.9	32.2	26.0	20.3	8.61	—

* 34 W = *P. arabinosum*; 19 = *P. shermanii*; 49 W = *P. pentosaceum*.
** Calculated value on basis of mM CO_2 fixed equal the mM succinate.
*** Calculated from Equation 1.

These fermentations were set up in evacuated round bottom 300 ml flasks fitted with ground glass joints carrying a gas inlet and dropping funnel. The gas phase was the CO_2 liberated from the bicarbonate after addition of the phosphate buffer. Incubation at 30° with shaking. The fermentations were stopped by addition of acid and the CO_2 was removed by aeration into 3.0 N NaOH. The propionate and succinate were isolated by chromatography. Methods are given in text.

Fermentation 19: Medium 60 ml, 0.033 M NaH¹⁴CO₃, 0.3 M K-phosphate buffer pH 7.0, 0.08 M glycerol, 5 %, bacteria grown as described in Table III. Time 24 h.

Fermentations 20, 21, 22, 30 ml, No. 23, 60 ml, 0.125 M NaH¹⁴CO₃, 60 ml. 0.075 M K-phosphate buffer pH 5.9, 0.1 M glycerol, bacteria 5 %. Bacteria grown 5 days on glycerol 0.5 % yeast extract 0.5 %, 0.05 M K- phosphate buffer at pH 6.8, 1.0 mg Ca pentothenate, 1.0 mg thiamin HCl and 0.4 mg biotin per liter. Time 50 h, except No. 23 was 21 hours.

using cultures 19, 34W, and 49W but low fixation values were obtained. Among other factors tested was supplementation of the growth medium with B vitamins, and with the bacteria from such media somewhat better fixation was obtained; representative results are shown in Table VIII. A complete analysis of the products was not attempted in these fermentations. The non-volatile and votatile acids were titrated and the propionate and succinate were isolated by chromatography. It is seen in Fermentation No. 21 and No. 23 that the results are very similar to those previously obtained with *P. pentosaceum*[8]. For example in No. 21 the specific activity of the propionate (9.85 cpm/μM) was half that of the final CO$_2$ (19.7 cpm/μM) and there was considerable dilution of the added ^{14}CO$_2$. In this case of the calculated CO$_{2\,used}$ was 52.5 and the ^{12}CO$_2$ produced was 30.3 as compared to approximately 34.1 required by the scheme of Fig. 1. It is noted in Fermentation 20 that a really substantial amount of CO$_2$ was fixed, 31.4 mM, and the carboxyls of succinate and propionate have a high specific acticity. Nevertheless the dilution of the ^{14}CO$_2$ was not large and the calculated CO$_2$ produced was only 11.0 mM per 100 mM of fermented glycerol. This shows that there can be formation of propionate and also substantial fixation of CO$_2$ into propionate without a large turnover of CO$_2$.

At present it is not possible to give an adequate explanation of the variation in capacity of different cell preparations of fix CO$_2$. It is usually has been assumed that the primary fixation reaction in the propionic acid bacteria is in oxalacetate. Actually no studies have been made with these bacteria on CO$_2$ fixation in oxalacetate and subsequent to the original proposal a number of other mechanisms for fixation have been found which may play a part. Interest in the possibility that fixation of CO$_2$ may occur by combination with propionate[39] has been stimulated by the recent studies of BARBAN AND AJL[22], DELWICHE *et al.*[25], LARSEN[40], LARDY[41], and our investigation on randomization of the isotope of propionate-3-^{14}C and incorporation of the latter into succinate. An important question is whether or not the CO$_2$ is fixed directly in propionate to yield succinate. LARDY[41] has proposed a very intriguing scheme for CO$_2$ fixation in which the propionate is activated by formation of an acyl linkage with the sulfhydryl group on the enzyme. The methyl group is pictured as reacting with a second sulfhydryl thus forming a ring structure. This is followed by a cleavage of the acyl linkage. Carbonic acid is activated by reacting with a sulfhydryl and combination with the propionate then occurs to yield succinate. It is apparent that this scheme offers possibilities of explaining the formation of a "C$_1$" from succinate that is not in equilibrium with CO$_2$ and also a mechanism for randomization of the α and β carbons propionate. It is of interest that fixation of CO$_2$ in oxalacetate, malate and succinate could in each case occur by an identical C$_3$ + CO$_2$ reaction in the sulfhydryl complex, the major difference in the reaction brought about by the enzymes being the stage at which the C$_4$-sulfhydryl complex is cleaved. Thus oxidation of propionate to the pyruvate level might occur as the sulfhydryl complex and fixation take place at the oxalacetate level. The cleavage of the C$_4$ acid might occur only after succinate is formed by reduction of the formed oxalacetate. The non-equilibration of succinate with fumarate and malate as found by BARBAN AND AJL[22] might thus be explained.

The variation in the capacity of different cell preparations to fix or exchange CO$_2$ may lie in their ability to catalyze the reaction "C$_1$" $\rightleftharpoons$ CO$_2$ or to form the "C$_1$" sulfhydryl complex.

It is of interest that CO$_2$ is fixed only in the carboxyl group whereas formaldehyde is fixed in every position of propionate, succinate, and acetate[13]. Thus the "C$_1$" formed

References p. 221/222.

from CO_2 is not convertible to the "C_1" from formaldehyde metabolism. It thus seems likely that two different C_1 compounds may play a role in the fermentation.

NaF inhibition of CO_2 utilization. It was observed by WOOD AND WERKMAN[38] that NaF inhibited the net fixation of CO_2 in glycerol fermentations. Accompanying this, there was inhibition of succinate formation. In the fermentations of glucose, the inhibition of succinate formation was not complete and it seemed possible that there was a fluoride intensitive mechanism of succinate production which was independent of CO_2 fixation. However, it was observed in unpublished experiemnts[5] (p. 149), that the NaF did not prevent the incorporation of $^{13}CO_2$ into the carboxyl groups of propionate and succinate during glucose or glycerol dissimilation. These observations seemed of sufficient interest to warrant further investigation. The results are shown in Table IX. Unfortunately, the final CO_2 collections were not quantitative due to an accident so that the net CO_2 fixed or produced could not be determined directly. However, it is apparent from Table IX that NaF inhibited the formation of non-volatile acids. It has been shown[24,38] that in glycerol fermentations succinate is the only non-volatile acid formed

TABLE IX

EFFECT OF NaF ON FERMENTATION BY CULTURE 19 (*P. shermanii*)

No.	Substrate	NaF Present	Substrate fermented mM/100ml	Volatile acid meq/100 mM substrate	Non-volatile acid meq/100 mM substrate	Non-reducing sugar* mM/100 mM substrate	Initial CO_2 cpm/μM	Final CO_2 cpm/μM	Average CO_2 cpm/μM	Propionate cpm/μM	Succinate cpm/μM
21	Glycerol	No	9.33	68	44		25.2	19.7	22.4	9.85	15.8
24	Glycerol	Yes	4.56	54	4.1		25.2	23.6	24.4	4.71	11.1
25	Glucose	No	4.96	129	39	19.5	25.2	15.2	20.2	12.04	19.8
26	Glucose	Yes	4.69	136	6.5	8.6	25.2	14.7	20.0	8.86	17.1

Fermentations were set up the same as Fermentations 20, 21, and 22 in Table VIII except that when glucose was used it was 0.05 M, the NaF was 0.015 M, and the cells were 2.3%. The propionate and succinate were isolated by chromatography and were oxidized to CO_2 for radioactivity measurement. Procedures are given in the text. The ^{14}C distribution in the succinate, propionate and acetate of Fermentation 25 is shown in Table VII.
* See footnote to Table I.

and that an almost equivalent amount of CO_2 is utilized. It is therefore quite certain that NaF inhibited CO_2 utilization and succinate formation in the present experiment The CO_2 produced in Fermentation 21 has been calculated to be 30.3 mM per 100 mM of glycerol, Table VIII. For this calculation the assumption was made that the net CO_2 fixed was equal to the succinate formed. On a similar basis it may be calculated that the CO_2 produced in Fermentation 24 was 16.7 mM when NaF was added. It is noted that in both the glycerol and glucose fermentations the specific activity of the propionate and succinate was reduced in the presence of NaF.

Two possible explanations of the results are suggested. One is that there are two mechanisms of fixation of CO_2 occurring simultaneously and that one of these leads to a net uptake of CO_2 and formation of succinate and is inhibited by NaF, whereas the second is insensitive to NaF and does not lead to a net uptake of CO_2. It is possible that the fluoride sensitive mechanism involves phosphopyruvate and that NaF prevents the generation of the phosphopyruvate which is essential for the fixation. This possibility is attractive because UTTER AND KURAHASHI[42] have recently shown that the fixation of

References p. 221/222.

CO_2 in oxalacetate by chicken liver enzymes involves phosphopyruvate and the reaction occurs as follows:

$$\text{Phosphopyruvate} + CO_2 + \text{ADP} \rightleftharpoons \text{Oxalacetate} + \text{ATP}$$

The fluoride intensitive mechanism might be responsible for the randomization of propionate-3-^{14}C and the reaction through which propionate is formed or equilibrated with C^4-dicarboxylic acids. As noted previously, this reaction may be more complex than a direct reversible decarboxylation of succinate.

The other explanation is that only one mechanism of fixation is involved and that the inhibition is never complete but is sufficient to reduce the fixation to a point where there no longer is a net uptake of CO_2.

At the present time there is insufficient data to decide between these two alternatives or other possibilities which have not been discussed.

There is one other point of interest in the fluoride experiments. This is the fact that that the formation of the non-reducing carbohydrate from glucose[43] is inhibited by fluoride[38]. At present nothing is known about this compound.

METHODS

The following designations have been assigned to the various strains of propionic acid bacteria used in these fermentations: 19 *P. shermanii*, 34W *P. arabinosum*, 49W *P. pentosaceum*.

The procedures and methods employed in the fermentations reported in Tables I and II are the same as those used by WOOD AND WERKMAN[24].

The analytical procedures employed for the experiments reported in Tables III, IV, VI, and VII were as follows:

At the conclusion of the incubation period the medium was made acid with $5 N H_2SO_4$ and the CO_2 was swept out with N_2. The CO_2 was trapped in $3 N$ sodium hydroxide in a weighed CO_2 collector. After the CO_2 was removed, the bacteria were centrifuged in a Sorval centrifuge, and were washed by suspending in 20 ml of distilled water and recentrifuged. This washing was repeated twice. The solutions were neutralized, combined, and diluted to volume.

The unfermented polyhydric alcohols were determined on an aliquot by the periodate method[44], the pyruvic acid by ceric sulfate oxidation[45] and the residual glucose by the SOMOGYI method[46]. The remainder of the solution was distilled to one-half its volume and the neutral volatile alcohols were determined in the distillate[47].

The residue of this distillation was acidified to congo red and extracted continuously with ether 32–48 hrs. The volatile acids were removed from the extract by twelve volume distillation and were titrated. The respective acids were separated on a silica gel column according to the method described by ELSDEN[48], with some modification. The dried sodium salts were converted to the acid with 200 per cent, excess of $3 N$ sulfuric acid, and the excess water removed by mixing with silica (Merck's CP powdered). The dry powder was put on the column and the propionic and acetic acids removed with 2.5 per cent butanol in chloroform. Thirty per cent, butanol in chloroform was used to remove the formic acid. The eluates from the column was collected in a dilute sodium hydroxide solution and separated from the solvent by shaking in a separatory funnel. The volatile acids were regenerated by acid steam distillation and titrated.

The formic acid fraction from such a column was not pure, being contaminated with acetic acid and pyruvic acid (the latter in the fermentation of pyruvate). It was rechromatogrammed on a silica column, using an external indicator (phenolphthalein) according to the method given by ISHERWOOD[49]. That the acid titrated was formic acid was demonstrated by the specific analytical method for formic acid[50]. It was further identified by oxidation to CO_2 with mercuric oxide.

The acetic acid obtained from the column was rechromatogrammed to remove all traces of contaminating propionic acid.

The non-volatile acids were separated on a silica column using the external indicator method[48]. The solvents were removed from the solution by the procedure described for volatile acids and the acid was recovered by ether extraction, and titrated. It was acidified to congo red and oxidized at 100° C with potassium permanganate and the acid was again obtained by ether extraction. It was then sublimed under high vacuum at 115 to 125° C. This procedure gave pure succinate as judged by

References p. 221/222.

mixed melting point and by the isotope dilution method. No attempt was made to obtain carbon balances in the fermentations reported in Tables VIII and IX. The propionate and succinate were obtained by chromatogramming aliquots of the volatile and non-volatile acids and they were purified by the procedure given above.

Degradation procedures

The propionic acid was degraded by a modification of the procedure described by WOOD et al.[51]. 1.5 to 2.0 mM of sodium propionate were dried for 3 h at 120 ° to 130° C. One ml of benzoyl chloride and 0.5 ml of bromine were added and refluxed for 2 hrs. Eighty to 100 ml of water followed by 7 g of potassium carbonate were then added to the mixture. This mixture was then refluxed for 7 h to obtain lactic acid. The lactic acid was then degraded by the method of WOOD et al[51].

The degradation of succinate was accomplished by the SCHMIDT reaction. 0.3 to 0.5 mM of succinic acid and 2 ml of phosphoric acid (47 g of P_2O_5 and 100 ml of 90 %. H_3PO_4) were placed in an apparatus similar to that described by PHARES[52] for degrading volatile acids by the SCHMIDT reaction. Fifty mg of sodium azide which had been activated by treatment with acetone were added and the mixture was heated at 60° C for 30 min. The reaction vessel was then heated on a steam bath for 3 h. This procedure was repeated two more times adding 50 mg of sodium azide each time. A 40–50 per cent. yield of the carboxyl groups was obtained.

Total oxidation of any material was accomplished by use of the wet combustion mixture as described by VAN SLYKE[53].

All samples were counted as barium carbonate using an end window Geiger-Muller tube.

The authors wish to express their appreciation to Mr RUNE STERNHOLM for assistance in some of the degradations.

SUMMARY

The fermentation of 3, 4, 5 and 6 carbon compounds by the propionic acid bacteria have been investigated by quantitative determination of the products and by estimating the CO_2 turnover and distributuon of the fixed CO_2 in the products. It has been found that there is a remarkable similarity in the quantitative relationship of the products of all the substrates, which is independent of the length of the carbon chain. If a cleavage of the 4 or 5 carbon substrates to C_1 or C_2 compounds occurs, these cleavage products are largely converted to succinate and propionate by secondary reactions. The CO_2 turnover was quite low and did not indicate that CO_2 is formed as a primary cleavage product from erythritol or adonitol. With these substrates, the distribution of fixed CO_2 in the products was identical to that found from C_3 and C_6 compounds and thus no evidence of a unique mechanism of fermentation was obtained by this method.

CO_2 turnover was investigated in relation to the problem of the mechanism of formation of propionate. Under certain conditions, it was found that the CO_2 turnover was much lower than that required by a mechanism in which succinate is decarboxylated to propionate and CO_2. It is suggested that the formation of propionate from a C_4 dicarboxylic acid may involve a "C_1" which is not CO_2 but may be converted to CO_2.

Considerable variation has been found in the ability of different cell preparations to fix CO_2. The best fixation was obtained with cells grown on a glycerol, yeast extract, phosphate, vitamin-B medium. NaF inhibits completely the net fixation of CO_2 but it does not prevent the incorporation of $^{14}CO_2$ into the propionate and succinate.

RÉSUMÉ

Les auteurs ont étudié la fermentation des corps en C_3, C_4, C_5 et C_6 par les bactéries propioniques en dosant les produits formées et en déterminant la vitesse de renouvellement du CO_2 et la distribution du CO_2 fixé dans ces produits. Il y a une similitude remarquable dans la proportion des produits formés à partir de tous les substrats, quelle que soit la longueur de leur chaîne carbonée. Si les produits en C_4 ou C_5 se clivent en donnant des produits en C_1 ou C_2, ces produits de clivage sont en grande partie transformés en succinate et en propionate par des réactions secondaires. La vitesse de renouvellement du CO_2 est très faible et 'nindique pas que CO_2 soit le produit de clivage primaire de l'érythritol ou de l'adonitol. Avec ces substrats, la distribution du CO_2 fixé dans les produits formés est identique à celle que l'on trouve avec des corps en C_3 et en C_6. Cette méthode ne donne donc pas la preuve que la mécanisme de fermentation est unique.

References p. 221/222.

Le renouvellement du CO$_2$ a été étudié en relation avec le problème du mécanisme de la formation du propionate. Dans certaines conditions, le renouvellement du CO$_2$ est beaucoup plus lent que ne l'exigerait un mécanisme dans lequel le succinate serait décarboxylé en propionate et CO$_2$. On peut supposer que la formation de propionate à partir d'un acide dicarboxylique en C$_4$ met en jeu un corps en C$_1$, que ne serait pas CO$_2$ mais qui pourrait être transformé en CO$_2$.

La capacité de fixer CO$_2$ varie considérablement selon les préparations cellulaires, La fixation la meilleure a lieu quand les cellules sont cultivées sur un milieu renfermant du glycérol, de l'extrait de levure, un phosphate et de la vitamine B. NaF inhibe complètement la fixation globale de CO$_2$ mais il n'empêche pas l'incorporation de ^{14}CO$_2$ dans le propionate et le succinate.

ZUSAMMENFASSUNG

Die Vergärung der 3-, 4-, 5- und 6-Kohlenstoffverbindungen durch Propionsäurebakterien ist durch die quantitative Bestimmung der Produkte und des CO$_2$-Umsatzes, und die Verteilung des in diesen Produkten festgelegten CO$_2$ untersucht worden. Es wurde gefunden, dass eine beträchtliche Ähnlichkeit in der quantitativen Beziehung der Produkte all dieser Substrate besteht, die unabhängig ist von der Länge der Kohlenstoffkette. Wenn eine Spaltung der 4- oder 5-Kohlenstoffsubstrate in C$_1$- oder C$_2$-Verbindungen eintritt, dann werden die Spaltprodukte weitgehend in Folgereaktionen in bernsteinsaures Salz und Propionat umgewandelt. Der CO$_2$-Umsatz war ziemlich niedrig und es war kein Anzeichen vorhanden, dass CO$_2$ als primäres Spaltprodukt aus Erythrit oder Adonit gebildet wurde. Bei diesen Substraten war die Verteilung des festgelegten CO$_2$ in den Produkten identisch mit der bei den C$_3$- und C$_6$-Verbindungen gefundenen und es konnte daher mit dieser Methode kein Anzeichen für einen einheitlichen Gärungsverlauf erhalten werden.

Der CO$_2$-Umsatz wurde in Bezug auf das Problem des Propionatbildungsmechanismus untersucht. Es wurde gefunden, dass der CO$_2$-Umsatz unter gewissen Bedingungen viel niedriger war als ein Mechanismus bei dem bernsteinsaures Salz zu Propionat und CO$_2$ decarboxyliert wird, erfordern würde. Es wird vermutet, dass bei der Bildung von Propionat aus einer C$_4$-Dicarbonsäure ein "C$_1$" beteiligt ist, das nicht CO$_2$ ist, aber in CO$_2$ umgewandelt werden kann.

Es wurden bei verschiedenen Zellpräparaten beträchtliche Unterschiede gefunden in der Fähigkeit CO$_2$ zu fixieren. Die beste Fixierung wurde bei Zellen erhalten, die auf einem Glycerin-Hefeextrakt-Phosphat-Vitamin B-Medium gewachsen waren. NaF hemmt die reine CO$_2$-Fixierung vollständig, aber es verhindert nicht den Einbau von ^{14}CO$_2$ in Propionat und bernsteinsaures Salz.

REFERENCES

[1] R. W. STONE AND C. H. WERKMAN, *Biochem. J.*, 31 (1937) 1516.
[2] H. G. WOOD, R. W. STONE AND C. H. WERKMAN, *Biochem. J.*, 31 (1937) 349.
[3] H. A. BARKER AND F. LIPMANN, *J. Biol. Chem.*, 179 (1949) 247.
[4] H. A. KREBS AND L. V. EGGLESTON, *Biochem. J.*, 35 (1941) 676.
[5] C. H. WERKMAN AND H. G. WOOD, *Advances in Enzymology*, 2 (1942) 135.
[6] E. A. DELWICHE, *J. Bact.*, 56 (1948) 811.
[7] A. T. JOHNS, *J. Gen. Microbiology*, 5 (1951) 1337.
[8] H. G. WOOD, C. H. WERKMAN, A. HEMINGWAY AND A. O. NIER, *J. Biol. Chem.*, 139 (1941) 365.
[9] C. H. WERKMAN, R. W. STONE AND H. G. WOOD, *Enzymologia*, 4 (1937) 24.
[10] H. G. WOOD AND C. H. WERKMAN, *Biochem. J.*, 30 (1936) 618.
[11] R. W. STONE, H. G. WOOD AND C. H. WERKMAN, *Biochem. J.*, 30 (1936) 324.
[12] S. F. CARSON AND E. A. DELWICHE, *Federation Proc.*, 11 (1952) 194.
[13] F. W. LEAVER AND H. G. WOOD, *J. Cell and Comp. Physiol.*, in press.
[14] E. B. FRED, W. H. PETERSON AND J. A. ANDERSON, *J. Biol. Chem.*, 48 (1921) 385.
[15] H. GEST AND J. O. LAMPEN, *J. Biol. Chem.*, 194 (1952) 555.
[16] I. BERNSTEIN, *J. Biol. Chem.*, in press.
[17] D. A. RAPPOPORT, H. A. BARKER AND W. Z. HASSID, *Arch. Biochem. Biophys.*, 31 (1951) 326.
[18] S. AKABORI, K. UEHARA AND I. MURAMATSU, *Proc. Japan Acad.*, 28 (1952) 39.
[19] B. L. HORECKER AND P. Z. SMYRNIOTIS, *J. Am. Chem. Soc.*, 75 (1953) 1009.
[20] E. RACKER, G. DE LA HABA AND I. G. LEDER, *J. Am. Chem. Soc.*, 75 (1953) 1010.
[21] C. ERB, *Respiratory behavior of the propionic acid bacteria*, Thesis, Iowa State College (1934).
[22] S. BARBAN AND S. AJL, *J. Biol. Chem.*, 192 (1952) 63.
[23] H. A. BARKER, M. D. KAMEN AND V. HAAS, *Proc. Natl. Acad. Sci.*, 31 (1945) 335.
[24] H. G. WOOD AND C. H. WERKMAN, *Biochem. J.*, 32 (1938) 1262.
[25] E. A. DELWICHE, E. F. PHARES AND S. F. CARSON, *Federation Proc.*, 12 (1953) 194.
[26] H. R. WHITELEY, *J. Am. Chem. Soc.*, 75 (1953) 1518.

[27] M. F. Utter, F. Lipmann and C. H. Werkman, *J. Biol. Chem.*, 158 (1945) 521.
[28] J. Wilson, L. O. Krampitz and C. H. Werkman, *Biochem. J.*, 42 (1948) 598.
[29] H. J. Strecker, H. G. Wood, and L. O. Krampitz, *J. Biol. Chem.*, 182 (1950) 525.
[30] W. Sakami, *J. Biol. Chem.*, 176 (1948) 995.
[31] I. Siegel and J. Lafaye, *Proc. Soc. Exptl. Biol. and Med.*, 74 (1950) 620.
[32] F. W. Leaver, *J. Am. Chem. Soc.*, 72 (1950) 5326.
[33] H. G. Wood and C. H. Werkman, *J. Bact.*, 30 (1935) 652.
[34] F. W. Leaver, *J. Am. Chem. Soc.*, 73 (1951) 2974.
[35] B. P. Cardon and H. A. Barker, *Arch. Biochem.*, 12 (1947) 165.
[36] A. T. Johns, *J. Gen. Microbiology*, 6 (1952) 123.
[37] F. W. Leaver, *Federation Proc.*, 12 (1953) 471.
[38] H. G. Wood and C. H. Werkman, *Biochem. J.*, 34 (1940) 129.
[39] V. Hartelius, *Biochem. Z.*, 305 (1940) 396.
[40] H. Larsen, *J. Biol. Chem.*, 193 (1952) 167.
[41] H. Lardy, *Proc. Natl. Acad. Sci.*, 38 (1952) 1003.
[42] M. F. Utter and K. Kurahashi, *J. Am. Chem. Soc.* 75 (1953) 758.
[43] H. G. Wood and C. H. Werkman, *J. Biol. Chem.*, 105 (1934) 63.
[44] P. Fleury and J. Lange, *J. Pharm. Chem.*, 17 (1933) 107.
[45] C. Fromageot and P. Deunevelle, *Biochem. Z.*, 279 (1935) 174.
[46] M. Somogyi, *J. Biol. Chem.*, 86 (1930) 655.
[47] G. L. Stahly, O. L. Osburn and C. H. Werkman, *Analyst*, 59 (1934) 319.
[48] S. R. Elsden, *Biochem. J.*, 40 (1946) 252.
[49] F. A. Isherwood, *Biochem. J.*, 40 (1946) 688.
[50] W. M. Grant, *J. Am. Chem. Soc.*, 20 (1948) 267.
[51] H. G. Wood, C. H. Werkman, A. Hemingway and A. O. Nier, *Proc. Soc. Exp. Biol. Med.*, 46 (1941) 313.
[52] E. F. Phares, *Arch. Biochem. Biophys.*, 33 (1951) 173.
[53] D. D. van Slyke, *J. Biol. Chem.*, 136 (1940) 309.

Received April 21, 1953

ENZYMIC SYNTHESIS AND
BREAKDOWN OF A PYRIMIDINE, OROTIC ACID

I. DIHYDRO-OROTIC DEHYDROGENASE

by

IRVING LIEBERMAN* AND ARTHUR KORNBERG

*National Institutes of Health, Bethesda, Maryland and The Department of Microbiology,
Washington University School of Medicine, St. Louis, Missouri (U.S.A.)*

Orotic acid (4-carboxyuracil) was first isolated from cow's milk[1] and has since been observed to be a growth factor for *Neurospora* mutants[2] and bacteria[3–7], and to be accumulated in large amounts by some mutant strains of *Neurospora*[8]. Recent experiments with intact rats[9–11], rat liver slices[12, 13], and growing cultures of *Lactobacillus bulgaricus* 09[14] have provided evidence that orotic acid, or a compound metabolically related to it, is a precursor of nucleic acid pyrimidines. Of great interest is the finding that ureidosuccinic acid (USA) can partially replace the orotic acid requirement of *L. bulgaricus* and that ^{14}C-labelled USA like orotic acid is incorporated with relatively little dilution into the pyrimidine nucleotides of the growing bacteria[14].

In order to obtain some definitive information about the pathways of orotic acid breakdown and clues to the mechanism of its biosynthesis, a bacterial organism was isolated by enrichment culture which was able to metabolize this compound rapidly. With enzyme preparations derived from this organism, evidence has been obtained to support the following scheme for orotic acid breakdown and synthesis[15]:

(1)

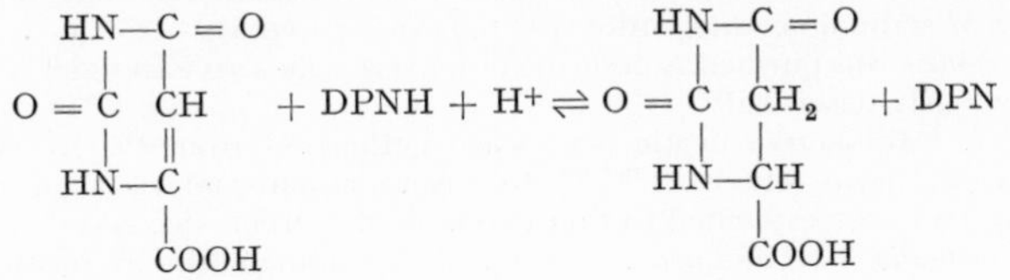

$$
\begin{array}{ccc}
\text{HN—C = O} & & \text{HN—C = O} \\
\quad|\quad| & & \quad|\quad| \\
\text{O = C CH} + \text{DPNH} + \text{H}^+ \rightleftharpoons & \text{O = C CH}_2 & + \text{DPN} \\
\quad|\quad\| & & \quad|\quad| \\
\text{HN—C} & & \text{HN—CH} \\
\quad| & & \quad| \\
\text{COOH} & & \text{COOH} \\
\text{Orotic acid} & & \text{Dihydro-orotic acid}
\end{array}
$$

(2)

$$
\begin{array}{ccc}
\text{HN—C = O} & & \text{COOH} \\
\quad|\quad| & & | \\
\text{O = C CH}_2 & & \text{CH}_2 \\
\quad|\quad| & + \text{H}_2\text{O} \rightleftharpoons & | \\
\text{HN—CH} & & \text{HN—CH} \\
\quad| & & \quad|\quad| \\
\text{COOH} & & \text{O = C COOH} \\
& & | \\
& & \text{NH}_2 \\
\text{Dihydro-orotic acid} & & \text{Ureidosuccinic acid}
\end{array}
$$

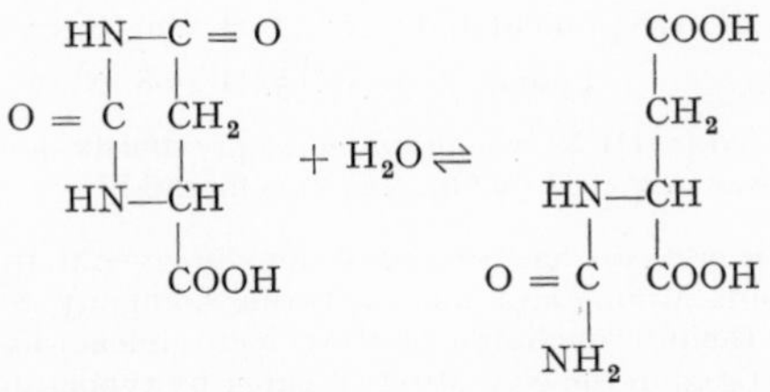

* Aided by a Fellowship from The National Foundation for Infantile Paralysis.

References p. 234.

(3)

Ureidosuccinic acid   5-(Acetic acid)-
                             hydantoin

The enzyme that catalyzes reaction (1), the reversible reduction of orotic acid to di-hydro-orotic acid, has been partially purified and named dihydro-orotic dehydrogenase. The purpose of this report is to present the evidence for reaction (1).

METHODS

Isolation and growth of the organism. The organism used in these studies is an obligate anaerobe isolated from San Francisco Bay mud by enrichment culture, by one of us (AK), in the laboratory of Dr. H. A. BARKER*.

The growth medium consisted of 2% tryptone, 0.05% Difco yeast extract, 0.2% orotic acid, and 0.05% sodium thioglycolate. For the preparation of stock test tube cultures, the medium was adjusted to pH 7.0 with 1 M KOH prior to autoclaving (15 minutes at 15 pounds pressure). Anaerobic conditions were maintained with a pyrogallol-Na_2CO_3 seal. Large cultures were grown in Erlenmeyer flasks (1 to 6 liters) without an anaerobic seal. After autoclaving for 20–30 minutes at 15 pounds pressure, the medium was cooled, neutralized with a sterile 50% K_2CO_3 solution and sterile water was added to the neck of the flask. The inoculum (one or two fresh stock cultures) was added promptly. Growth appeared to be complete in 16–20 hours at 30° C.

Preparation of the cell-free extract. The cells were harvested in a Sharples supercentrifuge and resuspended in 0.01 M sodium orotate (7 ml per liter of culture), potassium phosphate buffer (1 M, pH 7.0, 0.4 ml per liter of culture) and cysteine (0.1 M, pH 7.0, 0.4 ml per liter of culture). This cell suspension was incubated *in vacuo* at 26° C for 20 minutes. More active extracts appeared to be obtained when this step was included in the procedure. After centrifugation, the cells were suspended in ice cold water (about 5 ml per liter of culture), and an aliquot of the suspension (about 6 ml) was shaken with 6 g of glass beads (0.10–0.15 mm diameter)** in a Mickle vibrator for 15 minutes at 2° C. The mixture was centrifuged in a Sorvall centrifuge (at *ca.* 10,000 g) and the precipitate was washed once with cold water. The volume of the extract (combined supernatant solutions) was adjusted to 10 ml per liter of culture. If the purification procedure was not initiated at once, the extract was acidified to pH 6.5 with 2 M sodium acetate buffer (pH 6.0) and stored at —10° C.

Glucose dehydrogenase was purified as described by STRECKER AND KORKES[16]. *Lactic dehydrogenase* was prepared as previously described[17].

2-^{14}C-*Orotic acid.* Radioactive orotic acid was synthesized from ^{14}C-KCNO and DL-aspartic acid as described by NYC AND MITCHELL[18]***. Non-isotopic material was a commercial preparation whose absorption spectrum corresponded to that given by MITCHELL AND NYC[19].

Fusion product of maleic acid and urea. This compound, named dihydro-orotic acid by BACHSTEZ AND CAVALLINI[20], was prepared by their method. The recrystallized product gave the following analysis† when calculated for dihydro-orotic acid.

$C_5H_6O_4N_2$ Calculated C 37.97, H 3.79, N 17.72

        Found   C 38.15, H 4.08, N 17.77

Diphosphopyridine nucleotide (DPN) was prepared as previously described[21]. *Reduced diphospho-pyridine nucleotide* (DPNH) was prepared by OHLMEYER's method[22].

---

* The name *Zymobacterium oroticum* has been provisionally given to this organism by Dr. BARKER.
** Obtained from Minnesota Mining and Manufacturing Company, St. Paul, Minnesota.
*** In the preparation of the intermediate 5-(carboxymethylidene)-hydantoin, 4.28 g bromine were used, rather than the 1.28 g stated in the Nyc-Mitchell paper by typographical error. We are indebted to S. R. KORNBERG for this synthesis.
† Microanalyses were performed by the Microanalytical Laboratory of the National Institutes of Health under the supervision of Dr. W. C. ALFORD.

References p. 234.

DETERMINATIONS

Assay of dihydro-orotic dehydrogenase. DPNH, which is essential to the first step in the break-down of orotic acid, was generated by the addition of glucose dehydrogenase, glucose, and DPN. The test system contained 0.1 ml of $MgCl_2$ (0.15 M), 0.1 ml of potassium phosphate buffer (1 M, pH 6.1), 0.04 ml of sodium orotate (0.01 M), 0.2 ml of cysteine (0.1 M, pH 7.0), 0.03 ml of DPN (0.001 M), 0.2 ml of glucose (1 M), 250 units of glucose dehydrogenase, and the enzyme preparation in a volume of 3.0 ml. All the components except the glucose dehydrogenase were mixed and incubated at room temperature for 5 minutes. The glucose dehydrogenase was then added and the rate of orotate removal was followed in the Beckman DU spectrophotometer by the decrease in optical density at 280 mμ. A unit of enzyme was defined as the amount producing an optical density decrease of 0.100 in a 6 minute interval. In general, not more than 4 units of activity were used for the assay. Specific activity was defined as units of activity per mg of protein.

Under the conditions of the assay, the rate of orotate reduction was proportional to the amount of enzyme. Thus the decrease in optical density at 280 mμ in 6 minutes was found to be 0.000, 0.080, 0.137, 0.217, and 0.296 with 0.00, 0.03, 0.05, 0.07, and 0.10 ml of enzyme solution, respectively. In the absence of glucose, glucose dehydrogenase, or DPN, no removal of orotate was observed.

Glucose was estimated spectrophotometrically with hexokinase[*][23] (freed of glucose by dialysis against 0.01 M sodium acetate solution, pH 5.4) and *Zwischenferment*[24]. The assay was carried out as described[25] for the estimation of adenosine triphosphate (ATP) except that excess ATP (0.2 micro-mole) was added. Glucose (0.05–0.10 micromole) was added last to initiate the reaction.

Protein was determined by the method of LOWRY *et al.*[26].

[14]C-containing samples were in general plated as infinitely thin layers on aluminium discs and measured in a gas flow counter.

RESULTS

Purification of dihydro-orotic dehydrogenase

Protamine fraction. Purification of the enzyme was carried out at 0–2° C. 100 ml of freshly prepared cell-free extract were diluted with an equal volume of water and 15 ml of a 1% solution of protamine sulfate (Eli Lilly) were added with stirring. After 5 minutes, the precipitate was collected by centrifugation and the supernatant solution discarded. 100 ml of sodium citrate buffer (0.5 M, pH 6.0) were added to the hard and difficultly soluble precipitate. After 12–24 hours the softened precipitate was dissolved to a considerable extent by homogenization with a glass pestle, 200 ml of water were added with stirring, and the resultant stringy precipitate was discarded after centrifugation. The supernatant solution (Protamine, Table I) was essentially free of nucleic acid as indicated by the ratio of optical densities at 280 and 260 mμ (0.98).

TABLE I

PURIFICATION OF DIHYDRO-OROTIC DEHYDROGENASE

Enzyme fraction	Volume of solution ml	Units	Specific activity units per mg protein	Overall recovery %
Cell-free extract	100	4590	22.8	
Protamine	300	3180	26.5	69.3
Ammonium sulfate	120	2420	84.1	52.7
Acid ammonium sulfate	62	1850	175	40.3

For details of the fractionation procedure see the text.

Ammonium sulfate fraction. To the protamine fraction were now added with stirring 100 g of ammonium sulfate. After 5 minutes, the precipitate was removed by

---

[*] Kindly supplied by Dr. F. E. HUNTER, Jr.

References p. 234.

centrifugation and upon further addition of 25.2 g of ammonium sulfate to the supernatant solution another precipitate was formed. This precipitate was collected by centrifugation and dissolved in 120 ml of water (Ammonium sulfate, Table I).

Acid ammonium sulfate fraction. 30 ml of sodium formate buffer (0.5 M, pH 4.2), and then 36 g of ammonium sulfate were added to the ammonium sulfate fraction with stirring. After 5 minutes the precipitate was removed by centrifugation. 18 g of ammonium sulfate were added to the supernatant solution and the precipitate that formed was collected and dissolved in 62 ml of sodium acetate buffer (0.01 M, pH 6.0) (Acid ammonium sulfate, Table I).

Further purification of the activity (three- to five-fold) could be obtained by subjecting the acid ammonium sulfate fraction to column chromatography with Dowex 1, formate form, 2% cross-linked, and eluting with phosphate buffer. The yields were too variable to warrant inclusion of this step in the routine purification procedure.

Stoichiometric relationship of orotate and DPNH. The requirement for DPN, glucose, and glucose dehydrogenase for orotate reduction could be replaced with DPNH. With the purified enzyme preparation, oxidation of DPNH was accompanied by the removal of an equimolar amount of orotate (Table II). The essentially complete utilization of the

TABLE II

THE EQUIVALENCE OF DPNH AND OROTATE DISAPPEARANCE

	Exp. 1	*Exp. 2*
	Micromoles	
DPNH added	0.159	0.318
Δ Orotic acid	—0.147	—0.329

The reaction mixtures (in glass stoppered cuvettes) contained in 3.0 ml, 15 micromoles of $MgCl_2$, 100 micromoles of potassium phosphate buffer (pH 6.1), 20 micromoles of cysteine (pH 7.0), 0.4 micromole of sodium orotate, 4.1 units of enzyme (specific activity 178) and the indicated amount of DPNH. The DPNH was added after repeated flushing with H_2 and the reaction was followed spectrophotometrically at 280 mμ. Interference by DPNH oxidase, which contaminated the enzyme preparation, was almost completely eliminated in this anaerobic atmosphere and by the rapid rate of the orotate reduction (complete in 2–4 minutes).

DPNH by orotate in relatively low concentrations under conditions which appear to limit the reaction to this single step (see below) suggests that the equilibrium of the reaction is greatly in favour of orotate reduction.

Stoichiometric relationship of orotate and glucose. Under the standard conditions of assay for dihydro-orotic dehydrogenase (see Methods) and in large scale experiments, the DPNH was present in catalytic amounts and was constantly regenerated by the oxidation of glucose according to the following equations:

$$\text{Glucose} + \text{DPN} \xrightarrow{\text{glucose dehydrogenase}} \text{gluconate} + \text{DPNH} + \text{H}^+ \qquad (4)$$
$$\text{Orotate} + \text{DPNH} + \text{H}^+ \xrightarrow{\text{dihydro-orotic dehydrogenase}} \text{dihydro-orotate} + \text{DPN} \qquad (5)$$
$$\text{Sum: Glucose} + \text{orotate} \longrightarrow \text{gluconate} + \text{dihydro-orotate}. \qquad (6)$$

In order to establish that orotate reduction under these conditions involves the utilization of an equimolar amount of glucose, a quantitative experiment was carried out.

References p. 234.

The reaction mixture in a Thunberg tube consisted of 24.4 micromoles of glucose, 15 micromoles of $MgCl_2$, 100 micromoles of potassium phosphate buffer (pH 6.1), 10 micromoles of sodium orotate, 20 micromoles of cysteine (pH 7.0), and 51 units of dihydro-orotic dehydrogenase (specific activity 86). DPN (0.05 micromole) and 500 units of glucose dehydrogenase were placed in the side-arm. The total volume was 3.0 ml. The tube was evacuated, filled with helium, and re-evacuated; the process was then repeated. After tipping, incubation was carried out at 35° C for 180 minutes. A control tube contained no glucose. After incubation, the tubes were placed in a boiling water bath for 2 minutes, centrifuged, and aliquots of the supernatart solutions were used for the estimation of orotate and glucose. The anaerobic atmosphere was provided to avoid interference by DPNH oxidase which contaminated the enzyme preparation.

With the removal of 5.88 micromoles of orotate, the consumption of 5.50 micromoles of glucose was observed.

Isolation of the product of orotate reduction. Radioautography of paper chromatograms of the product(s) of the action of purified dihydro-orotic dehydrogenase on orotate-2-^{14}C showed essentially one spot. This substance could be adsorbed from reaction mixtures on Dowex 1, formate form, and appeared on elution as a discrete peak in an area distinct from known compounds.

To obtain a sufficient amount of this compound for its identification, a large scale reaction was carried out with 0.64 millimole of 2-^{14}C-orotate ($1.38 \cdot 10^6$ cpm.) and 1420 units of purified enzyme (specific activity 152). The reaction mixture also contained the remaining components of the standard assay system, in 50-fold greater amounts. During incubation at 34° C, aliquots were removed at intervals and spectrophotometrically tested for orotate disappearance. When the reaction was complete, 4 N HCl was added until the solution became acid to thymol blue; the precipitated protein was then discarded.

After adjusting the pH of the supernatant solution to 7.0 with 1 M KOH, the solution was subjected to ion-exchange chromatography on a column of Dowex 1, formate form (height, 11.0 cm; diameter, 4.2 cm). The eluting fluid was 0.055 M sodium formate solution adjusted to pH 3.2 with formic acid. The product, detected by radioactivity measurement, appeared between 20.8 and 25.8 resin bed volumes of eluant and represented at least 80% of the counts applied to the column. The radioactive fractions were combined (915 ml) and passed through Dowex 50, hydrogen ion form (resin bed volume of 150 ml), to remove the sodium ions. Water and formic acid were removed under reduced pressure (at a water bath temperature of 40–45° C). The residue was dried over KOH in a vacuum desiccator, then dissolved in hot water and crystallized in the cold. Upon recrystallization from water, 53 mg of hard white crystals were obtained representing a 53% recovery from orotate, assuming the product to have the molecular weight of dihydro-orotic acid.

Elementary analysis of the compound as compared with that of dihydro-orotic acid was as follows:

$C_5H_6O_4N_2$ Calculated C, 37.97, H 3.79, N 17.72
Found   C, 37.48, H 3.82, N 17.69.

The compound melted at 269–271° with some decomposition. No weight loss occurred at 77° *in vacuo*. Titration of a solution containing 1.00 mg of the compound to a phenol red endpoint required 6.06 micromoles of NaOH (0.010 N) yielding an equivalent weight 96% of that calculated for dihydro-orotic acid.

On the basis of the evidence thus far presented, the enzymic product has been provisionally considered to be dihydro-orotic acid.

References p. 234.

Specificity of DPNH and influence of DPNH concentration on orotate reduction.
With the purified enzyme preparation no observable reduction of orotate occurred in
the absence of added DPN. With TPN, the reaction rate was less than 2 % of that observed with DPN, and no inhibiting effect on the reaction (with DPN) was noted.

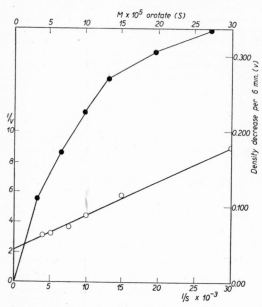

Fig. 1. The rate of orotate reduction as a function of orotate concentration.

The reaction mixtures containing 2.7 units of dihydro-orotic dehydrogenase (specific activity 86) were prepared as for the standard assay (see Methods) except that varying amounts of sodium orotate (molar concentrations = S) were used. The progress of the reaction was followed by measuring the decrease in optical density at 280 mμ during a 6 minute interval (v). The solid circles represent the decrease in optical density as a function of orotate concentration. The open circles represent a LINEWEAVER-BURK plot[27].

The rate of orotate reduction appeared to be dependent on DPNH concentration since it was found to be proportional to the amount of glucose dehydrogenase when this enzyme was added in limiting quantities. In one experiment, with 9.5 units of purified enzyme, the decrease in optical density at 280 mμ in 4 minutes was found to be 0.151, 0.301, 0.572, and 0.565, with 62.5, 125, 250, and 310 units of glucose dehydrogenase, respectively. With 4 units or less of dihydro-orotic dehydrogenase, glucose dehydrogenase at a level of 250 units did not limit the rate of the reaction. The concentration of glucose used in the assay system was 0.067 M, and it appeared to be sufficient to allow a maximum rate of orotate reduction. Decreasing the concentration of glucose to 0.033 M caused a decrease of less than 10 % in the reaction rate. Approximately half the maximum rate was obtained with 0.008 M glucose.

Specificity of dihydro-orotic dehydrogenase and the influence of orotate concentration on rate of reaction. The possibility that dihydro-orotic dehydrogenase can catalyze the reduction of other pyrimidines was investigated. No activity and no inhibition of orotate reduction was observed with uracil, cytosine, 5-methylcytosine, or thymine.

The rate of orotate reduction was studied as a function of orotate concentration (Fig. 1). When the data were plotted according to LINEWEAVER AND BURK[27], as shown in the figure, a straight line was obtained. K_s was calculated to be $1.1 \cdot 10^{-4}\ M$.

The effect of pH and other factors on orotate reduction

pH. The pH of the assay medium was 6.4–6.5. At pH 7.0, the initial rate of the reaction was the same as at 6.5, but the enzyme appeared to be less stable and the rate declined more rapidly than at the lower pH. At pH 5.5 and 7.8, the initial rates of reaction were 13 and 65 %, respectively, of that at pH 6.5.

References p. 234.

Mg^{+2}. While the presence of added Mg^{+2} had little effect on the initial rate of the reaction, an effect was apparent when the reaction proceeded for longer periods. Thus, at 0, $2 \cdot 10^{-3}\ M$, and $5 \cdot 10^{-3}\ M\ Mg^{+2}$, the decrease in optical density at 280 mμ in 6 minutes was found to be 0.225, 0.240, and 0.261, respectively, whereas at 20 minutes the density decreases were 0.355, 0.426, and 0.503.

Cysteine. Freshly prepared cell-free extracts showed little or no stimulation upon the addition of cysteine. The reaction rate with the purified enzyme preparation, however, was increased up to twofold in the presence of 0.002–0.007 M cysteine. Larger amounts of cysteine appeared to have an inhibitory effect.

Oxidation of dihydro-orotate to orotate. The reversibility of the conversion of orotate to dihydro-orotate was demonstrated with the purified enzyme. Dihydro-orotate (0.263 micromole) was incubated with 26 units of the enzyme under the usual assay conditions except that glucose and glucose dehydrogenase were omitted. The oxidation of reduced DPN was presumably achieved by the action of DPNH oxidase which was present in the enzyme preparation. A substance having the absorption spectrum of orotate was formed from dihydro-orotate in theoretical yield and complete removal of this material could be effected by the addition of glucose and glucose dehydrogenase (Fig. 2, 3).

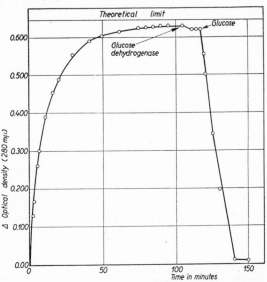

Fig. 2. The oxidation of dihydro-orotate to orotate.
    The incubation mixture in the experimental cuvette contained 15 micromoles of $MgCl_2$, 100 micromoles of potassium phosphate buffer (pH 6.1), 30 micromoles of cysteine (pH 7.0), 26 units of dihydro-orotic dehydrogenase (specific activity 184), 0.05 micromole of DPN, and 0.263 micromole of dihydro-orotic acid (enzymic origin) in a volume of 3.0 ml. The incubation mixture in the blank cell contained no dihydro-orotic acid. 250 units of glucose dehydrogenase and 200 micromoles of glucose were added at the times indicated.

Unlike the reduction of orotate to dihydro-orotate, which does not proceed in the absence of added DPN, the oxidation of dihydro-orotate by the same purified enzyme preparation was observed to occur at the same rate with or without added DPN.

In order to establish that dihydro-orotate oxidation does involve DPN reduction the reaction was studied under anaerobic conditions and in the presence of pyruvate and lactic dehydrogenase. As shown in Fig. 4, little orotate synthesis was observed in the absence of a DPNH oxidant such as the oxygen-DPNH oxidase or the pyruvate-lactic dehydrogenase systems.

The non-identity of natural dihydro-orotic acid and the synthetic fusion product. The fusion product of maleic acid and urea was considered to be dihydro-orotic acid by BACHSTEZ AND CAVALLINI[20], although they offered no proof of structure. This compound can be compared to the product of enzymic reduction of orotic acid in the following respects:

References p. 234.

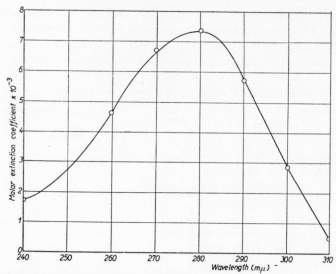

Fig. 3. A comparison of the absorption spectra of orotate and the product of dihydro-orotate oxidation. The curve represents the absorption spectrum of sodium orotate in phosphate buffer (0.033 *M*, pH 6.4). The circles represent the values obtained upon complete oxidation of dihydro-orotate under the conditions described in Fig. 2.

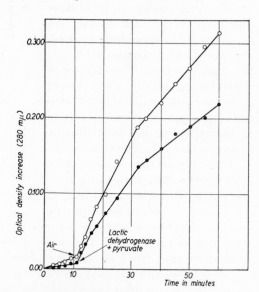

Fig. 4. The requirement for DPNH removal in dihydro-orotate oxidation.

The reaction mixtures prepared in each of two cuvettes fitted to Thunberg tubes contained in 3.0 ml, 15 micromoles of MgCl$_2$, 100 micromoles of potassium phosphate buffer (pH 6.1), 20 micromoles of cysteine (pH 7.0), 0.03 micromole of DPN, 0.53 micromole of dihydro-orotic acid, and 8.0 units of dihydro-orotic dehydrogenase (Protamine Fraction, see Table I). In addition, 20 micromoles of sodium pyruvate and 0.05 ml of lactic dehydrogenase were placed in the sidearm of one of the Thunberg tubes. The tubes were evacuated, filled with helium, and re-evacuated; this procedure was then repeated. The progress of the reaction was followed spectrophotometrically at 280 mμ. At the indicated time, one tube was opened to air, the other, containing the lactic dehydrogenase and pyruvate, was tipped.

1. *Ultraviolet absorption* of the fusion product (free acid) shows a peak at 220 mμ with molar extinction coefficients of $2 \cdot 10^4$ and $1 \cdot 10^4$ at 220 and 240 mμ, respectively. The enzymic compound (free acid) possesses only an end absorption with molar extinction coefficients at 220 and 240 mμ of $2 \cdot 10^3$ and $3 \cdot 10^2$, respectively. 2. *Melting point* of the fusion compound was found to be 264–265° uncor. (lit. 247–249°); the biological product melts at 269–271°. 3. *Elementary analyses* of the natural and synthetic compounds are in close agreement with that calculated for dihydro-orotic acid. 4. *Reaction with cysteine* of the synthetic compound, presumably due to the presence of an olefinic

References p. 234.

bond, was observed spectrophotometrically (the ultraviolet absorption of 0.4 micromole of the fusion product disappeared in 20 minutes when incubated in 3.0 ml of $3.3 \cdot 10^{-3}$ M cysteine at neutral pH). It appears doubtful that a similar reaction occurs with the enzymic compound since it is produced in the presence of cysteine and is oxidized to orotate in the presence of cysteine. 5. *Enzymic* oxidation to orotate (by dihydro-orotic dehydrogenase) was observed only with the natural product; the synthetic product was inert. 6. *Growth factor activity for L. bulgaricus 09* was not detectable with the fusion product while the biological product completely replaced the orotate requirement of the bacterium (see Fig. 5.)

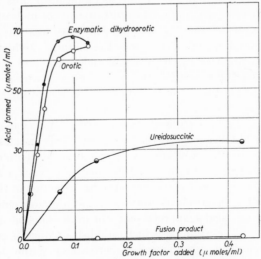

Fig. 5. The production of acid by *Lactobacillus bulgaricus 09* in the presence of orotic acid and related compounds.

Enzymic dihydro-orotic acid as a growth factor for Lactobacillus bulgaricus 09. Since this strain has been shown[7] to require orotic acid or ureidosuccinic acid for growth, it was of interest to determine the effects of enzymic dihydro-orotic acid and the urea-maleic acid fusion product upon this organism.

To 6.0 ml of double strength medium[7] were added aseptically the indicated amounts of the test compounds and sterile water to 7.0 ml. After inoculation of the organism[7], incubation was carried out at 37° C for 64 hours. Aliquots from each tube were titrated with 0.01 N NaOH using a microburette. A blank value of 18.3 micromoles per ml, the titratable material present in the control tubes receiving no growth factor additions, was subtracted.

Solutions of the compounds under test were sterilized by autoclaving* and varying amounts of each were aseptically added to the double strength basal medium of WRIGHT *et al.*[7]. The inoculum was prepared as described by WRIGHT *et al.*[7] and bacterial growth was measured at 64 hours turbidimetrically and by titrating aliquots of the culture with 0.010 N NaOH using phenol red as indicator. Growth was complete at 64 hours but none was apparent in the control tubes which received no growth factor additions.

From the results of the titrimetric determinations (Fig. 5), it can be seen that enzymic dihydro-orotate completely replaced the orotate requirement of the lactobacilli while growth was not supported by the synthetic compound. The synthetic product did not inhibit the activity of added orotate. Thus, with 0.12 micromole of the synthetic compound and 0.05 micromole of orotate per ml. of medium, 42.6 micromoles of acid per ml were formed, as compared with 43.7 micromoles of acid with orotate alone.

---

* Synthetic dihydro-orotic acid has the same ultraviolet absorption spectrum before and after autoclaving. This was taken to indicate that it had not been altered during the sterilization process. After autoclaving, enzymic dihydro-orotic acid behaved identically with the untreated material, both enzymically and spectrophotometrically.

References p. 234.

DISCUSSION

The first step in the metabolism of orotic acid by this anaerobic bacterium is a reduction involving the utilization of one mole of DPNH. The crystalline product isolated from this reaction has an elementary analysis and equivalent weight compatible with dihydro-orotic acid. Since this natural product is distinguishable from the compound synthesized by the fusion of maleic acid and urea and also claimed to be dihydro-orotic acid[20], it is possible that two isomeric forms are represented. Unlike the synthetic compound, the natural product is rapidly and quantitatively oxidized to orotic acid by the bacterial enzyme preparation and serves as a growth factor for *Lactobacillus bulgaricus* 09. The latter observation provides some evidence that the enzymic reduction of orotic acid takes place at the C_4–C_5 bond since ureidosuccinic acid and orotic acid were shown to be the only effective pyrimidine nucleotide precursors for the bacterium[7], and a dihydro-orotic acid of this configuration is a logical intermediate between these two compounds. Further evidence for reduction of the C_4–C_5 bond is the observed enzymic interconversion of orotic acid and ureidosuccinic acid[15] in which this form of dihydro-orotic acid again represents the most plausible intermediate.

These findings which establish a reduction product of a pyrimidine as the immediate metabolic precursor (and derivative) of the pyrimidine do not appear to be limited to the activities of this anaerobic bacterium. Rather, they are consistent with the findings of other workers that the reduced forms of uracil and thymine are metabolically active. FINK *et al.*[28] have demonstrated that rat liver slices convert large quantities of dihydro-thymine and dihydrouracil to β-amino*iso*butyric acid and β-alanine, respectively. While thymine and uracil were relatively inert in their system, it seems likely, as they suggest, that the pathways of thymine and uracil metabolism involve the reduced derivatives which were not produced by the *in vitro* system used. The isolation of dihydrouracil from beef spleen[29] and its active utilization as a nitrogen source by *Torula utilis*[30] may be taken as additional evidence for regarding the dihydropyrimidines as important metabolic intermediates. The finding[30] that the maleic acid-urea fusion product[20] is the only pyrimidine derivative metabolized by *Saccharomyces cerevisiae* is difficult to evaluate in view of the uncertainty regarding its structure.

So little is known about the mechanism of the biological synthesis of pyrimidine nucleotides that it is impossible to determine the validity of the general impression that orotic acid serves as a direct precursor. It is conceivable, for example, that dihydro-orotic rather than orotic acid may be the immediate precursor of nucleic acid pyrimidines. The availability of dihydro-orotic acid may now facilitate attempts to resolve this and related questions.

SUMMARY

1. An enzyme was partially purified from extracts of an anaerobic soil bacterium isolated by enrichment culture on orotic acid. The enzyme, named dihydro-orotic dehydrogenase, was shown to catalyze the reaction:

$$\text{Orotate} + \text{DPNH} + \text{H}^+ \rightleftharpoons \text{Dihydro-orotate} + \text{DPN}.$$

2. The product of the enzymic reduction of orotic acid was isolated in crystalline form and shown to have the correct elementary analysis and equivalent weight for dihydro-orotic acid; it is provisionally considered to be a dihydro-orotic acid saturated at the C_4–C_5 bond.

3. The equilibrium of the reaction strongly favours orotic acid reduction; oxidation of dihydro-orotic acid was demonstrable only with the aid of a system to remove DPNH.

References p. 234.

4. Dihydro-orotic acid was as effective as orotic acid in supporting the growth of *Lactobacillus bulgaricus* 09, an organism which utilizes orotic acid and ureidosuccinic acid for the synthesis of nucleic acid pyrimidines.

5. The fusion product of maleic acid and urea, which has the elementary composition of dihydro-orotic acid, was inert with dihydro-orotic dehydrogenase and as a growth factor for *L. bulgaricus* 09. It was further distinguishable from dihydro-orotic acid of enzymic origin on the basis of ultraviolet spectrum and chemical properties.

6. The significance of dihydropyrimidines in pyrimidine metabolism is discussed.

RÉSUMÉ

1. À partir d'extraits d'une bactérie anaérobie du sol, isolée par culture enrichissante sur de l'acide orotique, un enzyme a été partiellement purifié. Cet enzyme, appelé "dihydro-orotique-déshydrogénase", catalyse la réaction:

$$\text{Orotate} + \text{DPNH} + \text{H}^+ \rightleftharpoons \text{Dihydro-orotate} + \text{DPN}$$

2. Le produit de la réduction enzymatique de l'acide orotique a été isolé sous forme cristallisée. L'analyse élémentaire et le poids équivalent correspondent à l'acide dihydro-orotique. Provisoirement, on considère qu'il s'agit d'acide dihydro-orotique saturé en 4–5.

3. L'équilibre de la réaction est en faveur de la réduction de l'acide orotique; l'oxydation de l'acide dihydro-orotique n'a pu être démontrée qu'à l'aide d'un système éliminant le DPNH.

4. L'acide dihydro-orotique excerce la même action stimulante que l'acide orotique lui-même sur la croissance de *Lactobacillus bulgaricus* 09, organisme qui utilise les acides orotique et uréido-succinique pour synthétiser les pyrimidines d'acides nucléiques.

5. Le produit de fusion d'acide maléique et d'urée qui a la même composition élémentaire que l'acide dihydro-orotique est inerte vis-à-vis du "dihydro-orotique-déshydrogénase" et comme facteur de croissance de *L. bulgaricus* 09. De plus, ce produit se distingue de l'acide dihydro-orotique d'origine enzymatique par son spectre dans l'ultraviolet et ses propriétés chimiques.

6. La signification des dihydropyrimidines dans le métabolisme des pyrimidines a été discutée.

ZUSAMMENFASSUNG

1. Aus den Extrakten eines anaerobischen Bodenbakteriums, das durch Anreicherung einer Kultur mit Orotsäure isoliert wurde, wurde ein Enzym teilweise gereinigt. Es wurde gefunden, dass das Dihydro-orotsäuredehydrogenase genannte Enzym die Reaktion

$$\text{Orotsaures Salz} + \text{DPNH} + \text{H}^+ \rightleftharpoons \text{Dihydro-orotsaures Salz} + \text{DPN}$$

katalysiert.

2. Das Produkt der enzymatischen Reduktion der Orotsäure wurde in kristalliner Form isoliert und es wurde gezeigt, dass es die korrekte Elementaranalyse und das Äquivalentgewicht für Dihydro-orotsäure besitzt; es wird bis auf weiteres als eine an der C_4–C_5-Bindung gesättigte Dihydro-orotsäure betrachtet.

3. Das Reaktionsgleichgewicht begünstigt sehr stark die Reduktion der Orotsäure; die Oxydation der Dihydro-orotsäure konnte nur mit Hilfe eines das DPNH entfernenden Systems gezeigt werden.

4. Dihydro-orotsäure war ebenso wirksam wie Orotsäure bei der Unterstützung des Wachstums von *Lactobacillus bulgaricus* 09, eines Organismus, der Orotsäure und Ureidobernsteinsäure zur Synthese von Nucleinsäurepyrimidinen benützt.

5. Das Schmelzprodukt von Maleinsäure und Harnstoff, das die Elementarzusammensetzung der Dihydro-orotsäure besitzt, war inert gegenüber Dihydro-orotsäuredehydrogenase und als Wachstumsfaktor für *L. bulgaricus* 09. Es unterschied sich weiterhin von Dihydro-orotsäure enzymatischen Ursprungs auf Grund seines Ultravioletspektrums und seiner chemischen Eigenschaften.

6. Die Bedeutung der Dihydropyrimidine im Pyrimidinstoffwechsel wird besprochen.

REFERENCES

[1] G. BISCARO AND E. BELLONI, *Chem. Cent.*, II (1905) 64.
[2] H. S. LORING AND J. G. PIERCE, *J. Biol. Chem.*, 153 (1944) 61.
[3] H. J. ROGERS, *Nature*, 153 (1944) 251.
[4] F. W. CHATTAWAY, *Nature*, 153 (1944) 250.
[5] O. P. WIELAND, J. AVENER, E. M. BOGGIANO, N. BOHONOS, B. L. HUTCHINGS AND J. H. WILLIAMS, *J. Biol. Chem.*, 186 (1950) 737.
[6] J. W. HUFF, D. K. BOSSHARDT, L. D. WRIGHT, D. S. SPICER, K. A. VALENTIK AND H. R. SKEGGS, *Proc. Soc. Exp. Biol. Med.*, 75 (1950) 297.
[7] L. D. WRIGHT, K. A. VALENTIK, D. S. SPICER, J. W. HUFF AND H. R. SKEGGS, *Proc. Soc. Exp. Biol. Med.*, 75 (1950) 293.
[8] H. K. MITCHELL, M. B. HOULAHAN AND J. F. NYC, *J. Biol. Chem.*, 172 (1948) 525.
[9] H. ARVIDSON, N. A. ELIASSON, E. HAMMARSTEN, P. REICHARD, H. VON UBISCH AND S. BERGSTRÖM, *J. Biol. Chem.*, 179 (1949) 169.
[10] P. REICHARD, *Acta Chem. Scand.*, 3 (1949) 422.
[11] R. B. HURLBERT AND V. R. POTTER, *J. Biol. Chem.*, 195 (1952) 257.
[12] L. L. WEED, M. EDMONDS AND D. W. WILSON, *Proc. Soc. Exp. Biol. Med.*, 75 (1950) 192.
[13] L. L. WEED AND D. W. WILSON, *J. Biol. Chem.*, 189 (1951) 435.
[14] L. D. WRIGHT, C. S. MILLER, H. R. SKEGGS, J. W. HUFF, L. L. WEED AND D. W. WILSON, *J. Am. Chem. Soc.*, 73 (1951) 1898.
[15] I. LIEBERMAN AND A. KORNBERG, *Federation Proc.*, 12 (1953) 239.
[16] H. J. STRECKER AND S. KORKES, *J. Biol. Chem.*, 196 (1952) 769.
[17] A. KORNBERG AND W. E. PRICER, Jr., *J. Biol. Chem.*, 193 (1951) 481.
[18] J. F. NYC AND H. K. MITCHELL, *J. Am. Chem. Soc.*, 69 (1947) 1382.
[19] H. K. MITCHELL AND J. F. NYC, *J. Am. Chem. Soc.*, 69 (1947) 674.
[20] M. BACHSTEZ AND G. CAVALLINI, *Ber. chem. Ges.*, 66B (1933) 681.
[21] A. KORNBERG AND W. E. PRICER, Jr., *Biochemical Preparations*, Vol. 3 (in press).
[22] P. OHLMEYER, *Biochem. Z.*, 297 (1938) 66.
[23] L. BERGER, M. W. SLEIN, S. P. COLOWICK AND C. F. CORI, *J. Gen. Physiol.*, 29 (1946) 379.
[24] A. KORNBERG, *J. Biol. Chem.*, 182 (1950) 805.
[25] A. KORNBERG, *J. Biol. Chem.*, 182 (1950) 779.
[26] O. H. LOWRY, N. J. ROSEBROUGH, A. L. FARR AND R. J. RANDALL, *J. Biol. Chem.*, 193 (1951) 265..
[27] H. LINEWEAVER AND D. BURK, *J. Am. Chem. Soc.*, 56 (1934) 658.
[28] R. M. FINK, K. FINK AND R. B. HENDERSON, *J. Biol. Chem.*, 201 (1953) 349.
[29] C. FUNK, A. J. MERRITT AND A. EHRLICH, *Arch. Biochem.*, 35 (1952) 468.
[30] F. J. DI CARLO, A. S. SCHULTZ AND A. M. KENT, *J. Biol. Chem.*, 199 (1952) 333.

Received April 23, 1953

ENZYMIC CONVERSION OF PHOSPHORYLASE *a*
TO PHOSPHORYLASE *b*

by

PATRICIA J. KELLER* AND GERTY T. CORI

*Department of Biological Chemistry, Washington University School of Medicine,
St. Louis, Missouri (U.S.A.)*

Two forms of rabbit muscle phosphorylase were described by CORI AND GREEN in 1943: phosphorylase *a* which exhibits 60 to 70% of maximal activity without the addition of adenylic acid (adenosine-5'-phosphate), and phosphorylase *b* which has no or minimal activity unless adenylic acid is added to the reaction mixture[1]. In the presence of adenylic acid, both forms are equally active. Extracts of muscle and other tissues were shown to contain an enzyme called PR (prosthetic group-removing) which converts phosphorylase *a* to the *b* form[1]. It was at that time believed that phosphorylase *a* contained firmly bound adenylic acid and that the PR enzyme removed it from the protein. However, in 1944 it was stated that all attempts to demonstrate free adenylic acid (or pentose) after PR action gave negative results[2]. Subsequent attempts to show the presence of adenine in phosphorylase *a* were also unsuccessful[3].

Molecular changes of greater magnitude than removal of a prosthetic group have recently been found to accompany the conversion of phosphorylase *a* to phosphorylase *b*. A smaller protein, which can be identified as phosphorylase *b*, is formed in the reaction catalyzed by PR. Sedimentation patterns in the ultracentrifuge show this second molecular species to be absent from solutions of crystalline phosphorylase *a* but present in all reaction mixtures in which conversion to phosphorylase *b* has occurred.

The extent of conversion of phosphorylase *a* to phosphorylase *b* during PR action is determined by assaying enzymic activity in the presence and in the absence of adenylic acid. Results are expressed as % of specific activities (activity without/activity with adenylic acid, × 100). From these data the relative proportions of the *a* and *b* forms of phosphorylase in reaction mixtures have been calculated[1].

Fig. 1A shows the sedimentation pattern of a 0.6% solution of phosphorylase *a*, which is homogeneous in the ultracentrifuge. This preparation was 66% as active in the absence as in the presence of adenylic acid. The activation of phosphorylase *a* by adenylic acid would seem from this to be real and not due to contaminating phosphorylase *b*. The sedimentation constant ($s_{20, w}$) of phosphorylase *a* is 13.2 Svedberg units.

Concomitant changes in ultracentrifugal and enzymic behavior when phosphorylase *a* is incubated with the PR enzyme have been followed. Figs. 1B, 1C, 1D, and 1E show

---

* Fellow of the National Institutes of Health, United States Public Health Service. This report has been taken from a dissertation to be submitted by P. J. KELLER in partial fulfilment of the requirements for the degree of Doctor of Philosophy in Biological Chemistry, Washington University.

References p. 238.

30 Minute Picture	$\dfrac{Activity - AMP}{Activity + AMP} \times 100$	Enzymic Assay % as a.	% as b.	Area Analysis % as a.	% as b.
A.	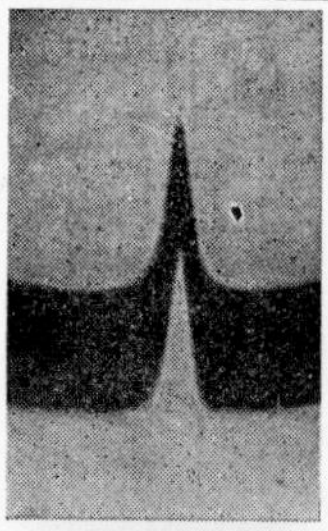 66	100	0	100	0
B.	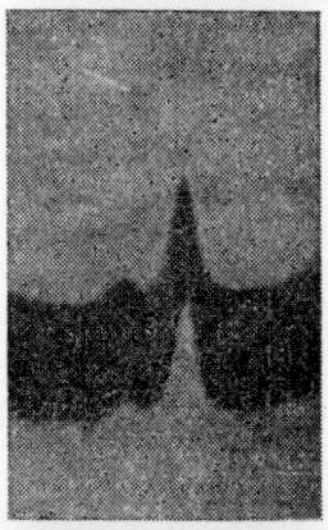 54	81	19	78	22
C.	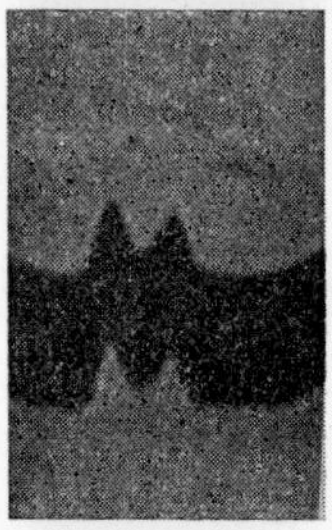 33	51	49	52	48
D.	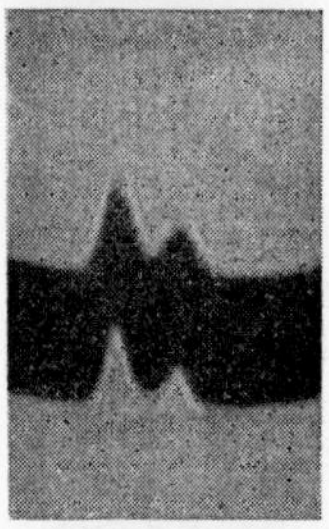 22	33	67	34	66
E.	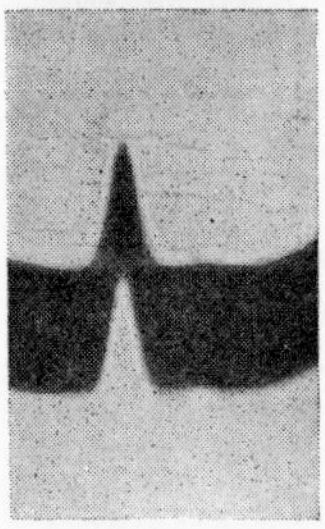 5	5	95	7	93

Fig. 1. Sedimentation patterns (A): of phosphorylase *a*, and (B), (C), (D) and (E): of reaction mixtures of phosphorylase *a* and PR in which increasing amounts of phosphorylase *a* have been converted to phosphorylase *b*. Centrifugations were carried out in the Spinco ultracentrifuge operating at a speed of 59,780 r.p.m.

References p. 238.

the sedimentation patterns of reaction mixtures in which increasing amounts of phosphorylase *a* have been converted to the *b* form. The purified PR enzyme used in these experiments represented no more than three % of the total protein present, and the concentration did not exceed 0.015%. At this concentration no protein peak for the PR enzyme would be visible. A second protein component, with a sedimentation constant of 8.2, can be seen to arise at the expense of phosphorylase *a*. In Fig. 1E the conversion is almost complete. The area of the smaller protein in % of the total protein is at all times equivalent to the enzymically determined proportion of phosphorylase *b*. Addition of adenylic acid (0.001 *M*) to the enzyme solution during ultracentrifugation had no effect on the rate of sedimentation nor on the relative proportions of the two proteins.

The protein product of the PR-catalyzed reaction behaves as a single molecular species throughout the course of centrifugation. This suggested that phosphorylase *a* is split by PR into equal or nearly equal parts. Molecular weight determinations have shown this to be the case. The molecular weights of phosphorylases *a* and *b* have been calculated using the constants and formula listed in Table I. The partial specific volumes ($\overline{V}_{20}$) were determined, using the Linderstrom-Lang gradient tube as described by TAYLOR[6].

TABLE I

MOLECULAR CONSTANTS OF PHOSPHORYLASES *a* AND *b*

Constant	Phosphorylase a.	Phosphorylase b.
$S_{20,\,w}$ *	13.2	8.2
$D_{20,\,w} \times 10^7$	2.6	3.3 **
$\overline{V}_{20}$	0.751	0.751
M.W. ***	495,000	242,000

    * expressed as Svedberg units
   ** determined by GREEN[5]
 *** calculated from M.W. $= \dfrac{RT_s}{D(1-\overline{V}_{20})}$

The sedimentation constant of phosphorylase *a* reported here, namely 13.2, is of the same order as that found by ONCLEY in 1943 which was 13.7. Phosphorylase *b* was not centrifuged at that time.

The diffusion constants for enzymes *a* and *b* call for some comment. ONCLEY[4] determined the diffusion constant for phosphorylase *a* in a neutralized cysteine-glycerophosphate buffer. The experiment was done at 25° C. Pictures were taken between 625 and 2036 minutes. ONCLEY reports formation of insoluble cystine as well as the appearance of skewed curves during the course of the experiment. Despite these difficulties a value between 3.2* and 3.8* seemed reasonable. The molecular weight calculated by ONCLEY was set between 340,000 and 400,000.

GREEN, in 1944, determined the diffusion constant of phosphorylase *b* and found it to be 3.3[5*]. The apparent similarity of diffusion constants for phosphorylase *a* and *b* pointed to molecular weights of the same order of magnitude.

In the present experiment, versene (ethylenediaminetetraacetic acid) was used instead of cysteine to solubilize phosphorylase *a*, and a five-time recrystallized preparation of enzyme was used. The experiment was run at 2° C. The same value (2.6) was found

---

* $D_{20,\,w} \times 10^7$

for ascending and descending limbs of the diffusion cell and the curves were symmetrical between 138 and 4000 minutes.

In retrospect it would seem that during ONCLEY's measurements phosphorylase a was being converted to b by traces of PR which may adhere to phosphorylase even through several recrystallizations.

How the PR enzyme effects the halving of phosphorylase a is the subject of further investigation. While prosthetic group-removing enzyme is a misnomer, it is proposed to retain the name PR (phosphorylase-rupturing enzyme). In chromatographic experiments neither peptide fragments nor free amino acids were found to be released in the a to b conversion. It may be recalled that crystalline trypsin will convert phosphorylase a to a form enzymically identical with phosphorylase b^2. At pH 6 this reaction proceeds preferentially to general proteolysis. However, the PR enzyme shows neither proteolytic nor esteratic activity when tested with substrates which are acted upon by trypsin. The identity or non-identity of trypsin-formed phosphorylase b and the PR product is also being investigated.

Miss CARMELITA LOWRY's technical assistance is gratefully acknowledged.

SUMMARY

Phosphorylase b,the product of the action of a muscle enzyme (PR) on crystalline rabbit muscle phosphorylase a, has one half the molecular weight of the a form. The molecular weights are 242,000 and 495,000 respectively.

RÉSUMÉ

La phosphorylase b, produite par l'action d'un enzyme du muscle (PR) sur la phosphorylase a cristallisée du muscle de lapin, a un poids moléculaire inférieure de moitié de celui de la forme a. Les poids moléculaires sont respectivement 242,000 et 495,000.

ZUSAMMENFASSUNG

Das Produkt der Einwirkung eines Muskelenzyms (PR) auf kristalline Kaninchenmuskel-phosphorylase a, die Phosphorylase b hat die Hälfte des Molekulargewichts der a-Form. Die Molekulargewichte sind 242,000 bzw. 495,000.

REFERENCES

[1] G. T. CORI AND A. A. GREEN, J. Biol. Chem., 151 (1943) 31.
[2] G. T. CORI AND C. F. CORI, J. Biol. Chem., 158 (1944) 321.
[3] S. F. VELICK AND L. F. WICKS, J. Biol. Chem., 190 (1951) 741.
[4] J. L. ONCLEY, J. Biol. Chem., 151 (1943) 21.
[5] A. A. GREEN, J. Biol. Chem., 158, (1944) 315.
[6] J. F. TAYLOR, Federation Proc., 9 (1950) No. 1.

Received April 23, 1953

THE PATHWAYS OF ACETATE OXIDATION*

by

E. S. GUZMAN BARRON AND F. GHIRETTI**

*Chemical Division, Department of Medicine,
The University of Chicago, Ill. (U.S.A.).*

The modern concepts of cellular respiration and of biological oxidations to a large extent were born from the discoveries of WARBURG. WARBURG isolated and crystallized the activating proteins; he discovered two of the three oxidation-reduction systems that mediate in the transfer of electrons from substrate to molecular oxygen, the pyridine nucleotides and the flavoproteins; and he also discovered the last link to oxygen among the iron-porphyrin enzymes, cytochrome oxidase or *Sauerstoffübertragendes Ferment*. WARBURG AND MICHAELIS formulated the fundamental principles. They trail-blazed the road. It is for the generations who succeed them in this search to clear the road and to penetrate into the mechanism of biological oxidation-reductions. Once the mechanism of the first phase of carbohydrate metabolism — the anaerobic reactions from glucose to pyruvic acid—were understood (thanks to WARBURG and MEYERHOF), there remained the oxidative phase, starting from the oxidation of pyruvic acid to acetate or acetyl-coenzyme A. The pathways of acetate oxidation have been diligently searched during the last fifteen years, without, however, general agreement about their relative importance in cellular respiration, or even in some cases about their existence. In animal tissues, both vertebrate and invertebrate, all the published experiments support the contention that oxidation of acetate proceeds *via* the tricarboxylic acid cycle[1,2], *i.e.*, by the condensation of acetylcoenzyme A with oxalacetate. In plants, oxidation proceeds also through this pathway[3,4]. In some moulds and bacteria, specially in those micro-organisms growing in acetate as the main carbon source, there have been proposed two alternative pathways, the dicarboxylic acid cycle[6-9] or oxidation to glycolic acid[10]. Other alternative pathways have also been suggested[11-13]. Solution of this problem is complicated by the semipermeable properties of the cell membrane, which in many cases is impermeable to di- and tri-carboxylic acids even when these are present largely as undissociated acids. It was decided to reinvestigate the possible existence of alternative pathways in those cells which had been presented as oxidizing acetate either by the dicarboxylic acid cycle or through glycolic acid. In all these cells were found the enzymes for the synthesis of citric acid and for the oxidation of *iso*citric acid, a demonstration that acetate can be oxidized *via* the tricarboxylic acid cycle. There was also, however, in these cells, as well as in other cells and tissues examined, anaerobic oxidation of acetate in the presence of coenzyme A, diphosphopyridine nucleotide (DPN), and flavin

* This work was supported by grants from the Biological Sciences Division of the Office of Naval Research and by the Douglas Smith Foundation for Medical Research of the University of Chicago.
** Fellow of the Public Health Service, National Cancer Institute.

References p. 249.

adenine dinucleotide (FAD). This enzyme, we believe, is responsible for the formation of the oxalacetic acid necessary to initiate the citric acid cycle.

EXPERIMENTAL

Methods. Aerobacter aerogenes and *Corynebacterium creatinovorans* were obtained from the American Type Culture collection. *Merulius niveus* and *M. tremellosus* were kindly provided by Dr. WILLIAM J. ROBBINS of the New York Botanical Garden. *Tetrahymena geleii* was kindly provided by Dr. G. M. KIDDER. *Pseudomonas fluorescens* and *Aspergillus fumigatus* were isolated at the laboratory. All bacteria were grown in the medium described by BARRON *et al.*[8] with acetate as the main source of carbon. The moulds were grown in the medium used by NORD AND VITUCCI[14] with acetate as the main source of carbon. *Tetrahymena* was grown in Kidder's yeast-peptone medium containing acetate and glucose. The bacteria were grown generally at 38°. Moulds were grown at 30° in flat-bottomed bottles with continuous shaking. Protozoa were grown at 30° in a dark room and in flat-bottomed bottles. The bacteria were washed three times by centrifugation. The moulds were filtered through gauze and washed several times with distilled water. Fleischmann baker's yeast was washed three times, and oxygen was bubbled through the suspension for six hours. It was then centrifuged again and suspended in water. Oxygen uptake and CO_2 formation were measured manometrically with the usual Warburg technique in vessels of different size. Cell-free extracts of micro-organisms were prepared by grinding the cells in a mechanical mortar at 3° for 3 to 4 hours in the presence of alumina, A-303. During the grinding process the paste was kept moist by addition of drops of 0.154M KCl. The mortar was washed with the KCl solution, and the suspension was centrifuged in a Sorvall angle centrifuge at 8,000 r.p.m. at 3°. The supernatant fluid was a clear golden yellow or green yellow solution. Yeast cells were broken in the press described by HUGHES[15]. Citric acid was determined by the method of ETTINGER *et al.*[16]; pyruvic and α-ketoglutaric acids, according to FRIEDEMANN AND HAUGEN[17]; malic acid, according to HUMMEL[18]; glycolic acid, according to LINK *et al.*[4]; oxalic acid, by titration with permanganate of the precipitated calcium oxalate. For the detection of organic acids by paper chromatography the method of LUGG AND OVERELL[30] was employed after several uni- and bi-dimensional methods were tested; unidimensional descending chromatography with

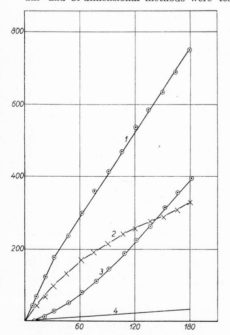

Fig. 1. Rate of Oxidation of Citrate, α-ketoglutarate, succinate, and acetate by *A. aerogenes*. Abcissa, time in minutes; Ordinate, O_2 uptake in μl. 1. Succinate; 2. α-ketoglutarate; 3. Acetate; 4. Citrate.

References p. 249.

Whatman No. 1 filter paper and redistilled mesityl oxide–4N formic acid (1:1) as solvent was used. The chromatograms were run for 8 hours at 18°. The papers were dried overnight in a hood and were developed with a bromocresol green and thymol blue solution. The activity of *iso*citric dehydrogenase in cell-free extracts was determined spectrophotometrically by measuring at 340 mμ the rate of reduction of triphosphopyridine nucleotide (TPN). In these experiments the quartz cells contained 1 ml of cell-free extract; 0.7 ml of 0.1M phosphate, pH 7.46; 0.1 ml of 0.2M MgCl$_2$; 0.5 ml of TPN (200 micrograms); 1.6 ml of H$_2$O. At time zero, 0.1 ml of 0.1M *iso*citrate was added. Reactions were run at room temperature (±26°). For citric acid synthesis, the following system was employed: 1 ml of cell-free extract; 0.2 ml of 0.1M K cysteine; 0.2 ml of 0.04M of MgCl$_2$; 0.2 ml of 0.2M K oxalacetate; 0.2 ml of 0.1M acetyl phosphate; and 0.1 ml of coenzyme A containing 150 units. The vessels were incubated at 26° for two hours, at the end of which 2 ml of 20% CCl$_3$COOH was added, and citric acid was determined in the filtrate.

Coenzyme A (150 units per mg) was kindly provided by Dr. F. LIPMANN; TPN and *iso*citric acid, by Dr. S. OCHOA.

Oxidation of intermediates of the di- and tricarboxylic acid cycles. It is known that most organic acids do not penetrate the cell membrane except as undissociated acids[20] and that as a consequence it is necessary in many cases to lower the pH value of the solution to increase

TABLE I

OXIDATION OF INTERMEDIATES OF THE CITRIC ACID CYCLE BY *Merulius niveus*

Phosphate buffer, 0.03M, pH 5.54. Substrates, 0.01M. Temp. 26°. Time 120 minutes.

Substrate	O_2 Uptake, $\mu l.$
None	156
Acetate	440
Citrate	156
Succinate	157
Malate	157
Pyruvate	169
Glycolate	169

the ratio of the undissociated acid. BARRON *et al.*[8] thus found that *Corynebacterium creatinovorans*, which did not oxidize succinate at pH 7, did oxidize it rapidly at pH 5.5. Citrate was not oxidized at any pH. Therefore, pH 5.5 was used in these experiments.

Aerobacter aerogenes, grown repeatedly in an acetate medium, oxidized ketoglutarate succinate, and acetate at a rapid rate; and citrate at a very slow rate (Fig. 1). *Merulius niveus* oxidized acetate at a rapid rate; pyruvate and glycolate slightly; succinate, citrate, and malonate not at all (Table I). *Pseudomonas fluorescens*, which — like *C. creatinovorans* – does not ferment glucose, oxidized acetate to 70% of complete oxidation (Fig. 2). It oxidized pyruvate readily although in the absence of oxygen no dismutation occurred (Fig. 3); acetate and succinate at about the same speed; ketoglut-

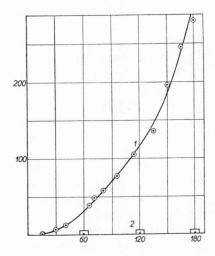

Fig. 3. Oxidation of Pyruvate by *Pseudomonas fluorescens*. Phosphate buffer, 0.03M pH 6.9 for O_2 uptake; bicarbonate – N_2:CO_2 pH 7.2 for dismutation and CO_2 formation. K pyruvate, 0.01M (30 micromoles.) Abscissa, time in minutes. Ordinate, O_2 uptake or CO_2 production im μl (blank subtracted). 1. O_2 uptake; 2. CO_2 production.

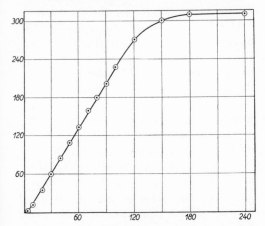

Fig. 2. Oxidation of Acetate by *Pseudomonas fluorescens*. Buffer, 0.03M phosphate, pH 6.9. Acetate, 10 micromoles. Abscissa, time in minutes. Ordinate, O_2 uptake in μl (blank subtracted).

arate less rapidly; and citrate very slowly (Table II). It is known that ketoglutarate accumulates during the oxidation of glucose by these bacteria[21]. *Tetrahymena geleii*

References p. 249.

TABLE II

OXIDATION OF INTERMEDIATES OF THE CITRIC ACID CYCLE

BY *Pseudomonas fluorescens*

Buffer, 0.05M phosphate, pH. 5.5; substrate, 0.01M. Figures give μl per mg dry weight per hour.

Substrate	O_2 Uptake
None	28.4
Acetate	178.5
Acetate + malonate	158
Succinate	136.5
Succinate + malonate	145
Citrate	56
a-Ketoglutarate	57.4
Pyruvate	74.4
Glycolate	30

oxidizes acetate readily and, according to SEAMAN[22], accumulates succinate in the presence of malonate. (The succinate figures given by him were too small to be considered reliable). *Tetrahymena geleii* obtained from 24-hour cultures oxidized acetate, citrate, and succinate. Although pyruvate did not increase the O_2 uptake, there was definite utilization. Malonate inhibited acetate oxidation, as found by SEAMAN (Table III).

Citric acid synthesis and isocitric acid oxidation. Neither kinetic nor isotope experiments are reliable tools to determine whether acetate is oxidized by the dicarboxylic acid pathway. Since these two pathways differ only by addition to the latter of a synthesis reaction and two more oxidative steps, it was necessary to look for these steps in the cells we were studying by preparing cell-free extracts and measuring citric acid synthesis and *iso*citric acid oxidation under optimum conditions for these enzymatic reactions. Cell-free extracts of *M. tremellosus, M. niveus, C. creatinovorans, Rhyzopus nigricans,* and *A. aerogenes* contained OCHOA's condensing enzyme for the synthesis of citric acid on addition of acetyl phosphate, oxalacetate, and coenzyme A (Table IV). The cell-free extracts of *Tetrahymena geleii* contained so much citric acid that search for the enzyme was considered unnecessary. All these cell-free extracts, including those of *Tetrahymena,* contained *iso*citric dehydrogenase, as shown by the reduction of TPN on addition of *iso*citrate (Table V). OCHOA found the condensing enzyme in cell-free extracts of *Pseudomonas fluorescences* [23].

Additional evidence that oxidation of acetate by the moulds *M. niveus,* and *M. tremellosus* occurs *via* the citric acid cycle was obtained by the determination of the citric acid cycle intermediate-oxidation products. For these experiments the moulds were grown at 30° with continuous shaking for 7 days. The filtered media were reduced in volume under vacuum, and determinations were made in aliquots of these solutions. In all the specimens were found by chemical analysis citric, a-ketoglutaric, malic, glycolic, and oxalic acids. By paper chromatography succinic and fumaric acids were identified (Table VI). The a-keto acid, which was determined as the coloured complex of the phenylhydrazone derivative, was assigned to a-ketoglutaric acid because the absorption spectrum was identical to that of the phenylhydrazone complex of a sample of a-ketoglutaric acid.

The effect of malonate on the oxidation of acetate. Malonate inhibition experiments with bacterial cells are sometimes difficult to interpret because of the possible lack of penetration through the cell membrane. In some cases this difficulty is surmounted by

References p. 249.

increasing the acidity of the solution, increasing the concentration of malonate, or decreasing the number of cells. In yeast cells at pH 4.0 with phthalate buffer, it was found that the effect of malonate depended on the amount of yeast used per vessel. With 51 mg of yeast, there was practically no inhibition (7.5% inhibition). When the amount of yeast was reduced to 5.1 mg malonate inhibited the oxidation of acetate by

TABLE III

OXIDATION OF INTERMEDIATES OF THE CITRIC ACID CYCLE

BY *Tetrahymena geleii*

Phosphate buffer, 0.03M, pH 5.54. Substrates, 0.01M except pyruvate, 0.005M. Malonate, 0.02M. Temp. 26°. Time, 180 min.

Substrate	O_2 Uptake c.mm.	Utilization c.mm.
None	300	
Acetate	471	
Citrate	373	141
Pyruvate	300	123
Succinate	343	

TABLE IV

OXIDATION OF ACETATE, *iso*CITRATE, AND SUCCINATE BY MICRO-ORGANISMS.

SYNTHESIS OF CITRIC ACID BY THEIR CELL-FREE EXTRACTS.

Oxidation: Buffer, K-phosphate, 0.03M, pH 5.53; substrate, 0.01M; temp. 38°.
Citrate Synthesis: cell-free extract, 1ml; K-phosphate buffer, pH 7.4, 25 μM; MgCl$_2$, 4μM; Cysteine, 10μM; K oxalacetate, 20μM; Acetyphosphate, 10μM; Coenzyme A, 50 units. Temp. 26°. Time of incubation, 2 hours. Figures refer to μM citric acid formed per mg protein.

Micro-organism	O_2 Uptake, blank substracted Acetate	Isocitrate	Succinate	Citrate Synthesis
	c.mm.	c.mm.	c.mm.	μM
M. tremellosus	100	0	460	6.77
M. niveus	609	0	3	0.205
C. creatinovorans	89	0	88	0.035
A. aereobacter	284	0	290	0.015

TABLE V

OXIDATION OF *iso*CITRATE BY CELL-FREE EXTRACTS OF MICRO-ORGANISMS

WHICH DO NOT OXIDIZE ADDED ISOCITRATE

System: cell-free extract, 1 ml; K phosphate buffer, pH 7.56, 0.1 M, 0.5 ml; MgCl$_2$, 0.2M, 0.1 ml; K *iso*citrate, 2.16 μM, 0.2 ml; H$_2$O, 1.1 ml. TPN, 0.16 μM, 0.1 ml added at time 0. Temp. 36°.

Micro-organism	Protein	Reduction of 0.073 μM TPN	Reduction rate calc. per mg protein
	mgs	seconds	seconds
M. tremellosus	0.506	594	297
M. niveus	1.29	186	144
C. creatinovorans	1.9	445	239
A. aerogenes	1.44	508	352
Tetrahymena geleii	1.33	280	372
R. nigricans	1.05	250	263

References p. 249.

TABLE VI

INTERMEDIATES OF THE CITRIC ACID CYCLE FOUND IN THE CULTURE MEDIA OF
CERTAIN MOULDS GROWN IN ACETATE AS THE MAIN SOURCE OF OXIDIZABLE MATERIAL
The figures give micrograms per ml of culture media, blank subtracted.

	Aspergillus	M. niveus	M. tremellosus
Citric acid	5.0	2.1	3.6
α-Ketoglutaric acid	2.4	3.6	2.1
Pyruvic acid*			
Malic acid	5.1	1.7	2.5
Succinic acid**	+	+	+
Fumaric acid**	+	+	+
Oxalic acid	73.0	15.0	31.0
Glycolic acid	76	18	14.4

* Determined as α-ketoglutarate
** Detected by paper chromatography.

TABLE VII

EFFECT OF MALONATE ON THE OXIDATION OF ACETATE BY MICRO-ORGANISMS
Acetate, 0.01M; Malonate, 0.01M. Temp. 38°. Incubation time 90 minutes. All figures blank
subtracted.

Micro-organism	pH	O_2 Uptake	
		Control c.mm.	Malonate c.mm.
Baker's yeast, 51 mgs/vessel	4.0	1030	952
,, ,, 12.5 mgs	4.0	1524	407
,, ,, 5.1 mgs	4.0	162.1	40
Corynebacterium creatinovorans	5.54	770	100
Pseudomonas fluorescens	5.54	749	638
Merulius niveus	5.54	548	560
Tetrahymena geleii	5.54	471	475
Rhyzopus nigricans	5.54	249	250

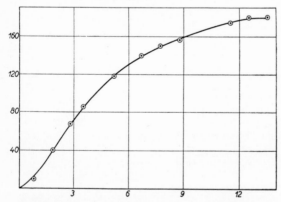

Fig. 4. Oxidation of malonic acid by *Aerobacter aerogenes*. Buffer 0.03 M phosphate pH 7.0. Malonate 10 micromoles. Abscissa time in hours. Ordinate O_2 uptake in c.mm. Figures given are blank subtracted. Temp. 37.5°. Calculated O_2 uptake for complete oxidation malonate 448 c.mm; found 179.7 c.mm (40% of total oxidation).

References p. **249**.

75%. LYNEN, aware of the membrane impermeability of yeast, obtained malonate inhibition by disturbing the membrane on treatment of yeast cells with liquid nitrogen[24]. At pH 5.54, the lowest pH for respiration of these microorganisms, acetate oxidation by *C. creatinovorans* was inhibited 87%; by *Pseudomonas fluorescens*, 15%; by *Tetrahymena geleii*, completely. The membrane of moulds seems more impermeable to malonate: malonate had no effect at all on the oxidation of acetate by *M. niveus* or *R. nigricans*.

Malonate was oxidized by *Aerobacter aerogenes* after an induction time, which increased as the cell concentration decreased. Oxidation stopped when 40% of the added malonate was oxidized (Fig. 4). The R.Q. value of this oxidation was 1.47 an indication of complete oxidation ($HOOCCH_2COOH + 2 O_2 = 3 CO_2 + 2H_2O$). The induction time, which may last as long as two hours when the amount of bacteria is small, was thought to be due to a slow decarboxylation of malonate preceding the oxidation ($HOOCCH_2COOH = CO_2 + CH_3COOH$). There was, however, no CO_2 production when the bacterial suspension was incubated in the presence of malonate with nitrogen as the gas phase. In spite of this oxidation, malonate inhibited effectively acetate oxidation (Fig. 5).

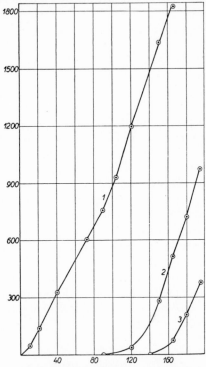

Fig. 5. Effect of Malonate on the Oxidation of Acetate by *A. aerogenes*. Phosphate buffer 0,03M, pH 5.54. Acetate, and malonate, 0.01M. Abscissa, time in minutes. Ordinate, O_2 uptake in μl. 1. Acetate; 2. Acetate + malonate; 3. Malonate (all figures blank subtracted). Temp. 38°.

Inhibition of acetate oxidation by malonate may be considered as evidence that the oxidation proceeds through the dicarboxylic or the tricarboxylic acid pathway. There would be no inhibition if the oxidation proceeded through another pathway which had no succinate as an intermediate oxidation product. Negative experiments, however may mean only lack of penetration of malonate. Thus acetate oxidation by moulds was not inhibited by malonate, although there were found in the culture media all the intermediates of the citric acid cycle. Malonate inhibition experiments could be utilized as an indication of the presence of the dicarboxylic acid cycle by determination of citric and succinic acids after oxidation of acetate in the presence and in the absence of malonate. It is known that baker's yeast produces citric and succinic acids on oxidation of acetic acid[25], and that the pathway of this oxidation, mainly the tricarboxylic acid cycle, can also be the dicarboxylic acid cycle[26],[27]. In agreement with these views, on oxidation of acetate by yeast at pH 4.0 there were found 44 mm³ of citrate, and traces of succinate, whereas in the presence of malonate citrate was four times as low and succinate increased considerably (Table VIII). In *Corynebacterium creatinovorans*, BARRON et al.[8], found on oxidation of acetate in the presence of malonate an accumulation of succinate with no citric acid formation. These experiments were repeated, using paper chromatography for the detection of the intermediate acids formed. At pH 5.54, in the presence of acetate, 2,030 mm³ of O_2 were used up. After ether extraction of the acidified solution citric and α-ketoglutaric acids were detected, an indication that oxidation of acetate proceeded *via* the citric acid cycle. In the presence of malonate, there was an uptake of 200 mm³ and in the paper chromatograms only succinic acid was detected. In *Aerobacter aerogenes* at pH 5.54 there was an O_2 uptake of 2,280 mm³ in the presence of acetate; in the paper chromatograms there were detected citric, α-ketoglutaric, and succinic acids. With acetate plus malonate, there was an O_2 uptake of 520 mm³; in the

TABLE VIII

CITRIC AND SUCCINIC ACIDS FORMED IN BAKER'S YEAST
DURING THE OXIDATION OF ACETATE

Buffer, 0.1M phthalate pH 4.0, 10 ml; yeast suspended in water, 10 ml (46.6 mgs); 2.5 ml of acetate, 0.2M; 2.5 ml of malonate, 0.1M; 1.0 ml. KOH, 3N. Time, 180 minutes. Temp. 38°.

Determinations	Acetate c.mm.	Acetate + Malonate c.mm.
O$_2$ uptake	4166	900
Citrate	43.8	11.7
Succinate	10	164

paper chromatograms only succinic acid was found. In all these experiments 1ml of 1N H$_2$SO$_4$ was added to the Warburg vessels at the end of the incubation period; the samples were boiled for a few minutes, and after centrifugation the solutions were extracted with ether for 24 hours in the Kutscher-Steudel extractors. Malonate was previously oxidized with permanganate.

The anaerobic oxidation of acetate. Cell-free extracts of *Corynebacterium creatinovorans* were found to oxidize acetate anaerobically, as shown by the reduction of methylene blue[3]. This anaerobic oxidation was attributed to the oxidative condensation to succinate because on oxidation of acetate in the presence of malonate there was accumulation of succinate and no citrate formation. Similar cell-free extracts prepared from 24-hour cultures of *A. aerogenes*, after 24 hours dialysis at 3° against 0.154M KCl, failed to reduce methylene blue on addition of acetate, unless the following components were added: Coenzyme A, DPN, FAD, and MgCl$_2$ (Table IX). Omission of any one of these compo-

TABLE IX

ANAEROBIC OXIDATION OF ACETATE BY DIALYZED CELL-FREE EXTRACTS
OF AEROBACTER AEROGENES (24 HOURS CULTURE)

Additions	ml	ml	ml	ml	ml	ml
Cell-free extract	0.3	0.3	0.3	0.3	0.3	0.3
Phosphate, 0.1M, pH 7.0	0.65	0.65	0.65	0.65	0.65	0.65
Acetate, 0.2M	0.25	0.25	0.25	0.25	0.25	—
DPN 700 micrograms	0.1	0.1	0.1	0.1	—	0.1
Coenzyme A, 86 units	0.1	0.1	0.1	—	—	0.1
FAD, 35 micrograms	0.1	0.1	—	0.1	0.1	0.1
Mg Cl$_2$, 0.2M	0.1	—	—	—	—	—
Methylene blue, 0.0005M	0.3	0.3	0.3	0.3	0.3	0.3
Water	1.1	1.2	1.3	1.3	1.4	1.45
Reduction of M.B. in minutes	30	45	none	none	none	none

nents inhibited dye reduction. Furthermore, it was found that addition of –SH reagents, such as iodosobenzoate or *p*-Cl-Hg benzoate also produced inhibition. Whether this inhibition is due to combination with the –SH group of coenzyme A or with the –SH groups of the protein is not known. DPN was reduced at very slow rate in extracts from *C. creatinovorans*. Anaerobic oxidation of acetate in the presence of the components above mentioned has also been found in cell-free extracts of baker's yeast, *Pseudomonas fluorescens*, *Aspergillus*, and *Tetrahymena geleii*. It seems that this enzyme, which may be called acetic dehydrogenase, is present not only in those cells which were believed to

References p. 249.

oxidize acetate *only* by the dicarboxylic acid pathway but in other cells as well. The enzyme has been found in the mitochondria of rat liver, of pigeon breast muscle, and in rat skeletal muscle. It has not yet been possible to isolate the protein component, and efforts are now being directed towards this goal.

DISCUSSION

The oxidation of acetate by the tricarboxylic acid cycle requires the presence of citrogenase, OCHOA'S condensing enzyme, and of isocitric acid dehydrogenase. Once these two enzymes have been found in a particular cell or tissue, it may be concluded that acetate metabolism can proceed *via* the citric acid cycle. Search for these two enzymes in microorganisms thought to oxidize acetate through alternative pathways has demonstrated their presence. Both enzymes were found in *Aerobacter aerogenes*, *Corynebacterium creatinovorans* and *Rhyzopus nigricans*, previously considered to oxidize acetate *via* the dicarboxylic acid cycle alone[6-9]. They were also found in the moulds *M. niveus* and *M. tremellosus*, which had been thought to oxidize acetate *via* glycolic acid[10]. Moreover, the culture fluid of these moulds contained citric, α-ketoglutaric, succinic, and malic acids – all intermediates of the citric acid cycle. The presence of glycolic acid in the culture fluid of these moulds (as found by us) and in Aspergillus (as found by WEINHOUSE[28]) must be due to hydrolysis of malic acid by the enzyme malic hydrolase, which was found in plants by LINK *et al.*[4]. The protozoa *Tetrahymena geleii* was also found to oxidize acetate *via* the citric acid cycle.

Although the citric acid cycle is thus extended to cover the mechanism of acetate oxidation in cells hitherto considered to utilize alternative pathways, the origin of the oxalacetic acid necessary for condensation with acetylcoenzyme A needs to be explained. Oxidation of acetate proceeds in these cells after an induction time of variable length. The accumulation of succinic acid on oxidation of acetate in the presence of malonate *without* citric acid or glycolic acid formation is proof that acetic acid does oxidize to succinic acid. In cell-free extracts of bacteria and moulds, as well as in mitochondria of liver and muscle, there was found an enzyme system which oxidized acetate anaerobically as shown by the reduction of methylene blue. Furthermore, it was found that after dialysis oxidation of acetate required the addition of coenzyme A, DPN, FAD and Mg^{+2}. From these experiments the anaerobic oxidation of acetate may be postulated to proceed as follows:

a) $2 \text{ Acetyl-S-CoA} + \text{DPN} + 2H_2O \rightleftharpoons \text{HOOC–CH}_2\text{CH}_2\text{COOH} + \text{DPNH} + H^+ + 2 \text{ HSCoA}$

b) $\text{DPNH} + H^+ + \text{FAD} \rightleftharpoons \text{DPN} + \text{FADH}_2$

c) $\text{FADH}_2 + \text{MB} \rightleftharpoons \text{FAD} + \text{MBH}_2$.

The first reaction proceeds at a slow rate because of the low oxidation-reduction potential of DPN as compared with that of acetate ⇌ succinate. It was found in fact that reaction stopped when only 0.02% of the DPN was reduced. Once succinate is formed, the production of oxalacetic acid is easily seen through its stepwise oxidation to fumarate, fumarate – malate, and malate – oxalacetate. It is our belief that this enzyme is universally present in all cells and that it is the source of the oxalacetate required to initiate the oxidation of acetate *via* the citric acid cycle. It is quite possible that impairment of this enzyme is responsible for the large aerobic glycolysis found by

WARBURG in tumor tissues, since WEINHOUSE [29] found no difference in the activity of the enzymes of the citric acid cycle. The dicarboxylic acid pathway may thus be considered as the priming mechanism for the oxidation of acetate through the citric acid cycle.

SUMMARY

In micro-organisms considered to oxidize acetate *via* the dicarboxylic acid cycle or by oxidation to glycolic acid, there were found the enzymes for the synthesis of citric acid and for the oxidation of *iso*citric acid. The culture media of moulds believed to oxidize acetate *via* glycolic acid contained citric, α-ketoglutaric, succinic, malic, and glycolic acids. In most of these organisms malonate inhibited acetate oxidation. In the absence of malonate, citric acid was detected chromatographically from solutions where acetate was oxidized whereas in the presence of malonate only succinate was detected. Formation of succinate from acetate seems to occur by the oxidative condensation of acetylcoenzyme A to succinate. Cell-free extracts of bacteria, moulds, yeast, and animal tissues contain the enzyme which oxidizes acetate in the presence of coenzyme A, flavine adenine dinucleotide, DPN, and Mg^{+2}. It is postulated that all cells oxidize acetate *via* citric acid cycle but also possess the dicarboxylic acid cycle which provides the oxalacetate required for citric acid formation.

RÉSUMÉ

Les auteurs ont trouvé, chez des microorganismes considérés comme oxydant l'acétate par l'intermédiaire du cycle dicarboxylique ou comme l'oxydant en acide glycolique, les enzymes nécessaires à la synthèse de l'acide citrique et à l'oxydation de l'acide *iso*-citrique. Les milieux de culture de moisissures qui oxydent, croit-on, l'acétate en acide glycolique, renferment les acides citriques, α-cétoglutarique, succinique, malique et glycolique. Chez la plupart de ces organismes, le malonate inhibe l'oxydation de l'acétate. En absence de malonate, l'acide citrique est décelable par chromatographie dans des solutions où l'acétate est oxydé, tandis qu'en présence de malonate l'acide succinique seul peut être décelé. La formation de succinate à partir d'acétate doit résulter d'une condensation oxydative de l'acétyl coenzyme A en succinate. Des extraits acellulaires de bactéries, de moisissures, de levures et de tissus animaux renferment l'enzyme qui oxyde l'acétate en présence de coenzyme A, de flavine adénine dinucléotide, de DPN et de Mg^{+2}. Les auteurs supposent que toutes les cellules oxydent l'acétate par l'intermédiaire du cycle citrique mais peuvent également l'oxyder par l'intermédiaire du cycle dicarboxylique qui donne naissance à l'oxaloacétate nécessaire à la formation d'acide citrique.

ZUSAMMENFASSUNG

Es wurden die Enzyme für die Zitronensäuresynthese und für die Oxydation von Isozitronensäure von Mikroorganismen gefunden, bei denen man vermutet, dass die Acetatoxydation über den Dicarbonsäurecyclus oder durch Oxydation zu Glycolsäure verläuft. Das Kulturmedium der Pilze, die Acetat über Glycolsäure oxydieren sollen, enthalten Zitronensäure, α-Ketoglutarsäure, Bernsteinsäure, Apfel- und Glycolsäure. Bei den meisten dieser Organismen hemmt Malonat die Acetatoxydation. Beim Abwesenheit von Malonat wurde Zitronensäure in Lösungen, in denen Acetat oxydiert wurde, chromatographisch nachgewiesen, während bei Gegenwart von Malonat nur Bernsteinsaures Salz entdeckt werden konnte. Es scheint, dass die Bildung von bernsteinsaurem Salz aus Acetat bei der oxydativen Kondensation von Acetylcoenzym A und bernsteinsaurem Salz stattfindet. Zellfreie Extrakte von Bakterien, Pilzen, Hefe und tierischen Geweben enthalten das Enzym, das Acetat in Gegenwart von Coenzym A, Flavin-adenin-dinucleotid, DPN und Mg^{+2} oxydiert. Es wird postuliert, dass alle Zellen Acetat über den Zitronensäurecyclus oxydieren, aber ebenfalls den Dicarbonsäurecyclus besitzen, der für das für die Zitronensäurebildung erforderliche Oxalacetat sorgt.

References p. 249.

REFERENCES

[1] H. A. KREBS, *Harvey Lectures*, 44 (1950) 165
[2] E. S. G. BARRON, W. P. SIGHTS, AND V. WILDER, *Arch. f. exptl. Path. u. Phar.* (in press).
[3] E. S. G. BARRON, G. K. K. LINK, R. M. KLEIN, AND B.E. MICHEL, *Arch.Biochem.*, 28 (1950) 377.
[4] G. K. K. LINK, R. M. KLEIN AND E. S. G. BARRON, *J. Exp. Bot.*, 3 (1952) 216.
[5] A. MILLERD, J. BONNER, B. AXELROD AND R. BANDURSKI, *Proc. Natl. Acad. Sci. U.S.*, 37 (1951) 855.
[6] S. J. AJL, *Bacteriol. Rev.*, 15 (1951) 211.
[7] S. DAGLEY, E. A. DAWES AND G. A. MORRISON, *J. Gen. Microbiol.*, 5 (1951) 508.
[8] E. S. G. BARRON, M. I. ARDAO AND M. HEARON, *Arch. Biochem.*, 29 (1950) 130.
[9] J. W. FOSTER, S. F. CARSON, D. S. ANTHONY, J. B. DAVIES, W. E. LEFFERSON AND M. V. LONG, *Natl. Acad. Sci. U. S.*, 35 (1949) 663.
[10] F. F. NORD AND J. C. VITUCCI, *Adv. in Enzymology*, 8 (1948) 253.
[11] H. A. KREBS, in *Symposium sur le Cycle Tricarboxylique. II. Congrès International de Biochimie, Paris*, 1952. p. 42.
[12] K. BLOCK, *Ann. Rev. Biochem.*, 21 (1952) 273.
[13] E. S. G. BARRON, in *Symposium sur le Cycle Tricarboxylique. II. Congrès International de Biochimie, Paris*, 1952, p. 94.
[14] F. F. NORD AND J. C. VITUCCI, *Arch. Biochem.*, 14 (1947) 229.
[15] D. E. HUGHES, *Brit. J. Exp. Pathol.*, 32 (1051) 97.
[16] R. H. ETTINGER, L. R. GOLDBAUM AND L. H. SMITH, *J. Biol. Chem.*, 199 (1952) 531.
[17] T. E. FRIEDEMANN, AND G. HAUGEN, *J. Biol. Chem.*, 147 (1943) 415.
[18] J. P. HUMMEL, *J. Biol. Chem.*, 180 (1949) 1225.
[19] S. J. AJL, *J. Gen. Physiol.*, 35 (1951) 115.
[20] W. J. V. OSTERHOUT, *J. Gen. Physiol.*, 8 (1925) 131.
[21] H. J. KOEPSELL, F. H. STODOLA AND E. S. SHARPE, *J. Am. Chem. Soc.*, 74 (1952) 5142.
[22] G. R. SEAMAN, *J. Biol. Chem.*, 196 (1950) 97.
[23] S. OCHOA, J. R. STERN AND M. C. SCHNEIDER, *J. Biol. Chem.*, 193 (1951) 691.
[24] F. LYNEN, *Ann.*, 554 (1943) 40.
[25] H. WIELAND AND R. SONDERHOFF, *Ann.*, 499 (1932) 213.
[26] S. WEINHOUSE AND R. H. MILLINGTON, *J. Am. Chem. Soc.*, 69 (1947) 3089.
[27] F. LYNEN, *Ann.*, 558 (1945) 47.
[28] S. WEINHOUSE, in *Phosphorus Metabolism*, W. D. MCELROY AND B. GLASS, Baltimore, 1951, p. 282.
[29] S. WEINHOUSE, R. H. MILLINGTON AND C. E. WENNER, *Cancer Res.*, 11 (1951) 845.
[30] J. W. H. LUGG AND B. T. OVERELL, *Nature*, 160 (1947) 87.

Received April 23, 1953

THE ROLE OF PHOSPHOGLYCOSYL COMPOUNDS
IN THE BIOSYNTHESIS OF NUCLEOSIDES AND NUCLEOTIDES

by

HERMAN M. KALCKAR

Universitetets Institut for Cytofysiologi, Copenhagen (Denmark)

Our growing understanding of the function of inorganic phosphate in biological synthesis stems back to the early discoveries of ARTHUR HARDEN and OTTO MEYERHOF. The coupling of the phosphate uptake with carbohydrate metabolism is of two essentially different types. The first type of coupling, with oxido-reductive processes, remained a mystery until OTTO WARBURG and his group in 1939, having isolated the crystalline enzyme as well as the pure coenzyme system of phosphotriose oxidation, were able to identify the primary product of phosphate coupling as 1,3-diphosphoglyceric acid. This was the first acylphosphate discovered in biological systems. From the work of LIPMANN, LYNEN and RACKER we know now that the primary attack of orthophosphate in the coupled oxidations is a fission of an acyl mercapto linkage. Thus the carbonyl groups in phosphoglyceraldehyde or in pyruvate do not react directly with phosphate. The sequence of reactions seems to start with a complex between the carbonyl group and a coenzyme mercapto (SH) group. This complex is oxidized and the resulting acyl complex undergoes enzymic fission, orthophosphate (or pyrophosphate) yielding acylphosphate and a free mercapto group.

The second type of coupling involves a more direct reaction between phosphate and a substituted aldehyde group and was described by CARL AND GERTY CORI in 1937, when they discovered the phosphorolytic fission of the 1–4 glycosidic linkages of glycogen. This type of phosphorolytic fission, which is readily reversed, was shown by DOUDOROFF and co-workers to play a role in the synthesis of many disaccharides. The primary product formed in enzymic phosphorolysis of glycosidic linkages is a phosphoglycosyl compound, and these 1-esters can exchange their phosphate group enzymatically with a sugar. The work on the phosphorolytic fission of the glycosidic linkages of di-and poly-saccharides turned out to be of importance as well for a close understanding of many features in nucleoside and nucleotide metabolism. The present article deals with some recent work on the importance of phosphoglycosyl compounds in nucleoside and nucleo-tide biosynthesis.

Nucleoside phosphorylases. The building blocks of nucleic acids contain an N-ribosyl linkage. It was found that nucleoside phosphorylase, an enzyme isolated from mammalian liver, brings about a liberation of phosphoribosyl or deoxyribosyl groups[1, 2]. The phos-phopentosyl compounds react readily with nitrogenous bases to form nucleosides.

References p. 263/264.

We have for example:

ribosyl-hypoxanthine + phosphate ⇌ ribosyl-phosphate + hypoxanthine

or

deoxyribosyl-hypoxanthine + phosphate ⇌ deoxyribosyl-phosphate + hypoxanthine

Hypoxanthine can be continuously removed by xanthine oxidase which catalyzes an oxidation to uric acid. By addition of two enzymes, nucleoside phosphorylase and xanthine oxidase, it is possible to follow the phosphorolysis of hypoxanthine-pentosyl compounds spectrophotometrically since the uric acid formed manifests itself by a conspicuously high absorbtion maximum at 2900 A; at the same time the phosphorolysis is brought to an end and the phosphopentosyl compounds which accumulate can be isolated. If the phosphopentosyl compounds are incubated with hypoxanthine or guanine and purine nucleoside phosphorylase, the purine ribosides are resynthesized and inorganic phosphate is liberated[1,2]. In the corresponding enzymic resynthesis of hypoxanthine deoxyriboside it was shown that the product had high growth factor activity towards *Thermobacterium acidophilus* R26 which is a deoxyribosyl requiring lactic acid bacterium[3]. The enzymic equilibrium is towards purine incorporation both when studied with ribosyl-phosphate and with deoxyribosyl-phosphate (see Fig.).

This type of reaction clearly revealed that the reactive component was a type of reactive ribosyl (or deoxyribosyl) as follows

$$\text{RO:} \overset{\downarrow\,+\,\vert}{\underset{\underset{H}{..}}{C}} \overset{\vert\!\!-\!\!-O\!\!-\!\!-}{}$$

which can attach to a N-base or a phosphate anion. This means that the fission of ribosyl phosphate takes place between the carbon number 1 of the ribose and the oxygen of the phosphate. Later studies using ^{18}O have shown that fission occurs in an analogous way between the carbon and oxygen in the enzymic splitting of glucose-1-phosphate in polysaccharide synthesis[4]. It has been demonstrated that arsenate exerts a hydrolytic effect if added to glycosyl phosphorylases[5,6]. We are here once more reminded of the corresponding observations made by WARBURG and his group, *i.e.* the hydrolytic formation of 3-phosphoglycerate in the presence of arsenate. Apparently glycosyl arsenates as well as acyl arsenates undergo spontaneous fission in water. MANSON AND LAMPEN have also found that addition of arsenate to nucleoside phosphorylase in the presence of deoxyribosides yields free deoxyribose[7].

Properties of pentosyl phosphates. The two pentose-1-phosphoric esters are highly acid labile, especially deoxyribose-1-phosphate, which is 50% dephosphorylated at 20° within 15 minutes at pH 4[8] and thus is an example of one of the most acid labile compounds of this type hitherto described. Ribo-furanose-1-phosphate is fairly stable at pH 4 but highly acid labile in strong mineral acid (in 0.5 N sulfuric acid at 20° it is hydrolyzed to the extent of 50% within 2.5 minutes[9]). Ribose-1-phosphate can therefore be studied by the LOWRY-LOPEZ phosphate determination at pH 4[9]. The properties of the pentose-1-phosphates are summarized in Table V together with other phosphoglycosyl compounds. Although the pentose-1-phosphates are formed from β-nucleosides[10], it is nevertheless difficult to make any suggestions with regard to the configuration of the phosphopentosyl compounds. Enzymic phosphorolytic fission of the 1-4-α-glycosidic linkages of glycogen and starch yields α-glucose-1-phosphate, as does the corresponding fission of sucrose[11,12]. In contrast, the α-1-4-glycosidic linkage of maltose yields β-glucose-1-phosphate[13]. Whether there may be a single inversion, a double inversion or no inversion at all, is at the present stage impossible to predict, especially for ribosides.

Specificity of the nitrogenous bases. The fact that the phosphorolysis of the purine and pyrimidine nucleosides is not catalyzed by the same enzyme has been established beyond any doubt (DEUTSCH AND LASER[14], KLEIN[15], MANSON AND LAMPEN[16]). PAEGE AND SCHLENCK[17] have described a pyrimidine nucleoside phosphorylase present in *E. coli* which is specific for uridine. As to the question whether the same enzyme can catalyze the phosphorolysis of ribosides and deoxyribosides, or whether two enzymes are required, nothing definite can be stated. Studies on rat liver purine nucleoside phosphorylase might indicate a common enzyme for the two pentoses[2]; the behaviour of bacterial enzymes indicats that here two independent enzymes may be operating[18, 19].

The specificity of the liver purine nucleoside phosphorylase with respect to the nitrogenous aglycone is very unpredictable. Hypoxanthine and guanine ribosides or deoxyribosides are swiftly phosphorolyzed. The corresponding xanthine compounds react very slowly, however, and the synthesis of the corresponding purines is of the same order with respect to rate.

Surprisingly enough adenine is not an active participant in nucleoside phosphorylation; correspondingly a direct phosphorolytic fission of adenosine does not occur, and the attack on this compound is preceded by a deamination of adenosine to inosine. An exception to these observations has recently been reported. *E. coli* contains an enzyme which specifically catalyzes the phosphorolysis of adenosine[18].

Purine derivatives as antigrowth factors and mutagens and their relation to nucleoside phosphorylase. Amongst the many unpredictable facts concerning the specificity of this enzyme is the finding by FRIEDKIN[20] that 8-azoguanine, incubated with ribose-1-phosphate or deoxyribose-1-phosphate in the presence of liver nucleoside phosphorylase, gives excellent yields of the corresponding azoguanine nucleosides. According to KIDDER[21] 8-azoguanine is a strong antigrowth factor for *Tetrahymena gelii*, a micro-organism which requires guanine as a growth factor. Also certain tumors are inhibited by azoguanine[21]. FRIEDKIN's findings raise the problem as to whether the participation of azoguanine in nucleoside (or nucleotide) metabolism can account for the suppression of growth. The enzymatically formed azoguanine ribosides were assayed by KIDDER for growth inhibition on *Tetrahymena gelii* and were found to exert, on a molar basis, half the inhibitory effect of free azoguanine. A detailed study of the incorporation of azoguanine into nucleotides and nucleic acids (bypassing of nucleosides?) has not yet been performed, but experiments using isotopically labelled azoguanine[22] lend support to the theory[21] that this substance can give rise to the formation of abnormal nucleotides and nucleic acids. The author of the present review is, however, inclined to bring up another aspect which might help to interpret the data collected on the effect of azoguanine on the growth of certain mammary carcinoma in mice[21]. FRIEDKIN's experiments show that azoguanine forms ribosyl or deoxyribosyl compounds very effectively. This could imply that under conditions (or in certain types of tumors) where the availability or the rate of formation of ribosyl (espec. deoxyribosyl) is such as to barely suffice for rapid growth, a side tracking by azoguanine will manifest itself biologically. The conditions hinted at could be rapid expansive growth during which the rate of biosynthesis of pentosyl in general becomes a limiting factor. If azoguanine acts like a ribosyl or deoxyribosyl trap it would greatly inhibit growth under such circumstances. The same type of effect may play a role for the antimutagenic effect of guanosine, inosine and adenosine (NOVICK

References p. 263/264.

AND SZILARD[23]), as these compounds are able to reverse the mutagenic action of dimethyl-xanthine, azoguanine, and other purine derivatives[24]. If ribosides which are potential ribosyl phosphate producers can incorporate some of the mutagenic purine derivatives the latter will not appear in the deoxyribonucleic acids, which may again imply that they are barred from producing mutations. In this case the ribosyl compounds may function as a trap for mutagenic purines. The fact that the nucleosides also suppress the normal or "spontaneous" mutation rate adds to the interest of the whole phenomenon.

Phosphorolysis of pyridinium nucleosides. ROWEN AND KORNBERG[25] have found that nicotine-amide riboside (the pyridinium (N⁺) riboside) undergoes a phosphorolysis catalyzed by a liver enzyme which seems to be identical with the purine nucleoside phosphorylase. The reaction is reversible. This observation is particularly surprising because the pyridinium (N⁺) riboside linkage does not have the typical properties of a substituted glycosidic linkage. It is, for instance, more labile towards alkali than towards acid[26]. The reduced nicotine-amide riboside (monohydropyridine riboside) is much more labile towards acids than towards alkali[26]., *i.e.* like a typical glycoside; yet the reduced form is inert towards the enzyme. Since a pyridinium compound is converted by enzymic phosphorolysis into a pyridine compound with a liberation of one hydrogen ion, it is clear that the equilibrium:

"pyridinium (N⁺) riboside" + phosphate $\rightleftharpoons$ "pyridine" + ribose-1-phosphate + H⁺

depends on pH. In a buffer at neutral pH the reaction will go predominantly from left to right. At pH 7.4, expressing concentrations as mmols per ml K is [27]:

$$K = \frac{\text{N}^+\text{-riboside} \times \text{P}}{\text{nicotinamide} \times \text{rib-1-P}} = 10^{-3}$$

The ΔF of hydrolysis of the N⁺ ribosyl bond at pH 7 is close to 8000 cals (*cf.*[27]) of which almost half is furnished by the dissociation of hydrogen ions. The ΔF hydrolysis of a phosphoglycosyl compound like glucose-1-phosphate or ribose-1-phosphate amounts presumably to 4500–5000 cals.

Transglycosidases. Phosphopentosyl compounds are not obligatory intermediaries in nucleoside metabolism. MACNUTT[28] has discovered the existence of a trans-N-glycosidase in *Lactobacillus helveticus* and other lactic acid bacteria, requiring deoxy-ribosides or B_{12}. This enzyme catalyzes the following type of reaction: purine deoxy-riboside + pyrimidine $\rightleftharpoons$ pyrimidine deoxyriboside + purine. All the purines and pyrimidines occurring in nucleic acids, as well as the corresponding deaminated deriva-tives, can be participants. A corresponding trans-N-glycosidase for ribosides may also be present but a study of such an enzyme is not possible in crude extracts of *L. helveticus* due to the presence of a powerful hydrolytic enzyme, ribosidase[29]. Ribosidases have also been found in other micro-organisms[30].

It has been shown that sucrose phosphorylase can also act as a trans-O-glycosidase between ketoses (*e.g.* direct enzymic conversion of sucrose into α glucosido-sorboside[5]). We have been comparing a trans-N-glycosidase from *L. delbrückii* with a nucleoside phosphorylase from *L. casei*. It can be seen from Table I that the trans-N-glycosidase does not show phosphorylase activity nor does the phosphorylase show trans-N-glycosi-dase activity[29]. The interesting spleen enzyme trans-nicotinamide-glycosidase attacking DPN[27] has apparently no phosphorylase activity.

The mechanism by which glycosyl phosphorylases or transferases operate will be discussed elsewhere. Recent studies by FRIEDKIN[20] have shown that deoxyribosyl

References p. 263/264.

TABLE I

INCUBATION OF HYPOXANTHINE DEOXYRIBOSIDE (80 μG) WITH BACTERIAL EXTRACTS
(0.5 MG PROTEIN) FOR 2 H AT 35° PH 7.0. ANALYSIS OF PROTEIN-FREE FILTRATES FOR URIC ACID

Enzyme	μg Purine liberated		
None	0	0	0
L. casei	3.4	32.0	3.4
L. delbruckii	4.8	4.0	15.8

(KALCKAR[19])

phosphate, in the presence of the specific phosphorylase, does not exchange with inorganic phosphate (^{32}P labelled) except in the presence of the nitrogenous bases.

The question of a prosthetic group for transglycosidases or phosphorylases, especially of the type of LELOIR's uridine diphospho-glycosyl compound, has been in the minds of several investigators, including ourselves[31,*32,33]. Polysaccharides, disaccharides, nucleosides or phosphoglycosyls might play the role of glycosyl donors with uridine diphosphate as acceptor. The UDP-glycosyl formed could then donate the glycosyl to acceptors including inorganic phosphate. Whether the recent report[34] that uridine diphospho-glucuronate is the cofactor of glucuronide synthesis can be classified as an example of this type of reaction remains to be seen.

The physiological role of nucleoside phosphorylases. The demonstration of nucleoside formation from pentosyl phosphates and in particular the demonstration of highly active growth factors for micro-organisms formed from deoxyribosyl phosphate and purine by liver nucleoside phosphorylase, might very well lead an investigator to believe that this could be the clue to an understanding of nucleotide and nucleic acid synthesis. This may be the case if the discussion is confined to biosyntheses in micro-organism. It must, however, be borne in mind that the enzymes used originated from rat liver, and the logical question is, therefore, how does this enzymic step reaction benefit the nucleotide and nucleic acid synthesis in the rat organism? Since radioactive pentoses so far have not been accessible, the fate of the pentoses of inosine or its deoxyribo analogue has yet to be determined. We can, therefore, only discuss the importance of nucleoside phosphorylase for the incorporation of N-bases into nucleic acids. For an evaluation of this problem the inertness of adenine in this enzymic step is bound to become a crucial point. Without adenine as an active partner the role of this group of enzymes of nucleotide and nucleic acid synthesis must somehow be more or less indirect. This is particularly evident from the studies performed on the intact rat with isotopically labelled purines. BROWN and co-workers[35] have found that adenine is incorporated into nucleic acids on a large scale, the hypoxanthine of inosine to a small extent and free hypoxanthine not at all. The fact that riboside-bound hypoxanthine is definitely incorporated, whereas the free hypoxanthine is not, points towards the existence of important alternative pathways for nucleotide synthesis from ribose-1-phosphate. The formation of

---

* KALCKAR AND CUTOLO[31] have found that addition of UDP or UDPG to inosine nucleoside phosphorylase and xanthine oxidase brought about an increase in the rate of liberation of uric acid as compared with the samples without the uridine nucleotides. The rates were, however, much slower than those obtained by addition of free phosphate. It has not been possible to demonstrate a formation of uridyl phospho-1-ribose. The formation of this compound by the action of uridyl transferase (see later) has not been observed.

References p. 263/264.

ribose-1-phosphate stems either from ingested inosine or from hexosephosphates generated in ordinary carbohydrate metabolism[36].

Role of ribose-1,5-diphosphate in nucleotide formation and in the biosynthesis of purines. The possibility of alternative pathways for ribose-1-phosphate as an inter mediary metabolite, is a crucial point in a discussion of nucleotide synthesis. Two independent investigators studying hypoxanthine synthesis in pigeon liver have found evidence for ribose-5-phosphate as the carrier of both incomplete purine precursors and complete purines. GREENBERG[37] found that ^{14}C labelled formic acid added to pigeon liver extract appeared in the hypoxanthine of 5-inosinic acid (hypoxanthine-ribose-5-phosphate) in markedly higher concentration than in that of inosine of free hypoxanthine (*cf.* Table II). Inosine had a conspicuously low isotope concentration and GREENBERG was therefore led to believe that in the synthesis of purine nucleotides the nucleosides were bypassed.

TABLE II

INOSINE NOT PRECURSOR OF IMP-5 IN DE NOVO SYNTHESIS
Specific activity, cts./per/μM

Inosine-5-phosohate	Inosine	Hypoxanthine
18,600	9,900	4,730

Experiment H-27, vessel 1. System 1 ml of 1:2 liver homogenate 1 μM of inosine, 12 μM of ^{14}C-formate (68·10^3 cts. per μmol), time 21 minutes.

From G. R. GREENBERG, *J. Biol. Chem.*, 190 (1951) 623.

The nucleosides were considered to be breakdown products from nucleic acids and nucleotides and not steps on the biosynthetic pathway to the latter compounds. Such a bypassing of nucleosides was also indicated in some studies on nicotinamide nucleotide synthesis in hemolysates[38]. A third observation of importance was the stimulation of inosinic acid synthesis in pigeon liver extract by the combined action of adenosine triphosphate and ribose-5-phosphate (BUCHANAN[39]).

It will be noticed that the studies performed on unfractionated extracts of tissues have given, in general, some extra information about nucleotide metabolism and have given hints about the existence of reactions which have so far not been detected in more fractionated systems. Consequently we initiated studies on more or less intact or unfractionated liver preparations. BENNETT and I injected 8-^{14}C adenine into a perused rabbit liver and found that the adenine disappeared largely from the blood within 5 minutes. A large proportion was found in the adenylpyrophosphate (ADP,ATP) fraction[40]. GOLDWASSER studied the purine metabolism of liver slices and homogenates and found that a marked incorporation of adenine into nucleotide took place[41]. Homogenates of pigeon liver turned out as on so many previous occasions to be the most reproducible cell free system. The supernatant obtained from spinning at 100,000 *g* was practically free of microsomes and possessed all the activity. The adenine was incorporated into 5-adenylic acid or adenosine diphosphate[41]. SAFFRAN AND SCARANO[42] have found that the particle free extract is completely inactivated by dialysis but can be completely reactivated by adding ribose-5-phosphate and ATP. The ribose-5-phosphate can be replaced by ribose-1-phosphate (see Addendum, p. 262) but ribose-2-phosphate, ribose-3-phosphate, deoxyribose-1-phosphate and ribose are not active (Table III).

In contrast to the original extract, the dialyzed preparation incorporates adenine into AMP only. ATP could be shown to react with ribose-1-phosphate. The ATP-dependent enzyme is destroyed by heating at 65° for 5 minutes; preincubation of ribose 1-phosphate and ATP with the dialyzed extract, followed by heating at 65°, and then a further incubation with ^{14}C adenine, yielded ^{14}C-AMP, but there was not incorporation when the ribose-1-phosphate and ATP were added only after the heating step (Table IV)[42]. The enzyme catalyzing the incorporation of adenine into the diphosphoribose is heat stable in contrast to the enzymes which catalyze the formation of the diester.

TABLE III

FORMATION OF ^{14}C-AMP FROM ^{14}C-ADENINE BY A DIALYZED PIGEON-LIVER EXTRACT

	cts/min in 5-AMP
Dialyzed extract + ^{14}C-adenine	15
Dialyzed extract + ^{14}C-adenine + R-5-P + ATP	1868
Dialyzed extract + ^{14}C-adenine + R-1-P + ATP	2550
Dialyzed extract + ^{14}C-adenine + R-2 or 3-P + ATP	53
Dialyzed extract + ^{14}C-adenine + DR-1-P + ATP	30
Dialyzed extract + ^{14}C-adenine + ribose + ATP	90
Dialyzed extract + ^{14}C-adenine + ATP alone	22
Dialyzed extract + ^{14}C-adenine + R-1-P alone	82
Dialyzed extract + ^{14}C-adenine + α-G-1, 6-P$_2$ + R-1-P + phosphoglucomutase	1840
Dialyzed extract + ^{14}C-adenine + R-1-P + phosphoglucomutase*	1110

* Spectrophotometric assay showed the presence of G-1, 6-P$_2$ in the phosphoglucomutase preparation.

From SAFFRAN AND SCARANO[42].

TABLE IV

PREINCUBATION OF RIBOSE-MONOPHOSPHATE AND ATP

	cts./min in AMP	
	R-1-P	R-5-P
Preincubation with ribose-monophosphate and ATP Heating at 65° for 5′ Incubation with ^{14}C-adenine	1161	1066
Heating at 65° for 5′ Incubation with ribose-monophosphate, ATP and ^{14}C-adenine	0	0

From SAFFRAN AND SCARANO[42]

These observations were very close to a previous one made by the BUCHANAN group[39] in which they also found an enhancement of inosinic acid formation in pigeon liver by a combined action of ATP and ribose-5-phosphate. The obvious question was whether ATP phosphorylated ribose monophosphate (1 or 5-ester) to ribose-1,5-diphosphate. For further pursuit in this direction, SAFFRAN AND SCARANO were able to benefit from KLENOW's demonstration of this ester as the result of an enzymic interaction[43]. It is necessary at this point to add a few remarks about phosphoribomutase.

References p. 263/264.

The significance of phosphoribomutase in analogy with phosphoglucomutase[45] was first clearly recognized by SCHLENK[44]. Later MANSON AND LAMPEN found that deoxyribosides can be converted to deoxyribose-5-phosphate. KLENOW AND LARSEN found that phosphoribomutase from muscle and yeast[43] can be activated by small amounts of synthetic α-glucose-1,6-diphosphate. It should be added that the muscle ribomutase requires an activator only in the presence of 8-hydroxyquinoline. A clue to the understanding of the nature of activation of phosphoribomutase was given by the following type of reaction:

$$\text{ribose-1-phosphate} + \alpha\text{-glucose-1,6-diphosphate} \rightleftharpoons$$

$$\text{ribose-1,5-diphosphate} + \text{glucose-6-phosphate}$$

This reaction, which is analogous to Leloir's reaction between α-glucose-1,6-diphosphate and mannose-1-phosphate[46], can be pushed towards the right (and be demonstrated optically) by addition of "Zwischenferment" and triphosphopyridine nucleotide (TPN) in the presence of which the glucose-1-phosphate is oxidized[26]. The new diester, which was isolated by means of chromatography on a Dowex-1 column, has a strong cofactor activity in the phosphoribomutase test. Table V lists some of the properties of ribose-1,5-diphosphate. It will be noticed that although the 1-ester phosphate is acid labile it is not as labile as ribose-1-monophosphate.

TABLE V

STABILITY OF 1-ESTER P

	Neutral and weak alka-line react.	Acetate buffer pH 4.0	0.5 N H_2SO_4		Cofactor in phosphosugar mutase
	20^0	20^0	20^0	100^0	
α-Glucopyranose-1-phosphate	stable	stable	stable	labile	o
α-Glucopyranose-1,6-diphosphate*	stable	stable	stable	labile	+
Ribofuranose-1-phosphate	stable	stable	labile 50% in 2.5'		o
Ribopyranose-1-phosphate**	stable	stable	labile 50% in 90'	labile	o
Ribose-1,5-diphosphate	stable	stable	labile 50% in 5'		+
Deoxribofuranose-1-1-phosphate	stable	labile 50% in 15'	extr. labile	o	

* Synthetic preparation (courtesy Prof. POSTERNAK).
** Synthetic preparation (courtesy Prof. A. R. TODD).

With the knowledge about formation and properties of ribose-1,5-diphosphate in mind, SAFFRAN AND SCARANO were in a position to furnish further evidence for ribose-1,5-diphosphate as the ester which reacts with radioactive adenine yielding 5-adenylic acid. First of all they showed that incorporation of adenine can be increased just as much by preincubation of ribose-1-phosphate with α-glucose-1,6-diphosphate (synthetic, POSTERNAK) as with the former and ATP. Secondly the ribose ester formed after these preincubations possesses the properties described by KLENOW. It remains to study the reaction between ribose-1,5-diphosphate and adenine in more detail in order to prove that we are here in fact dealing with a simple nucleotide glycosylphosphorylase.

The role of ribose-1,5-diphosphate is probably not limited to the function as a co-phosphoribomutase and as an exchange substance for adenine and hypoxanthine. It may also be the substance which reacts with nicotinamide (cf. LEDER AND HANDLER[39]), and perhaps it can, in general, serve as a "ribotyl" (5-phosphoribosyl) unit for precursors of purines and pyrimidines.

Uridyl phosphoglycosyl compounds. Our interest in these novel types of nucleotide which were discovered by LOUIS LELOIR and his group[47], started with the idea that they could be considered as glycosyl compounds with a substituted phosphate instead of free phosphate (see formula p. 253).

In other words, could the uridine diphosphate be considered as a carrier of glycosyls? This aspect has already been discussed briefly, but since no direct experimental evidence is available at the present time to indicate that the UDPG (a or β?) can participate in glycosyl phosphorylation or transglycosidation, the idea must so far be classified as possible fruitful speculation.

From the start, however, LELOIR and his group put the spotlight on the potentialities of another bond. They found that UDPG is a coenzyme for the inversion of a-galactose-1-phosphate to a-glucose-1-phosphate. Two step reactions were proposed[48].

1.   Uridyl-phospho-1-glucose + phospho-1-galactose $\rightleftharpoons$
           Uridyl-phospho-1-galactose + phospho-1-glucose

2.   Uridyl-phospho-1-galactose $\rightleftharpoons$ Uridyl phospho-1-glucose.

The enzyme for reaction 1 has not been isolated but can be demonstrated separately after the galacto-inversion enzyme has been inactivated (see later). LELOIR[40] demonstrated reaction 2 separately by subsequent analysis of the sugars by paper chromatography. In equilibrium he found that 75% is in the form of uridylphospho-1-glucose (UDPG) and 25% in the form of uridylphospho-1-galactose. This type of reaction which so far is a real novelty in enzyme chemistry has been discussed in detail from a chemical point of view by LELOIR[46]. Apparently it does not conform with any of the known chemical mechanisms of inversions either. It was predicted by LELOIR in 1950[46] that UDPG probably would turn out to play a role in other enzymic reactions than the galactose inversion. Phosphopyruvate is able in the presence of the proper phosphokinase to phosphorylate uridine diphosphate (UDP) to uridine triphosphate (UTP)[49]. It was anticipated that the latter may play a role in the synthesis of UDPG through pyrophosphorolysis[49], a type of fission discovered a few years ago by KORNBERG.[50] It was later found[51] that ATP, UDP, and a-glucose-1-phosphate in the presence of mercaption juice from bakers yeast can give a distinct increase in the amount of UDPG present in the juice.

Uridyl transferases. We have found[52, 53] that brewery yeast as well as galactose adopted yeast (*Saccharomyces fragilis*) contains an enzyme which catalyzes a pyrophosphorolytic fission of UDPG. The specific enzyme UDPG pyrophosphorylase is abundant in the so-called "Zwischenferment" preparation (WARBURG AND CHRISTIAN 1932[54]) which is a protein precipitated with carbon dioxide at high aqueous dilutions (100 fold) of yeast maceration juice. This fraction can be further purified; the protein fractions precipitated in the range 0.6 to 0.7 saturated ammonium sulphate being the most active. For our investigations we have used the WARBURG-CHRISTIAN-LE PAGE "Zwischenferment" extensively because it turned out, by a stroke of fortune, to contain most of the enzymes needed for good micro assays and practically none which were undesirable.

The reaction is: UDPG + pyrophosphate $\rightleftharpoons$ UTP + a-G-1-P and the fission of UDPG occurs as shown in Fig. 1. This fission will release Cori-ester (a-glucose-1-phosphate) which upon addition of phosphoglucomutase (absent in our Zwischenferment preparation) would yield glucose-6-phosphate. Since Zwischenferment together with

References p. 263/264.

TPN will dehydrogenate the latter ester (WARBURG, CHRISTIAN AND GRIESE[26]) the rate of liberation of glucose ester can be followed in the ultraviolet range at 340 mμ by reduction of TPN (WARBURG, CHRISTIAN AND GRIESE[26]).

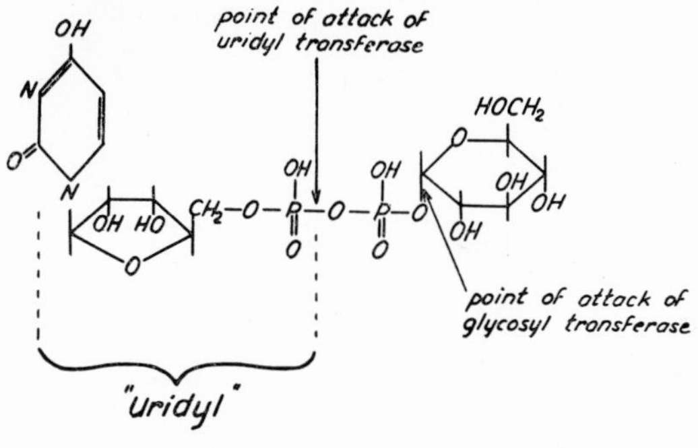

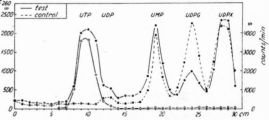

Fig. 1. Uridyl-Phospho-1-Glucose (UDPG)

[32]P labelled inorganic pyrophosphate was utilized in the reaction and for each mol radioactive pyrophosphate used one mol α-glucose-1-phosphate was liberated. If the cleavage took place at arrow number 1 (Fig. 1) the resulting nucleotide should be uridine triphosphate (UTP). It is possible to isolate the radioactive ester by barium precipitation, by chromatography through a column of Dowex Cl$^-$, by paper-ionophoresis and by paper chromatography (ethanol-ammonium acetate pH 7.0, (PALADINI AND LELOIR[55]). In all these procedures the isolated nucleotide behaves like a di- or tri-phosphate. In the chromatogram (see Fig. 2) it appears more charged than uridine diphosphate (UDP), moving, more slowly. Since it has one mol ^{32}P-pyrophosphate per mol uracil it seems evident that it is UTP and a chemical analysis confirmed this. UTP seems to act slowly as a phosphoryl donor in the hexokinase test[49]; interestingly enough, if a small amount of adenosine diphosphate (ADP) is present this reaction goes much faster[56]. UDP is not active in this test, which is a very sensitive assay for nucleoside triphosphates.

It is of particular interest, however, to describe the enzymic reaction in which UTP plays the role of a uridyl donor. This is in the "back reaction" of the pyrophosphorolysis, *i.e.* UTP plus α-glucose-1-phosphate in the presence of Zwischenferment gives

Fig. 2. Paper chromatogram of norite eluate of UDPG-pyrophosphorylase digest.
(from A. MUNCH-PETERSEN *et al.*[53]).
Reaction mixture: 0.2 μmol UDPG, 2 μmol inorganic pyrophosphate (8·10^4 cts/min), 50 μl phosphoglucomutase, 50 μl Zwischenferment (3.3 mg/ml), 3 ml Tris (Hydroxy methyl) amino methane HCl pH 8.0.
Control mixture: Same without pyrophosphate. After 45 min. incubation, the digest were acidified, adsorbed on norite and eluted with 50% ethanol. Chromatographed 44 hours in neutral solvent. Chromatogram scanned in the Beckmann 260 mμ

UDPGlucose (uridyl-phospho-glucose) plus inorganic pyrophosphate. If the latter is split by a specific pyrophosphatase the reaction is pulled and the formation of UDPGlucose from UTP and gluxose-1-phosphate is easy to demonstrate (see Fig. 3). The UDPG pyrophosporylase could logically be classified as a "uridyl transferase". In extracts from galactose adapted *Saccharomyces fragilis* it is simple to demonstrate that UTP reacts with α-galactose-1-phosphate[57]. In the final balance the presence of UTP brings about a conversion of a manyfold amount of galactose-1-phosphate to glucose-6-phosphate (see Fig. 4). The sequence of reactions is as follows:

i. UTP + α-galactose-1-phosphate $\rightleftharpoons$ UDPGalactose + pyrophosphate. This is the pyrophosphorylase reaction (uridyl transferase No. 1) presumably specific for galactose adapted yeast.

References p. 263/264.

ii. Pyrophosphate $+ H_2O \to 2$ orthophosphates. This is catalyzed by inorganic pyrophosphatase which is also present in crude *S. fragilis* extracts.

iii. UDPGalactose $\rightleftharpoons$ UDPGlucose. This is catalyzed by the inversion enzyme ("Galacto Waldenase") specific for galactose adapted yeast.

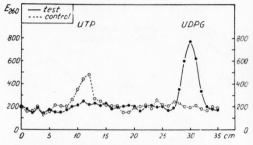

iv. UDPGlucose $+ \alpha$-galactose-1-phosphate $\rightleftharpoons$ UDPGalactose $+ \alpha$-glucose-1-phosphate. This is catalyzed by a non-pyrophosphorolytic uridyl transferase (No. 2) presumably specific for galactose adapted yeast.

v. α-glucose-1-phosphate $\rightleftharpoons$ glucose-6-phosphate catalyzed by phosphoglucomutase which is also present in unfractionated *S. fragilis* extracts.

vi. Glucose-6-phosphate $+ TPN^+ \rightleftharpoons 6$-phospho-gluconic acid $+$ reduced TPN. This is catalyzed by glucose-6-phosphate dehydrogenase, also present in crude *S. fragilis* extracts.

Since all the six step enzymes are present in dialyzed *S. fragilis* extract the addition

Fig. 3. Paper chromatogram of norite eluate of UTP-pyrophosphorylase digest. (from A. MUNCH-PETERSEN *et al.*[53]).

Reaction mixture: 0.2 μmol UTP, 10 μmol glucose-phosphate, 100 μl inorganic pyrophosphatase, 50 μl Zwischenferment, 1 ml Tris (hydroxy methyl) amino methane HCl pH 8.0

Control mixture: Same without glucose-1-phosphate. After 50 min. incubation the gigests were acidified, adsorbed on norite and eluted with 50% ethanol. Chromatographed 44 hours in neutral solvent. Chromatogram scanned in the Beckmann at 260 mμ.

of TPN 30 minutes after α-galactose-1-phosphate and UTP have been added to a dialyzed *S. fragilis* extract will bring about a rapid density increase at 340 mμ due to the reduction of TPN by the accumulated glucose-6-phosphate. Of the six step enzymes mentioned number iv deserves a few comments. This enzyme which can best be demonstrated in diluted extracts of *S. fragilis* manifests itself by a formation of 1 mol glucose-1-phosphate per mol UDPG and galactose-1-phosphate consumed. Since addition of inorganic pyrophosphate is superfluous (occasionally inhibitory) and the presence of pyrophosphatase apparently does not interfere, it is clearly a non-pyrophosphorolytic uridyl transferase where the uridyl acceptors are α-galactose-1-phosphate and α-glucose-1-phosphate[57], resp. It is presumably the same enzyme which catalyzes the following reaction:

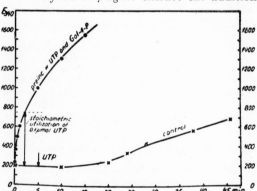

Fig. 4. Spectrophotometric analysis (TPN reduction) of glucose-6-phosphate from UTP and gaalctose-1-phosphate in *S. fragilis* extract. (from H. M. KALCKAR, A. MUNCH-PETERSEN AND B. BRAGANZA[57].

Reaction mixture: 0.1 μmol UTP, 0.6 μmol Gal-1-P*, 50 μl dialyzed *S. fragilis* extract (approx. 250 μg protein), 50 μl 0.1 M Tris (hydroxy methyl) amino methane HCl, pH 8.0. Control mixture: Same without UTP. After 30 min incubation excess of TPN was added (time zero on the graph). At 5 min 0.1 μmol UTP was added to the control.

---

* Courtesy LELOIR AND REISSIG. Ba-salt, subjected to reprecipitation with ethanol acid labile P estimated.

References p. 263/264.

uridyl-phospho-1-glucose (UDP Glucose) $+$ (^{32}P) phospho-1-glucose $\rightleftharpoons$ uridyl (^{32}P) phospho-1-glucose $+$ phospho-1-glucose.

This reaction as well as the reactions with galactose-1-phosphate does not take place in Zwischenferment preparations.

TRUCCO[51] has found that ATP $+$ UDP can act as "Co-Waldenase" in the conversion of galactose-1-phosphate to glucose-1-phosphate in dialyzed S. fragilis extracts. The catalytic effect of UTP which we have demonstrated is presumably a step reaction in TRUCCO's system. In general the demonstration of such reactions shows that the so-called "Co Waldenase" test is not specific for UDPGlucose or UDPGalactose if performed in crude dialyzed extracts of S. fragilis. The UDPGlucose pyrophosphorolytic test with "Zwischenferment" and TPN seems at the present time to be the most specific test for UDPGlucose.

The occurrence of other uridyl phosphoglucosyl compounds

i. "UDPX" from yeast; this component has most recently been identified by LELOIR and his colleagues as uridyl phospho-1-(N-acetyl 2-amino) glucose[58].

ii. "UDPX" compounds from Staphylococcus aureus metabolizing in the presence of penicillin.[59] PARK[60] has identified these compounds.

Compound 1: (N-acetyl, 2 amino) uronic acid.

Compound 2: Same type with extra incorporated alanine.

Compound 3: same type with extra incorporated peptide (containing D and L amino acids).

iii. Uridyl phospho-1-glucuronic acid[61].

PARK AND JOHNSON's discovery of the effect of penicillin on the accumulation of uridine diphosphoglycosyl compounds of type ii poses the problem whether this antibiotic exerts a strong inhibition on a step enzyme of the uridyl transferase type. If about 0.5 Oxford unit of penicillin is added to a growing culture of staphylococci cell division stops but expansion of the cells continues for another ¾ to 1 hour during which time the normal amount of "UDPX" is increased more than fifty fold. This accumulation of uridine nucleotides seems to be at the expense of the formation of ribonucleic acid (see next section). The recent observations that a uridine nucleotide which seems to have a β-phospho-1-glucuronic acid as the P-glycosyl component and works as a coenzyme for the glucuronide synthesis[34] has already been discussed briefly. In this case there is reason to believe that the exchange fission may take place at the glycosyl linkage. One cannot help thinking that polysaccharides of a type like hyaluronic acid may serve as glycosyl donors for UDP thus giving rise to the formation of UDPGluronic acid and UDPX substances such as these classified under i and ii.

Biosynthesis of nucleic acid linkages. It has in general been found that labelled purines and pyrimidines if incorporated into nucleic acids are rapidly incorporated into the 5-nucleotides of the corresponding N-bases. Administration of labelled adenine to a perfused liver or to liver homogenates appears within a few minutes after the addition of the purine in 5-adenylic acid, ADP, and ATP[40,41]. In sea urchin embryos ^{14}C adenine is incorporated rapidly into the 5-nucleotides and into deoxyribonucleic acid and slowly into ribonucleic acid[62]. Labelled orotic acid, which seems to be the only free pyrimidine to be incorporated into the nucleic acids of the rat organism[61], appears first in 5-uridylic acid nucleotides[63]. Correspondingly, in micro-organisms capable of using

References p. 263/264.

uracil for nucleic acid synthesis, labelled uracil can be detected in 5-uridylic compounds[64]. It has, moreover, been found that addition of penicillin causes the staphylococci to cut down on the incorporation of uracil into ribonucleic acid with a corresponding increased incorporation in the derivatives of 5-nucleotides[64]. It seems likely therefore that the 5-nucleotides, their polyphosphates or other derivatives are precursors of nucleic acid units, especially those of ribonucleic acids. As discussed earlier in this review the incorporation of nitrogenous bases for nucleic acid synthesis is complex. Nucleosides are mainly bypassed and it seems that in the case of *Lactobacillus helveticus* which needs uracil, more complex nucleotides than the simple 5-nucleotides are needed[65]. One could well image that UTP, reacting with free nucleosides or nucleosides bound as end-groups in a ribonucleic acid chain, could form nucleic acid linkages through pyrophosphorolysis. In other words it seems worthwhile to search for uridyl transferases in which nucleosides or end-groups of nucleic acids can be used as uridyl acceptors.

As usual, progress in this field depends on the development of new, ingenious and bold methods, especially of the kind with which OTTO WARBURG has provided us to such a generous extent.

ACKNOWLEDGEMENT

The studies on nucleotide metabolism performed in Universitets Institut for Cytofysiologi have been supported by grants from the following foundations: Carlsbergfondet, Lederle Laboratories, American Cyanamid Company, Instituto Sieroterapico Italiano, Nordisk Insulinfond, The Rockefeller Foundation and The Williams Waterman Fund of The Research Corporation.

Addendum (July 8, 1953)

In our laboratory SCARANO (unpublished work) has recently isolated an enzyme from pigeon liver, phosphoribokinase, which catalyzes the phosphorylation of ribose-5-phosphate in the 1-position, yielding ribose-1,5-diphosphate. ATP is phosphoryl donor. The fractionated enzyme was freed from phosphoribomutase and consequently ribose-1-phosphate does not serve any more as a phosphate acceptor. Adenine is the only nitrogenous compound which reacts rapidly with the ribose-1,5-diphosphate in the heated fraction of the pigeon liver homogenate after high-speed centrifugation.

SUMMARY

In the biosynthesis of nucleosides and nucleotides the intermediate formation of ribose (or deoxyribose)-1-phosphate and their corresponding 5-esters may play a prominent role in the animal organism; the pathway seems to involve a phosphorylation (by ATP) of the 1 position of ribose-5-phosphate yielding ribose-1,5-diphosphate. This new diester can also be obtained from ribose-1-phosphate and glucose-1,6-diphosphate in the presence of phosphoglucomutase. In pigeon liver extracts there are strong indications that ribose-1,5-diphosphate can exchange its 1-ester phosphate with adenine, hypoxanthine or incomplete purine precursors.

Glucose-1-phosphate and galactose-1-phosphate (both α-glycosyl compounds) also play a role as acceptors of uridyl radicals catalyzed by a special class of enzymes, uridyl transferases. Uridine triphosphate plus one of these enzymes incubated with one or the other of the two above-mentioned 1-esters yields LELOIR's UDP-glucose or UDP-galactose, the so-called "CoWaldenases".

Conversely, the latter compound incubated with inorganic pyrophosphate and a uridyl-transferase gives rise to the formation of uridine triphosphate (UTP). UTP may, through the action of another uridyl transferase, play a role in the incorporation of the uridyl radical into nucleic acids.

References p. 263/264.

RÉSUMÉ

Au cours de la synthèse biologique des nucléosides et des nucléotides dans l'organisme animal, la formation intermédiaire de ribose (ou désoxyribose)-1-phosphate et des esters en 5 correspondants joue probablement un rôle important; la suite des réactions comprendrait une phosphorylation (par l'ATP) de la position 1 du ribose-5-phosphate donnant du ribose-1,5-diphosphate. Ce nouveau diester peut également provenir du ribose-1-phosphate et du glucose-1,6-diphosphate en présence d'une phosphoglucomutase. Dans les extraits de foie de pigeon, il parait bien que le ribose-1,5-diphosphate peut échanger son phosphate en position 1 avec l'adénine, l'hypoxanthine ou des précurseurs puriques incomplets.

Le glucose-1-phosphate et le galactose-1-phosphate (qui sont tous les deux des corps α-glycosyliques) jouent également le rôle d'accepteurs de radicaux uridyliques en présence d'enzymes particuliers, les uridyl transférases. L'uridine triphosphate et l'un de ces enzymes incubés avec l'un ou l'autre de ces deux esters donne l'UDP glucose de LELOIR ou l'UDP galactose, appelés aussi "CoWaldenases".

Inversement, le dernier corps incubé avec un pyrophosphate minéral et une uridyl-transférase donne naissance à de l'uridine triphosphate (UTP). L'UTP peut, grâce à une autre uridyl transférase, jouer un rôle dans l'incorporation du radical uridylique dans les acides nucléiques.

ZUSAMMENFASSUNG

Bei der Biosynthese von Nucleosiden und Nucleotiden kann die intermediäre Bildung von Ribose- (oder Desoxyribose-) 1-phosphat und der zugehörigen 5-Ester im tierischen Organismus eine hervorragende Rolle spielen. Die Reaktion scheint eine Phosphorylierung (mit ATP) der 1-Stellung des Ribose-5-phosphats zu Ribose-1,5-diphosphat zu enthalten. Dieser neue Diester kann ebenso von Ribose-1-phosphat und Glucose-1,6-diphosphat bei Gegenwart von Phosphoglucomutase erhalten werden. Es sind deutliche Anzeichen vorhanden, dass Ribose-1,5-diphosphat in Taubenleberextrakten das 1-Esterphosphat gegen Adenin, Hypoxanthin oder unvollständige Purinvorläufer austauschen kann.

Glucose-1-phosphat und Galaktose-1-phosphat (beide sind α-Glucosylverbindungen) spielen ebenfalls eine Rolle als Acceptoren von Uridylradikalen. Diese Reaktion wird von einer besonderen Klasse von Enzymen, den Uridyltransferasen katalysiert. Mit einem der beiden obenerwähnten 1-Ester bebrütetes Uridintriphosphat plus eines dieser Enzyme gibt die sogn. "CoWaldenasen", LELOIR's UDP-Glucose oder UDP-Galaktose.

Umgekehrt verursacht die Bebrütung von letzterer Verbindung mit anorganischem Pyrophosphat und einer Uridyltransferase die Bildung von Uridintriphosphat (UTP). Durch die Wirkung einer anderen Uridyltransferase kann UTP eine Rolle beim Einbau des Uridylradikals in Nucleinsäuren spielen.

REFERENCES

[1] H. M. KALCKAR, *J. Biol. Chem.*, 167 (1947) 477.
[2] M. FRIEDKIN AND H. M. KALCKAR, *J. Biol. Chem.*, 184 (1950) 437.
[3] E. HOFF-JØRGENSEN, M. FRIEDKIN AND H. M. KALCKAR, *J. Biol. Chem.*, 184 (1950) 461.
[4] M. COHN, *J. Biol. Chem.*, 180 (1949) 771.
[5] M. DOUDOROFF, H. A. BARKER AND W. Z. HASSID, *J. Biol. Chem.* 170 (1947) 147.
[6] J. KATZ, W. Z. HASSID AND M. DOUDOROFF, *Nature*, 161 (1948) 96.
[7] L. A. MANSON AND J. O. LAMPEN, *J. Biol. Chem.*, 191 (1951) 95.
[8] M. FRIEDKIN, *J. Biol. Chem.*, 184 (1950) 449.
[9] O. H. LOWRY AND J. A. LOPEZ, *J. Biol. Chem.*, 162 (1946) 421.
[10] B. LYTHGOE AND A. R. TODD, *Structure and Synthesis of Nucleotides, Symposia Soc. Exp. Biol.*, 1 (1947) 15.
[11] C. F. CORI, S. P. COLOWICK AND G. T. CORI, *J. Biol. Chem.*, 121 (1937) 465.
[12] M. J. DOUDOROFF, *J. Biol. Chem.*, 151 (1943) 351.
[13] C. FITTING AND M. DOUDOROFF, *J. Biol. Chem.*, 199 (1952) 153.
[14] W. DEUTSCH AND R. LASER, *Z. physiol. Chem.*, 186 (1929) 1.
[15] W. KLEIN, *Z. physiol. Chem.*, 231 (1935) 125.
[16] L. A. MANSON AND J. O. LAMPEN, *J. Biol. Chem.*, 193 (1951) 539.
[17] L. M. PAEGE AND F. SCHLENK, *Arch. Biochem.*, 28 (1950) 348.
[18] J. O. LAMPEN, in MCELROY AND GLASS, *Symposium on Phosphorus Metabolism.*, II (1952) 363.
[19] H. M. KALCKAR, *Publ. d. Staz. Zool. di Napoli*, 23 (1951) 93, Table 2.

[20] M. FRIEDKIN, submitted for public. 1953.
[21] G. W. KIDDER, V. C. DEWEY AND R. E. PARKS, *Science*, 109 (1948) 511.
[22] J. H. MITCHELL, H. D. SKIPPER AND L. L. BENNETT, *Cancer Res.*, 10 (1950) 647.
[23] A. NOVICK AND L. SZILARD, *Nature*, 170 (1952) 926.
[24] N. FRIES AND B. KIHLMAN, *Nature*, 162 (1948) 573.
[25] J. W. ROWEN AND A. KORNBERG, *J. Biol. Chem.*, 193 (1951) 497.
[26] O. WARBURG, W. CHRISTIAN AND A. GRIESE, *Biochem. Z.*, 282 (1935) 157.
[27] L. S. ZATMAN, N. O. KAPLAN AND S. P. COLOWICK, *J. Biol. Chem.*, 200 (1953) 147.
[28] W. S. MACNUTT, *Biochem. J.*, 50 (1952) 384.
[29] H. M. KALCKAR, in ZECHMEISTER's *Fortschritte d. Chem. org. Naturstoffe*, IX (1952) 374.
[30] C. E. CARTER, *J. Am. Chem. Soc.*, 73 (1951) 1508.
[32] H. M. KALCKAR AND E. CUTOLO, unpublished work.
[32] M. BUELL, *Federation Proc.*, 11 (1952) 192.
[33] J. G. BUCHANAN, J. A. BASSHAM, A. A. BENSON, D. F. BRADLAY, M. CALVIN, L. L. DAUS, M. GOODMAN, P. M. HAYES, V. H. LYNCH, L. T. NORRIS AND A. T. WILSON, in MCELROY AND GLASS, *Symp. on Phosphorus Metabolism*, II (1952) 453.
[34] G. J. DUTTON AND I. D. E. STOREY, *Proc. Biochem. Soc. Biochem. J.*, 53 (1953) XXXVII.
[35] B. A. LOWY, J. DAVOLL AND G. B. BROWN, *J. Biol. Chem.* 197 (1952) 591.
[36] B. L. HORECKER, in MCELROY AND GLASS *Symp. on Phosphorus Metab.*, I (1951) 117.
[37] G. R. GREENBERG, *J. Biol. Chem.*, 190 (1951) 611.
[38] J. G. LEDER AND PH. HANDLER, *J. Biol. Chem.*, 190 (1951) 611.
[39] J. M. BUCHANAN, in MCELROY AND GLASS *Symp. on Phosphorus Metabolism*, II (1952) 406.
[40] E. BENNETT AND H. M. KALCKAR, unpublished.
[41] E. GOLDWASSER, *Nature*, 171 (1953) 126.
[42] M. SAFFRAN AND E. SCARANO, unpublished.
[43] H. KLENOW AND B. LARSEN, *Arch. Biochem.*, 37 (1952) 488.
[44] F. SCHLENK AND M. J. WALDVOGEL, *Arch. Biochem.*, 9 (1946) 455.
[45] E. W. SUTHERLAND, S. P. COLOWICK AND C. F. CORI, *J. Biol. Chem.*, 140 (1941) 309.
[46] L. F. LELOIR, in MCELROY AND GLASS, *Symp. On Phosphorus Metabolism*, I (1951) 67.
[47] R. CAPUTTO, L. F. LELOIR, C. E. CARDINI AND A. C. PALADINI, *J. Biol. Chem.*, 184 (1950) 333.
[48] L. F. LELOIR, *Arch. Biochem.*, 33 (1951) 186.
[49] A. KORNBERG, in MCELROY AND GLASS, *Symp. on Phosphorus Metabolism*, I (1932) 438.
[50] A. KORNBERG, *J. Biol. Chem.*, 182 (1950) 779.
[51] R. E. TRUCCO, *Arch. Biochem.*, 34 (1951) 482.
[52] H. M. KALCKAR AND E. CUTOLO, IIe Congr. Internat. de Biochimie, (1952) 260.
[53] A. MUNCH-PETERSEN, H. M. KALCKAR, E. B. SMITH AND E. CUTOLO, unpublished.
[54] O. WARBURG AND W. CHRISTIAN, *Biochem.*, 254 (1932) 438.
[55] A. C. PALADINI AND L. F. LELOIR, *Biochem. J.*, 51 (1952) 426.
[56] P. BERG AND W. K. JOKLIK, unpublished.
[57] H. M. KALCKAR, A. MUNCH-PETERSEN AND B. BRAGANCA, unpublished.
[58] L. F. LELOIR, unpublished.
[59] J. T. PARK AND M. J. JOHNSON, *J. Biol. Chem.*, 179 (1949) 585.
[60] J. T. PARK, in MCELROY AND GLASS, *Symposium on Phosphorus Metabolism*, I (1951) 93.
[61] S. BERGSTRÖM, H. ARVIDSON, E. HAMMERSTEN, N. A. ELIASSON, P. REICHARD AND H. V. UBISCH, *J. Biol. Chem.*, 179 (1949) 163.
[62] E. SCARANO AND H. M. KALCKAR, *Publ. di Staz. Zool. di Napoli*, in press.
[63] R. B. HIRLBERT, *Federation Proc.*, XII (1953) 222.
[64] J. STROMINGER, in MCELROY AND GLASS, *Symp. on Phosphorus Metabolism*, II (1952) 422.
[65] R. B. MERRYFIELD AND D. W. WOOLLEY, *Federation Proc.*, 11 (1952) 258.

Received May 1st, 1953

PRECIPITABILITY OF SMALL QUANTITIES OF
CELL CONSTITUENTS AND METABOLITES AS INSOLUBLE
RADIOACTIVE COMPOUNDS*

by

C. NEUBERG AND A. GRAUER

*Department of Biochemistry, New York Medical College, New York (U.S.A.)
and the Forschungsinstitut Gastein (Austria).*

Apart from physical methods, cyto- and histo-chemistry usually rely on visual demonstration of objects by means of characteristic precipitations or stains. Examples of this type are found in the long proven specific staining of certain cell constituents such as the nuclei with basic dyestuffs. These cases are concerned with preformed objects whereas in other instances the cell constituents to be determined are made visible by an in situ transformation as *e.g.* in the Feulgen tests for polysaccharides, plasmogen and desoxyribonucleic acid[1,2]. The staining technique is based on the isolation or transformation of primarily non-staining substances into staining compounds. This may be achieved by purely chemical measures or by enzymes. DUBOS AND BRACHET's method[1] of demonstration of ribonucleates represents a method of the latter type. The enzyme ribonuclease is used to produce the characteristic staining compound from the ribonucleic acid substrate. Conversely, enzymes may be determined, if they yield a specific, well defined and staining reaction product. This applies to the technique of TAKAMATSU as well as GOMORI[1] for identification of phosphatases. In this process, phosphate enzymatically produced from suitable phosphorylated substrates is transformed into black staining cobalt- or lead-phosphate. This method of enzymic production of an insoluble precipitate is based on the ability of the phosphatases to split off insoluble alkaline earth phosphate from various substrates such as calcium salts of sugar- or glycero-phosphates as first shown and recognized as significant by NEUBERG and collaborators[3].

The principal physical methods are specific absorption and electron microscope photography of the objects to be demonstrated as well as manifestations of fluorescence. Recently, radioautography has been added. This last method, however, preponderantly indicates accumulation and migration in organs or tissues without demonstrating localization of a process within a single cell.

In the purely chemical as well as in the physical characterization of substances either distinctly preformed or artificially produced in situ, conservation of the morphological localization as well as specificity of the reaction to be applied are prerequisites.

* This investigation was supported by contracts of the U.S. Atomic Energy Commission and the Office of Naval Research and the American Cancer Society on recommendation by the Committee of Growth of the National Research Council with the New York Medical College.

References p. 272.

An ideal method would be the histochemical characterization of specific cell ingredients by local fixation through specific precipitation reactions. Nucleic acids may thus be characterized according to OPIE AND LAVIN[4] by suitable application of La-acetate. The latter will form a compound with ribonucleic acid which will withstand the action of ribonuclease whereas basophilia of the original substance will be retained.

The reactions of nucleic acids with the salts of various rare earths have long been known and recommended for characterization of nucleic acids[5]. The fate of radioactive lanthanum has been studied by EKSTEIN AND LEWIN[6], WURM[7] and STERN et al.[8] in normal as well as pathological tissue.

We have investigated the specificity of suitable precipitation reactions. In consideration of the problems of radioautography, we studied the precipitability of natural substances mainly by salts of the elements thorium, lanthanum and uranium. The initial data could be obtained by means of the natural, only slightly radioactive metal compounds. Salts of the rare earths as well as of thorium and uranium with various organic substances have been prepared years ago mainly because they represented a certain analytical and preparative interest. (For details see the manuals.) The large number of important cell constituents, ingredients of tissue liquids and metabolites which are precipitated by the above metal salts over a wide range of pH constituted somewhat of a surprise.

These salts will precipitate aliphatic, hydroaromatic and aromatic acids as well as certain amino acids, peptides and peptone-like substances in addition to special plant constituents such as aliphatic and cyclic polyhydroxy-acids.

It seems remarkable that some of the most significant phosphorylated intermediates of carbohydrate metabolism are precipitated rather completely. Phytates and the nucleotides are precipitated as well as the nucleic acids. It also seems noteworthy that all products of the di- and tri-carboxylic acid cycles are precipitated. Details are shown in the following tables.

This precipitability of numerous naturally occurring substances by the above-mentioned metal salts—and that number may be further considerably increased—might be used in micro-chemical methods of determination. Results obtained by this method, however, should be carefully interpreted since there is no specificity as such. Specificity, on the other hand, may be frequently obtained by combining the radioactive forms of the above metals with the substances to be precipitated labelled with regard to various elements. Thus a number of possibilities might be developed for purposes of radioautography[9]. With different types and intensities of radiation even the more simple criteria such as provided by the Geiger counter might prove adequate.

The precipitation reaction is highly sensitive (for limits see later). If there is no direct flaking of distinct particles, adsorption will prove successful. Suitable adsorbents for analogous purposes have previously been recommended[10]. Obviously these materials must be free of radiating isotopes. The chromatographic separation of substances of similar precipitability has of course been successfully carried out and described previously.

The principle of double and multiple labelling is applicable also in the precipitation of inorganic salts (see later).

References p. 272.

DATA
THORIUM*

Na or K salts **	Precipitate	Remarks
Palmitic acid	+	only slightly s. on warming in NH_4 citrate
Stearic acid	+	
Oleic acid	+	
Malonic acid	+	s. in excess of malonate
Malic acid	+	s. in excess of malate
Fumaric acid	+	
Itaconic acid	+	
Oxaloacetic acid	+	
α-Ketoglutaric acid	+	ins. in excess of ketoglutarate
Citric acid	+	
*I*socitric acid	+	
Aconitic acid	+	
Tartaric acid	+	
Saccharic acid	+	
Menthol glucuronide	+	
Pectic acid	+	stiff jelly
Benzoic acid	+	ins. in excess of benzoate
Mandelic acid	+	
Cinnamic acid	+	
Gallic acid	+	s. in excess of gallate
Tannic acid	+	ins. in excess of tannate
Cholic acid	+	almost ins. in excess of cholate
Desoxycholic acid	+	s. in excess of desoxycholate
Glycocholic acid	+	ppt. resinous, s. in excess of $Th(NO_3)_4$ sol.
Taurocholic acid	+	
Fructose-6-phosphate	—	Ba salt used
Fructose-1,6-diphosphate	+	Mg salt used
Glycerophosphoric acid	slight ppt.	ppt. increases on addition of Na-acetate, remains incomplete
Phosphoglyceric acid	+	ppt. only on warming
Phytic acid	+	ins. in excess of phytate
Guanylic acid	+	
Adenosine-3-phosphoric acid	+	s. in excess of adenosine-3-phosphate
Adenosine-5-phosphoric acid	+	s. in excess of adenosine-5-phosphate
Adenosinediphosphoric acid	+	s. in excess of $Th(NO_2)_4$
Adenosinetriphosphoric acid	+	s. in excess of ribonucleate on warming
Ribonucleic acid	+	slightly s. in excess of ribonucleate on warming
Desoxyribonucleic acid	+	s. in excess of desoxyribonucleate

Amino acids or salts	Precipitate	Remarks
Na hippurate	+	slightly s. in excess of hippurate
Tyrosine	—	
Leucyltyrosine	—	
Glycyltyrosine	—	
Tryptophan	—	
Acetyltryptophan	—	
Arginine HCl	—	
Lysine HCl	—	
Histidine	—	
Na Aspartate	+	slightly s. in excess of aspartate
Asparagine	—	
Na acid glutamate	+	s. in excess of glutamate
Cysteine Na	—	
Methionine	—	
Glutathione Na	+	
Witte-peptone	—	
Silk peptone	+	s. in excess of $Th(NO_3)_4$

* used as $M/10$ solutions of $Th(NO_3)_4$.   ** used as $M/10$ or $M/100$ solutions.
Almost all the precipitates are soluble in solutions of triammonium- or trisodium citrate.

17

LANTHANUM*

Na or K salts**	Precipitate	Remarks
Palmitic acid	+	
Stearic acid	+	
Oleic acid	+	
Malonic acid	+	s. in excess of malonate
Succinic acid	+	ins. in hot water or excess of succinate
Malic acid	+	very s. in Mg-fumarate, s. in excess of both reagents
Fumaric acid	+	s. in excess of fumarate
Itaconic acid	+	
Oxaloacetic acid	+	
α-Ketoglutaric acid	+	
Citric acid	+	ppt. at first jellylike, becomes flaky, s. in Na-fumarate
*I*socitric acid	+	s. in excess of *iso*citrate
Aconitic acid	+	somewhat s. in excess of aconitate
Tartaric acid	+	s. in excess of tartrate
Saccharic acid	+	
Mucic acid	+	
Menthol glucuronide	+	ppt. even in acid solution, small indistinct needles
Pectic acid	+	ppt (stiff jelly)
Benzoic acid	+	almost ins. in excess of benzoate
Mandelic acid	+	
Cinnamic acid	+	
Gallic acid	+	s. in excess of gallate
Tannic acid	+	ins. in excess of tannate
Cholic acid	+	almost ins. in excess of cholate
Desoxycholic acid	+	ppt. jellylike, ins. in excess of desoxycholate
Glycocholic acid	+	almost ins. in excess of glycocholate
Taurocholic acid	+	
Abietic acid	+	
Copaivic acid	+	
Chaulmoogric acid	+	
Fructose-1,6-diphosphate	+	Mg salt used, ppt. s. in NH_4 tartrate
Glycerophosphoric acid	+	Na and Mg salts used, ppt. ins. in NH_4Cl
Phosphoglyceric acid	+	
Phytic acid	+	
Guanylic acid	+	s. in M $NaPO_3$, $K_4P_2O_7$ monoethanolamine metaphosphate, ins. in excess of guanylate, slightly s. in 50% acetic ac.
Adenosine-3-phosphoric acid	+	The free acid ppt. with La-acetate
Adenosine-5-phosphoric acid	+	idem
Adenosinediphosphoric acid	+	s. in excess of $LaCl_3$
Adenosinetriphosphoric acid	+	s. in excess of ATP

* used as $M/10$ solutions of $LaCl_3$ or $La(NO_3)_3$, occasionally La-acetate.
** used in $M/10$ or $M/100$ solutions
   Almost all the precipitates are s. in solutions of triammonium-or trisodiumcitrate.

LANTHANUM

Amino acids or salts	Precipitate	Remarks
Na hippurate	+	s. in excess of hippurate
Tyrosine	—	
Leucyltyrosine	—	
Glycyltyrosine	—	
Tryptophan	—	
Acetyltryptophan	—	
Arginine HCl	—	
Lysine HCl	—	
Histidine HCl	—	
Asparagine	—	
Na glutamate	—	pH 6 to 7
Cysteine Na	+	
Methionine	—	
Glutathione Na	—	
Witte-peptone		
Silk peptone		incompletely s. in excess of each of the reactants

URANIUM*

Na or K salts**	Precipitate	Remarks
Palmitic acid	+	
Stearic acid	+	
Oleic acid	+	
Malonic acid	—	
Succinic acid	+	ppt. slowly, better on warming, s. in excess of succinate
Malic acid	—	
Fumaric acid	—	
Itaconic acid	—	
Oxaloacetic acid	—	
a-Ketoglutaric acid	—	
Citric acid	—	no ppt. even on warming
*I*socitric acid	—	
Mentholglucuronide	+	
Pectic acid	+	ppt. jellylike
Benzoic acid	+	s. in excess of benzoate
Cinnamic acid	+	
Gallic acid	—	dark brown color
Tannic acid	+	dark brown color and ppt. s. in excess of tannate
Glycocholic acid	+	only slight ppt.
Taurocholic acid	+	
Copaivic acid	+	
Fructose-1,6-diphosphate	+	Mg salt used, s. in M $NaPO_3$, $K_4P_2O_7$, monoethanolamine metaphosphate
Guanylic acid	+	s. in M $NaPO_3$, $K_4P_2O_7$, monoethanolamine metaphosphate
Adenosine-3-phosphoric acid	+	s. in excess of adenosine-3-phosphate, s. in NH_4 citrate only on warming
Adenosine-5-phosphoric acid	+	only slightly s. in excess of adenosine-5-phosphate; very s. in NH_4 citrate
Adenosinediphosphoric acid	+	s. in NH_4 citrate
Adenosinetriphosphoric acid	+	white ppt., s. in excess of ATP-Na; s. in NH_4 citrate with yellow color

* used as $M/10$ solution of uranyl acetate.
** used as $M/10$ or $M/100$ solutions.
Almost all ppt. are soluble in solutions of triammonium- or trisodium citrate.

URANIUM

Amino acids or salts	Precipitate	Remarks
Na hippurate	—	
Tyrosine	—	
Leucyltyrosine	—	
Glycyltyrosine	—	
Tryptophane	—	
Acetyltryptophan	—	
Arginine HCl	—	
Lysine HCl	—	
Histidine HCl	—	
Asparagine	—	
Na glutamate	+	s. in excess of glutamate
Methionine	—	
Glutathione Na	+	ppt. yellow-white, indistinct needles
Witte-peptone	—	
Silk peptone	+	s. in NH_4 citrate

In order to obtain some criteria for the practical applicability of the process as described above some experiments were carried out to determine the minimum quantities which are detectable.

a. *Fructose- 1,6-diphosphate*

0.1 ml of an $M/100$ solution + 0.9 ml H_2O yield a flaky precipitation with thorium-nitrate, uranylacetate or lanthanumchloride, especially on warming. The precipitants were applied in suitable concentrations.

b. *Phosphoglycerate*

The limits of precipitability were similar to those under a.

c. *Glycerophosphate*

Precipitation was obtained only in tenfold concentration with $LaCl_3$ and $Th(NO_3)_4$, but not with uranyl acetate.

d. *Na-phytate*

Phytic acid will react in similar concentration as a. and b.

e. The same is true for *Fumarates*.

f. *Citrate*

Will precipitate in similar concentration as a., b. and d. with $Th(NO_3)_4$ and $LaCl_3$; uranyl acetate yields no precipitation.

There should be an excess of the metal salts over the compounds to be precipitated, since the latter tend to redissolve the resulting precipitates more or less readily.

For the purposes of the present investigations the composition of the insoluble or hardly soluble compounds in itself is immaterial. In the following some of the analyses will be reported.

References p. 272.

La-salt of fructose-1,6-diphosphate

Prepared from the pure Mg salt of fructose-1,6-diphosphate with $LaCl_3$ and dried in vacuo to constance of weight shows the composition $[C_6H_{10}O_4(POH)_2]_3La$. This corresponds to the otherwise[11] known type of acid salts of the sugar phosphate.

La-salt of D-(—)3-phosphoglyceric acid

Air dried it shows the composition $(C_3H_5O_7P)_3La_2 \cdot 3H_2O$. The crystal water is completely lost at $105\,°C$.

La-salt of fumaric acid

After drying in vacuo it has the following composition $(C_4H_2O_4)_3La_2$.

Condensed inorganic phosphates such as pyro- and triphosphates will yield precipitates with La-, Th- and uranyl-salts. These precipitates are soluble in meta- and pyro-phosphates. The *orthophosphates* of the above 3 metals especially on slight warming are soluble in Na-salts of pyro- and triphosphoric acid, as well as in NH_4-citrate.

Some useful effects have also been obtained with *other metal salts* e.g. $Y(NO_3)_3$, $Zr(NO_3)_4$, $In_2(SO_4)_3$, $Ce(NO_3)_3$, $PrCl_3$, $NdCl_3$.

Fructose-diphosphate is precipitated with these salts. Its yttrium salt is soluble in an excess of $Y(NO_3)_3$, but is reprecipitated on warming. The Zr-fructose-diphosphate is soluble in monoethanolamine metaphosphate.

Adenosinediphosphate yields a precipitate with $PrCl_3$ which is soluble in an excess of $PrCl_3$. The same result is obtained with $NdCl_3$.

Na-isocitrate yields precipitations with $Y(NO_3)_3$, $In_2(SO)_4)_3$, $Ce(NO_3)_3$, $PrCl_3$, $NdCl_3$.

Some of the precipitations will appear on warming only. If the precipitating metal salts are very acid, they will dissolve the resulting precipitates; the latter are also soluble in an excess of the used organic reactants.

Other metal compounds may possibly also be used for purposes of identification. It was found that ferric, cupric, silver- and lead-salts of fumaric acid are precipitated to a great extent, in some instances even quantitatively by means of Na-fumarate. Fe- and Ag-nitrate are in praxi completely precipitated by sodium fumarate.

We gratefully acknowledge the helpful assistance of Dr. MARIANNE KREIDL.

We thank Prof. Dr. F. SCHEMINSKY (Innsbruck) for laboratory facilities at the radiology station at his Forschungsinstitut in Gastein (Austria).

SUMMARY

The reported data show that many metabolites and cell constituents even in considerable dilution may be precipitated by soluble salts of thorium, lanthanum and uranium. Characterization of the resulting compounds is facilitated if the precipitants and possibly also the substances to be precipitated are radioactive.

RÉSUMÉ

Les résultats exposés montrent que de nombreux métabolites et constituants cellulaires peuvent être précipités, même à des dilutions considérables, par des sels solubles de thorium, de lanthane ou d'uranium. La caractérisation des composés formés est facilitée si les réactifs précipitants et si possible également les substances à précipiter sont radioactives.

References p. 272.

ZUSAMMENFASSUNG

Die mitgeteilten Befunde lehren, dass viele Stoffwechselerzeugnisse sowie Zellinhaltssubstanzen auch in beträchtlicher Verdünnung durch lösliche Salze des Thoriums, Lanthans und Urans niedergeschlagen werden können. Eine Charakterisierung der entstehenden Verbindungen wird erleichtert, wenn die Fällungsmittel und gegebenenfalls auch die zu fällenden Producte radioaktiv sind.

REFERENCES

[1] For bibliography see D. GLICK, *Techniques of Histo- and Cyto-Chemistry*, Interscience Publ. New York 1949. – A. L. DOUNCE in SUMNER-MYRBÄCK, *The Enzymes*, Vol. I, part 1, pag. 187, Academic Press, New York, 1950.

[2] R. C. MILLICAN AND R. W. MOWRY, *Federation Proc.*, 12 (1953) 352; G. Z. WILLIAMS and ass., *Federation Proc.*, 12 (1953) 406; D. MAZIA et al., *Biol. Bull.* 104 (1953) 57; H. SPATZ, *Mitt. aus der Max-Planck-Ges. Heft*, 5 (1953) 32.

[3] C. NEUBERG AND K. DJENAB, *Biochem. Z.*, 82 (1917) 391; C. NEUBERG AND E. SIMON, *Phosphatasen, Handb. der biolog. Arbeitsmethoden*, Abtl. IV, Teil 1, p. 615 and 621, 1927. – M. MORIL, *C. A.*, 26 (1932) 2781; R. ROBISON, *The significance of phosphoric esters in metabolism*, New York Univ. Press 1932. – More recent publications are C. NEUBERG AND A. FISCHER, *Enzymologia*, 2 (1938) 241 and 360.–.D. GLICK AND E. E. FISCHER, *Science*, 102 (1945) 429.

[4] L. E. OPIE AND G. J. LAVIN, *J. Exptl. Med.*, 84 (1946) 107.

[5] E. CHARGAFF and ass., *J. Biol. Chem.*, 173 (1948) 263; 177 (1949) 405, 417 and 429, where also the older literature is quoted.

[6] D. M. EKSTEIN AND R. LEWIN, *Cancer Res.*, 11 (1951) 246.

[7] M. WURM, *J. Biol. Chem.*, 192 (1951) 707.

[8] D. LASZLO, D. M. EKSTEIN, R. LEWIN AND K. G. STERN, *J. Natl. Cancer Inst.*, 13 (1952) 559.

[9] M. CALVIN, Harrison Howe Lecture before the Rochester Section of the *Am. Chem. Soc. Novb.* 22, 1952.

[10] C. NEUBERG AND E. STRAUSS, *Arch. Biochem.*, 7 (1945) 211.

[11] C. NEUBERG, H. LUSTIG AND M. A. ROTHENBERG, *Arch. Biochem.* 3 (1943) 33.

Received May 1st, 1953

ON THE COMPOUNDS OF FERRICYTOCHROME C
APPEARING IN ACID SOLUTION

by

E. BOERI*, A. EHRENBERG, K. G. PAUL AND H. THEORELL

*Biochemical Department and the Wallenberg Laboratory of
Physiological Chemistry, Medical Nobel Institute, Stockholm (Sweden)*

Twelve years ago THEORELL AND ÅKESON[1] found that ferricytochrome c shows five different types of absorption spectra at different pH values. These investigations were extended from pH —0.3 to 13.8, because the absorption data seemed to show that ferricytochrome was so stable that only reversible changes would occur within this remarkably wide range. KEILIN AND HARTREE, in 1940[2], had stated that cytochrome c as judged by their enzymic test was entirely stable in 0.3 M HCl at room temperature for 18 hours, whereas a decrease of 50% in activity followed in 0.1 M KOH at the same temperature and for the same time. PAUL[3] more recently demonstrated that the enzymic activity of cytochrome c, as determined with succinic oxidase from kidneys and succinic acid is somewhat less stable to extreme pH values. He found the limits for practically indefinite stability to be pH 1.6 and 12.3. Below pH 1.6 down to 0.66 there was a slow decrease of the activity. The inactivation in this region seemed slow enough to permit spectrophotometric and magnetic experiments to be made during the first half or perhaps whole hour after acidification without any serious degree of disturbance from inactivation.

In the following we shall thus restrict ourselves to experiments at pH values higher than around 1.

The spectrophotometrically determined dissociation curve indicated a pK of 2.5. Magnetometric measurements[4] indicated that the essentially covalent bonds in ferricytochrome c in neutral solution were shifted to essentially ionic bonds in acid solution. An attempt to correlate the spectrophotometric and magnetic values with one another gave curves that did not agree entirely. At that time we did not know whether the discrepancies were due to experimental errors, or to some unknown factor interfering. Since we have now at our disposal an accurate magnetometric apparatus requiring only small amounts of material[5], it appeared to be of interest to reinvestigate the spectrophotometric and magnetic properties of ferricytochrome c in acid solution. The magnetic apparatus has in the last year been considerably improved, as will be described elsewhere.

For several years we have had reason to believe that chloride ions influence the light absorption of ferricytochrome c in acid solutions[6]. The existence of a fluoride compound of cytochrome c around pH 3 was reported as early as 1941[1]. MAEHLY[7] recently found that acidification with HCl, or some other acids, of a solution of horse radish peroxidase (HRP) was followed by spectral changes in the Soret band region, from which

---

* Rockefeller Foundation Fellow.

References p. 282.

the formation of four compounds, A, B, C, and D, in time sequence could be demonstrated.

As will be shown in this work, chloride ions form a compound with ferricytochrome *c* in acid solution. Its properties have here been studied spectrophotometrically and magnetometrically. A theory of the structure of the Cl-compound is advanced. It presents a sequence of dipoles resembling the arrangement in ionic crystals.

METHODS

Spectrophotometric measurements were made in a Beckman spectrophotometer model DU, in most cases in 1 cm cells. In some preliminary experiments cells of varied depths were used in order to check whether the absorption values at different hydrogen ion and salt concentrations remained constant at widely different concentrations of cytochrome *c*. It was found that a 300-fold variation of this concentration did not influence the results.

The pH-measurements were made with glass electrodes, calibrated against Pt–H_2 electrodes. KCl-agar was used for connection in order to diminish the diffusion of chloride ions into the solution.

All the experiments were carried out in rooms maintained at 20°C.

MATERIAL

Four different specimens of cytochrome *c* were used. The first one, prepared according to THEORELL AND ÅKESON[8], contained 0.417 % Fe, and the second and third ones, prepared according to KEILIN AND HARTREE[9], 0.387 and 0.437 %, respectively. Specimen 4, also prepared according to KEILIN AND HARTREE, gave only 0.317 % Fe. During this preparation it was felt desirable to avoid vacuum evaporation, hence all volumes were kept small to permit freeze-drying. This might explain the incomplete removal of protein impurities. All preparations were examined for contaminating hemoproteins by means of treatment with acid acetone in the cold. In preparation 3 about 5 % of the total iron was found to be non-cytochrome heme-iron. The other three gave negative tests.

The procedure of TSOU[10] was employed for the determination of the content of autoxidizable cytochrome *c*. Preparation 3 contained 2 % of autoxidizable cytochrome; preparations 2 and 4 none. Preparation 1 was not tested during the time it was used. Preparations 1 and 2 were used only for spectrophotometric experiments, 3 and 4 for the magnetic. The content of autoxidizable cytochrome has been found to increase gradually when a preparation is stored at low temperature (0–4°). Specimen 1 was found to contain 50 % autoxidizable material five months later. It was therefore carefully examined to determine whether this caused any changes in the light absorption in the Soret band region at those acidities and chloride ion concentrations used in our experiments. Remarkably enough it was found that the high autoxidizability did not seem to have any influence upon the spectrophotometric results. Moreover, it was noticed that exposure of an aliquot portion to low pH and high chloride ion concentration for a few hours resulted in a reduction of the amount of autoxidizable cytochrome *c* from 50 to 16 %. This observation might be connected with the observation of PAUL[3] that exposure of ferricytochrome *c* to chlorides at acid reaction (*e.g.* pH 1.63) caused a marked (30 %) increase of its enzymic activity. For the removal of trichloroacetic acid from cytochrome *c* we generally dialyze our preparations against dilute ammonia, while KEILIN AND HARTREE prescribe dialysis against 0.5 % KCl. Whereas we occasionally find a small percentage of autoxidizable cytochrome *c* in our fresh preparations, KEILIN AND HARTREE do not seem to find any; the difference may be attributed to a protecting or restoring action of the chloride.

RESULTS

Experiments. It is seen from Fig. 1 that the maximum of the Soret band, in agreement with the earlier findings[1], changes from 408 mμ in neutral solution ("type III") to 395 mμ at pH 1.7 ("type II"). If only these two forms were present we would expect, however, to see an isosbestic point in the region 400–405 mμ. This is not the case; the variable intersection between the curves indicates that one or more other compounds interfere with the results.

It was found that the concentration of chloride ions had a decisive influence upon the absorption spectrum. Fig. 2 illustrates how the addition of sodium chloride to cyto-

References p. 282.

chrome c in 0.1 M HCl causes a decrease of the light absorption and a shift of the maximum from 395 mμ to slightly above 400 mμ. In this case we have an isosbestic point at 402 mμ.

Since the change in light absorption was maximal at 395 mμ we made a series of determinations at this wavelength at different hydrogen and chloride ion concentrations. The results are summarized in Fig. 3.

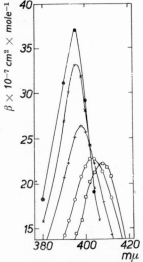

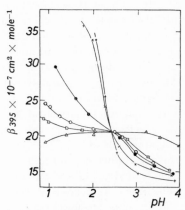

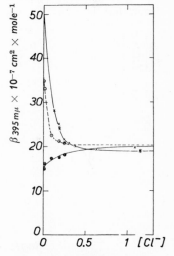

Fig. 3. Curves showing how the extinction at 395 mμ varies with pH at different [Cl$^-$]: 0.009 (+), 0.019 (×), 0.094 (●), 0.189 (○), 0.250 (□), and 2.83 (△) M NaCl.

Fig. 1. Soret band of ferricytochrome c at different pH values and low [Cl$^-$]. Solutions of cytochrome c with a final concentration of 4 μM and varied pH were made by mixing a stock solution of cytochrome c with 0.1M HCl and water. The [Cl$^-$] thus increased with the acidity in this experiment.
pH 3.36 (□), 2.53 (○), 2.20 (+), 1.87 (×) and 1.70 (●).

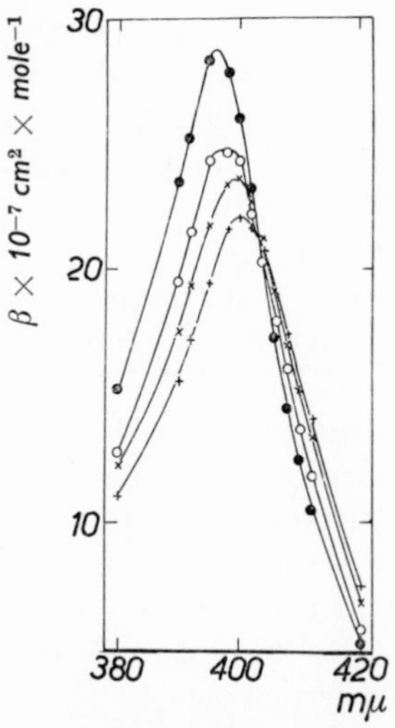

Fig. 2. Soret band of cytochrome c in 0.10 M HCl (●) and after addition of 0.066 (○), 0.132 (×), and 0.528 (+) M NaCl. The total [Cl$^-$] was thus 0.1, 0.166, 0.232 and 0.628 respectively.

It is seen that variations in pH between 4 and 1 bring about very great changes in extinction at low chloride concentrations; at increasing [Cl$^-$] the curves more and more approach a constant level of $\beta^* \sim 20 \cdot 10^7$ cm^2 × mole^{-1}. This indicates the formation of a chloride compound of ferricytochrome c in this acid region.

Fig. 4 shows the variation in light absorption upon the addition of increasing amounts of chloride at pH 1.0, 2.0 and 3.0. It is seen how the curves at increasing [Cl$^-$] again approach the level $\beta = 20 \cdot 10^7$ cm^2 × mole^{-1}.

Fig. 4. The extinction at 395 mμ as a function of [Cl$^-$] at different pH: 1.0 (×), 2.0 (○), and 3.0 (●).

Evidently a hitherto unknown compound is formed by the addition of hydrochloric acid or sodium chloride to ferricytochrome c in slightly

* $\beta = \dfrac{1}{c} \times \dfrac{1}{d} \times \ln \dfrac{I_0}{I}$, where c = concentration in moles/ml;
d = optical depth of solution.

References p. 282.

acid solution. This effect arises through an interaction between hydrogen and chloride ions. The cation of the added salt seems to play no role; potassium or calcium chloride gave the same results as sodium chloride.

Some other anions were also investigated. Br^- and SO_4^{-2} gave effects similar to Cl^-, but the absorption coefficients were slightly different.

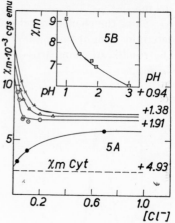

In view of these new facts it seemed interesting to reinvestigate the magnetic susceptibility of ferricytochrome c in acid solution. In Fig. 5A we have plotted the new data on the paramagnetic susceptibility, χ_m, for the cytochrome iron at 20 °C at varied $[Cl^-]$ and pH. At low $[Cl^-]$ χ_m is strongly dependent on pH, just as the light absorption, but at higher $[Cl^-]$ the curves converge and reach horizontal asymptotes. Contrary to the spectrophotometric values, the magnetic ones do not approach exactly the same value; the levels of the asymptotes depend to a certain degree on the pH, as indicated in Fig. 5B. Two different concentrations of cytochrome were used for these determinations, 1.54 and 0.77 mM. The lower concentration was used in such determinations where it was important to reach a low pH with a minimum of Cl^-; in these cases the buffering capacity of the cytochrome played a certain role.

Fig. 5A. Magnetic susceptibility of cytochrome c plus NaCl at different pH: 1.5 (×), 1.8 (△), 2.0 (O), and 3.0 (●). Single values at $[Cl^-] = 1.0$ (+), pH given in figure.

Fig. 5B. Variation of χ_m of the chloride compound with pH.

Evaluation of experimental data. Spectrophotometry. From Fig. 3 it is immediately seen that the curve for the lowest chloride ion content (0.009 M) has the general form of a part of a dissociation curve. The asymptotic level at pH 5.5 is experimentally determined ($\beta_{395, pH 5.5} = 14.0 \cdot 10^7$ cm² × mole⁻¹) but the level at low pH is unknown.

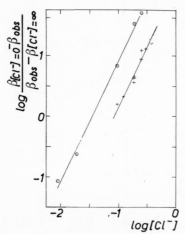

By plotting $\log \dfrac{\beta_{obs} - \beta_{pH\ 5.5}}{\beta_{low\ pH} - \beta_{obs}}$ against pH for the experimental points (pH, $\beta_{395} \times 10^{-7}$): (2.04, 33.5); (2.24, 25.6);(2.40, 20.8) and (2.54, 17.3) it was found by trial and error that the value of $\beta_{395,\ low\ pH} = 48 \cdot 10^7$ cm² × mole⁻¹ gives a straight line with $n_{H+} = 2.0$ and a pH$_{50\%}$ 2.10. We conclude that an increase in hydrogen ion concentration leads to a new compound by the simultaneous addition of two protons to ferricytochrome c. If the neutral cytochrome is denoted Cyt, we may designate the new compound Cyt⁻2H⁺. The values of $\beta_{395,\ Cyt-2H+}$ and pH$_{50\%}$ obtained in this way must be somewhat too low because of the small amount of chloride ions present. They can, however, be used in the calculations of the influence of chloride ions.

Fig. 6. Graphical determination of the number n and $[Cl^-]_{50\%}$ for the reaction with Cl^- at pH 1.0 (+) and 2.0 (O).

At pH 1.0 we had $\beta_{395\ m\mu,\ [Cl^-]\ =\ \infty} = 18.7 \cdot 10^7$, and $\beta_{395\ m\mu,\ [Cl^-]\ =\ 0.009} = 48 \cdot 10^7$ cm²/mole. Thus we can plot $\log \dfrac{48 \cdot 10^7 - \beta_{obs}}{\beta_{obs} - 18.7 \cdot 10^7}$ versus $\log [Cl^-]$, as in Fig. 6. Some of the experimental data derive from Fig. 3, others from separate experiments not mentioned before.

At pH = 2.0 the value of $\beta_{395, [Cl^-] = 0}$ could be rather accurately determined by extrapolation to 36×10^7, as in Fig. 4. The β-values for different $[Cl^-]$ at pH 2.0 were taken graphically from Fig. 3. $\beta_{395, Cl^- = \infty} = 20.5 \cdot 10^7$.

$\log \dfrac{36 \cdot 10^7 - \beta_{obs}}{\beta_{obs} - 20.5 \cdot 10^7}$ is plotted against $[Cl^-]$ in Fig. 6. At pH = 3 the changes in light absorption were too small to allow accurate calculations.

Evidently the results prove that the acid ferricytochrome c, with two protons added, forms a compound with two chloride ions per molecule, since $n_{Cl^-} = 2$ ("Cyt-2H+-2Cl-"). Thus the following relations are valid

$$\frac{[Cyt]\,[H^+]^2}{[Cyt-2H^+]} = K_{H^+}; \tag{1}$$

$$\frac{[Cyt-2H^+]\,[Cl^-]^2}{[Cyt-2H^+-2Cl^-]} = K_{Cl^-} \tag{2}$$

We shall now calculate the value of K_{Cl^-} at pH 1, 2 and 3. At pH = 1 less than 0.6% of the total cytochrome is in the form of Cyt, and can be neglected. At $\log [Cl^-] = -1.07$, $[Cyt-2H^+] = [Cyt-2H^+-2Cl^-]$ (see Fig. 6). This gives

$$K_{Cl^-,\,pH\,1} = 10^{-2.14} = 7 \cdot 10^{-3}\,M^2.$$

At pH 2 Cyt, Cyt-2H+ and Cyt-2H+-2Cl- may all be present in considerable amounts. Since $[Cyt] \approx [Cyt-2H^+]$ at pH 2.10 and $[Cyt] + [Cyt-2H^+] = [Cyt-2H^+ -2Cl^-]$ at $[Cl^-] = 0.035\,M$ (see Fig. 6) we could calculate the mole fractions of the three compounds at pH 2 and $[Cl^-] = 0.035$ to $[Cyt] = 0.194$; $[Cyt-2H^+] = 0.306$; and $[Cyt-2H^+-2Cl^-] = 0.500$. Inserting these values into eq. (2) gives $K_{Cl^-,\,pH\,=\,2} = 0.7 \cdot 10^{-3}\,M^2$.

A very uncertain value at pH = 3 could be calculated from Fig. 4 and 5, in which the midpoints of the transitions seem to appear near $[Cl^-] = 0.1$; this gave the value

$$K_{Cl^-,\,pH\,3} = 2(\pm 1) \cdot 10^{-3}\,M^2$$

It was now possible to calculate the true values for $\beta_{395, 2H^+}$ and $pH_{50\%}$ for the transition Cyt+2H+ ⇌ Cyt-2H+. We thus found

$$\beta_{395,\,Cyt-2H^+} = 50 \cdot 10^7\,cm^2 \times mole^{-1}, \text{ and } pH_{50\%} = 2.12.$$

The difference from the preliminary values at $[Cl^-] = 0.009\,M$, $48 \cdot 10^7$, resp. 2.10 is so small that obviously practically no errors had been introduced by using the preliminary values.

We could now derive the β-values for the whole Soret-band of the pure Cyt-2H+. Of course one must remember that this compound cannot exist in a pure state, but only in equilibrium with Cyt and some anion compound. The light absorption of pure Cyt was directly measured at pH = 5.5, and that of Cyt-2H+-2Cl- at $[Cl^-] = 2.83\,M$ and at pH 1.5-3.5.

The curve for pure Cyt-2H+ could be calculated only in the pH-range 1.7 to 2.2, because outside these values the contributions of Cyt-2H+ in the equilibrium with Cyt-2H+-2Cl- and Cyt become too small for obtaining reliable values. From five sets

References p. 282.

of measurements we derived the following values for the top of the Soret band of Cyt–$2H^+$ at 395 mμ

$$pH:\ 1.70,\ 1.84,\ 1.87,\ 2.06,\ 2.20$$
$$\beta_{395}:\ 46.5,\ 48.4,\ 46.4,\ 51.8,\ 46.3$$

The mean value, 48 ($\pm$ 1) $\cdot 10^7$ cm^2 $\times$ mole^{-1}, is in as good agreement as could be expected with the value $\beta_{395} = 50 \cdot 10^7$ obtained from the points at [Cl$^-$] $= 0.009\ M$ in Fig. 3.

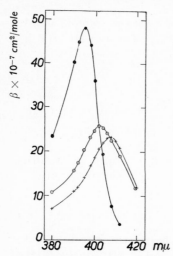

Fig. 7. Soret bands of Cyt (+), measured at pH 5.5, of Cyt–$2H^+$–$2Cl^-$ (O), measured at pH 1.5–3.5 and [Cl$^-$] = 2.83, and of Cyt–$2H^+$ (●), calculated.

The value is exceptionally high for a hemoprotein and of the same order of magnitude as the values for porphyrins in acid solutions[11]. The Soret bands of the three compounds Cyt, Cyt–$2H^+$–$2Cl^-$, and Cyt–$2H^+$ are shown in Fig. 7.

Magnetometry. χ_m for Cyt was found $= 2120 \cdot 10^{-6}$ cgs emu. This value is somewhat lower than that found in the earlier investigation[4] but is probably more correct, since our present preparations were purer than the older ones, and the new value ($\mu = 2.24$ Bohr magnetons) is in better agreement with the value expected for one odd electron, 1.73 Bohr magnetons $+$ an orbital contribution.

The χ_m for Cyt–$2H^+$–$2Cl^-$ was taken from Fig. 5B. It is unexpected that the paramagnetic susceptibility of this compound should vary between pH 1.5 and 3, where the spectrophotometric values remain practically unchanged, but heme-linked groups that are spectrophotometrically inoperable, though magnetometrically operable, have been reported for other hemoproteins[12, 13]. Whereas the paramagnetic susceptibility between pH 3.0 and 1.5 increases only from 6000 to 7400 $\cdot 10^{-6}$, and thus remains in the neighbourhood of the theoretical value for three odd electrons, $\chi_m = 6400 \cdot 10^{-6}$, a much more rapid increase in χ_m occurs below pH 1.5, where the light absorption at 395 mμ begins to decrease (Fig. 3). We believe that these changes below pH 1.5 are connected with the appearance of "type I" in the earlier work[1].

The paramagnetic susceptibility of pure Cyt–$2H^+$ was calculated from six determinations at low [Cl$^-$] and pH-values giving the highest possible molar fractions of Cyt–$2H^+$. The values are given in Table I. The mean value of χ_m is $= 16,200$ ($\pm$ 600) $\cdot 10^{-6}$, corresponding to $\mu = 6.17$ ($\pm$ 0.14) Bohr magnetons. This value is somewhat higher than

TABLE I

pH	Cl⁻ M	Mole fraction calculated for			$\chi_m \times 10^6$ in cgs emu		
		Cyt	Cyt–2H⁺–2Cl⁻	Cyt–2H⁺	Observed	for Cyt–2H⁺–2Cl⁻	for Cyt–2H⁺
1.55	0.056	0.029	0.568	0.403	10 390	7 350	15 300
1.51	0.080	0.015	0.733	0.252	9 320	7 400	15 400
1.80	0.060	0.054	0.708	0.236	9 500	7 100	18 500
1.80	0.090	0.029	0.847	0.125	7 800	7 100	13 800
2.01	0.030	0.206	0.450	0.343	9 300	6 850	16 800
2.02	0.040	0.162	0.585	0.256	8 610	6 850	16 700

References p. 282.

the theoretical maximum for five odd electrons, 5.92. Considering the uncertainty of the calculations, this difference is insignificant. Our conclusion is that in Cyt–2H$^+$ the iron is held by essentially ionic bonds.

DISCUSSION

On the basis of these results we arrive at the following picture of the compounds of ferricytochrome c in acid solution. The links between the iron atom and the hemichrome-forming group in Cyt can be broken by two protons. The two dissociation steps are very strongly linked, ($n = 2$), the entrance of one proton greatly facilitating the entrance of the second one. Two chloride ions can enter into Cyt–2H$^+$. The interaction between the two steps is again so strong that $n = 2$. We may thus represent the relations between the three compounds by the formula:

$$
\underset{\substack{\text{Cyt}\\ \text{1 odd electron, d}^2\text{sp}^3\text{ bonds}}}{
\begin{array}{c}
\overline{N} \\
\text{N} \overset{+}{|} \text{N} \\
\text{N} {>} \text{Fe} {<} \text{N} \\
\text{N}
\end{array}
}
\quad \underset{- 2H^+}{\overset{+ 2H^+}{\rightleftarrows}} \quad
\underset{\substack{\text{Cyt–2H}^+\\ \text{5 odd electrons, essentially}\\ \text{ionic bonds}}}{
\begin{array}{c}
{\equiv}\text{NH} \\
\text{N}^- \quad \text{N} \\
\text{Fe}^{+++} \\
\text{N} \quad \text{N}^- \\
\text{HN} \\
+
\end{array}
}
\quad \underset{- 7Cl^-}{\overset{+ 2Cl^-}{\rightleftarrows}} \quad
\underset{\substack{\text{Cyt–2H}^+\text{–2Cl}^-\\ \text{3 odd electrons, dsp}^2\text{ bonds}}}{
\begin{array}{c}
{\equiv}\overset{+}{\text{NH}} \\
\text{Cl}^- \\
\text{N} {>} \text{Fe}^+ {<} \text{N} \\
\text{Cl}^- \\
\text{HN} \\
+
\end{array}
}
$$

As seen in the formula, we presume that the chloride ions are interposed between positive nitrogen and iron atoms, forming a dipole chain system. Neither a ferric ion, nor a positively charged nitrogen atom alone would be able to form compounds of low dissociation constants with chloride ions. But in this case the nitrogen atoms probably are held by the protein part in essentially intact positions relative to the iron after the entrance of the two protons. We may recall that in cytochrome c the prosthetic group and the protein part are firmly joined by two thioether linkages[14,15]. It is, therefore, easy to imagine that anions must be strongly attracted into the gaps between ${\equiv}$N$^+$H and Fe$^+$. There is an interesting sort of interaction between protons and anions; they cooperate synergistically in the formation of the dipole chain. The distance between ${\equiv}$N$^+$H and Fe$^+$ must be of decisive importance for the association of the anions. The larger K_{Cl^-} at pH 1, compared with that of pH 2, can be explained if we assume that a deformation of the protein part the molecule takes place at low pH, increasing the distance between ${\equiv}$N$^+$H and Fe$^+$.

The results from 1941[1,4] suggested that the iron-linked nitrogen atoms were split off one after the other at widely different pH values, giving three types (III, II, I) of ferricytochrome c with the transitions occurring at pH 2.5 and 0.5 respectively. "Type III" corresponds to "Cyt" in this paper, while "Type II" must have included both Cyt–2H$^+$ and Cyt–2H$^+$–2Cl$^-$. The older results were based on spectrophotometric determinations in visible light (470 and 650 mμ) In connection with the present investigation a few experiments were made at 620 mμ. They indicated a chloride-sensitive dissociation constant pK 2.5, in agreement with the old value. However, we now observed a slow drift of the optical density with time amounting to a few per cent. This observation remains to be interpreted. Such complications did not seem to appear in the Soret band region.

References p. 282.

"Type I"[1] must have been a more or less denatured product, since the enzymic activity is lost at such acidities, which are low enough to bring about its appearance.

A comparison of the old and new magnetic data discloses that the former values generally were higher. The preparations used at that time were of low purity (0.7) and they might accordingly have contained some non-cytochrome iron. Our preparation 3 gave $\chi_m = 2600 \cdot 10^{-6}$ cgs emu for Cyt as compared to $\chi_m = 2120$ for preparation 4.

A priori one would not expect to find close analogies between the reactions occurring with ferricytochrome c and horse radish peroxidase (HRP) or catalase upon acidification. Ferricytochrome c at neutral pH is undoubtedly a hemichrome with nitrogen attached to the iron atom by covalent bonds on both sides of the ferri-porphyrin disc, whereas in HRP and catalase the iron atom is held by essentially ionic bonds. It has been supposed to be linked on one side to the protein and on the other to a water molecule or a hydroxyl ion. Moreover, cytochrome c is stable and gives reversible compounds in the acidity range applied, whereas the acid compounds of HRP and catalase studied by MAEHLY[7] seem to be irreversibly altered products, with the exception of HRP-chloride, "Compound A".

Nevertheless certain parallels can be found between the present results on cytochrome c and those of MAEHLY on HRP. MAEHLY's "Compound A" has its Soret band maximum at 407.5 mμ, $\beta = 20 \cdot 10^7$ (recalc.), while Cyt–2H$^+$–2Cl$^-$ has its maximum at 402 mμ, $\beta = 25.8 \cdot 10^7$. This difference is the same as the one found by THEORELL between the wavelengths of the band maxima of certain protohemin compounds and comparable derivatives of cytochrome c. The displacement of the bands depends upon the fact that in the prosthetic group of cytochrome c the number of conjugated double bonds is reduced by two because of the thioether structure at the side chains in positions 2 and 4. MAEHLY has not published any calculation of the number of chloride ions involved in the formation fo Compound A.

MAEHLY's "Compound B" and our Cyt–2H$^+$ are rather similar. The wavelengths of the Soret band maxima are 396.5 and 395 mμ respectively, thus at 11 and 7 mμ shorter wavelengths than for the corresponding chloride compounds. The intensities of the bands are, however, rather different: $\beta_{\text{Comp. B}} = 30 \cdot 10^7$ (calc. from $\varepsilon = 130$ cm^{-1} $\times$ mM^{-1}) and $\beta_{\text{Cyt–2H+}} = 50 \cdot 10^7$ cm$^2 \times$ mole^{-1}. MAEHLY points out that the value $\varepsilon = 130$ is obtained only in the absence of halogen ions. Sulphuric acid developed Compound B, but a further addition of sulphate ions did not cause any additional spectral change, contrary to what was the case with cytochrome c. The transformation from HRP to Compound B involved only one proton; the same value was found for the corresponding change in catalase (Fig. 10 and 11 in (7)). Kinetic experiments, however, indicated that the rate of acid splitting was proportional to the square of [H$^+$]. In order to explain this, MAEHLY considered the simultaneous breaking of one iron-protein bond and one bond between a propionic acid residue and the protein. MAEHLY's conversion B→C is perhaps comparable to the strong increase of the dissociation constant (K_{Cl^-}) between Cl$^-$ and Cyt–2H$^+$ when pH is changed from 2 to 1. Denaturation of the HRP protein or reversible change of shape of the cytochrome c upon acidification to pH 1 could both lead to a diminished affinity for chloride ions.

In summary a comparison of the reactions of HRP and cytochrome c in acid solutions discloses certain similarities; the interpretation of the data is less certain for HRP than for cytochrome c, because HRP in contradistinction to cytochrome c undergoes irreversible changes under the experimental conditions. Nevertheless it appears possible

References p. 282.

that the differences in the mode of linkage between hemin and protein in HRP and cytochrome c are smaller than previously believed.

LEWIS, working in this institute[16], has found that the splitting of ferrihemoglobin or ferrimyoglobin into hemin + colourless protein by means of HCl plus acetone occurred at a considerably higher pH if NaCl was added. A similar but less pronounced effect was observed for sulphate ions.

The cooperation of anions, $e.g.$ Cl$^-$, with protons in the splitting of heme-protein bonds thus appears to be a general phenomenon. Cytochrome c is the first case in which it has been possible to give a structural explanation of this anion effect.

ACKNOWLEDGEMENTS

The authors' thanks are due to the Rockefeller Foundation for a fellowship to one of us (E.B.) and to Knut och Alice Wallenbergs Stiftelse, Magn. Bergvalls Stiftelse and the Rockefeller Foundation for financial support.

SUMMARY

1. The absorption spectra in the Soret band region and the magnetic properties of ferricytochrome c at various chloride ion concentrations have been reinvestigated within the range pH 1–5.

2. The form of ferricytochrome c, which exists at neutral pH ("Cyt", $\beta_{max} = 23.3 \cdot 10^7$ cm^2 × mole^{-1} at 408 mμ) changes upon acidification to an acid form ("Cyt-2H$^+$", $\beta_{max} = 50 \cdot 10^7$ cm^2 × mole^{-1} at 395 mμ) with the simultaneous uptake of two protons ($n = 2$). Half of the total spectral change is reached at pH 2.12. Simultaneously to the spectral change the paramagnetic susceptibility increases from $\chi_m = 2120$ (1 odd electron) to $16,200 \cdot 10^{-6}$ cgs emu (5 odd electrons). The values for Cyt-2H$^+$ have been obtained by extrapolation to [Cl$^-$] = 0.

3. When increasing amounts of chloride ions are added to a solution, containing cytochrome c mainly as Cyt-2H$^+$, the cytochrome is gradually converted into another form, denoted Cyt-2H$^+$-2Cl$^-$ ($\beta_{max} = 25.8 \cdot 10^7$ cm^2 × mole^{-1} at 402 mμ). Two chloride ions are taken up simultaneously ($n = 2$). K_{Cl^-} was found to be $7 \cdot 10^{-3}$ M^2 at pH 1 and about ten times lower at pH 2 and 3. Parallelling these spectral changes the paramagnetic susceptibility decreases to $\chi_m = 6000$ at pH 3 and $7400 \cdot 10^{-6}$ cgs emu at pH 1.5 (3 odd electrons). The differences in K_{Cl^-} and χ_m of Cyt-2H$^+$-2Cl$^-$ at pH 1–1.5 are tentatively explained as depending upon protein disconfiguration due to the acid milieu.

4. The change from Cyt to Cyt-2H$^+$ is interpreted as corresponding to a replacement of covalent links between the iron atom and the two hemichrome-forming groups of the protein moiety by ionic links. In Cyt-2H$^+$-2Cl$^-$ a dipole chain arrangement is assumed.

RÉSUMÉ

1. L'étude des spectres d'absorption dans la région de la bande de Soret et des propriétés magnétiques du ferricytochrome c, en présence de diverses concentrations d'ions chlorures, a été reprise entre pH 1 et pH 5.

2. Le ferricytochrome c se présente à pH neutre sous une forme ("Cyt", $\beta_{max} = 23.3 \cdot 10^7$ cm^2 × mole^{-1} à 408 mμ) qui, paracidification, donne une forme acide ("Cyt"-2 H$^+$, $\beta_{max} = 50 \cdot 10^7$ cm^2 × mol^{-1} à 395 mμ), en fixant deux protons en même temps ($n = 2$). La moitié du changement spectral est atteinte à pH 2.12. En même temps que le spectre se modifie, la susceptibilité paramagnétique augmente de $\chi_m = 2120$ (1 électron non aparié) à $16,200 \cdot 10^{-6}$ unités C.G.S. (5 électrons non apariés). Ces valeurs pour Cyt-2H$^+$ ont été obtenues par extrapolation en supposant [Cl$^-$] = 0.

3. Quand on augmente la quantité d'ions chlorure ajoutés à une solution contenant la plus grande partie du cytochrome c sous sa forme Cyt-2H$^+$, le cytochrome prend progressivement une autre forme désignée par Cyt-2H$^+$-2 Cl$^-$ ($\beta_{max} = 25.8 \cdot 10^7$ cm^2 × mol^{-1} à 402 mμ). Deux ions chlorures sont fixés en même temps ($n = 2$). K_{Cl^-} est de $7 \cdot 10^{-3}$ M^2 à pH 1 et environ dix fois plus faible à pH 2 et 3. Parallèlement à ces modifications du spectre, la susceptibilité paramagnétique décroît jusqu'à $\chi_m = 6000$ à pH 3 et $7400 \cdot 10^{-6}$ unités C.G.S. à pH 1.5 (3 électrons non apariés). Il est possible que les différences de K_{Cl^-} et χ_m de Cyt-2H$^+$-2 Cl$^-$ à pH 1–1.5, s'expliquent par une modification de la configuration de la protéine, due à l'acidité du milieu.

References p. 282.

4. Le passage de Cyt à Cyt-2H$^+$ peut s'interpréter comme correspondant au remplacement de deux liaisons de covalence entre l'atome de fer et les hémichromogènes de la partie protéique par des liaisons ioniques. Dans Cyt-2H$^+$-2Cl$^-$ les auteurs supposent un arrangement de chaîne dipolaire.

ZUSAMMENFASSUNG

1. Die Absorptionsspektren in der Soretbandregion und die magnetischen Eigenschaften von Ferricytochrom c bei verschiedenen Chlorionenkonzentrationen wurden im pH-Bereich 1–5 nochmals untersucht.

2. Die bei neutralem pH bestehende Form des Ferricytochroms c ("Cyt", $\beta_{max} = 23.3 \cdot 10^7$ cm^2 × Mol^{-1} bei 408 mμ) geht unter gleichzeitiger Aufnahme von zwei Protonen ($n = 2$) beim Ansäuern in eine saure Form über ("Cyt-2H$^+$", $\beta_{max} = 50 \cdot 10^7$ cm^2 × Mol^{-1} bei 395 mμ). Die Hälfte der gesamten spektralen Veränderung ist bei pH 2.12 erreicht. Gleichzeitig mit der spektralen Veränderung nimmt die paramagnetische Suszeptibilität von $\chi_m = 2120$ (1 einsames Elektron) auf 16,200·10^{-6} cgs eme (5 einsame Elektronen) zu. Die Werte für Cyt-2H$^+$ wurden durch Extrapolation auf [Cl$^-$] = 0 erhalten.

3. Wenn zu einer Cytochrom c hauptsächlich als Cyt-2H$^+$ enthaltenden Lösung steigende Mengen Chlorionen hinzugefügt werden, dann wird Cytochrom allmählich in eine als Cyt-2H$^+$-2Cl$^-$ ($\beta_{max} = 25.8·10^7$ cm^2 × Mol^{-1} bei 402 mμ) bezeichnete Form übergeführt. Zwei Chlorionen werden gleichzeitig aufgenommen ($n = 2$). Für K_{Cl^-} wurde der Wert $7·10^{-3}$ M^2 bei pH 1 und ein ungefähr 10 mal geringerer Wert bei pH 2 und 3 gefunden. Parallel zu dieser spektralen Veränderungen fällt die paramagnetische Suszeptibilität auf $\chi_m = 6000$ bei pH 3 und 7400·10^6 cgs eme bei pH 1.5 (3 einsame Elektronen). Die Unterschiede der K_{Cl^-} und χ_m-Werte von Cyt-2H$^+$-2Cl$^-$ bei pH 1–1.5 werden versuchsweise als abhängig von einer in saurem Medium stattfindenden Proteindiskonfiguration erklärt.

4. Die Veränderung die Cyt beim Übergang in Cyt-2H$^+$ untergeht wird als ein dem Ersatz der covalenten Bindungen zwischen dem Eisenatom und 2 hemichrombildenden Gruppen der Proteinhälften durch Ionenbindungen entsprechenden Vorgang interpretiert. In Cyt-2H$^+$-2Cl$^-$ wird eine Dipolkettenanordnung angenommen.

REFERENCES

[1] H. THEORELL AND Å. ÅKESON, *J. Am. Chem. Soc.*, 63 (1941) 1812.
[2] D. KEILIN AND E. F. HARTREE, *Proc. Roy. Soc. (London) B*, 122 (1940) 277.
[3] K. G. PAUL, *Acta Chem. Scand.*, 2 (1948) 430.
[4] H. THEORELL, *J. Am. Chem. Soc.*, 63 (1941) 1820.
[5] H. THEORELL AND A. EHRENBERG, *Arkiv Fysik*, 3 (1951) 299.
[6] K. G. PAUL, *Heme-linked Groups of Cytochrome c* (Dissertation, Stockholm, 1951).
[7] A. C. MAEHLY, *Biochim. Biophys. Acta*, 8 (1952) 1, and personal communication.
[8] H. THEORELL AND Å. ÅKESON, *J. Am. Chem. Soc.*, 63 (1941) 1804.
[9] D. KEILIN AND E. F. HARTREE, *Biochem. J.*, 39 (1945) 289.
[10] C. L. TSOU, *Biochem. J.* 49 (1951) 362.
[11] K. G. PAUL, *Scand. J. Clin. Lab. Invest.*, in press.
[12] CH. D. CORYELL, F. STITT AND L. PAULING, *J. Am. Chem. Soc.*, 59 (1937) 633.
[13] H. THEORELL AND A. EHRENBERG, *Acta Chem. Scand.*, 5 (1951) 823.
[14] H. THEORELL, *Biochem. Z.*, 298 (1938) 242.
[15] K. G. PAUL, *Acta Chem. Scand.*, 4 (1950) 239.
[16] U. J. LEWIS, to be published.

Received May 11th, 1953

INFLUENCE DU MANGANÈSE SUR LA STABILITÉ DU LYSOZYME

II. RÔLE PROTECTEUR DU MANGANÈSE LORS DE L'HYDROLYSE DU LYSOZYME PAR LA TRYPSINE[*]

par

LUIGI GORINI, FRANÇOISE FELIX et CLAUDE FROMAGEOT

Laboratoire de Chimie biologique de la Faculté des Sciences, Paris (France)

Le lysozyme est un matériel particulièrement favorable à l'étude du rôle éventuel d'un métal dans les relations existant, chez une protéine, entre dénaturation et sensibilité à l'action de la trypsine. La dénaturation du lysozyme peut en effet être facilement suivie par la perte de son activité enzymatique; on sait[2] d'autre part que, à l'exclusion de nombreux autres métaux bivalents, le manganèse (introduit sous forme d'ion Mn^{++}) réduit jusqu'à dix fois (pour une concentration de $10^{-2} M$) la vitesse de sa dénaturation thermique irréversible. Si, comme cela a déjà été établi dans le cas d'autres protéines, la trypsine est capable de protéolyser le lysozyme seulement après que celui-ci ait été dénaturé, on peut *a priori* s'attendre à ce que le manganèse exerce vis à vis de cette protéolyse un effet protecteur analogue à celui qui a été décrit[3] pour le calcium dans le cas de la serumalbumine par exemple.

En fait, le présent travail montre que: 1. La vitesse de la protéolyse par la trypsine du lysozyme enzymatiquement actif est limitée par la vitesse d'une réaction dont l'énergie d'activation est relativement élevée; 2. le manganèse protège fortement le lysozyme contre l'action de la trypsine; 3. lorsque le lysozyme a été préalablement inactivé par la chaleur, il devient directement hydrolysable par la trypsine, et l'action protectrice du manganèse ne se manifeste plus; 4. lorsque le lysozyme a été seulement partiellement inactivé, l'action du manganèse au cours de l'hydrolyse de la protéine par la trypsine permet de démontrer que ce lysozyme est alors constitué par un mélange de molécules ayant conservé leur activité lysante et de molécules tout à fait inactives, et non pas par des molécules qui, toutes identiques entre elles, ne seraient que partiellement actives.

PARTIE EXPÉRIMENTALE

Techniques

Le lysozyme (poids moléculaire = 14,800)[4] est dissous dans une solution tampon de borate $5 \cdot 10^{-2} M$ à pH 7.9[2]. La trypsine[**] est dissoute dans l'eau; la solution obtenue est diluée au moment de l'expérience par la solution tampon de borate. Le manganèse est introduit sous forme de $MnCl_2$. Le

---

[*] Des observations préliminaires à ce travail ont fait l'objet d'une communication au IIème Congrès International de Biochimie, Paris, 1952[1].
[**] Trypsine cristallisée provenant de Worthington, Freehold. Avant d'être utilisé, l'enzyme est débarrassé par dialyse du sulfate de magnésium qui l'accompagne au moment de sa livraison. Son poids moléculaire est considéré comme étant de 17,700[5].

Bibliographie p. 288.

milieu réactionnel est constitué par le mélange, en proportions définies, de solution de lysozyme et de solution de trypsine. Les concentrations indiquées pour chacune de ces deux substances, de même que pour le métal, sont leurs concentrations finales dans le mélange. La protéolyse du lysozyme (pH 7.9, milieu tampon borate) est suivie soit par le dosage du lysozyme encore actif, soit par celui des produits d'hydrolyse. Le lysozyme encore actif est déterminé en mesurant la vitesse de lyse d'une suspension de *Micrococcus lysodeikticus* dans les conditions déjà décrites[2]. La température de 25°, à laquelle est faite cette détermination, est suffisamment basse pour arrêter pratiquement toute protéolyse; il a été d'autre part vérifié que la présence de trypsine aux concentrations réalisées ici n'exerce aucune influence sur l'activité du lysozyme. En ce qui concerne les produits d'hydrolyse, leur dosage est fait en mesurant l'extinction à 280 mμ du liquide surnageant obtenu après centrifugation du mélange résultant de l'addition de 5 ml d'acide trichloracétique à 5 % à 3 ml du milieu réactionnel. Au cours de ces mesures, on tient compte de la présence éventuelle des produits d'hydrolyse de la trypsine elle-même.

Action de la trypsine sur le lysozyme actif

L'action de la trypsine sur le lysozyme actif a déjà fait l'objet de quelques observations[6]. L'étude de cette action est faite ici en suivant en fonction du temps la perte progressive d'activité du lysozyme maintenu en présence de trypsine; cette méthode est en effet plus sensible que celle basée sur la mesure des produits d'hydrolyse. Toutefois, au cours d'expériences préliminaires réalisées en mettant en œuvre une concentration relativement élevée de lysozyme ($8.5 \cdot 10^{-6}M$), de telle sorte que les produits d'hydrolyse formés soient en quantité appréciable, il a été vérifié que le dosage de ces produits d'hydrolyse fournit des résultats en parfait accord avec ceux donnés par la mesure de l'activité lysante (Tableau I).

TABLEAU I

PROTÉOLYSE PAR LA TRYPSINE DU LYSOZYME ACTIF,
SUIVIE SOIT PAR LA DÉTERMINATION DE L'ACTIVITÉ RÉSIDUELLE (A),
SOIT PAR CELLE DES PRODUITS D'HYDROLYSE APPARUS (B)

Lysozyme $8.5 \cdot 10^{-6}$ M; Trypsine $5 \cdot 10^{-6}$ M; Ca^{++} 10^{-2} M^{*}; Température 36°.

Temsp (heures)	% de lysozyme hydrolysé	
	A	B**
0	0	0
4	14	13
8	27	27
16	45	46
25	55	57
32	57	60

* Ca^{++} n'ayant pas d'influence sur la protéolyse du lysozyme est ajouté pour stabiliser la trypsine.
** Calculé à partir de la valeur de l'extinction due au lysozyme total obtenue en substituant de l'eau à l'acide trichloracétique.

Les expériences ultérieures portant sur le lysozyme actif mettent en œuvre des concentrations de lysozyme environ dix fois plus faibles, car nous avons observé que la sensibilité du lysozyme vis à vis de la trypsine est d'autant plus forte que le lysozyme est plus dilué. Ce fait, assez remarquable, mis en relation avec le fait que la stabilité du lysozyme à l'inactivation thermique à 60° varie aussi dans le même sens que la concentration[2], suggère déjà l'existence d'un point commun dans le mécanisme d'action de la chaleur et dans celui de la trypsine.

Bibliographie p. 288.

Influence de la température

L'action de la trypsine sur le lysozyme actif, pratiquement nulle à 25°, devient appréciable à 36°. A cette température elle est toutefois très lente; en absence de tout métal, et avec du lysozyme en solution diluée ($10^{-6}\ M$), il faut attendre plusieurs heures pour obtenir une inactivation significative du lysozyme. En présence de manganèse ($10^{-2}\ M$) on ne constate aucune attaque du lysozyme (Tableau III). L'influence du métal est donc déjà nette; mais les résultats quantitatifs obtenus à la température en

question ne peuvent guère servir à une étude cinétique précise du fait que les expériences doivent ici durer trop longtemps pour que la concentration en trypsine reste constante surtout en l'absence de tout métal. Nous avons donc étudié la réaction à 45° et à 48°. La figure 1 représente les résultats obtenus à 48° pour des concentrations de lysozyme de $10^{-6}\ M$ et de trypsine de $0.8\cdot10^{-6}\ M$ en présence de différentes concentrations de manganèse. Considérant la réaction en question comme une réaction du premier ordre, nous avons calculé la valeur de sa constante de vitesse dans les différents cas (Tableau II). L'énergie E d'activation de cette réaction, entre 45° et 48°, en absence de manganèse, calculée d'après la formule d'Arrhenius

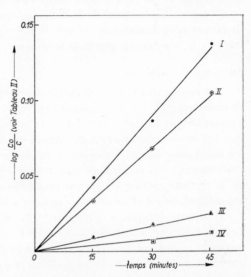

Fig. 1. Influence du manganèse sur la vitesse d'inactivation du lysozyme par la trypsine à 48°. Concentration en Mn++: I o; II $10^{-4}\ M$; III 10^{-3} M; IV $10^{-2}\ M$.

$$\text{Log } K = -\frac{E}{2.3\,R}\cdot\frac{1}{T} + Constante,\text{ à}$$

TABLEAU II

INFLUENCE DE LA TEMPÉRATURE ET DE Mn++ SUR LA VITESSE
D'INACTIVATION DU LYSOZYME PAR LA TRYPSINE

K = Constante de vitesse d'inactivation calculée d'apres la formule:

$$\text{Log } \frac{C_0}{C} = \frac{K}{2.3}\cdot t$$

où C_0 et C sont les concentrations en lysozyme actif aux temps zéro et t.

$$C_0 = 10^{-6}\ M.$$

Température d'inactivation	Concentration moléculaire de Trypsine . 10^6	Concentration moléculaire de Mn++	$K/sec\cdot10^5$
45°	o	o	o
	0.8	o	4.7
	0.8	10^{-2}	$\sim$o
48°	o	o	o
	0.8	o	11.5
	0.8	10^{-4}	8.8
	0.8	10^{-3}	2.3
	0.8	10^{-2}	1.0

Bibliographie p. 288.

partir des valeurs du Tableau II, est de l'ordre de 57,000 cal/mol. Cette énergie, très supérieure à celle d'une réaction d'hydrolyse enzymatique, est au contraire comparable à celle de la réaction d'inactivation thermique précédemment calculée[2]. Ceci suggère que l'hydrolyse par la trypsine du lysozyme actif est limitée par une réaction analogue à celle qui se manifeste à des températures plus élevées en l'absence de trypsine. Toutefois, il ne nous paraît pas encore possible de dire quelle est la nature de la réaction en question. Quoi qu'il en soit, le fait qu'il existe, dans les conditions du Tableau I, un parallélisme entre la perte d'activité lysante et l'hydrolyse du lysozyme actif sous l'action de la trypsine, montre que si le lysozyme actif, en présence de trypsine, se transforme en une forme inactive avant d'être hydrolysé, cette forme inactive ne s'accumule pas dans le milieu.

Influence du manganèse

La comparaison des constantes de vitesse d'inactivation en présence et en absence de manganèse (Tableau II) met en évidence l'action de ce métal. La diminution de vitesse provoquée par le manganèse est du même ordre de grandeur que celle observée dans le cas de l'inactivation thermique (vitesse environ dix fois plus petite pour $Mn^{++} 10^{-2} M$)[2]. Le manganèse agirait ainsi soit en déplaçant un équilibre éventuel vers la forme active du lysozyme, soit en rendant cette forme active moins sensible à une action dénaturante de la trypsine, action s'exerçant préalablement à son action hydrolysante[7]. L'influence du manganèse est d'autant plus remarquable que ce métal, comme le calcium, favorise l'action protéolytique de la trypsine[8,9,10]; on aurait donc pu s'attendre à ce que la protéolyse du lysozyme s'accroisse au lieu d'être inhibée. Mais on sait déjà[3] que l'influence que les métaux ont sur une protéolyse par la trypsine est la résultante des actions qu'ils exercent sur l'une et sur l'autre des deux protéines en présence: la trypsine et son substrat. Le Tableau III montre ce qui se passe dans le cas du lysozyme, soumis à l'action de la trypsine en présence de manganèse, de calcium et de magnésium. Le manganèse exerçant son action surtout sur le lysozyme, diminue la protéolyse; le calcium dépourvu d'action sur le lysozyme, mais protégeant la trypsine, permet une protéolyse plus grande; le magnésium étant pratiquement sans effet sur les deux protéines, n'influence pas la protéolyse.

TABLEAU III

INFLUENCE DE CERTAINS IONS MÉTALLIQUES SUR LA STABILITÉ
DU LYSOZYME EN PRÉSENCE DE TRYPSINE

Lysozyme $10^{-6} M$; Trypsine $3 \cdot 10^{-6} M$; Métaux $10^{-2} M$; Température 36°.

Temps (heures)	Activité résiduelle du lysozyme en % de l'activité initiale			
	Tampon seul	Mg^{++}	Ca^{++}	Mn^{++}
0	100	100	100	100
1.5	89	89	86	100
3	55	55	50	100
4.5	50	50	42	98

Action de la trypsine sur le lysozyme inactif

L'étude de l'action de la trypsine sur le lysozyme ayant préalablement subi une

Bibliographie p. 288.

inactivation thermique a porté sur du lysozyme ayant subi un traitement basé sur les considérations suivantes; les solutions de lysozyme à inactiver doivent être suffisamment concentrées pour fournir des valeurs convenables lors du dosage des produits d'hydro-lyse, seule méthode de mesure applicable ici. Or, de telles solutions à 60° ne s'inactivent que lentement, alors qu'à des températures plus élevées, leur inactivation est accompa-gnée d'une précipitation[2]. On est donc amené à préparer une solution de "lysozyme dénaturé standard" en traitant à 70° pendant 60 minutes une solution de lysozyme ac-tif $1.7 \cdot 10^{-4}$ M dans du tampon borate à pH 7.9, puis en centrifugeant pour éliminer le léger louche qui s'est formé; cette solution de "lysozyme dénaturé standard" a conservé environ 40% de son activité initiale. Pour mieux définir l'état de dénaturation d'une telle préparation, il convient de savoir si dans la solution on a affaire à des molécules ayant toutes subi une inactivation partielle, ou à un mélange de molécules actives et de molécules inactives; or, si on suit à 25° l'action de la trypsine ($2 \cdot 10^{-7}$ M) sur une telle solution, on constate que la perte d'activité lysante et l'apparition de produits d'hydro-lyse ne sont *plus* parallèles: alors que le premier phénomène ne se manifeste pratiquement pas, même après six heures, les produits d'hydrolyse apparaissent dès le début pour atteindre dans le même temps 25% de ce qui correspondrait à l'hydrolyse de la totalité du lysozyme présent. Il est donc évident, que, dans les conditions réalisées, les molécules de lysozyme hydrolysées par la trypsine ne sont pas celles qui ont conservé leur activité. De plus, ces dernières molécules se comportent d'une façon analogue à celle des molé-cules du lysozyme actif: en effet, si on dilue la solution de "lysozyme dénaturé standard" dans des proportions telles qu'on ait, en lysozyme actif, une concentration de 10^{-6} M, on observe en présence de trypsine 10^{-6} M à 36° une vitesse d'inactivation tout à fait comparable à celle obtenue avec une solution de même concentration en lysozyme cris-tallisé actif. En présence de manganèse 10^{-2} M, aucune protéolyse n'est décelable même après six heures. On est donc conduit à considérer la solution de "lysozyme dénaturé standard" comme contenant approximativement 40% de molécules de lysozyme actif et 60% de molécules de lysozyme inactif.

Ces observations jointes au fait qu'à 25° l'action de la trypsine sur le lysozyme actif est pratiquement inexistante, indiquent que, quoique la solution de "lysozyme déna-turé standard" consiste en un mélange d'au moins deux espèces de molécules, il est pos-sible de l'utiliser pour étudier l'action de la trypsine sur le lysozyme inactivé.

Cette étude montre que, en l'absence de manganèse ou de calcium, une solution de "lyso-zyme dénaturé standard" dont la concentration en lysozyme inactif est $9 \cdot 10^{-5}$ M, est hydrolysée par la trypsine $2 \cdot 10^{-7}$ M suivant une réaction d'ordre zéro (concentration du substrat saturante) pendant les vingt premières minutes de la réaction; 10% du substrat sont alors hydrolysés (Δ extinction du surnageant trichloracétique après 20 minutes = 0.130). En présence de manganèse ou de calcium (10^{-2} M), cette protéolyse est accrue d'environ 10%. Si la concentration du substrat, au lieu d'être saturante, est limitante ($3.4 \cdot 10^{-5} M$), la présence des métaux en question provoque un accroissement du même ordre de la protéolyse. Ainsi, contrairement à ce qui se passe dans le cas de la protéolyse par la trypsine du lysozyme actif, la protéolyse du lysozyme inactif n'est pas diminuée par la présence de manganèse; au contraire, ce métal, tout comme le calcium, favorise l'action protéolytique en stabilisant la trypsine.

Le fait que en présence de manganèse la trypsine n'agit pas sur le lysozyme actif, même à 36°, permet de comparer à 25° et à 36° les vitesses de protéolyse par la trypsine ($2 \cdot 10^{-7}$ M) du lysozyme inactif ($9 \cdot 10^{-5}$ M) en présence de manganèse (10^{-2} M). Cette comparaison montre que le rapport de ces vitesses est de 2.2, ce qui correspond bien à l'ordre de grandeur de Q_{10} d'une réaction de protéolyse enzymatique au voisinage des températures en question.

Que l'identification comme substrat de la trypsine, des molécules de lysozyme dénaturées de façon différente (dénaturées à température élevée ou dénaturées à la température ordinaire en présence de trypsine) soit justifiée ou non, le présent travail n'en permet pas moins de conclure que l'hydrolyse par la trypsine du lysozyme actif nécessite une inactivation préalable de ce lysozyme et que c'est sur cette réaction d' inactivation que le manganèse exerce son influence.

RÉSUMÉ

L'étude de l'influence du manganèse sur la protéolyse par la trypsine soit du lysozyme actif soit du lysozyme inactivé par la chaleur, montre que la présence de ce métal réduit considérablement (10 fois pour Mn 10^{-2} M) la vitesse d'hydrolyse du lysozyme actif et laisse inchangée celle du lysozyme inactivé par la chaleur. D'autre part, l'importance considérable de la température sur l'hydrolyse du lysozyme actif par la trypsine suggère que l'action hydrolysante de la trypsine est limitée par une réaction de dénaturation du lysozyme; l'énergie d'activation de cette dernière réaction peut être calculée comme égale à 57,000 cal/mol. C'est vis à vis de cette réaction que le manganèse exerce son action inhibitrice.

SUMMARY

Manganese considerably (10 times for Mn 10^{-2} M) diminishes the rate of hydrolysis by trypsin of enzymically active lysozyme, while it has no effect on the hydrolysis of heat inactivated lysozyme. This fact, coupled with the large energy of activation (57,000 cal/mol) of the proteolysis of active lysozyme, suggests that the rate of hydrolysis by trypsin is limited by the rate of denaturation of lysozyme. It is on this latter reaction that manganese exerts its inhibiting action.

ZUSAMMENFASSUNG

Mangan vermindert merklich (10 mal für Mn 10^{-2} M), die tryptische Hydrolyse von enzymatisch-aktivem Lysozym während er keine Wirkung auf die Hydrolyse von durch Hitze inaktiviertem Lysozym ausübt. Die grosse Aktivationsenergie (57,000 kal/mol) der Proteolyse des aktiven Lysozyms lässt ausserdem vermuten dass seine tryptische Hydrolysegeschwindigkeit durch die Geschwindigkeit einer Denaturierungsreaktion begrenzt ist, auf welche Mangan seine hemmende Wirkung ausübt.

BIBLIOGRAPHIE

[1] L. GORINI ET F. FELIX, *IIème Congrès International de Biochimie*, Paris 1952. Résumé des communications, p. 232.
[2] L. GORINI ET F. FELIX, *Biochim. Biophys. Acta*, 10 (1953) 128.
[3] L.GORINI ET L. AUDRAIN, *Biochim. Biophys. Acta*, 9 (1952) 180.
[4] C. FROMAGEOT ET M. PRIVAT DE GARILHE, *Biochim. Biophys. Acta*, 4 (1950) 509.
[5] H. GOLDENBERG ET A. D. McLAREN, *J. Am. Chem. Soc.*, 73 (1951) 1131
[6] G. ALDERTON, W. H. WARD ET H. L. FEVOLD, *J. Biol. Chem.* 157 (1945) 43.
[7] K. LINDERSTRÖM-LANG, *Cold Spring Harbor Symposia Quant. Biol.*, 14 (1949) 117.
[8] L. GORINI, *Biochim. Biophys. Acta*, 7 (1951) 318.
[9] M. BIER ET F. F. NORD, *Arch. Biochem. Biophys.*, 33 (1951) 320.
[10] M. M. GREEN, J. A. GLADNER, L. W. CUNNINGHAM, JR., ET H. NEURATH, *J. Am. Chem. Soc.*, 74 (1952) 2122.

Reçu le 29 Mai 1953

NEW METHODS FOR THE STUDY OF THE
CARBON MONOXIDE COMPOUNDS OF RESPIRATORY ENZYMES[*]

by

BRITTON CHANCE, LUCILE SMITH AND LAROY CASTOR[**]

*Johnson Research Foundation, University of Pennsylvania,
Philadelphia, Pennsylvania (U.S.A.)*

In the past few years it has been possible to improve considerably and to extend the range of three basic methods for the study of respiratory enzymes, especially their carbon monoxide compounds. Visual spectroscopy—used first by MacMunn in 1885[1] to discover the histohemins, by Keilin in 1925[2] to identify and to study the cytochromes in detail, and by Warburg and his co-workers to identify the CO compound of the respiratory enzyme in *Acetobacter pasteurianum*[3]—until recently has had no successful competitor for the study of the absorption bands of the respiratory enzymes in suspensions of intact cells or in muscle tissue. But improved photoelectric surfaces and electronic techniques have in our hands and more recently in the hands of others[4] brought sharply into focus the absorption spectra that could at best be only dimly perceived by earlier photoelectric techniques such as were used by Warburg and Christian to show the presence of flavoprotein in *Bacterium delbrückii*[5] and by Haas to measure the speed of reduction of cytochrome c in *Torula utilis*[6]. It is now possible to observe the reduction of respiratory enzymes in the range 320 to 660 mμ in many types of respiring cell suspensions. In bakers' yeast, for example, the reaction kinetics and spectra of the pyridine nucleotides, flavoproteins and cytochromes of types a, a_3, b and c can be separately studied by rapid and sensitive spectroscopic methods[7,8]. In some cases the sensitivity exceeds that achieved by highly skilful visual observers since we can regularly record the 590 mμ band of cytochrome a_1 in cultures of *Azotobacter chroococcum*. More recently these spectroscopic methods have been improved so that they are suitable for measuring the changes in optical density caused by the formation of the carbon monoxide compounds[9] of the respiratory enzymes[10] or cytochrome oxidases[11] of the cell suspensions.

About ten years ago Bücher and Negelein developed an "optical method" for the study of the kinetics of photodissociation of the CO compounds of the soluble pigments myoglobin and hemoglobin[12]. By introducing new electronic techniques, we now have developed a more sensitive method for use with turbid cell suspensions, first, for demonstrating that the photodissociation of the cytochrome a_3–CO compound actually occurs[13], secondly, for obtaining "photodissociation spectra" of the CO compounds of respiratory enzymes[13], and thirdly, for obtaining accurate values for the molecular extinction of the a-bands of the CO compounds of the respiratory enzymes by direct meas-

[*] This research was supported in part by the National Institutes of Health, United States Public Health Service, by the Office of Naval Research, and by the National Science Foundation.
[**] Lalor Foundation predoctoral fellow.

References p. 297/298.

urements of the kinetics of photodissociation and recombination of the CO compounds[14]. The latter method is much more direct than the manometric method[15,16] which responds too slowly to permit a direct measurement of the kinetics of photodissociation. We find the molecular extinction coefficient of the a-band of cytochrome a_3–CO to be $\varepsilon = 12$ cm^{-1} $\times$ mM^{-1} for bakers' yeast cells and for heart muscle homogenates[14].

The classical manometric method for determining the relative photochemical action spectrum for the reversal of carbon monoxide inhibition of respiration that was developed twenty-five years ago[17] has been until now the only method so far available. Although this manometric method has given excellent spectra, there seem to be large changes in the heights of the major absorption bands and in the details of the subsidiary bands when the temperature is lowered[18,19]. Also, MELNICK'S action spectrum for yeast[20] does not agree in detail with that of KUBOWITZ AND HAAS[18] nor does his 450 mμ peak for heart muscle preparation agree with any of the other data on cytochrome a_3[13,19]. Thus a new method that permits monochromatic illumination of the sample over a wide range of wavelengths is highly desirable. We can report here preliminary experiments with an apparatus for measuring photochemical action spectra in a drop of cell suspension[21] with the aid of the platinum microelectrode[22,23]. We have not yet perfected the fourth and logical development of these techniques—the plotting of the photochemical action spectra from data on the direct measurement of the photodissociation kinetics for a number of wavelengths of monochromatic photodissociating light, but such an apparatus appears feasible.

We have surveyed the respiratory pigments of various materials with these sensitive methods[24] and have recently focussed our attention upon a rather different "CO-binding pigment" found in *Staphylococcus albus* and in other bacteria. Our absorption spectrum (difference spectrum) for this CO compound shows peaks at 416 mμ[9], 535 and 570 mμ[25], and the photodissociation spectrum shows close agreement with the absorption spectrum; the peak of the Soret band lies at 415 mμ[13]. We here present quantitative data on the kinetics of photodissociation of this CO-binding pigment and find that it is considerably less light-sensitive at 589 mμ than the enzyme of yeast or muscle, but that it has a distinctive band at 546 mμ. Our preliminary value for the molecular extinction of the CO-binding pigment at this wavelength is $\varepsilon = 5$ cm$^{-1} \times$ mM^{-1}. We have also determined the relative photochemical action spectrum for this pigment and find that the action spectrum in the Soret region has a peak at 418 mμ, in agreement with our absorption and photodissociation difference spectra and distinctly different from the 430 mμ peak for yeast and muscle[21]. Our results suggest that this "CO-binding pigment" is a new respiratory enzyme that has a prosthetic group closely allied to that of the protohemin enzymes and distinctly different from the dichroic hemin enzymes, and should therefore be classed as a completely new type of respiratory enzyme.

*Absorption difference spectra**

One of the more useful methods for obtaining difference spectra is illustrated by Fig. 1. This method utilizes the light chopping and demodulating system developed by CHANCE for a double-beam spectrophotometer[8] and an automatic gain control circuit (agc) developed by R.C.A.[26], together with a number of ingenious improvements devised by Dr. C. C. YANG[27]. The apparatus consists of a source of high intensity monochromatic light that is split into two paths by a vibrating mirror (60 cps) and illuminates

* *Footnote see page 292.*

two suspensions of respiring cells of equal concentration. Cuvette A is taken to be the reference cell and the photocurrent obtained upon illuminating that cuvette is maintained at a predetermined level by an automatic gain control circuit that receives its signal from the contacts of the first demodulator and adjusts the dynode voltage of the photomultiplier to the appropriate value for constant photocurrent regardless of the intensity of the light illuminating the cuvette, the transmission through the sample, or the sensitivity of the photosurface. This constitutes the "100% transmission" signal. When cuvette B is illuminated, a signal representing the actual transmission is received from the first demodulator and is measured by a second demodulator. In order to record optical densities, the percent transmission is converted into logarithms by a segmented logarithmic characteristic consisting of ten diodes[28, 29]. The optical density values are then plotted by a servo recorder (Leeds and Northrup Speedomax). In order to have a linear wavelength scale on the chart, an appropriately loaded potentiometer operates in the feedback circuit of the chart drive servomechanism[30].

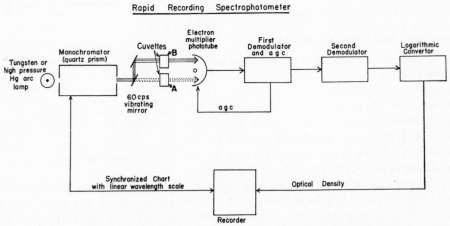

Fig. 1. A schematic diagram of the operation of a spectrophotometer suitable for recording the spectra of the respiratory pigments of cell suspensions and tissue homogenates. agc represents "automatic gain control" (MD-25).

The apparatus has a noise level of $\sim 1 \cdot 10^{-4}$ in optical density and operates with a spectral interval of 2 mμ or less when the cuvettes are filled with a turbid suspension of respiring cells. The spectrum is plotted at the rate of a few millimicrons per second.

In studies with turbid cell suspensions, it is important to gather both the transmitted and the scattered light from the cell suspension in order to obtain adequate sensitivity. This we accomplish by placing the phototube near the cell suspension and thereby avoid the lens and prism as were used earlier by WARBURG AND CHRISTIAN[6].

In actual use, a "base-line" is plotted with cuvettes A and B filled with equal concentrations of oxidized cells. Then the substrate is added to the cell suspension in cuvette B so that the oxygen is consumed and the absorption bands of the reduced cytochromes are recorded. Next the substrate is added to cuvette A and a second base-line is drawn. CO is finally bubbled through cuvette B to form the CO-reduced compound and the spectrum of the CO compound is plotted. (For further details see reference 9.)

Thus this apparatus is especially useful for plotting difference spectra, for example, the spectrum representing the difference between the reduced and oxidized forms of the respiratory pigments of *S. albus* illustrated by the trace labelled "reduced" in Fig. 2.

And the trace labelled "reduced + CO" represents the difference between the CO compounds and the reduced forms of the respiratory pigments. In this case one observes a distinct peak at 416 mμ and a trough at 432 mμ, as contrasted to the peak and trough of the corresponding spectrum for the yeast cells which lie at 430 and 445 mμ respectively.

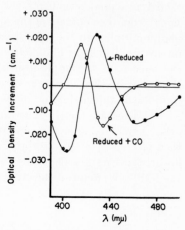

Similar studies can be carried out for *S. albus* in the visible region of the spectrum and peaks at 535 and 570 mμ are reported by SMITH[25].

Fig. 2 when compared with Fig. 3B of reference 9 shows that cultures of *S. albus* may be treated so as to increase considerably their relative content of this CO-binding pigment.

Fig. 2. The absorption difference spectra for a culture of *Staphylococcus albus* obtained by means of the apparatus of Fig. 1. The trace labelled "reduced" represents the differences between the reduced and oxidized cytochromes and the trace labeled "reduced + CO" represents the difference between the CO compound and the reduced form. Similar data can readily be obtained in the visible region (0-37).

Photodissociation difference spectra

Because their experimental conditions were inappropriate, KEILIN AND HARTREE were not able to demonstrate the photochemical dissociation of the CO compound of cytochrome a_3. We have recently been able to accomplish this by a differential spectrophotometric method that is suitable for the observation of changes in absorption due to the photodissociation reaction within the respiring cell.

This experiment is considerably more difficult than that carried out by BÜCHER AND NEGELEIN on clear solutions of hemoglobin and myoglobin carbon monoxide. It is not possible to use here the favorable optical geometry that they used—a short optical path for the photodissociating light and a long path for the measuring of light. With turbid cell suspensions, we require a fairly large surface area of the suspension near the measuring photosurface (see p. 291, 2nd paragraph under Fig. 1). Thus we have used a square cuvette in which the photodissociating and the measuring paths are both equal to one cm.

Another novel feature of the method that we use is the ability to vary the measuring wavelength and thereby to obtain a "photodissociation difference spectrum"* of the CO compound. Since the turbid suspensions scatter photodissociating light of very high intensity in the direction of the measuring phototube, our method has three features that avoid interference with the spectrophotometric measurement by the photodissociating light.

---

* In order to distinguish between the three types of spectra of the CO compounds that are discussed in this paper, it is useful to define the three terms:

Absorption difference spectrum. This is a spectrum representing the change of light absorption caused by a chemical change of the pigment, for example, from oxidized to reduced (a reduced-oxidized spectrum), or from reduced to the CO compound (a CO-reduced spectrum).

Photodissociation difference spectrum. This is a spectrum representing the change of light absorption caused by a photochemical reaction, for example, the photochemical dissociation of a CO compound of a reduced cytochrome in which case a CO-reduced spectrum is obtained.

Photochemical action spectrum. This is an absolute (not difference) spectrum. The ordinates are inversely proportional to the quantum intensity required at each wavelength to produce a given rate of photochemical decomposition of the CO compound.

References p. 297/298.

First, the photodissociation is accomplished by illuminating the cell suspension with yellow light, for example, the 589 mμ line of the Na arc or the 578 mμ of the Hg arc, other portions of the spectrum of these line sources being readily eliminated by appropriate filters having the characteristics shown in Fig. 3. The observation of the photodissociation of CO compounds is made in the region of the Soret band (410–480 mμ) and the photocell is rendered insensitive to the yellow light not only by the nature of its surface (Cs–Sb) but also by the blue colour filter combination shown by the solid curve of Fig. 3.

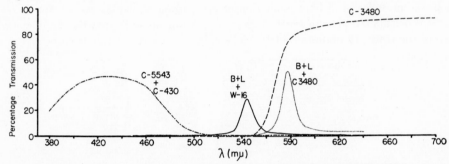

Fig. 3. Transmission curves for optical filters used to isolate photodissociating light (above 520 mμ) from spectrophotometric wavelengths (410–480 mμ). C represents Corning glass filters, W represents Wratten filter, and B + L represents Bausch and Lomb interference filters (MD-27).

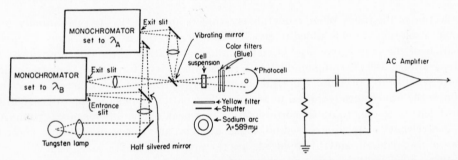

Fig. 4. A schematic diagram of a double-beam spectrophotometer suitable for measuring the kinetics of the photochemical decomposition of the CO compounds of the respiratory enzymes within intact cells. The characteristics of the optical filters are given in Fig. 3. The wavelengths λ_A and λ_B are set in the region 410–480 mμ (MD-28).

Secondly, as Fig. 4 shows, the differential double-beam spectrophotometer employs two wavelengths of light, one a reference wavelength, for example 480 mμ where no appreciable optical density changes due to photodissociation are to be expected, and the other an adjustable wavelength (in the region 410–480 mμ). The photoelectric circuit measures the differences of the light transmission changes at the two wavelengths, and this difference is not affected by leakage of yellow light through the colour filters.

Thirdly, to discriminate further against light leakage, the two beams of monochromatic light are chopped by a vibrating mirror at 60 cps so that first one and then the other is incident upon the sample and the photocell. Thus the output current from the photocell consists of a square 60 cps wave, the amplitude of which represents the difference of light transmission at the two wavelengths of light[8]. Since the arc lamps for

References p. 297/298.

causing photodissociation are operated on well-filtered direct current, there is no alternating component of the yellow light that leaks through the filters.

By means of these three design factors, the filtered light from a 100 watt Na or Hg lamp a few inches from the sample cell causes no deflection of the trace of the spectrophotometer. The only detectable effect of the light leakage is an increase in the shot noise output of the photoelectric circuit.

A typical record of the photodissociation and recombination of the CO compound in bakers' yeast cells is shown in Fig. 5. Starting with the steady-state oxidized yeast cells in the presence of alcohol, reduction of cytochrome a_3 causes the abrupt increase of optical density at 445 mμ (with respect to 480 mμ) as indicated by the downward sweep of the trace. Illumination of the cells with the Na arc at this time results in no

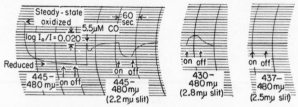

Fig. 5. An example of the measurement of a photodissociation difference spectrum of the cytochrome a_3–CO compound of bakers' yeast cells with the apparatus of Fig. 4. The points "on" and "off" represent the moments at which the photodissociating light is turned on and off. Illuminating light is 589 mμ. (25° C) (Expt. 145e).

deflection of the trace. When reduction is complete and the cells are substantially anaerobic, a solution of CO is added to give a final concentration of 5.5 μM, causing the formation of the cytochrome a_3–CO compound. Illumination of the cells now causes the dissociation of the CO compound while darkness allows its reformation, the latter change corresponding to a decrease of optical density and to a trough in the difference spectrum. If now the wavelength is shifted to 430 mμ, illumination causes the opposite sign of optical density change to occur, corresponding to a peak in the difference spectrum. And if a wavelength of 437 mμ is used no change at all occurs; this is an isosbestic point between the reduced and CO-reduced spectra providing a good control against possible artifacts.

These deflections, plotted as a function of wavelength, form a "difference spectrum" that represents the differences between the absorption of the CO compound and the reduced form of cytochrome a_3. The peak of this difference spectrum would be expected to lie very close to that of the absolute photochemical absorption spectrum of the respiratory enzyme at 430 mμ[17] because, as KEILIN AND HARTREE already have shown[11], the respiratory enzyme has many of the properties of cytochrome a_3. The result obtained with direct methods affords a conclusive proof of the identity of the respiratory enzyme of *T. utilis* and cytochrome a_3 of heart muscle preparations.

S. albus shows a rather different pigment with a peak at 415 mμ and a trough a 433 mμ as shown in Fig. 6 [13].

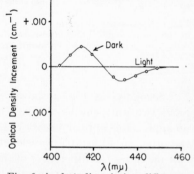

Fig. 6. A photodissociation difference spectrum for the "CO-binding pigment" of *Staphylococcus albus* obtained with the apparatus of Fig. 4 (948 c).

References p. 297/298.

In order to demonstrate that our method for measuring the photodissociation spectrum gives a result that agrees accurately with the actual absorption spectrum, we compare in Fig. 7 the spectrum obtained by subtracting the ferromyoglobin–CO spectrum from that of ferromyoglobin (BEZNAK[31]) with a photodissociation spectrum obtained with this apparatus. The agreement of the data shows that the photodissociation method gives nearly as accurate results as the direct measurement of the absorption spectra.

It should be noted that exact coincidence of the peaks of the absorption photodissociation difference spectra with those of the relative photochemical action spectra is not to be expected. Fig. 7 (Curve A) clearly shows that for protohemin pigments the peak of the difference spectrum lies 2.5 mμ below that of the absolute spectrum and, in the case of the dichroic hemin enzyme lactoperoxidase, the displacement is 1.5 mμ[13]. Thus the displacement is small, but significant.

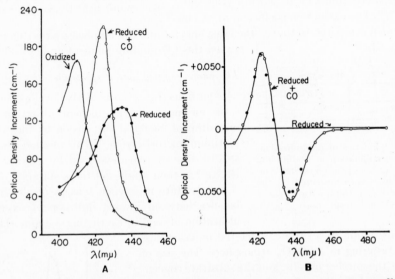

Fig 7. (A), the oxidized, reduced, and reduced-CO spectra for myoglobin (from BEZNAK[31]) and (B), (open circles), the difference spectrum of the CO compound. Solid circles of (B) show experimental data on the photodissociation spectrum of myoglobin-CO obtained by the method of Fig. 4. In order to facilitate the comparison, the ordinates of the photodissociation curve were multiplied by a constant factor to cause the two sets of data to match at the peak of the curve (1 μM Mgb, pH = 7.0, 2.9 μM CO) (Expt. 143a).

Calculation of the molecular extinction coefficients

By measuring the kinetics of photodissociation and recombination of the CO compound on a faster time scale as in Fig. 8, the molecular extinction coefficient may be calculated in a manner similar to that used by BÜCHER AND KASPERS[33] provided the intensity of the photodissociating light is known. But instead of a bolometer we use myoglobin–CO as a standard and thereby avoid the need for an accurate measurement of the light intensity as well as the distribution of intensities in the cuvette. To simulate light scattering when myoglobin is used, *Escherichia coli* are added to give the same scattering effects as the yeast cells (see reference 14 for details). On this basis, we have computed the values of the molecular extinction coefficients for the CO compounds in heart muscle homogenates, bakers' yeast cells, *A. pasteurianum*, and *Bacillus subtilis*[14], and find ε_{589} = 12 cm^{-1} × mM^{-1} for the cytochromes of type a_3. (Reference 14 gives detailed data on the experimental controls and also the method of calculating the results.)

In our previous studies the sensitivity of the apparatus was insufficient to give any quantitative idea of the molecular extinction coefficients of the "CO-binding pigment" of *S. albus*. We now have increased the sensitivity, and satisfactory kinetic data may be obtained as in Fig. 8. A preliminary value can be given for the molecular extinction coefficient of the band at 546 mμ, $\varepsilon = 5$ cm^{-1} × mM^{-1}, about half that of the value for myoglobin–CO at 580 mμ (10.6 cm^{-1} × mM^{-1})[32]. The extinction coefficient at 589 mμ

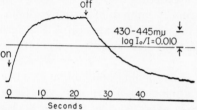

Fig. 8. The kinetics of photodissociation and recombination of the cytochrome a_3–CO compound in bakers' yeast cells as measured by the method of Fig. 4 (Expt. measured by the method of Fig. 4. Illuminating light is 589 mμ (Expt. 144).

is very small compared to that of the yeast enzyme and this emphasizes the difference between this CO-binding pigment and cytochrome a_3.

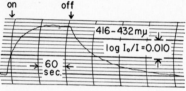

Fig. 9. The kinetics of photodissociation and recombination of "CO-binding pigment" in a suspension of *Staphylococcus albus* cells as measured by the method of Fig. 4. Illuminating light is 578 mμ (Expt. 144).

The photochemical action spectrum

One of us (L.C.) has recently developed an apparatus for measuring photochemical action spectra in a drop of bacterial suspension by means of the platinum microelectrode[21]. This method utilizes the steady-state system developed by CONNELLY AND BRINK[23] in their studies of the respiration of nerve. A steady-state in oxygen tension results from the balance between inward diffusion of oxygen and utilization of oxygen by the nerve tissue. The same

conditions obtain in a drop of bacterial or yeast suspension respiring in a CO–O$_2$ atmosphere. The size of the drop, the number of cells, and the substrate concentration are adjusted so that the steady-state oxygen concentration for maximal effectiveness of the photochemical reaction is obtained. Illumination of the drop will displace this steady-state and the change of oxygen concentration is sensitively recorded by the platinum microelectrode.

Our results for *S. albus* show a Soret band at 418 mμ definitely displaced from the 430 mμ peak measured for yeast cells with the same apparatus. A preliminary action spectrum for the respiratory enzyme in *S. albus* in the Soret region is shown in Fig. 10.

In the visible region of the spectrum, the peaks of the CO compound are found to lie at 535 and 566 mμ in fairly good agreement with the peaks of the absorption difference spectrum that lie at 535 and 570 mμ[25]. These values are similar to those for hemoproteins

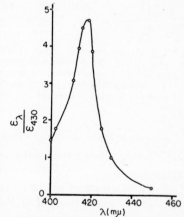

Fig. 10. A relative photochemical action spectrum of the CO-binding pigment in *Staphylococcus albus*. Similar data are readily obtained in the visible region of the spectrum (25°) (0–38).

References p. 297/298.

that have protohemin as their prosthetic group and lead us to suggest that this new respiratory enzyme has a protohemin prosthetic group instead of a dichroic hemin and that it should be classified as a completely new type of respiratory enzyme.

SUMMARY

Several highly refined physical methods have been described for the study of the CO compounds of the respiratory pigments of living cell suspensions. These methods reveal significant differences in the respiratory enzymes of different bacterial cells and our results suggest that *Staphylococcus albus* contains a new respiratory enzyme that has a prosthetic group closely related to the protohemin enzymes and that this respiratory pigment should be classified as a completely new type of respiratory enzyme.

RÉSUMÉ

Plusieurs méthodes physiques très fines pour l'étude des composés oxycarbonés des pigments respiratoires de cellules vivantes en suspension ont été décrites. Ces méthodes révèlent des différences significatives entre les enzymes respiratoires de différentes bactéries et nos résultats suggèrent que *Staphylococcus albus* renferme un nouvel enzyme respiratoire dont le groupement prosthétique est très voisin des enzymes protohémines. Ce pigment respiratoire doit être rangé dans un groupe complètement nouveau des enzymes respiratoires.

ZUSAMMENFASSUNG

Mehrere höchst verfeinerte physikalische Methoden für die Untersuchung der Atmungspigmente von Suspensionen lebender Zellen werden beschrieben. Diese Methoden erlauben bedeutsame Unterschiede zwischen Atmungsfermenten verschiedener Bakterien aufzufinden. Unsere Versuche machen es wahrscheinlich dass *Staphylococcus albus* ein Pigment enthält dessen prosthetische Gruppe mit den Protohäminfermenten nahe verwandt ist, aber als ein ganz neuer Typ von Atmungsferment angesehen werden muss und entsprechend eine Klasse für sich bildet.

REFERENCES

[1] C. A. MacMunn, *Phil. Trans. Royal Soc. London*, 177, (1885) 267.
[2] D. Keilin, *Proc. Roy. Soc. London, Series B*, 98 (1925) 312.
[3] O. Warburg and E. Negelein, *Biochem. Z.*, 262 (1933) 237.
[4] H. Lundegårdh, *Arkiv. Kemi*, 5 (1952) 97.
[5] O. Warburg and W. Christian, *Biochem. Z.*, 266 (1933) 399.
[6] E. Haas, *Naturwissenschaften*, 22 (1934) 207.
[7] B. Chance, *Nature*, 169 (1952) 215.
[8] B. Chance, *Rev. Sci. Instruments*, 22 (1951) 619.
[9] B. Chance, *J. Biol. Chem.*, 202 (1953) 383.
[10] O. Warburg, *Schwermetalle als Wirkungsgruppen von Fermenten*, Chapter 8, Freiburg (1949).
[11] D. Keilin and E. F. Hartree, *Proc. Roy. Soc. London, Series B*, 127 (1939) 167.
[12] T. Bücher and E. Negelein, *Biochem. Z.*, 311 (1942) 163.
[13] B. Chance, *J. Biol. Chem.*, 202 (1953) 397.
[14] B. Chance, *J. Biol. Chem.*, 202 (1953) 407.
[15] O. Warburg and E. Negelein, *Biochem. Z.*, 202 (1928) 202.
[16] O. Warburg and E. Negelein, *Biochem. Z.*, 214 (1929) 64.
[17] O. Warburg and E. Negelein, *Biochem. Z.*, 193 (1928) 339.
[18] F. Kubowitz and E. Haas, *Biochem. Z.*, 255 (1952) 247.
[19] D. Keilin and E. F. Hartree, *Nature*, 171 (1953) 413.
[20] J. L. Melnick, *J. Biol. Chem.*, 141 (1941) 269.
[21] L. N. Castor and B. Chance, to be published.
[22] P. W. Davies and F. Brink, *Rev. Sci. Instruments*, 13 (1942) 524.

[23] C. M. CONNELLY AND F. BRINK, *Rev. Sci. Instruments*, August, 1953.
[24] L. SMITH, to be published.
[25] L. SMITH, *Federation Proc.* 12 (1953) 270.
[26] Radio Corporation of America, personal communication on a normalizing amplifier (1949).
[27] C. C. YANG, *Proc. Institute of Radio Engineers*, 40 (1952) 220.
[28] B. CHANCE, V. HUGHES, E. MacNICHOL, D. SAYRE AND F. C. WILLIAMS, *Waveforms*, Chapter 8, New York (1949).
[29] B. CHANCE, F. C. WILLIAMS, C. C. YANG, J. BUSSER AND J. HIGGINS, *Rev. Sci. Instruments*, 22 (1948) 683.
[30] I. GREENWOOD, J. HOLDAM AND D. MacRAE, Electronic Instruments, p. 94, New York (1948).
[31] M. BEZNAK, *Acta Chem. Scand.*, 2 (1948) 333.
[32] H. THEORELL, *Biochem. Z.*, 268 (1934) 55.
[33] T. BÜCHER AND J. KASPERS, *Biochim. Biophys. Acta*, 1 (1947) 21.

Received May 29, 1953

ENZYMES OF FATTY ACID METABOLISM*

by

FEODOR LYNEN

Biochemische Abteilung, Chemisches Universitäts-Laboratorium, München (Deutschland)

AND

SEVERO OCHOA

Department of Pharmacology, New York University College of Medicine, New York, N.Y. (U.S.A.)

Work of recent years (for reviews see [3, 5, 30]) has thrown much light on the mechanism of the β-oxidation of fatty acids formulated by KNOOP in 1904[32]. Through the use of isotopic tracer techniques[74, 53, 75] and of cell-free tissue preparations capable of oxidizing fatty acids[50, 43, 37–40, 20, 15, 16] it was established that the two-carbon units removed successively from fatty acid chains during β-oxidation are identical to the two-carbon units derived from carbohydrate through the oxidative decarboxylation of pyruvic acid[39]. Further, these units can either condense with one another—or with longer fatty acid chains—to bring about fatty acid synthesis, or can undergo oxidation via the citric acid cycle[74, 53, 6, 39, 40, 20]. Work with extracts of *Clostridium kluyveri* demonstrated that fatty acid synthesis occurs by a reversal of β-oxidation[61–63, 28]. Evidence was also obtained that in the process of synthesis, in both bacteria[4, 66] and animal tissues[1, 78, 52], the methyl end of "acetic acid" units is added to the carboxyl end of a fatty acid chain.

Further progress was hampered by the failure to detect intermediates during fatty acid oxidation or synthesis although from the early work of DAKIN[14] the corresponding α,β-unsaturated, β-hydroxy- and β-keto derivatives would be expected to be involved. Such a view would be in agreement with the observations that, at least in some tissues, the above compounds are oxidized at about the same rate as the corresponding fatty acids[31, 20].

The finding that fatty acids are not oxidized unless they undergo a preliminary activation and the fact that this activation is dependent on the generation of energy-rich phosphate[50, 43, 37, 38, 42, 20, 33, 61, 62, 63, 29, 15, 16] suggested that the actual intermediates might not occur as the free acids[28]. The identification of the two-carbon unit as S-acetyl coenzyme A** [46, 47, 65, 51, 71, 34, 59, 45] shed new light on the problem and strongly suggested

* The experimental work reported in this paper was aided by grants from the Deutsche Forschungsgemeinschaft and the Firma C. H. Boehringer Sohn, Ingelheim (University of Munich), and the United States Public Health Service, the American Cancer Society (recommended by the Commitee on Growth of the National Research Council), and by a contract (N6onr279, T.O. 6) between the Office of Naval Research and New York University College of Medicine. The authors are indebted to the Rockefeller Foundation for travelling fellowships which facilitated collaboration between their two laboratories.

** The following abbreviations are used: Coenzyme A (reduced), CoA, CoÃ-SH or CoA-SH; S-acyl coenzyme A derivatives, S-Acyl CoA, acyl-S-CoÃ, acyl-S-CoA, or simply acyl CoA; adenosine triphosphate, ATP; adenosine-5'-phosphate, AMP; pyrophosphate, PP; oxidized and reduced diphosphorpyridine nucleotide, DPN+ and DPNH; oxidized and reduced flavin adenine dinucleotide, FAD and FADH$_2$.

that the active intermediates might be the CoA derivatives of the fatty acids[47, 3, 30]. This belief was reinforced by the observation that S-acetyl CoA or the S-acyl derivatives of higher fatty acids can be generated enzymically through a reaction of the fatty acid with acyl phosphates in the presence of CoA[59, 60] or with CoA and ATP[11, 44, 15, 36, 49, 72, 23, 16, 41, 67]. Finally, work on the enzymic breakdown and synthesis of acetoacetate and other β-keto fatty acids[7, 76, 9, 24, 75, 58, 70, 64, 3, 21, 68, 22] opened the way for an understanding of the mechanism whereby fatty acid chains are shortened or elongated, by the removal or addition of acetyl CoA, during fatty acid oxidation or synthesis.

By employing synthetic S-acyl analogues of the fatty acid derivatives of CoA[48, 55] or the CoA fatty acid derivatives themselves[48, 69, 67] more recently made available by chemical or enzymatic synthesis, it has been possible to characterize and isolate from animal tissues some of the enzymes of fatty acid metabolism and obtain a clearer picture of the process as a whole. The development of rapid and sensitive optical methods of assay, whose introduction in enzymology we owe to OTTO WARBURG, has greatly facilitated the task of purifying the individual enzymes and studying their mechanism of action. The work described in this paper owes much to WARBURG's pioneering contributions which opened up new avenues of approach to dynamic biochemistry.

Fatty acid cycle

The results of the work summarized above and of the more recent work to be discussed in this paper show that fatty acid oxidation and synthesis proceed through the reactions illustrated in Fig. 1.

Fatty acid synthesis is accomplished through repetition of a cycle of four consecutive reactions: (a) condensation of two molecules of acetyl CoA to form acetoacetyl CoA and CoA–SH, (b) reduction of acetoacetyl CoA to β-hydroxybutyryl CoA, (c) dehydration of β-hydroxybutyryl CoA to crotonyl CoA, and (d) reduction of crotonyl CoA to butyryl CoA. A new cycle is started by the reaction of butyryl CoA with another molecule of acetyl CoA, to form β-keto-caproyl CoA + CoA–SH, and so forth. The cycle is repeated eight times until stearyl CoA is formed. All four reactions of the fatty acid cycle are reversible and fatty acid oxidation, once the fatty acid is

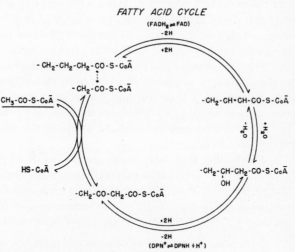

Fig. 1. Fatty acid cycle

activated through conversion to the corresponding acyl CoA derivative, proceeds by a reversal of the above sequence. The acetyl CoA split off at the end of each sequence is either oxidized via the citric acid cycle, by reacting with oxalacetate to form citrate and CoA–SH[51, 71], or is converted to acetoacetyl CoA + CoA–SH. In liver, acetoacetyl CoA is hydrolysed by a specific deacylase with formation of CoA–SH and acetoacetate[69a, 14a]. The presence of this enzyme would seem to account for the formation of free acetoacetate in this organ. In either case CoA–SH is made available for activation of further fatty acid molecules.

The equilibrium of reaction (a) is predominantly in favor of the thioclastic splitting of the β-ketoacyl CoA derivatives. For this reason the name β-ketothiolase, or simply thiolase, has been proposed for this class of enzymes[48]. The equilibrium of reaction (b) favors reduction of the β-keto derivative, hence the name β-ketoreductase has been proposed for this group of enzymes[48]. The name crotonase has been suggested[67] for the enzyme or enzymes catalyzing reaction (c) and, finally, the name ethylene reductase has been used[55] to designate the enzyme or enzymes catalyzing reaction (d).

There are two main mechanisms for activation of fatty acids, i.e., for the synthesis of their S-acyl CoA derivatives: (a) by a reaction with CoA–SH and ATP which, as we shall see later, results in the reversible formation of the corresponding acyl CoA, AMP and PP, and (b) by transfer of CoA from certain acyl CoA compounds such as acetyl CoA or succinyl CoA. Animal tissues, such as liver, heart, and kidney, utilize mainly the first mechanism while *C. kluyveri* utilizes the second. Extracts of this organism catalyze the reversible transfer of CoA from acetyl CoA to such fatty acids as propionate or butyrate[60]. Because of the presence of phosphotransacetylase[59], in the presence of CoA such extracts can utilize acetyl phosphate for activation.

A transferring enzyme of rather limited specificity is present in heart and probably in skeletal muscle and kidney but appears to be absent from liver. This enzyme catalyzes the reversible transfer of CoA from succinyl CoA to acetoacetate[21, 68, 69, 22]. Through the formation of acetoacetyl CoA the enzyme activates acetoacetate, produced in the liver and carried by the blood stream to the peripheral tissues, for oxidation in these tissues via the tricarboxylic acid cycle (see reference no. 8). The latter in turn generates the necessary succinyl CoA through the oxidation of α-ketoglutarate which, as shown by recent work[26, 54, 27], reacts with CoA–SH and DPN$^+$ to form succinyl CoA, CO_2, and DPNH.

S-acyl fatty acid derivatives

Synthetic S-acetoacetyl and S-crotonyl derivatives of N-acetyl thioethanolamine[48a] have been found to act as substrates of β-ketoreductase and ethylene reductase respectively[48, 55]. These structural analogues of the natural S-acyl CoA derivatives have therefore provided suitable substrates for the isolation of the two enzymes. Further, the two model compounds have characteristic absorption spectra. This made it possible not only to predict the optical properties of the corresponding natural substrates, i.e., S-acetoacetyl and S-crotonyl CoA, but also to develop convenient optical methods for the assay of several enzymes. Thus, the analogues have greatly facilitated the study of individual steps of fatty acid metabolism.

S-acetoacetyl-N-acetyl thioethanolamine was obtained as a colourless crystalline compound (m.p., 60°) through reaction of N-acetyl thioethanolamine with diketene. As a solid, the compound is in the keto form but it undergoes rapid enolization in solution as can be shown with the ferric chloride reaction and by the change in its absorption spectrum. At equilibrium the percentage of enol is higher in solutions of the thioester

$$CH_3-\underset{O}{\overset{O}{C}}-CH_2-\underset{O}{\overset{O}{C}}-S-CH_2-CH_2-NH-CO-CH_3 \rightleftharpoons CH_3-\underset{OH}{\overset{OH}{C}}=CH-\underset{O}{\overset{O}{C}}-S-CH_2-CH_2-NH-CO-CH_3$$

than in those of acetoacetic ethyl ester, a fact which was first observed by BAKER AND REID with acetoacetic thioethyl ester[2].

References p. 313/314.

The absorption spectrum of S-acetoacetyl-N-acetyl thioethanolamine is shown in Fig. 2. At pH 6.2 the compound has a band with a maximum at 233 mμ; this absorption

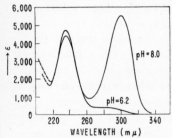

Fig. 2. Ultraviolet absorption spectrum of S-acetoacetyl-N-acetyl thioethanolamine.

peak is characteristic of the thioester bond[57],[60]. At pH 8.0 an additional band appears with a maximum at 303 mμ. This band is to be attributed to the formation of an enolate ion and, as shown in Fig. 3, depends on the pH. The increasing absorption parallels the increasing dissociation as the pH is raised. The pK' of the compound was found to be 8.54.

S-crotonyl-N-acetyl thioethanolamine was obtained in

$$CH_3—CH=CH—\overset{\displaystyle O}{\overset{\|}{C}}—S—CH_2—CH_2—NH—CO—CH_3$$

crystalline form (m.p., 61.5–62°) through reaction of crotonyl chloride with the lead salt of N-acetyl thioethanolamine[55].

Its absorption spectrum is shown, along with that of free crotonate, in Fig. 4. It is evident that with the binding of the unsaturated acid to sulfur there is a shift toward longer wavelengths of the absorption due to the double bond. Free crotonate has a maximum (not shown on the figure) at 204 m μ while the thioester has a maximum at 224 mμ. The thioester has an additional band at 263 mμ which is possible due

to the —$\overset{\displaystyle O}{\overset{\|}{C}}$—S-group. The shift of the two absorption maxima toward longer wavelengths may be a reflection of the resonance between the double bond and the thioester linkage, a fact which is of great importance for the chemical reactivity of the former.

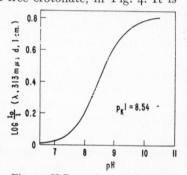

Fig. 3. pH Dependence of light absorption of S-acetoacetyl-N-acetyl thioethanolamine at 313 mμ. $c = 5 \cdot 10^{-5} M$; $d = 1.0$ cm.

A number of S-acyl CoA derivatives of fatty acids have now become available through chemical or enzymic synthesis. Solutions of acetoacetyl CoA can be readily prepared by the enzymic transfer of CoA from succinyl CoA to acetoacetate. This reaction has made possible the isolation of acetoacetyl CoA[69] and its routine preparation for the assay of β-ketothiolase. Succinyl CoA itself can be prepared enzymically with α-ketoglutaric dehydrogenase[54],[27] or by means of the reaction between succinate, CoA, and ATP, of KAUFMAN et al.[26],[27]. However, the compound can be obtained much more readily by the synthetic procedure of SIMON AND SHEMIN[56] with CoA–SH and succinic anhydride. The method of SIMON AND SHEMIN has further been applied to the preparation of other S-acyl CoA derivatives such as acetyl, propionyl, butyryl, and crotonyl CoA. S-acyl fatty acid derivatives have also been prepared by means of the enzymic reaction of fatty acids with CoA–SH and ATP[21a] and, in the case of the acetyl and propionyl derivatives, through the phosphotransacetylase catalyzed reaction between CoA–SH and the corresponding acyl phosphates[59]. Finally, S-acetoacetyl and S-β-hydroxybutyryl

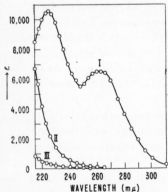

Fig. 4. Ultraviolet absorption spectra of S-crotonyl-N-acetyl thioethanolamine (I), crotonate (II), and N-acetyl thioethanolamine (III), at pH 7.0.

References p. 313/314.

CoA have recently become available through chemical synthesis. T. WIELAND[77] has succeeded in synthesizing these compounds by reaction of CoA–SH with the thio-esters of acetoacetic or β-hydroxybutyric acid and thiophenol. S-acetoacetyl CoA has also been prepared through the interaction of CoA–SH with diketene[14a].

The absorption spectra of acetoacetyl CoA and crotonyl CoA are essentially the same as those of their thioethanolamine analogues. The main difference is that, in contrast to N-acetyl thioethanolamine, CoA absorbs in the 260 mμ region because of its adenine group. This does not interfere with the enol band of acetoacetyl thioesters but interferes to some extent with the 263 mμ band of the crotonyl derivatives. However, the extinction coefficient of the latter compounds at this wavelength is very high and the interference of the adenine moiety of crotonyl CoA can be eliminated by addition of adenine nucleotide, for example adenylic acid, to the blank cell.

In contrast to the optical behavior of the acetoacetyl and crotonyl CoA derivatives, β-hydroxyacyl and saturated acyl CoA compounds show only the thioester band at 233 mμ in addition to the adenine band. It is therefore possible in enzymic experiments, to follow the appearance and disappearance of β-ketoacyl or dehydroacyl CoA compounds if β-hydroxyacyl or acyl CoA compounds are involved in the reaction. At pH 8.0 the enol absorption of acetoacetyl thioesters is markedly increased by magnesium ions[67a], probably through formation of a chelate structure. This increase in absorption can conveniently be made use of to increase the sensitivity of the optical enzyme tests.

ENZYMES OF FATTY ACID METABOLISM

Activating enzymes. As already stated the main mechanism for the activation of fatty acids in animal tissues is through a reaction of the fatty acid with CoA–SH, in the presence of ATP, to yield the corresponding S-acyl CoA, AMP, and PP. This reaction requires the presence of Mg ions. The first reaction of this type to be studied in detail was the activation of acetate by an enzyme present in liver, yeast, and other tissues[11]. The mechanism of the over-all reaction was established by LIPMANN *et al.*[44] with partially purified enzyme preparations from liver and yeast (Reaction 1). Similar results were obtained by HILZ AND LYNEN (unpublished experiments) with a highly purified enzyme

$$CH_3-COOH+HS-Co\bar{A}+ATP \rightleftharpoons CH_3-\overset{O}{\overset{\|}{C}}-S-Co\bar{A}+AMP+PP \qquad (1)$$

from yeast and by GREEN and collaborators[21, 23] with purified enzymes from heart muscle and liver. The acetate enzyme is active also with propionate.

Recent experiments[25] suggest that the over-all reaction occurs in three steps as indicated below:

(a) ATP + enzyme $\rightleftharpoons$ AMP-enzyme + PP
(b) AMP-enzyme + CoA $\rightleftharpoons$ CoA-enzyme + AMP
(c) CoA-enzyme + acetate $\rightleftharpoons$ acetyl-CoA + enzyme

The occurrence of reaction (a) is supported by the incorporation of labelled PP into ATP in the presence of a partially purified enzyme from yeast. This exchange is dependent upon the presence of Mg^{+2}. Reaction (c) is supported by the incorporation of isotopic acetate into acetyl CoA in the presence of the enzyme.

An enzyme catalyzing the activation of fatty acids from C_4 to C_{12} was isolated from ox liver in D. E. GREEN's laboratory[72]. The enzyme catalyzes Reaction 2. The same

References p. 313/314.

enzyme preparation was active on α,β-unsaturated and β-hydroxy derivatives. The formation of crotonyl- and β-hydroxybutyryl CoA by liver enzymes under similar

$$-CH_2-CH_2-COOH+HS-Co\bar{A}+ATP \rightleftharpoons -CH_2-CH_2-\overset{O}{\overset{\|}{C}}-S-Co\bar{A}+AMP+PP \qquad (2)$$

conditions has also been observed in other laboratories[41,67]. The activation of higher fatty acids, presumably C_{14} to $_{18}$, by ATP and HS-CoA is catalyzed by yet another enzyme discovered by KORNBERG AND PRICER[36,35] in liver. KORNBERG's enzyme catalyzes the formation of S-stearyl CoA, AMP, and PP from stearic acid, HS-CoA and ATP.

CoA transferases. In *Cl. kluyveri* extracts activation of fatty acids appears to occur predominantly by transfer of CoA from acetyl-S-CoA. The first enzyme of the CoA transferase type was discovered by STADTMAN in extracts of *Cl. kluyveri* and named CoA transphorase[60]. The enzyme catalyzes the reversible transfer of CoA from acetyl-CoA to propionate (Reaction 3).

$$CH_3-\overset{O}{\overset{\|}{C}}-S-Co\bar{A}+CH_3-CH_2-COOH \rightleftharpoons CH_3-COOH+CH_3-CH_2-\overset{O}{\overset{\|}{C}}-S-Co\bar{A} \qquad (3)$$

Cl. kluyveri extracts also catalyze the transfer of CoA from acetyl CoA to butyrate, vinyl acetate, and lactate[60a]. This enzyme (enzymes) is (are) similar to the succinyl-CoA-acetoacetate transferase of heart muscle but with different substrate specificity.

The reversible transfer of CoA from succinyl CoA to acetoacetate was discovered independently by GREEN and co workers[21,22] and by STERN *et al.*[68,69]. The enzyme which, as already mentioned, is present in heart and probably in skeletal muscle and kidney but not in liver, catalyzes Reaction 4. In the early stages of purification[69] the

$$HOOC-CH_2-CH_2-\overset{O}{\overset{\|}{C}}-S-Co\bar{A}+CH_3-CO-CH_2-COOH \rightleftharpoons$$
$$HOOC-CH_2-CH_2-COOH+CH_3-CO-CH_2-\overset{O}{\overset{\|}{C}}-S-Co\bar{A} \qquad (4)$$

enzyme assay was based on the rate of citric acid synthesis from succinyl CoA and acetoacetate in the presence of oxalacetate, an excess of thiolase, and crystalline citrate condensing enzyme, as indicated by the reactions below:

Succinyl—S—Co$\bar{A}$+acetoacetate $\rightleftharpoons$ succinate+acetoacetyl—S—Co$\bar{A}$ (transferase)
Acetoacetyl—S—Co$\bar{A}$+HS—Co$\bar{A}$ $\rightleftharpoons$ 2 acetyl—S—Co$\bar{A}$ (thiolase)
2 Acetyl—S—Co$\bar{A}$+2 oxalacetate+2 H$_2$O $\rightleftharpoons$ 2 citrate+2 HS—Co$\bar{A}$ (citrate condensing enzyme)

Sum: Succinyl—S—Co$\bar{A}$+acetoacetate+HS—Co$\bar{A}$+2 oxalacetate+2 H$_2$O $\rightleftharpoons$ Succinate+
2 citrate+2 HS—Co$\bar{A}$

A heated ammonium sulfate fraction from ox liver, free of transferase, was used as the source of thiolase. After removal of thiolase, the transferase assay was based on the increase in optical density at pH 8.1 and wavelength 305 mμ due to the formation of acetoacetyl-S-CoA. Although magnesium ions are not required for the reaction, as mentioned previously, Mg^{+2} markedly augments the light absorption and was added to the reaction mixture in order to increase the sensitivity of the assay.

The enzyme has been isolated from pig heart and purified about 700-fold over the initial phosphate extract[67a]. The purification involved ammonium sulfate and acetone fractionation, removal of inactive proteins by heat and by adsorption on Ca phosphate

References p. 313/314.

gel, fractionation with ethanol in the presence of Zn ions, and refractionation with ammonium sulfate.

Fig. 5 shows the appearance of the enol band of S-acetoacetyl thioesters when succinyl CoA is incubated with acetoacetate and transferase at pH 8.1, indicating the formation of S-acetoacetyl CoA. Within the range 290 to 330 mμ this band corresponds closely with the corresponding band of S-acetoacetyl-N-acetyl thioethanolamine. It may also be seen that most of the absorption in this region disappears after the further addition of CoA–SH and thiolase since the equilibrium position of the thiolase reaction favors the formation of acetyl CoA. The forward course and the reversal of the transferase

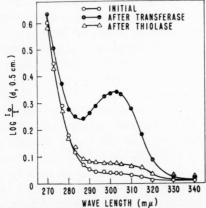

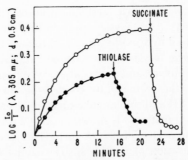

Fig. 5. Spectral changes accompanying the enzymatic synthesis and breakdown of S-acetoacetyl CoA at pH 8.1. Volume, 1.5 ml; $d = 0.5$ cm; temp. 25°.—O—O— S-Succinyl CoA ($\sim$ 0.1 μM). —●—●— After establishment of equilibrium on addition of acetoacetate (50 μM) and transferase (60 μg of protein). —△—△—After further addition of CoA–SH (0.15 μM) and thiolase (90 μg of protein). Acetoacetate and CoA–SH added to both blank and experimental cells. MgCl$_2$ (8.0 μM) present in reaction mixture.

Fig. 6. Optical demonstration of transferase and thiolase activities. Volume, 1.5 ml; $d = 0.5$ cm; pH, 8.1; temp., 25°. Upper curve: Transferase (17 μg of protein) added at zero time to a mixture of succinyl CoA ($\sim$ 0.11 μM) and acetoacetate (50 μM); succinate (40 μM) added at the arrow. Lower curve: Transferase (17 μg of protein) added at zero time to a mixture of succinyl CoA ($\sim$ 0.06 μM) and acetoacetate (50 μM); CoA–SH (0.15 μM) and thiolase (2.7 μg of protein) added at the arrow. Other details as in Fig. 5.

reaction as followed at 305 mμ are shown in Fig. 6. The upper curve shows the increase in absorption at 305 mμ on adding transferase to a mixture of succinyl CoA and acetoacetate and the reversal of the reaction by succinate after equilibrium was established. The equilibrium constant of the transferase reaction (K_{eq}=(Succinate) (acetoacetyl-S-CoA)/Succinyl-S-CoA) (acetoacetate)) is about 10^{-2} at pH 8.1.

The acetoacetyl CoA formed by the reaction between succinyl CoA and acetoacetate, in the presence of transferase, was isolated as a crude alcohol-insoluble barium salt and further purified by paper chromatography[69]. In ethanol-acetate its R_F is 0.52 at 24°, while that of acetoacetate is 0.75. Like acetyl CoA[46, 47], acetoacetyl CoA gives a positive sulfhydryl reaction with nitroprusside only after alkaline hydrolysis.

Some insight into the mechanism of action of the transferase has been gained by experiments with methylene labelled ^{14}C-succinate[19a]. When ^{14}C-succinate and succinyl-CoA are incubated with transferase a rapid exchange of free- and thioester-bound succinate occurs. This suggests the possibility that succinyl CoA, or acetoacetyl CoA, reacts with the enzyme to form a CoA-enzyme compound which retains the energy of the

References p. 313/314.

thioester bond and can transfer CoA to the free acid, acetoacetic or succinic. The reaction could be visualized as involving a carboxyl group of the enzyme as indicated below:

$$HOOC—CH_2—CH_2—\overset{O}{\overset{\|}{C}}—S—CoA + Enzyme—COOH \rightleftharpoons$$

$$HOOC—CH_2—CH_2—COOH + Enzyme—\overset{O}{\overset{\|}{C}}—S—CoA$$

$$Enzyme—\overset{O}{\overset{\|}{C}}—S—CoA + CH_3—CO—CH_2—COOH \rightleftharpoons$$

$$Enzyme—COOH + CH_3—CO—CH_2—\overset{O}{\overset{\|}{C}}—S—CoA$$

The best preparations of transferase so far obtained are free of thiolase and, under the conditions of the optical assay, catalyze the formation of 250 moles of acetoacetyl-CoA per minute per 100,000 g of enzyme at 25°. As assayed optically, the purified transferase catalyzes the transfer of CoA from succinyl CoA to acetoacetate, β-ketovalerate, β-keto*iso*caproate, and β-ketocaproate in order of decreasing activity. β-ketooctanoate is inactive. The enzyme catalyzes the transfer of CoA from acetoacetyl CoA to succinate but not to β-hydroxybyturate, crotonate, butyrate or octanoate.

β-keto thiolase. The enzyme catalyzing Reaction 5 has been partially purified from sheep liver[48] and more extensively from pig heart[50a]. The enzyme has also been referred to as the acetoacetate condensing enzyme[69]. In the lower curve of Fig. 6, addition of CoA-SH and thiolase to a mixture of succinyl CoA and acetoacetate previously incubated with transferase is shown to cause a decrease in optical density at 305 mμ due to cleavage of the acetoacetyl CoA formed by the CoA transfer reaction. The assay used for the purification of the pig heart enzyme was based on the decrease in optical density at

$$CH_3—CO—CH_2—\overset{O}{\overset{\|}{C}}—S—CoA + HS—CoA \rightleftharpoons 2 CH_3—\overset{O}{\overset{\|}{C}}—S—CoA \qquad (5)$$

pH 8.1 and wavelength 305 mμ with acetoacetyl CoA and CoA–SH as substrates in the presence of Mg^{+2}. Solutions of acetoacetyl CoA were prepared every few days by incubating synthetic succinyl CoA and acetoacetate with purified CoA-transferase. When the reaction reached equilibrium, the pH of the mixture was brought to 5.5 with acetic acid, the solution was heated to 75° for 2 minutes to destroy the transferase, cooled, centrifuged and the supernatant adjusted to pH 8.0. Acetoacetyl CoA was stable for several days if stored at −18° when not in use.

The enzyme has been purified about 300 fold over the initial phosphate extract through steps involving ammonium sulfate and acetone fractionation, removal of inactive proteins at pH 5.3, refractionation with ammonium sulfate, and low temperature ethanol fractionation in the presence of Zn ions. The time course of the reaction in the optical test with varying concentrations of purified pig heart enzyme is shown in Fig. 7.

The thioclastic cleavage of acetoacetyl CoA to acetyl CoA results not only in a decrease of light absorption

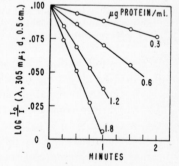

Fig. 7. Optical thiolase test. Tris (hydroxymethyl) amino - methane-HCl buffer pH 8.1, 200 μM; MgCl$_2$, 8.0 μM; reduced glutathione, 10.0 μM; CoA-SH, 0.15 μM; S-aceto-acetylCoA,~0.03 μM. Volume, 1.5 ml; $d = 0.5$ cm; temp., 25°.

at 305 mμ but also in a concomitant increase in the absorption in the 240 mμ region

References p. 313/314.

due to the formation of a second thioester bond, since two molecules of acetyl CoA are formed per molecule of acetoacetyl CoA disappearing. In the presence of CoA-SH, oxal-acetate, thiolase, and citrate condensing enzyme, acetoacetyl CoA yields two molecules of citrate per molecule of sulfhydryl (*i.e.*, per molecule of CoA–SH) appearing[69], accor-ding to the following reactions:

Acetoacetyl—S—CoÃ+HS—CoÃ $\rightleftharpoons$ 2 acetyl—S—CoÃ (thiolase)

2 Acetyl—S—CoÃ+2 oxalacetate+2 H$_2$O $\rightleftharpoons$ 2 citrate+2 HS—CoÃ (citrate condensing enzyme)

Sum: Acetoacetyl—S—CoÃ+HS—CoÃ+2 oxalacetate+2 H$_2$O $\rightleftharpoons$ 2 citrate+2 HS—CoÃ

The equilibrium position of the thiolase reaction is very far toward cleavage[48, 68, 69]. For this reason it was not feasible to use this reaction for the isolation of acetoacetyl CoA. Determinations of the equilibrium constant $(K'_{eq} = (\text{Acetyl-S-CoA})^2/(\text{Acetoacetyl CoA})(\text{CoA-SH}))$ by means of the optical method gave an approximate value of $5 \cdot 10^4$ at pH 8.1, and $1 \cdot 10^4$ at pH 9.0.

The reversibility of the reaction can be demonstrated by the optical method as previously reported[48]. The synthesis of acetoacetyl CoA from acetyl CoA can be followed directly at alkaline pH ($\sim$ 9.0) as a small increase in the optical density at 305 mμ in the presence of large amounts of acetyl CoA[48a], or indirectly through coupling with the β-keto reductase to effect the oxidation of reduced DPN[48].

The purified heart enzyme is highly specific for acetoacetyl CoA. β-Ketovaleryl CoA reacts at 20% of the rate of acetoacetyl CoA, and β-ketocaproyl- and *iso*caproyl-CoA react practically not at all. This is in contrast to the broader specificity of crude enzyme fractions[68] and indicates that there must be other thiolases, acting on S-β-ketoacyl CoA derivatives of higher chain length.

Under the conditions of the optical test, the best preparations of the heart enzyme so far obtained catalyze the cleavage of 3000 to 4000 moles of acetoacetyl CoA per minute per 100,000 g of enzyme at 25°. When coupled with β-keto reductase about 30 times more acetoacetate condensing enzyme must be used in the back reaction to reach the rates obtained in the direction of acetoacetyl CoA cleavage.

β-Ketothiolase has been found to be inhibited by sulfhydryl reagents such as iodoacetic acid or arsenoxide[48a]. This indicates that the enzyme is an "SH enzyme" and suggests the following mechanism of action:

(a) R—CH$_2$—CO—CH$_2$—$\overset{O}{\overset{\|}{C}}$—S—CoÃ+HS-Enzyme $\rightleftharpoons$ R—CH$_2$—$\overset{O}{\overset{\|}{C}}$—S-Enzyme+CH$_3$—$\overset{O}{\overset{\|}{C}}$—S—CoÃ

(b) R—CH$_2$—$\overset{O}{\overset{\|}{C}}$—S-Enzyme+HS—CoÃ $\rightleftharpoons$ R—CH$_2$—$\overset{O}{\overset{\|}{C}}$—S—CoÃ+HS-Enzyme

Such a mechanism is further supported by experiments[45a] with CoA labelled with ^{35}S. On incubation of propionyl-S-CoA with ^{35}S-H-CoA, in the presence of purified heart thiolase, radioactive propionyl-S-CoA is formed indicating the occurrence of the following reaction:

Propionyl S—CoÃ+HS-enzyme $\rightleftharpoons$ Propionyl-S-enzyme+HS—CoÃ

The above mechanism provides an explanation for the unequal isotope distribution in acetoacetate observed during oxidation of isotopic fatty acids in liver[10, 13, 12, 19, 18]. For example, octanoic acid labelled with ^{14}C in the carboxyl group can yield acetoacetate in which the ratio of the radioactivity in the carbonyl and carboxyl carbons is less than unity. Some acetoacetate labelled exclusively in the carboxyl group must arise when

References p. 313/314.

non-labelled acetoacetyl-S-CoA from the last four carbons of the fatty acid chain reacts with thiolase to give non-labelled acetyl-S-enzyme and this in turn reacts with labelled acetyl-S-CoA from the pool to yield $CH_3-CO-CH_2-\overset{\overset{O}{\|}}{C^*}-S-CoA$. This is shown schematically in Fig. 8 for the case of caproic acid.

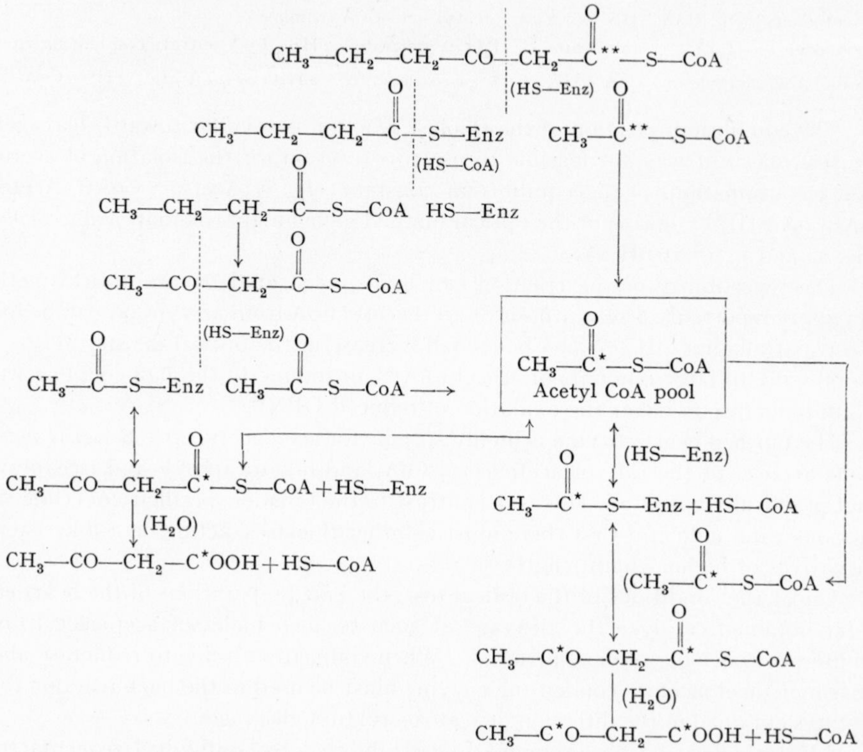

$$CH_3-CH_2-CH_2-CO\!-\!CH_2-\overset{\overset{O}{\|}}{C^{**}}-S-CoA$$

$$CH_3-CH_2-CH_2-\overset{\overset{O}{\|}}{C}\!-\!S-Enz \qquad CH_3-\overset{\overset{O}{\|}}{C^{**}}-S-CoA$$
$(HS-Enz)$

$(HS-CoA)$

$$CH_3-CH_2-CH_2-\overset{\overset{O}{\|}}{C}-S-CoA \qquad HS-Enz$$

$$CH_3-CO\!-\!CH_2-\overset{\overset{O}{\|}}{C}-S-CoA$$

$(HS-Enz)$

$$CH_3-\overset{\overset{O}{\|}}{C}-S-Enz \quad CH_3-\overset{\overset{O}{\|}}{C}-S-CoA \longrightarrow \qquad CH_3-\overset{\overset{O}{\|}}{C^*}-S-CoA$$
Acetyl CoA pool

$$CH_3-CO-CH_2-\overset{\overset{O}{\|}}{C^*}-S-CoA+HS-Enz \qquad CH_3-\overset{\overset{O}{\|}}{C^*}-S-Enz+HS-CoA$$
(H_2O)
$(HS-Enz)$

$$CH_3-CO-CH_2-C^*OOH+HS-CoA \qquad (CH_3-\overset{\overset{O}{\|}}{C^*}-S-CoA$$

$$CH_3-C^*O-CH_2-\overset{\overset{O}{\|}}{C^*}-S-CoA$$
(H_2O)

$$CH_3-C^*O-CH_2-C^*OOH+HS-CoA$$

Fig. 8. Asymmetric labelling of acetoacetate from carboxyl-labelled caproic acid.

β-keto-reductase. This enzyme catalyzes Reaction 6. The finding that

$$CH_3-CO-CH_2-\overset{\overset{O}{\|}}{C}-S-CoĀ+DPNH+H^+ \rightleftharpoons CH_3-CHOH-CH_2-\overset{\overset{O}{\|}}{C}-S-CoĀ+DPN^+ \quad (6)$$

the acetoacetyl-S-CoA analogue, S-acetoacetyl-N-acetyl thioethanolamine, was readily reduced by DPNH in the presence of enzyme solutions from various sources afforded a convenient assay for this enzyme. Employing this assay the enzyme was purified some 300-fold from sheep liver extracts by a procedure involving three steps: precipitation with ethanol, denaturation of inactive protein at 55°, and fractionation with ammonium sulfate[48]. The time course of the reaction in the optical test with varying concentrations of the purified enzyme is shown in Fig. 9.

The reaction is readily reversible but, at pH 7.35 with equimolecular amounts of DPNH and the acetoacetyl thioethanolamine derivative, it proceeds in the direction of reduction of the latter to the extent of 95 %. The equilibrium constant of the reaction (K'_{eq} = (S-β-hydroxybutyryl compound) (DPN$^+$)/(S-acetoacetyl compound) (DPNH)) has been found[48a] to be $5.2 \cdot 10^2$ at pH 7.0. The enzyme does not react with free acetoacetate or with ethyl acetoacetate; it also fails to react with S-acetoacetyl glutathione. With acetoacetyl-S-CoA the reaction is much faster than with the thioethanolamine derivative. This is undoubtedly due to the much higher affinity of the enzyme for the natural compound. In fact, in kinetic studies with S-acetoacetyl-N-acetyl thioethanolamine it was not possible to reach saturation of the enzyme with the analogue[48a].

In the presence of thiolase, β-keto reductase, and DPNH, the latter is oxidized on addition of acetyl-S-CoA; DPN+, β-hydroxybutyryl-S-CoA and HS-CoA are the reaction products[48]. This occurs according to the reactions below:

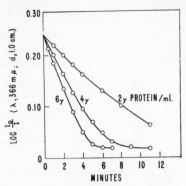

Fig. 9. Optical β-keto reductase test. Pyrophosphate buffer pH 7.4, 50 μM; DPNH, 0.13 μM; S-acetoacetyl-N-acetyl thioethanolamine, 5.0 μM. Volume, 2.0 ml; $d = 1.0$ cm; temp. 25°.

$$2\,CH_3-\overset{O}{\underset{\|}{C}}-S-CoA \rightleftharpoons HS-CoA+CH_3-CO-CH_2-\overset{O}{\underset{\|}{C}}-S-CoA \quad \text{(thiolase)}$$

$$CH_3-CO-CH_2-\overset{O}{\underset{\|}{C}}-S-CoA+DPNH+H^+ \rightleftharpoons CH_3-CHOH-CH_2-\overset{O}{\underset{\|}{C}}-S-CoA+DPN^+ \quad \text{(reductase)}$$

$$\textit{Sum:}\ 2\,CH_3-\overset{O}{\underset{\|}{C}}-S-CoA+DPNH+H^+ \rightleftharpoons CH_3-CHOH-CH_2-\overset{O}{\underset{\|}{C}}-S-CoA+HS-CoA+DPN^+$$

The formation of HS-CoA can be followed through the appearance of sulfhydryl groups. β-hydroxybutyryl-S-CoA was extracted from the acidified reaction mixture with p-cresol and converted into the corresponding hydroxamic acid by reaction with hydroxylamine. The β-hydroxybutyrohydroxamic acid was identified by paper chromatography (R_F in aqueous butanol, 0.29). On incubation of the natural β-hydroxybutyryl-S-CoA with DPN+ and purified β-ketoreductase at pH 9.05, the reduction of DPN+, followed at 340 mμ, is accompanied by the formation of acetoacetyl-S-CoA as shown by the increase in optical density at 303 mμ.

As previously mentioned both β-hydroxybutyryl- and acetoacetyl-S-CoA have recently become available synthetically. The course of the β-ketoreductase reaction with these two compounds[48a] is shown in Fig. 10.

LEHNINGER AND GREVILLE[41] have recently reported the interesting observation that liver contains two different p-ketoreductases. One of them catalyzes the reversible oxidation of free l-hydroxybutyrate by DPN+, the other catalyzes the reversible oxidation

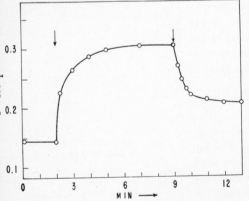

Fig. 10. Optical experiments with β-keto reductase. Pyrophosphate buffer pH 6.58, 100 μM; DPN+, 5.0 μM; S-β-hydroxybutyryl CoA, 2.0 μM. Volume, 2.0 ml; λ, 366 mμ; $d = 1.0$ cm; temp. 21°. β-keto reductase (1.5 mg of protein) added at the first arrow. S-acetoacetyl CoA (0.43 μM) added at the second arrow.

References p. 313/314.

of d-β-hydroxybutyryl-S-CoA by DPN$^+$. The latter reaction, which is undoubtedly catalyzed by the β-ketoreductase here described, was demonstrated by making use of the fact that liver also contains enzymes catalyzing the formation of d- or l-β-hydroxy-butyryl-S-CoA in the presence of ATP, CoA-SH, and d- or l-β-hydroxybutyrate.

The chain-length specificity of the β-ketoreductase is still unknown and it is not possible to decide at this time whether more than one enzyme is concerned with the CoA derivatives of β-keto and β-hydroxy acids from C_4 to C_{18}. The purified reductase described above has been found to act rapidly on S-β-ketocaproyl-N-acetyl thioethanolamine[48a].

Crotonase. Synthetic S-crotonyl CoA is converted to S-acetoacetyl CoA, in the presence of DPN, by crude enzyme preparations from heart or liver[67]. The reaction can be followed through the appearance of the absorption band of DPNH at 340 mμ or that of acetoacetyl-S-CoA at 305 mμ. Also, on addition of HS-CoA, citrate condensing enzyme, and oxalacetate, crotonyl-S-CoA acts as an acetyl donor for citrate synthesis; the required thiolase was present in the crude enzyme preparation used. These observations, together with the fact that reduced leucosafranine is oxidized by synthetic β-hydroxy-butyryl-S-CoA in the presence of partially purified preparations of ethylene reductase[55] indicate the occurrence of an enzyme catalyzing the reversible Reaction 7 below. The name crotonase has been suggested for this enzyme[67]. The enzyme has no action on free

$$CH_3{-}CH{=}CH{-}\overset{\displaystyle O}{\overset{\|}{C}}{-}S{-}Co\bar{A}+H_2O \rightleftharpoons CH_3{-}CHOH{-}CH_2{-}\overset{\displaystyle O}{\overset{\|}{C}}{-}S{-}Co\bar{A} \qquad (7)$$

crotonate or on the S-crotonyl derivatives of N-acetyl thioethanolamine, glutathione or thioglycolic acid.

As already mentioned the spectrum of S-crotonyl CoA is similar to that of S-crotonyl-N-acetyl thioethanolamine. This is readily apparent when the contribution of the adenine moiety of the CoA derivative is eliminated by reading S-crotonyl CoA against a solution containing an identical amount of the compound but previously subjected to alkaline hydrolysis. The difference spectrum so obtained[52a], illustrated in Fig. 11, shows absorption maxima at 224 and 263 mμ like S-crotonyl-N-acetyl thioethanolamine. The crotonyl CoA was obtained through reaction of CoA-SH with crotonic anhydride following the method of SIMON AND SHEMIN[56].

The decrease in light absorption at 263 mμ when crotonase acts on crotonyl CoA affords a simple method of assay for this enzyme. The purification of the enzyme from ox liver has recently been undertaken. Through steps involving denaturation of inactive proteins by acidification and heat, followed by acetone, ammonium sulfate and low temperature ethanol fractionation, preparations of the enzyme have been obtained representing about 100-fold purification over the original extract[52a]. The preparations are free of fumarase showing that fumarase and crotonase are distinct enzymes. Crotonase has a

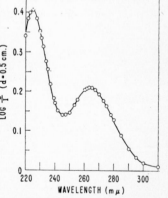

Fig. 11. Difference ultraviolet absorption spectrum of S-crotonyl CoA before and after alkaline hydrolysis of the thio-ester bond. $c \sim 6 \cdot 10^{-5}$ M in each cell; $d = 0.5$ cm; pH, 7.5. Crotonyl CoA in blank cell previously hydrolyzed with alkali.

remarkably high activity as may be seen in Fig. 12. which shows the time course of the reaction in the optical test with varying amounts of the enzyme. The equilibrium

References p. 313/314.

constant of the reaction has not yet been determined but it appears to favor the S-β-hydroxyacyl derivatives. Nothing can as yet be said as to the chain-length specificity of crotonase and consequently the occurrence of several enzymes of this type is not excluded.

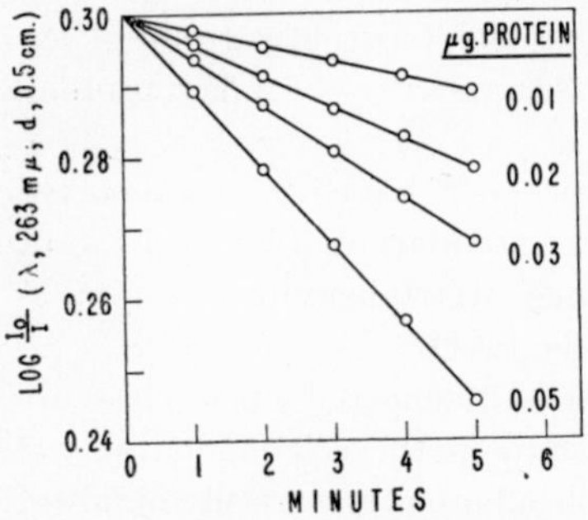

Crotonase would also appear to convert S-vinyl-acetyl CoA to the β-hydroxybutyryl derivative[21a]. If so, an equilibrium would be established between the S-acyl CoA derivatives of crotonic, vinylacetic, and β-hydroxybutyric acid. This might explain the observation that vinylacetate can be either oxidized or reduced by extracts of *C. kluyveri*[28,62]. The failure of crotonate to replace vinylacetate in this system[62] may have been due to failure of the bacterial extracts to activate crotonate.

Ethylene reductase. Ethylene reductase was detected in liver extracts[55] by a method similar to that employed by FISCHER AND EYSENBACH to study fumarate reductase[17]. Leucosafranine is oxidized by S-crotonyl-N-acetyl thioethanolamine, but not by free crotonate, in the presence of an enzyme from liver.

Fig. 12. Optical crotonase test. Tris (hydroxymethyl) aminomethane-HCl-buffer pH 7.5, 100 μM; egg albumin, 0.1 mg; ethylenediamine tetraacetate, 1.5 μM; S-crotonyl CoA, $\sim$ 0.5 μM. 2.0 μM of AMP in blank cell. Volume, 1.5 ml; d = 0.5 cm; temp., 25°.

The reaction is shown in Fig. 13. Here again a natural compound, in this case crotonyl-S-CoA, could be replaced by its readily synthesized thioethanolamine analogue. The

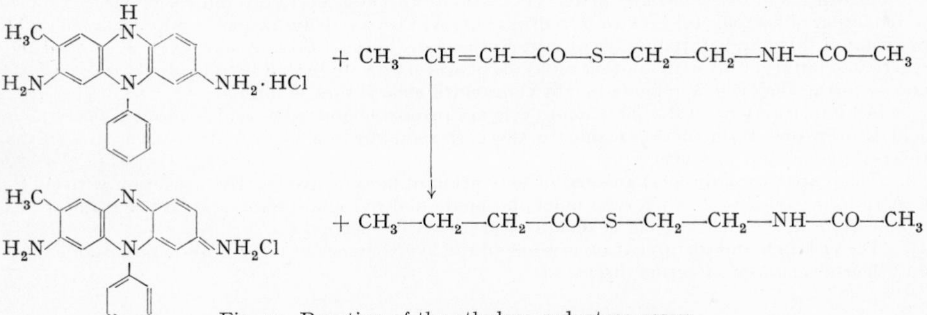

Fig. 13. Reaction of the ethylene reductase assay.

enzyme assay, in which the appearance of colour from the leucodye is followed, is illustrated in Fig. 14. By the use of this assay ethylene reductase was purified about 80-fold from sheep liver extracts through steps involving acetone fractionation, adsorption and elution from calcium phosphate gel, and ammonium sulfate fractionation. Solutions of the purified enzyme are yellow in colour. A colourless, almost inactive

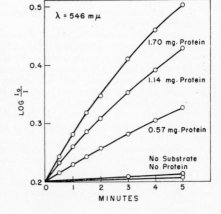

Fig. 14. Optical ethylene reductase test. Phosphate buffer pH 7.1, 140 μM; leucosafranine T, 0.5 μM; S-crotonyl-N-acetyl thioethanolamine, 2.6 μM. Volume, 2.1 ml; d = 0.5 cm; temp. 17°.

References p. 313/314.

protein can be precipitated from these solutions with ammonium sulfate at pH 3.6 as in the method of WARBURG AND CHRISTIAN[73] for the resolution of the flavoprotein D-amino acid oxidase. The activity of the protein can be restored by the addition of flavin adenine dinucleotide which has been found to be the prosthetic group of the enzyme. Thus, like fumarate reductase, ethylene reductase appears to be a flavoprotein. DPNH or TPNH cannot substitute for the leucodye.

In line with the above observations GREEN and co-workers[20a] have recently reported on the isolation of flavoproteins from ox liver catalyzing the oxidation of butyryl-S-CoA and some higher acyl-S-CoA derivatives in the presence of triphenyltetrazolium as hydrogen acceptor. The prosthetic group appears also to be FAD.

There is thus little doubt that the enzymes of the ethylene reductase class are flavoproteins. The nature of the electron transport system in the cell mediating the transfer of hydrogen from the reduced flavoprotein to molecular oxygen is still unknown. During fatty acid synthesis, hydrogens made available through oxidation of carbohydrate as reduced pyridine nucleotides must be transferred to the ethylene reductase flavoproteins to effect the reduction of the α,β-unsaturated S-acyl-CoA fatty acid derivatives. How such interaction takes place is also unknown.

SUMMARY

The intermediates in the biological breakdown and synthesis of fatty acids are S-acyl derivatives of coenzyme A.

Fatty acid synthesis is accomplished through repetition of a cycle of four consecutive reactions: a. Condensation of two molecules of acetyl CoA to form acetoacetyl CoA and coenzyme A (CoA–SH); b. reduction of acetoacetyl CoA to β-hydroxybutyryl CoA; c. dehydration of β-hydroxybutyryl CoA to crotonyl CoA, and d. reduction of crotonyl CoA to butyryl CoA. A new cycle is started by the reaction of butyryl CoA with another molecule of acetyl CoA, to form β-keto-caproyl CoA + CoA–SH, and so forth. The cycle is repeated eight times until stearyl CoA is formed.

All four reactions of the fatty acid cycle are reversible and fatty acid oxidation, once the fatty acid is activated through conversion to the corresponding S-acyl CoA derivative, proceeds by a reversal of the above sequence.

There are two main mechanisms for activation of fatty acids: (a) By a reaction with ATP and CoA to form S-acyl CoA, adenosine monophosphate and pyrophosphate, and (b) by transfer of CoA from certain acyl CoA compounds such as acetyl CoA or succinyl CoA.

The isolation and identification of some of the key enzymes of fatty acid metabolism is outlined and their mechanism of action discussed.

RÉSUMÉ

Les intermédiaires dans la dégradation et la synthèse biologique des acides gras sont des dérivés S-acylés du coenzyme A.

La synthèse des acides gras est le résultat de la répétition d'un cycle de 4 réactions consécutives: (a) condensation de deux molécules d'acétyl CoA conduisant à l'acétoacétyl CoA et au coenzyme A (CoA–SH), (b) réduction de l'acétoacétyl CoA en β-hydroxybutyryl CoA, (c) déshydratation du β-hydroxybutyryl CoA en crotonyl CoA, et (d) réduction du crotonyl CoA en butyryl CoA. Un nouveau cycle recommence par la réaction du butyryl CoA avec une autre molécule d'acétyl CoA, qui donne le β-cétocaproyl CoA + CoA–SH, et ainsi de suite. Le cycle se répète huit fois jusqu'à la formation du stéaryl CoA.

Les quatre réactions du cycle des acides gras sont réversibles et l'oxydation d'un acide gras, après son activation par transformation en dérivé S-acylé du CoA, suit le chemin inverse de la synthèse.

Il y a deux mécanismes principaux d'activation des acides gras: (a) par une réaction avec ATP et CoA qui donne du S-acyl CoA, de l'adénosine monophosphate et du pyrophosphate et (b) par transfert du CoA de certains acyl CoA, tels que l'acétyl CoA et le succinyl CoA.

L'isolement et l'identification de quelques-uns des enzymes essentiels au métabolisme des acides gras sont esquissés et leur mécanisme d'action discuté.

References p. 313/314.

ZUSAMMENFASSUNG

Die Zwischenprodukte bei dem biologischen Abbau und bei der Synthese der Fettsäuren sind S-Acylderivate des Coenzyms A.

Die Fettsäuresynthese wird erreicht durch die Wiederholung eines Kreislaufs von 4 aufeinander-folgenden Reaktionen: a. Der Kondensation von 2 Molekülen Acetyl-CoA zu Acetoacetyl-CoA und Coenzym A (CoA–SH), b. der Reduktion des Acetoacetyl-CoA zu β-Hydroxybutyryl-CoA, c. der Dehydratisierung des β-Hydroxybutyryl-CoA zu Crotonyl-CoA und d. der Reduktion des Crotonyl-CoA zu Butyryl-CoA. Ein neuer Kreislauf wird begonnen mit der Reaktion des Butyryl-CoA mit einem anderen Molekül Acetyl-CoA unter Bildung von β-Ketocaproyl-CoA und CoA–SH, usw. Dieser Kreislauf wird 8 mal wiederholt bis Stearyl-CoA gebildet ist.

Alle 4 Reaktionen des Fettsäurekreislaufs sind reversibel und die Fettsäureoxydation verläuft über die umgekehrten Stufen der obigen Folge, wenn einmal die Fettsäure durch Überführung in das entsprechende S-Acyl-CoA aktiviert ist. Es gibt 2 Hauptmechanismen für die Aktivierung der Fettsäuren: a. Eine Reaktion mit ATP und CoA unter Bildung von S-Acyl-CoA, Adenosin mono-phosphat und Pyrophosphat, und b. eine Überführung des CoA von gewissen Acyl-CoA-verbindungen wie Acetyl-CoA oder Succinyl-CoA.

Die Isolierung und Identifizierung einiger Schlüsselenzyme des Fettsäurestoffwechsels wird umrissen und der Wirkungsmechanismus besprochen.

REFERENCES

[1] H. S. ANKER, *J. Biol. Chem.*, 194 (1952) 177.
[2] R. B. BAKER AND E. E. REID, *J. Am. Chem. Soc.*, 51 (1929) 1567.
[3] H. A. BARKER, in W. D. MCELROY AND B. GLASS, *Phosphorus Metabolism*, Vol. I, p. 204, Johns Hopkins Press, Baltimore (1951).
[4] H. A. BARKER, M. D. KAMEN AND B. T. BORNSTEIN, *Proc. Natl. Acad. Sci.*, 31 (1945) 373.
[5] K. BLOCH, *Ann. Rev. Biochem.*, 21 (1952) 273.
[6] R. O. BRADY AND S. GURIN, *J. Biol. Chem.*, 186 (1950) 461.
[7] F. L. BREUSCH, *Science*, 97 (1943) 490; *Enzymologia*, 11 (1944) 169.
[8] F. L. BREUSCH, in *Symposium sur le Cycle Tricarboxylique*, IIe Congrés International de Biochmie, p. 35. Paris (1952).
[9] F. L. BREUSCH AND H. KESKIN, *Enzymologia*. 11 (1944) 243.
[10] J. M. BUCHANAN, W. SAKAMI AND S. GURIN, *J. Biol. Chem.*, 169 (1947) 411.
[11] T. C. CHOU AND F. LIPMANN, *J. Biol. Chem.*, 196 (1952) 89.
[12] D. I. CRANDALL, R. O. BRADY AND S. GURIN, *J. Biol. Chem.*, 181 (1949) 845.
[13] D. I. CRANDALL AND S. GURIN, *J. Biol. Chem.*, 181 (1949) 829.
[14] H. D. DAKIN, *J. Biol. Chem.*, 6 (1909) 203, 221.
[14a] K. DECKER AND F. LYNEN, unpublished.
[15] G. R. DRYSDALE AND H. A. LARDY, in W. D. MCELROY AND B. GLASS, *Phosphorus Metabolism*, Vol. II, p. 281. Johns Hopkins Press, Baltimore (1952).
[16] G. R. DRYSDALE AND H. A. LARDY, *J. Biol. Chem.*, 202 (1953) 119.
[17] F. G. FISCHER AND H. EYSENBACH, *Ann. Chem.*, 530 (1937) 99.
[18] R. P. GEYER, M. CUNNINGHAM AND J. PENDERGAST, *J. Biol. Chem.*, 185 (1950) 461; 188 (1950) 185.
[19] R. P. GEYER, L. W. MATTHEWS AND F. J. STARE, *J. Biol. Chem.*, 180 (1950) 1037.
[19a] C. GILVARG, unpublished.
[20] A. L. GRAFFLIN AND D. E. GREEN, *J. Biol. Chem.*, 176 (1948) 95.
[20a] D. E. GREEN, reported at meeting of Federation of Biological Societies, Chicago, April 1953.
[21] D. E. GREEN, *Science*, 115 (1952) 661.
[21a] D. E. GREEN, personal communication.
[22] D. E. GREEN, D. S. GOLDMAN, S. MII AND H. BEINERT, *J. Biol. Chem.*, 202 (1953) 137.
[23] M. P. HELE, *Federation Proc.*, 12 (1953) 216.
[24] F. E. HUNTER AND L. F. LELOIR, *J. Biol. Chem.*, 159 (1945) 295.
[25] M. E. JONES, F. LIPMANN, H. HILZ AND F. LYNEN, *J. Am. Chem. Soc.*, 75 (1953) 3285.
[26] S. KAUFMAN, in W. D. MCELROY AND B. GLASS, *Phosphorus Metabolism*, Vol. I, p. 370. Johns Hopkins Press, Baltimore (1951).
[27] S. KAUFMAN, C. GILVARG, O. CORI AND S. OCHOA, *J. Biol. Chem.* 203 (1953) 869.
[28] E. P. KENNEDY AND H. A. BARKER, *J. Biol. Chem.*, 191 (1951) 419.
[29] E. P. KENNEDY AND A. L. LEHNINGER, *J. Biol. Chem.*, 190 (1951) 361.
[30] E. P. KENNEDY AND A. L. LEHNINGER, in W. D. MCELROY AND B. GLASS, *Phosphorus Metabolism* Vol. II, p. 253. Johns Hopkins Press, Baltimore (1952).
[31] A. KLEINZELLER, *Biochem. J.*, 37 (1943) 678.
[32] F. KNOOP, *Beitr. Chem. Physiol. Pathol.*, 6 (1904) 150.

[33] W. E. KNOX, B. N. NOYCE AND V. H. AUERBACH, *J. Biol. Chem.*, 176 (1948) 117.
[34] S. KORKES, A. DEL CAMPILLO, I. C. GUNSALUS, AND S. OCHOA, *J. Biol. Chem.* 193 (1951) 721.
[35] A. KORNBERG, in W. D. MCELROY AND B. GLASS, *Phosphorus Metabolism*, Vol. II, p. 245. Johns Hopkins Press, Baltimore (1952).
[36] A. KORNBERG AND W. E. PRICER Jr., *J. Am. Chem. Soc.*, 74 (1952) 1617.
[37] A. L. LEHNINGER, *J. Biol. Chem.*, 154 (1944) 309; 157 (1944) 363.
[38] A. L. LEHNINGER, *J. Biol. Chem.*, 161 (1945) 437.
[39] A. L. LEHNINGER, *J. Biol. Chem.*, 161 (1945) 413; 164 (1946) 291.
[40] A. L. LEHNINGER, *J. Biol. Chem.*, 165 (1946) 131.
[41] A. L. LEHNINGER AND G. D. GREVILLE, *J. Am. Chem. Soc.*, 75 (1953) 1515.
[42] A. L. LEHNINGER AND E. P. KENNEDY, *J. Biol. Chem.*, 173 (1948) 753.
[43] L. F. LELOIR AND J. M. MUÑOZ, *J. Biol. Chem.*, 153 (1944) 53.
[44] F. LIPMANN, M. E. JONES, S. BLACK AND R. M. FLYNN, *J. Am. Chem. Soc.*, 74 (1952) 2384.
[45] J. W. LITTLEFIELD AND D. R. SANADI, *J. Biol. Chem.*, 199 (1952) 65.
[45a] F. LYNEN, unpublished experiments.
[46] F. LYNEN AND E. REICHERT, *Angew. Chem.*, 63 (1951) 47, 490.
[47] F. LYNEN, E. REICHERT AND L. RUEFF, *Ann. Chem.*, 574 (1951) 1.
[48] F. LYNEN, L. WESSELY, O. WIELAND AND L. RUEFF, *Angew. Chem.*, 64 (1952) 687.
[48a] F. LYNEN, G. VOGELMANN, L. WESSELY, O. WIELAND AND W. SEUBERT, unpublished.
[49] H. A. MAHLER, in W. D. MCELROY AND B. GLASS, *Phosphorus Metabolism*, Vol. II, p. 286. Johns Hopkins Press, Baltimore (1952).
[50] J. M. MUÑOZ AND L. F. LELOIR, *J. Biol. Chem.*, 147 (1943) 355.
[50a] S. OCHOA, J. HARTING AND M. C. SCHNEIDER, unpublished.
[51] S. OCHOA, J. R. STERN AND M. C. SCHNEIDER, *J. Biol. Chem.*, 193 (1951) 691.
[52] G. POPJÁK, G. D. HUNTER AND T. H. FRENCH, *Biochem. J.*, 54 (1953) 238.
[52a] I. RAW AND J. R. STERN, unpublished.
[53] D. RITTENBERG AND K. BLOCH, *J. Biol. Chem.*, 160 (1945) 417.
[54] D. R. SANADI AND J. W. LITTLEFIELD, *J. Biol. Chem.*, 201 (1953) 103.
[55] W. SEUBERT AND F. LYNEN, *J. Am. Chem. Soc.*, 75 (1953) 2787.
[56] E. J. SIMON AND D. SHEMIN, *J. Am. Chem. Soc.*, 75 (1953) 2520.
[57] B. SJÖBERG, *Z. physik. Chem.*, 52 B (1942) 209.
[58] M. SOODAK AND F. LIPMANN, *J. Biol. Chem.*, 175 (1948) 999.
[59] E. R. STADTMAN, *J. Biol. Chem.*, 196 (1952) 527, 535.
[60] E. R. STADTMAN, *Federation Proc.*, 11 (1952) 291; *Abstracts 122nd Meeting Am. Chem. Soc.*, 32 C (1952).
[60a] E. R. STADTMAN, personal communication.
[61] E. R. STADTMAN AND H. A. BARKER, *J. Biol. Chem.*, 180 (1949) 1085, 1095, 1117, 1169.
[62] E. R. STADTMAN AND H. A. BARKER, *J. Biol. Chem.*, 181 (1949) 221.
[63] E. R. STADTMAN AND H. A. BARKER, *J. Biol. Chem.*, 184 (1950) 769.
[64] E. R. STADTMAN, M. DOUDOROFF AND F. LIPMANN, *J. Biol. Chem.* 191 (1951) 377.
[65] E. R. STADTMAN, G. D. NOVELLI AND F. LIPMANN, *J. Biol. Chem.*, 191 (1951) 365.
[66] E. R. STADTMAN, T. C. STADTMAN AND H. A. BARKER, *J. Biol. Chem.*, 178 (1949) 677.
[67] J. R. STERN AND A. DEL CAMPILLO, *J. Am. Chem. Soc.*, 75 (1953) 2277.
[67a] J. R. STERN AND A. DEL CAMPILLO, unpublished.
[68] J. R. STERN, M. J. COON AND A. DEL CAMPILLO, *Nature*, 171 (1953) 28.
[69] J. R. STERN, M. J. COON AND A. DEL CAMPILLO, *J. Am. Chem. Soc.*, 75 (1953) 1517.
[69a] J. R. STERN, M. J. COON AND A. DEL CAMPILLO, unpublished observations.
[70] J. R. STERN AND S. OCHOA, *J. Biol. Chem.*, 191 (1951) 161.
[71] J. R. STERN, B. SHAPIRO, E. R. STADTMAN AND S. OCHOA, *J. Biol. Chem.*, 193 (1951) 703.
[72] S. WAKIL AND H. R. MAHLER, *Federation Proc.*, 12 (1953) 285.
[73] O. WARBURG AND W. CHRISTIAN, *Biochem. Z.*, 298 (1938) 150.
[74] S. WEINHOUSE, G. MEDES AND N. F. FLOYD, *J. Biol. Chem.* 155 (1944) 143.
[75] S. WEINHOUSE, G. MEDES AND N. F. FLOYD, *J. Biol. Chem.*, 166 (1946) 691.
[76] H. WIELAND AND C. ROSENTHAL, *Ann. Chem.*, 554 (1943) 241.
[77] T. WIÉLAND AND L. RUEFF, *Angew. Chem.*, 65 (1953) 186.
[78] I. ZABIN, *J. Biol. Chem.*, 189 (1951) 355.

Received June 22nd, 1953

CHOLINE ACETYLASE SPECIFICITY IN RELATION TO BIOLOGICAL FUNCTION*

by

RUTH BERMAN, IRWIN B. WILSON AND DAVID NACHMANSOHN

Department of Neurology, College of Physicians and Surgeons,
Columbia University, New York, N.Y. (U.S.A.)

INTRODUCTION

OTTO WARBURG's achievements have greatly influenced contemporary biology and biochemistry in many respects. One of the outstanding features of his work has been his early emphasis on energy-yielding chemical reactions in cells as a key for a better understanding of cellular function. It was this particular aspect which impressed OTTO MEYERHOF and – under the influence of OTTO WARBURG – attracted him to cellular physiology. The work of these two leaders on the energy transformations in cellular systems have revolutionized the thinking of our generation of biochemists.

From the studies of intermediate carbohydrate metabolism emerged the recognition that the paramount role of the glycolytic cycle is the generation of ATP. The energy of hydrolysis of this nucleotide is generally assumed to be used in the elementary process of muscular contraction. In studies aimed at the analysis of the elementary process of nerve impulse conduction and the sequence of energy transformations associated with this function, evidence has been obtained that the release of acetylcholine and its action upon a structural protein is the primary chemical reaction responsible for the generation of the bioelectric currents, which propagate the nerve impulse[1,2]. The action of acetylcholinesterase is the rapid hydrolysis of the ester enabling the nerve to return to its resting state. Since it was found, in experiments on electric fish, that the energy released by the breakdown of phosphorylated compounds is adequate to account for the total energy released during activity, it was postulated that the energy of ATP in hydrolysis is used for the resynthesis of the acetylcholine split in the primary process, in other words, provides the energy for acetylation. This postulate was borne out by experiment. It was shown, in 1943, that cell-free extracts of brain and electric tissue may acetylate choline in presence of ATP[3]. These experiments were the first demonstration that ATP provides energy for synthetic reactions outside the glycolytic cycle in addition to its role in muscular contraction. It initiated intensive studies in many laboratories on the mechanism of acetylation generally.

---

* This work was supported (in part) by the Medical Research and Development Board, Office of the Surgeon General, Department of the Army, Contract No. DA-49-007, and in part by the Division of Research Grants and Fellowships of the National Institutes of Health, H-740, United States Public Health Service.

References p. 324.

20

The acetylating enzyme requires a coenzyme, later called Coenzyme A (CoA), which was discovered simultaneously and independently in three laboratories in 1945 (LIP-MANN AND KAPLAN[4], LIPTON in BARRON's laboratory[5], NACHMANSOHN AND BERMAN[6]). The structure of CoA is today well established by the work of various laboratories, especially by the work of LIPMANN and his associates[7,8]. An essential progress was the isolation of acetyl CoA ("active acetate") by LYNEN AND REICHERT[9] and their discovery that this compound is an acetyl thioester. The thioester was postulated by LYNEN to be a new type of energy rich compound and this assumption was confirmed by the work of STERN, OCHOA AND LYNEN[10] and STADTMAN[11]. During the last few years the analysis of the mechanism of acetylation has made rapid progress, mainly by the work of LIPMANN, OCHOA, LYNEN, GREEN, BARKER and STADTMAN and their associates.

The availability of acetyl CoA makes possible an investigation of the specificity of choline acetylase, the enzyme which transfers the acetyl group from acetyl CoA to choline[12]. The molecular forces acting between the substrates and this enzyme appeared of special interest in view of the results obtained in studies of the molecular forces acting between acetylcholine and acetylcholinesterase[2, 13–15].

It is a great privilege and pleasure for the authors to present this first study on the specific features of choline acetylase and their biological significance as a tribute to Professor OTTO WARBURG on the occasion of his 70th birthday.

METHODS

Purification

Acetone-dried powder prepared from head ganglia of Squid[16] was extracted with 0.05 M K_2HPO_4 buffer of pH 7.4 and was centrifuged in the Spinco preparatory ultracentrifuge. The proteins of the supernatant solution were precipitated with an equal volume of 50 % ammonium sulfate and centrifuged. The precipitate was dissolved in 0.1 M K_2HPO_4 buffer of pH 7.8. The ammonium sulfate was removed by dialysis against 0.05 M K_2HPO_4 buffer of pH 7.4. Protamine sulfate, in a 2 % solution was added (1 mg per 10 mg protein) and the precipitate formed was removed by centrifugation. When large amounts of materials were used, an ammonium sulfate fractionation was carried out at this stage and the protein fractionated between 16 and 28 %. With smaller amounts the next step was carried out directly, consisting of treatment with 3.3 mg of calcium PO_4 gel per mg of protein at pH 6.2. The gel was centrifuged and eluted with 0.05 M phosphate buffer of pH 7.5 and the eluate discarded. Futher elution with 0.2 M phosphate buffer of pH 8.2 contained most of the enzyme. The eluate was again fractionated with ammonium sulfate, between 16 and 32 %.

The data of one preparation are given as example; although in this way only a 10-fold purification was obtained, the enzyme solution at this stage has a satisfactory stability and is adequate for the analysis desired, especially the deacylase activity present in the crude preparation is removed in this process.

	Specific activity *	Per cent. recovery
Crude extract	5.9	
1st Amm. sulfate	11	100
Protamine sulfate	10	60
Ca gel	40	60
2nd Amm. sulfate	58	45

Assay methods during purification

The enzyme activity was tested by assaying the acetylcholine formed with the method of HESTRIN[17]. The preparations used were the same as described in a previous paper[12], except for CoA. The CoA preparation was obtained from Pabst and was about 75 % pure. The reaction mixture contained the following components in micromoles per ml: choline chloride 50, $MgCl_2$ 5, tetraethyl pyro-

---

* μM ACh formed per mg protein per hour.

References p. 324.

phosphate 1, L–cysteine 20, CoA 0.05, acetyl phosphate 40, K_2HPO_4 buffer of pH 7 10. To the mixture were added 0.15 ml of transacetylase of an ammonium sulfate fractionation from *E. coli* extracts of 60 % saturation, and 0.05 ml of choline acetylase to be assayed. The total volume was 1 ml, the temperature was 32 °C. After 30 min the reaction was stopped by addition of 1 ml of 0.1 N HCl. After destroying the excess acetyl phosphate by boiling for 4 minutes at pH 4.5 the acethydroxamic acid formation was determined as usual. The protein concentration of the different enzyme fractions was determined by the biuret method developed for serum protein by GORNALL[18] and standardized against the Kjeldal method for determining protein nitrogen.

Preparation of acyl coenzymes

Acyl coenzymes were prepared by adding the corresponding acid anhydrides to the coenzyme in slightly alkaline medium as described by SIMON AND SHEMIN[19]. Benzoyl CoA was kindly supplied by Dr JOHN TAGGART. The amount of acyl CoA formed was determined by two methods: (i) the hydroxamic acid formation at neutral pH, at which presumably only the acyl group on the SH is tested, and (ii), the nitroprusside test for free SH groups described below. The hydroxamic acid test was calibrated against acetylthiocholine iodide solutions. According to both methods 95 to 100 % of the CoA was acylated.

Assay of the reactions mediated by choline acetylase by the nitroprusside test for free SH groups

If the reaction mixture contains acetyl CoA and choline as substrates and choline acetylase as enzyme, the enzymic activity may be tested either by bioassay of the acetylcholine formed, using the frog's rectus muscle, or by determining the remaining acetyl CoA by the use of hydroxylamine in neutral solution or by determining the appearance of free SH groups of CoA. Of the two chemical tests the latter is more sensitive and was used by adapting the method described by GRUNERT AND PHILIPS[20] to our special conditions.

The reaction mixture contained only acetyl CoA, choline and enzyme in buffer (0.1 M K_2HPO_4 of pH 7). The total volume was 1.0 ml. An aliquot of this solution (0.2 ml) was added to 0.1 ml of 0.033 N HCl and 1.2 ml of saturated sodium chloride solution. Solid NaCl (0.2 gram) was added to keep the system saturated. Following the inactivation of the enzyme, 0.1 ml of 0.033 N NaOH was added. The protein precipitate was removed by centrifugation; at this stage the mixture remains stable. An aliquot (0.8 ml) was used for spectrophotometric determination. To the aliquot were added 0.1 ml of 0.067 M sodium nitroprusside and 0.1 ml of a solution containing 1.5 sodium carbonate and 0.067 M NaCN. The optical density was determined in the Coleman Junior Spectrophotometer at 520 mμ exactly 30 seconds after the addition of the base. To correct for slight current changes in the spectrophotometer control tubes containing saturated NaCl, the nitroprusside and cyanide-carbonate reagents were tested between every 3 or 4 assays. If the assay mixture was not saturated with NaCl, a significant decrease in color was observed, whereas the presence of metaphosphoric acid was not found to be necessary for the experimental conditions used. There is a slight decrease in optical density if the phosphate concentration in the acid system exceeds 0.01 M, probably due to the effect of the buffer on the final pH, since the optimal pH of the colorimetric test is 10.

The nitroprusside test was calibrated against standard glutathione solution under identical conditions and with the same constituents as in the tests themselves. If the color developed per SH group is assumed to be the same in both cases, 1 mg of the Pabst CoA preparation would contain about 740 μg CoA, or close to 1 μM. In the calculations 1 mg of the CoA preparation was assumed to contain 1 μM of CoA.

Acyl CoA breaks down at pH 10, liberating SH groups. There is, therefore, an increase in colour between the time of addition of the alkali and the reading 30 seconds later. This increase is proportional to the amount of acyl CoA present at the time of the addition of alkali. Curves which indicate the amount of colour produced by various acyl CoA concentrations were used in two successive approximations to correct for this factor.

The stability of the different acyl Coenzymes differs considerably. Butyryl and acetyl CoA have about the same stability, but propionyl CoA breaks down almost twice as fast and benzoyl CoA even more rapidly.

Since the quantitative measurement of acetylation was based upon the appearance of mercaptan groups during the course of the reaction, it is necessary to establish the validity of the test. If, as is believed, the colour is produced by a complex involving the mercaptan, then the molar extinction coefficient should depend upon the precise nature of the mercaptan and colorimetric assay would require calibration with CoA. This latter procedure requires a sample of known composition and this was not readily available to us. However, it appeared likely that the molar extinction coefficient for glutathione might not differ greatly from that of CoA and could be used for the assays. Consistent results have been obtained by others on this assumption. Fortunately, this question could be tested by measuring the acetylation in an independent way, namely by assaying for acetylcholine directly: This latter comparison is necessary for establishing the validity of the method in general even aside from the question of extinction coefficients. The following figures compare the nitroprusside mercaptan assay based upon the glutathione extinction coefficient and the biological acetylcholine measurement:

Time (min)	μM of acetylcholine formed/ml	
	Bioassay	Nitroprusside test
30	0.33	0.34
60	0.67	0.65

These data validate the appearance of mercaptan as a measure of acetylation. However, it must be noted that there is a difference – not yet explained – between the two systems: In the full system including transacetylase, acetylphosphate etc. the activity was about 3 times as high as in the tests with choline acetylase alone.

RESULTS

Figs. 1 and 2 demonstrate the time course of the acetylation reaction for different concentrations of the substrates choline and acetyl CoA. The choline curves show very

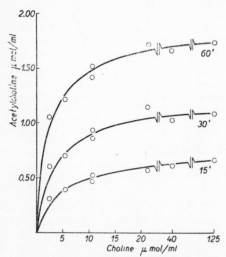

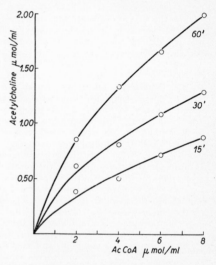

Fig. 1. Acetylation of choline by choline ace-tylase as function of choline concentration. The reaction mixture contained 140 μg en-zyme and the following components in μM per ml: Acetyl CoA 5, phosphate buffer pH 7, 90, choline as indicated in the graph. Total volume 1 ml, $t = 31\,^\circ C$.

Fig. 2. Acetylation of choline by choline ace-tylase as function of Acetyl CoA concentra-tion. The reaction mixture contained 140 μg enzyme and the following components in μM per ml: choline 10, phosphate buffer pH 7, 90, acetyl CoA as indicated in the graph. Total volume 1 ml, $t = 31\,^\circ C$.

marked enzyme saturation corresponding to a Michaelis-Menten constant of about $2 \cdot 10^{-3}$ M. The acetyl CoA curves on the other hand show far less saturation in the concentration range utilized and the data correspond to a Michaelis-Menten constant on the order of $5 \cdot 10^{-3}$ M. The curves are reasonably linear in time; the moderate rate decline at longer times being nearly accounted for by the decrease in the concentration of acetyl CoA.

Table I shows the reaction rate as a function of time and enzyme concentration. Again the moderate deviation from linearity at high enzyme concentration corresponds to a decrease in acetyl CoA as the reaction proceeds.

TABLE I

Acetylation of choline by choline acetylase as function of enzyme concentration.
The reaction mixture contained in addition to the enzyme as indictated the following components in μM per ml: Acetyl CoA 5, choline 20, phosphate buffer pH 7,90. Total volume 1 ml, $t = 31$°C.

	Choline acetylated in $\mu M/ml$			
Enzyme (μg)	55	110	220	440
Time (min)				
15	0.18	0.45	0.73	1.45
30	0.33	0.60	1.25	2.02
60	0.52	1.20	2.02	2.50

The approximate linearity of rate with time and enzyme concentration and the demonstration of enzyme saturation indicates that we have a stable enzyme system which we may reasonably anticipate to be free of complicating and unknown second-ary features.

The enzyme specificity toward the acetyl acceptor with regard to extent of methyla-tion of the aminoethanol is shown in Table II. The large difference between trime-thyl and dimethyl aminoethanol is of interest in comparison with the results obtained with less purified systems, in which case the trimethyl compound was only twice as good as the dimethyl. In crude preparations no difference was observed between the two compounds[12]. However, in those experiments acetyl CoA was not a substrate but only a catalytic intermediate being formed from acetate, ATP and CoA, and mediated by acetylkinase.

TABLE II

Effect of the number of methyl groups upon the acetylation of aminoethanols by choline acetylase.
The reaction mixture contained in addition to the enzyme as indicated below the following components in μM per ml: Acetyl CoA 5, aminoethanols 80, phosphate buffer pH 7, 50. Total volume
1.0 ml, $t = 31$°C.

	Methylaminoethanols acetylated in $\mu M/ml$		
	Trimethyl	Dimethyl	Monomethyl
Enzyme (mg)	0.14	1.4	1.4
Time (min)			
15	0.61	0.37	0.12
30	1.08	0.76	0.18
60	1.64	1.31	0.28

The increased disparity between the utilization of the two compounds with increased purity indicates that two (or more) enzymes are involved, at least in the crude preparations. We may not conclude, therefore, that the specificity pattern with the present enzyme preparation is necessarily that of a single enzyme but we can say that the major enzyme constituent is at least as discriminating in regard to a third methyl group as is indicated in the Table. Since the concentrations of the amino alcohols were very much higher than the Michaelis-Menten constant for choline the distinction is in the saturation rate and the question of relative binding is not involved.

The specificity pattern with respect to acyl CoA is shown in Fig. 3. In this case it would appear that both binding and rate factors are involved since the acyl CoA con-

References p. 324.

centration is about the Michaelis-Menten constant for acetyl CoA. The immeasurably low reactivity of butyryl CoA is not, however, due to poor binding. This is illustrated by the fact that butyryl CoA in equal concentration with acetyl CoA inhibits the rate of acylation of choline by approximately 80%.

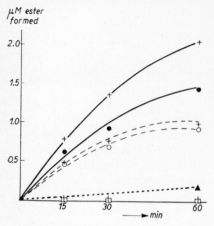

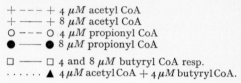

Fig. 3. Effect of the acyl group of CoA derivatives on the acylation of choline by choline acetylase. The reaction mixture contained 140 μg enzyme and the following components in μM per ml: choline 20, phosphate buffer, pH 7, 90, acyl CoA either 4 or 8. Total volume 1 ml, $t = 31°$ C.

+ ---- + 4 μM acetyl CoA
+ ——— + 8 μM acetyl CoA
O ---- O 4 μM propionyl CoA
● ——— ● 8 μM propionyl CoA

□ ——— □ 4 and 8 μM butyryl CoA resp.
...... ▲ 4 μM acetyl CoA + 4 μM butyryl CoA.

DISCUSSION

The specificity patters of choline acetylase assumes enhanced biological interest when the acetylase is recognized as part of a physiological system, the acetylcholine system, which is directly involved in conduction. It is important to compare this enzyme with the other members of the system to ascertain if any underlying unity exists.

It is consequently pertinent to describe, albeit very briefly, the mechanism of the system as it is presently envisaged[1,2]. Acetylcholine is in a bound state during rest; it is released in activity to react with a receptor and is finally destroyed by acetylcholine-esterase, a step essential for the rapid short range recovery of function. Complete recovery in a long range sense is accomplished by the resynthesis of acetylcholine mediated by choline acetylase.

The receptor, presumably a protein or a conjugated protein, is assumed to determine the membrane characteristics associated with such phenomena as ion permeability and electrical potential. The combination of ACh with the receptor alters its properties perhaps through change in configuration which brings about the characteristic changes in electrical potential, membrane resistance, and ionic flow observed during conduction of the nerve impulse and other types of conduction.

Four functions which appear to reside in four discrete proteins, have thus been delineated: storage, receptor, destroying and synthesizing functions. Of these proteins only the two enzymes, the acetylase and the esterase, have been obtained and studied in solution. The receptor has been studied by the response of intact structures so that the observations are affected by secondary features, e.g. permeability properties. We have little knowledge concerning the storage protein and therefore it will not be considered further. On the other hand, the esterase has been extensively studied with regard to its specificity pattern, forces of interaction and hydrolytic mechanism[2,13–15]. This information may be of considerable value in understanding the interaction of ACh with the other members of the system and aid in the design and interpretation of experiments particularly in the case of the receptor and storage proteins where direct experiments have not been carried out as yet. This follows from the fact that a small molecule, such

References p. 324.

as acetylcholine, has only a severly limited number of features which may contribute to its interaction with proteins. The elementary interactions between the atoms, or groups of atoms, of the ester and the enzyme are intrinsically weak. A relatively strong inter- action is effected by the sum of all or nearly all elementary interactions. All proteins which specifically interact with acetylcholine (or choline) must utilize most of the same elementary interactions and therefore be similarly constituted at the site of action. The exact consequence of the interaction may be determined by the omission of one or more of the elementary interactions or by the addition of repulsive forces, *e.g.* steric inhibitions peculiar to the particular protein.

The comparative specificity of the three proteins toward the acid moiety of appro- priate compounds is shown in Table III. In the case of the acetylase the compounds are CoA derivatives and choline is the acyl acceptor. Choline derivatives are the compounds for the esterase and receptor. Enzyme specificity is indicated in two categories:

a. overall catalytic proficiency
b. binding strength of the enzyme-substrate complex.

TABLE III

Acidic moiety	Acetylase		Esterase		Receptor
	a	b	a	b	
acetyl	100	100	100	100	100
propionyl	80–100	100	80–100	100	90–100
butyryl	< 1	∼ 200	0.7	∼ 150	80
benzoyl	< 1	—	0.05	∼ 300	1

a. catalytic proficiency.
b. binding strength

The two enzymes clearly show a parallel interaction pattern in both categories. In comparing the receptor to the enzymes it is significant that the receptor has no cata- lytic function and, therefore, only comparison of the binding strength of the enzyme with receptor response may be pertinent. Binding to the receptor is a necessary but not a sufficient condition for the response of the receptor. Again there is a strong parallelism except for the benzoate. Whether the weak response of the receptor to the benzoate is real or caused by secondary phenomena is not known.

The comparative specificity toward the extent of methylation is indicated in Table IV. The compounds tested with the acetylase are the aminoethanols using acetyl CoA as the acyl donor. The three categories of reaction considered for the esterase are

a. overall catalytic proficiency
b. substrate inhibition, usually attributed to the formation of an inactive ES_2 complex
c. reactivation of tetraethyl pyrophosphate inhibited enzyme[15,21]. The inhibited en- zyme is a diethyl phosphoryl enzyme and its reactivation is an enzymic process.

The β-aminoethyl acetates are the compounds for the esterase categories a and b and for the receptor. The amino alcohols are the compounds for category c of the esterase.

As with the acidic moieties there is a marked parallelism in the interaction of these compounds with the three proteins. In all but one instance the removal of a methyl group from the trimethyl derivative results in a very great diminution of interaction. To illustrate this fact just a few examples may be given. If a methyl group is removed

TABLE IV

Extent of methylation	Acetylase	Esterase			Receptor
		A	B	C	
trimethyl	100	100	100	100	100
dimethyl	8	45	< 5	< 5	∼ 1 – 0.1
monomethyl	8		—		—

A. hydrolysis
B. substrate inhibition at high concentration
C. reactivation of TEPP inhibited enzyme

from acetylcholine, it loses practically all its action on the frog rectus muscle. Comparison between a variety of tertiary amines and the corresponding quaternary ammonium salts on the depolarization of electric cells of electric tissue has shown similar striking differences (ALTAMIRANO et al., unpublished results of this Laboratory). Reactivation of acetylcholinesterase inhibited by tetraethyl pyrophosphate may be obtained with choline; but dimethyl ethanolamine is 100 times less effective.

The appearance of new chemical properties associated with the conjugate acid and base of the dimethyl derivatives does not seem to be of importance here, since these properties introduce additional possibilities of interaction and would hardly account for a decreased activity. This striking effect of the 3rd methyl group towards the 3 proteins of the system tested appears to indicate that the 3rd methyl group has a positive action of its own and this raises the question as to what a chemically saturated group can do. The quaternary portion of these molecules being of tetrahedral structure is more or less spherical so that the only way the protein could be "in contact" with the chemically functioning alcohol or ester group and simultaneously with all three methyl groups would be for the protein to envelop the molecule and this implies an altered protein configuration. Such a change would be of especial interest with regard to the functional properties of the receptor.

A positive response of all three proteins to the relatively inert methyl group could hardly be fortuitous and manifests a certain underlying unity. It is not difficult to conceive of relatively small changes in the protein which profoundly alter its function without changing its gross interaction with the various compounds here considered.

The specificity pattern of choline acetylase concerning the acyl part is biologically interesting in regard to the recent concepts of fatty acid oxidation developed in the laboratories of LYNEN, OCHOA, GREEN and others, where a whole sequence of acyl derivatives of CoA from stearyl CoA to acetyl CoA have been shown to be intermediates. It thus seems necessary for choline acetylase to have a sharp specificity with regard to the chain length of the acyl group if a whole series of choline esters are not to be formed formed which may have undesirable biological side effects. The acetylase is not required to discriminate against propionyl CoA because the β-oxidation mechanism precludes the formation of acyl CoA derivatives containing an odd number of carbon atoms in the acyl chain.

ACKNOWLEDGEMENTS

We would like to acknowledge gratefully the assistance of Mrs. IDA FREIBERGER aud MAX COHEN.

References p. 324.

SUMMARY

The specificity pattern of choline acetylase was tested with partially purified preparations, obtained from head ganglia of Squid, of a specific activity of about 40 to 80 μM of ester formed per mg protein per hour. The reaction mixture contained in addition to the enzyme only acyl derivatives of CoA and amino ethanols methylated with a varying number of methyl groups as substrates.

The acetylation of choline was tested as a function of acetyl CoA, of choline and of enzyme concentration. The choline curves showed marked saturation corresponding to a MICHAELIS-MENTEN constant of about $2 \cdot 10^{-3} M$. The acetyl CoA showed less saturation in the range tested; the data correspond to a MICHAELIS-MENTEN constant of the order of $5 \cdot 10^{-3} M$.

A striking differences was obtained in the acetylation of trimethyl, dimethyl and monomethyl ethanolamine. With the di- and monomethyl compounds the acetylation was only 8 and 2 % respectively, compared to that of trimethyl aminoethanol. This strong distinction by the enzyme toward the 3rd methyl group becomes of great biological interest in view of comparably strong effects of the 3rd methyl group towards the other proteins of the acetylcholine system. Loss of the 3rd methyl group leads to nearly complete loss of action upon the receptor protein which determines nerve membrane characteristics associated with such phenomena as ion permeability and electric potential. In the reactivation process of acetylcholinesterase inhibited by alkyl phosphates similar sharp differences between compounds with 2 and 3 methyl groups are observed in the interaction with the enzyme.

In view of the chemically saturated nature of a quaternary group and its tetrahedral structure it is suggested that its unique action may be attributed to an alteration of the protein configuration so as to envelope the molecule. This appears necessary if the protein is to interact simultaneously with the three methyl groups and the chemical functional group of the molecule. Such change in configuration may be necessary for full function of the proteins.

Among the acyl derivatives of CoA only propionyl CoA has a reactivity comparable to that of acetyl CoA. The enzyme does not mediate the reaction of butyryl CoA with choline, although the latter is bound by the enzyme even stronger than the acetyl CoA. This may have biological significance, since in contrast to propionyl CoA butyryl CoA is an intermediate of fatty acid metabolism and a ready formation of this choline ester may have undesirable effects.

RÉSUMÉ

La spécificité de la choline acétylase a été étudiée sur des préparations partiellement purifiées, obtenues à partir de ganglions céphaliques de calmar, et dont l'activité spécifique était d'environ 40 à 80 μM d'ester formé par mg de protéine et par heure. Le milieu réactionnel renfermait, outre l'enzyme, exclusivement des dérivés acétylés du CoA et des amino éthanols méthylés, portant un nombre variable de groupements méthyliques, comme substrats.

L'acétylation de la choline a été étudiée en fonction de la concentration en acétyl CoA, en choline et en enzyme. Les courbes de la choline présentent une saturation marquée correspondant à une constante de MICHAELIS-MENTEN d'environ $2 \cdot 10^{-3} M$. L'acétyl CoA présente une saturation moins nette dans le domaine des concentrations employées; les résultats correspondent à une constante de MICHAELIS-MENTEN de l'ordre de $5 \cdot 10^{-3} M$.

Une différence frappante existe entre l'acétylation de la triméthyl-, de la diméthyl- et de la monométhyléthanolamine. L'acétylation des composés di- et monométhylés n'est que 8 et 2 % respectivement, de celle du triméthylaminoéthanol. La forte spécificité de l'enzyme vis à vis du 3ème groupe méthylique présente un grand intérêt biologique, étant donné les effets comparables du 3ème groupe méthylique vis à vis d'autres protéines du système de l'acétylcholine. La perte du 3ème groupe méthylique entraine une perte d'action presque totale sur la protéine récepteur qui détermine les propriétés de la membrane de la fibre nerveuse, associées à des phénomènes tels que la perméabilité aux ions et le potentiel électrique. Au cours de la réactivation de l'acétylcholinestérase inhibée par des alkyl phosphates, des différences pareilles entre les substances avec deux et trois groupes méthyliques s'observent dans l'interaction avec l'enzyme.

Etant donné le caractère saturé d'un groupe quaternaire et sa structure tétraédrique, on peut supposer que sa seule action peut être une altération de la configuration de la protéine telle que cette dernière enveloppe la molécule. Ce phénomène doit être nécessaire, si la protéine doit réagir à la fois avec les trois groupes méthyliques et le groupe chimique fonctionnel de la molécule. De telles modifications de configuration semblent nécessaires pour que l'activité des protéines soit totale.

ZUSAMMENFASSUNG

Die Spezifität der Cholinacetylase wurde mit teilweise gereinigten, aus den Kopfganglien des Tintenfisches erhaltenen, Präparaten einer spezifischen Aktivität von 40–80 μM gebildeten Esters

References p. 324.

pro mg Protein pro Stunde untersucht. Die Reaktionsmischung enthielt zusätzlich zu dem Enzym nur Acylderivate des CoA und methylierte Aminoäthanole mit einer wechselnden Anzahl von Methylgruppen als Substrate.

Die Acetylierung des Cholins wurde untersucht als Funktion der Konzentration von Acetyl-CoA, von Cholin und Enzym. Die Cholinkurven zeigten eine ausgesprochene Sättigung, die einer MICHAELIS-MENTEN-Konstante von ungefähr $2 \cdot 10^{-3}$ M entspricht. Das Acetyl-CoA zeigte geringere Sättigung in dem überprüften Bereich; die Daten entsprechen einer MICHAELIS-MENTEN-Konstante von $5 \cdot 10^{-3}$ M.

Auffallende Unterschiede zeigten sich bei der Acetylierung von Trimethyl-, Dimethyl- und Monomethyläthanolamin. Bei den Di- und Monomethylverbindungen betrug die Acetylierung nur 8 bzw. 2% verglichen mit der des Trimethyläthanols. Dieses starke Unterscheidungsvermögen des Enzyms der dritten Methylgruppe gegenüber, erhält grosses biologisches Interesse, da auch die dritte Methylgruppe gegenüber den anderen Proteinen des Acetylcholinsystems vergleichbar starke Wirkung besitzt. Der Verlust der dritten Methylgruppe führt zu einem beinahe vollständigen Verschwinden der Wirkung gegenüber dem Receptorprotein, das die mit der Ionenpermeabilität und dem elektrischen Potential verbundenen Eigenschaften der Nervenmembran bestimmt. Bei dem Reaktivierungsprozess der von Alkylphosphaten gehemmten Acetylcholinesterase werden bei der Reaktion des Enzyms ähnliche scharfe Unterschiede zwischen Verbindungen mit zwei und drei Methylgruppen beobachtet.

Im Hinblick auf die chemisch abgesättigte Natur einer quaternären Gruppe und ihrer tetrahedrischen Struktur wird vermutet, dass ihre einzigartige Wirkung mit einer Veränderung der Proteinkonfiguration und damit mit einer Einhüllung des Moleküls verbunden ist. Dies erscheint nötig, da das Protein gleichzeitig mit den drei Methylgruppen und der chemisch funktionellen Gruppe des Moleküls reagieren muss. Derartige Konfigurationsänderungen scheinen für die volle Funktion des Proteins notwendig zu sein.

Unter den Acylderivaten des CoA hat nur Propionyl-CoA eine dem Acetyl-CoA vergleichbare Reaktivität. Das Enzym vermittelt nicht die Reaktion des Butyryl-CoA mit Cholin, obwohl letzteres sogar stärker als Acetyl-CoA vom Enzym gebunden wird. Dies kann biologische Bedeutung besitzen, da im Gegensatz zu Propionyl-CoA Butyryl-CoA ein Zwischenprodukt im Fettsäurestoffwechsel ist und eine leichte Bildung dieses Cholinesters unerwünschte Effekte mitsichbringen könnte.

REFERENCES

[1] D. NACHMANSOHN, in E.S.G. BARRON; *Modern Trends of Physiology and Biochemistry*, Academic Press, New York (1952) 229.
[2] D. NACHMANSOHN AND I. B. WILSON, *Advances in Enzymology*, XII (1951) 259.
[3] D. NACHMANSOHN AND A. L. MACHADO, *J. Neurophysiol.*, 6 (1943) 397.
[4] F. LIPMANN AND N. O. KAPLAN, *J. Biol. Chem.*, 162 (1946) 743.
[5] M. A. LIPTON, *Federation Proc.*, 5 (1946) 145.
[6] D. NACHMANSOHN AND M. BERMAN, *J. Biol. Chem.*, 165 (1946) 551.
[7] G. D. NOVELLI, in MC ELROY AND GLASS: *Phosphorus Metabolism I.* Johns Hopkins University Press (1951).
[8] E. E. SNELL, G. M. BROWN, V. J. PETERS, J. A. CRAIG, E. L. WITTLE, J. A. MOORE, V. M. McGLOHON and O. BIRD, *J. Am. Chem. Soc.*, 72 (1950) 5349.
[9] F. LYNEN, E. REICHERT AND L. RUEFF, *Liebig's Ann.* 1 (1951) 574.
[10] J. R. STERN, S. OCHOA and F. LYNEN, *J. Biol. Chem.*, 198 (1952) 313
[11] E. R. STADTMAN, *J. Biol. Chem.*, 196 (1952) 535.
[12] S. R. KOREY, B. DE BRAGANZA AND D. NACHMANSOHN, *J. Biol. Chem.*, 189 (1951) 705.
[13] I. B. WILSON, F. BERGMANN AND D. NACHMANSOHN, *J. Biol. Chem.*, 186 (1950) 781.
[14] I. B. WILSON, *J. Biol. Chem.*, 197 (1952) 215
[15] I. B. WILSON, *J. Biol. Chem.*, 199 (1952) 113.
[16] D. NACHMANSOHN AND M. S. WEISS, *J. Biol. Chem.*, 172 (1948) 677.
[17] S. HESTRIN, *J. Biol. Chem.*, 180 (1949) 249.
[18] A. GORNALL, *J. Biol. Chem.*, 177 (1949) 751
[19] E. SIMON AND D. SHEMIN, *J. Am. Chem. Soc.*, 75 (1953) 2520.
[20] R. R. GRUNERT AND PH. PHILIPS, *Arch. Biochem.*, 30 (1951) 217.
[21] I. B. WILSON, *J. Biol. Chem.*, 1950 (1951) 111.

Received June 24th, 1953.

ÜBER PYRROL-RADIKALE

von

RICHARD KUHN und HELMUTH KAINER

Max-Planck-Institut für Medizinische Forschung, Institut für Chemie, Heidelberg (Deutschland)

Schüttelt man eine farblose Lösung von Tetraphenyl-pyrrol[1] in Toluol* mit Bleidioxyd so färbt sie sich tief rot. Die filtrierte rote Lösung wird beim Abkühlen auf —60° (CO$_2$-Schnee/Äther) völlig farblos, um bei Raumtemperatur ihre ursprüngliche Farbe wieder anzunehmen. Dieses Spiel lässt sich unter Luftabschluss beliebig wiederholen.

Erhitzt man die rote Lösung, so vertieft sich die Farbe noch beträchtlich. Das Absorptionsspektrum ist in Fig. 1 dargestellt.

Die Erscheinungen erinnern an die temperaturabhängige Dissoziation von Tetraphenylhydrazin in 2 Mole Diphenylstickstoff[2] $(C_6H_5)_2N–N(C_6H_5)_2 \rightleftarrows 2(C_6H_5)_2N$ ... und legen die Annahme nahe, dass es sich beim Tetraphenyl-pyrrol (I) um die Bildung freier Radikale mit 2-wertigem Stickstoff (II) handelt:

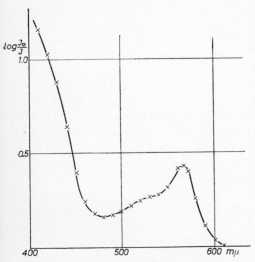

Fig. 1. Absorptionsspektrum einer 4%-igen Lösung von Tetraphenyl-pyrrol nach 10 Minuten langem Erhitzen mit PbO$_2$. Schichtdicke 1 mm.

Die roten Lösungen gehorchen, wie diejenigen des Diphenylstickstoffs, nicht dem Beer'schem Gesetz (Fig. 2). Im Gegensatz zu den olivgrünen Lösungen von Diphenylstickstoff sind sie jedoch gegen Sauerstoff empfindlich (Fig. 3), ohne dass die ausserordentliche O$_2$-Empfindlichkeit von Radikalen mit 3-wertigem Kohlenstoff erreicht wird**.

---

* An Stelle von Toluol kann man auch Benzol, Cyclohexan, Aceton, Chloroform, Dioxan und andere hydroxylfreie organische Lösungsmittel verwenden.

** Nachdem wir in unserer Arbeit über Ringerweiterung am Tetraphenylpyrrol, aus dem bei Einwirkung von Bleitetraacetat Tetra-phenyl-pyrazin entsteht[3] über das Auftreten roter Radikallösungen berichtet hatten, hat uns Herr Prof. Dr. G. WITTIG in freundlicher Weise darauf aufmerksam gemacht, dass in einer unter seiner Leitung ausgeführten Doktordissertation von O. UNGEMACH, Marburg/Lahn, 1932, die nicht veröffentlicht worden ist, die Rotfärbung bei Einwirkung von PbO$_2$ auf Tetraphenyl-pyrrol bereits beschrieben worden ist. Herrn Prof. Dr. G. WITTIG sind wir für die Überlassung eines Exemplares dieser Dissertation sehr dankbar. Aus ihr haben wir ersehen dass die Reaktionsfähigkeit mit O$_2$ und mit NO schon damals auffiel.

Literatur S. 328.

Sehr wahrscheinlich lässt sich das ungepaarte Elektron nicht streng am N-Atom lokalisieren, so dass das Dehydrotetraphenylpyrrol in geringem Masse auch als Radikal mit 3-wertigem Kohlenstoff (III ⟷ IV) zu reagieren vermag:

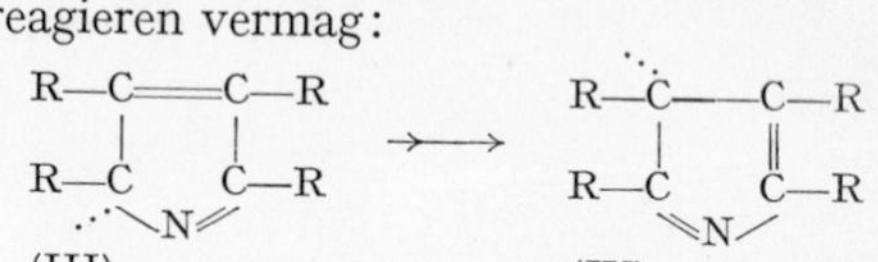

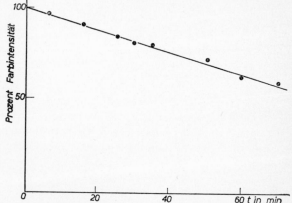

$$
\begin{array}{ccc}
R-C{=\!=}C-R & & R-\overset{\cdot\cdot}{C}\text{---}C-R \\
\mid\quad\quad\mid & \longrightarrow & \mid\quad\quad\parallel \\
R-C\quad\;\; C-R & & R-C\quad\;\; C-R \\
\;\;\overset{\cdot\cdot}{\diagdown}N\diagup & & \;\;\diagdown N\diagup \\
\text{(III)} & & \text{(IV)}
\end{array}
$$

Mit NO, NO$_2$, mit Triphenylmethyl und mit Phenyl-biphenylyl-keton-kalium erfolgt augenblicklich Entfärbung. Mit seinem C-Analogon, dem Pentaphenyl-cyklopentadienyl von ZIEGLER, tritt jedoch keine Umsetzung ein. Diphenylamin wird zu Tetraphenyl-hydrazin dehydriert. Dihydropyocyanin wird in die grüne Monohydroverbindung verwandelt. Das rote Tetraphenyl-pyrryl übertrifft an Dehydrierungsvermögen sogar das permanganatfarbige N,N-Diphenyl-N′-trinitrophenyl-hydrazyl von ST. GOLDSCHMIDT, das von seinem Entdecker als besonders starkes Oxydationsmittel für Amine und Phenole beschrieben worden ist:

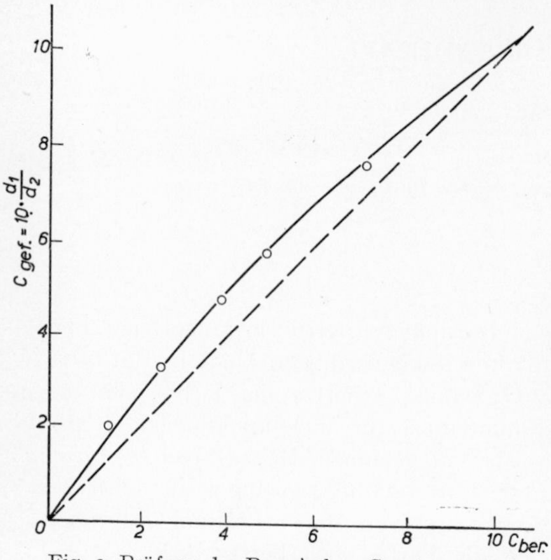

Fig. 2. Prüfung des BEER'schen Gesetzes. 2 %-ige Lösung von Tetraphenyl-pyrrol in Benzol, in der Wärme mit PbO$_2$ dehydriert. Messung der relativen Farbstärken im Duboscq-Kolorimeter unter Stickstoff. ——— gefundene Werte; – – – – theoretische Gerade bei Gültigkeit des BEER'schen Gesetzes.

Pyrryl + Hydrazin ⟶ Pyrrol + Hydrazyl
(rot)   (orange)   (farblos)   (violett)

Diese Reaktion kann zur quantitativen Bestimmung des Radikalgehaltes der roten Lösungen dienen, indem man das gebildete violette Hydrazyl mit Hydrochinon titriert.

Auf diese Weise fanden wir, dass der Gehalt an dehydriertem Tetraphenyl-pyrrol in unseren roten Lösungen durchschnittlich nur 2–4% d. Th. betrug. Dieselben Werte findet man bei direkter Titration mit Hydrochinon, das die roten Lösungen sofort entfärbt. Wieviel davon auf Radikale mit 2-wertigem Stickstoff und wieviel auf dimeres Dehydrierungsprodukt, das mit diesem im Gleichgewicht steht, entfällt, lässt sich noch nicht angeben. Verdampft man unter sorgfältigem Ausschluss von Luft rote Lösungen, so hinterbleibt eine rosa gefärbte krystalline Substanz, die im Hochvakuum wochenlang haltbar

Fig. 3. Sauerstoffempfindlichkeit. Abnahme der Farbstärke (Messungen mit dem Duboscq-Kolorimeter) einer benzolischen Lösung bei 20° C, wobei gelegentlich mit Luft umgeschüttelt wurde.

ist. Sie löst sich in organ. Solventien wieder auf mit tief roter Farbe. In der Hauptsache besteht sie laut Elementaranalysen und DEBYE-SCHERRER-Aufnahmen aus

Literatur S. 328.

unverändertem Tetraphenyl-pyrrol; Titrationen mit Hydrochinon ergaben einen Gehalt von 2–4% an Dehydrierungsprodukt.

Wie Tetraphenyl-pyrrol verhalten sich auch 2:3:4:5-Tetra-*p*-tolyl-pyrrol und 2:3-Diphenyl-4:5-di-*p*-tolyl-pyrrol gegen PbO_2. Eine Dehydrierung *p*-ständiger Methingruppen erfolgt also nicht. An Stelle von PbO_2 können auch $PbAc_4$, Naphthodichinon und Anthradichinon, die DIMROTH[4] als Verbindungen mit extrem hohem Oxydationspotential erkannt hat, angewandt werden. Dass auch bei den Tolylverbindungen, der Radikalgehalt der roten Lösungen einige wenige Prozent nicht übersteigt, hängt abgesehen von dem ungewöhnlich hohen Potential auch damit zusammen, dass die Radikale miteinander unter Bildung von Tetra-arylpyrazinen reagieren.

Nach fallendem Dehydrierungsvermögen ergibt sich die Reihenfolge:

> Tetraphenyl-pyrryl
> N,N-Diphenyl-N′-trinitrophenyl-hydrazyl[*]
> Diphenyl-stickstoff[*]
> Monohydro-pyocyanin

Pyrrolkörper scheinen zur Bildung freier Radikale verschiedener Art befähigt zu sein: von ungeladenen Radikalen mit 2-wertigem N, und von Radikal-ionen mit 3-wertigem positiv geladenen Stickstoff, wie die Darstellung des tiefblauen, paramagnetischen Pentaphenyl-pyrrolium-perchlorats[6] gezeigt hat. Ob sich Porphyrine, unter Verlust der beiden an N gebundenen H-Atome, zu Dehydroporphyrinen werden dehydrieren lassen, bedarf noch der Prüfung.

BESCHREIBUNG DER VERSUCHE

1. *Herstellung von Radikalmischkrystallen*

1 g Tetraphenyl-pyrrol, 4 g geglühtes Na_2SO_4 und 10 g PbO_2 (E. Merck) wurden in 50 ml trockenem, analysenreinem Benzol 2.5 Stdn. unter reinem Stickstoff auf 80–90° erhitzt (Wasserbad). Die tief rot gefärbte Lösung filtrierte man unter Luftausschluss ab und dampfte i.V. ein. Die zurückbleibende, schwach rosa gefärbte Substanz lösten wir in möglichst wenig heissem Benzol auf und fügten Petroläther (60–70°), hinzu. Dabei schieden sich reichlich schwach rosa gefärbte Krystalle ab. Sie gaben dem Tetraphenyl-pyrrol entsprechende Analysenzahlen.

$$C_{28}H_{21}N \quad (371.18) \quad \text{Ber. C } 90.52, \quad \text{H } 5.70, \quad \text{N } 3.77\%$$
$$\text{Gef. C } 90.81, \quad \text{H } 6.08, \quad \text{N } 3.78\%$$

148.6 mg Radikalmischkrystall verbrauchten 6.5 ml einer Hydrochinonlösung (14.9 mg Hydrochinon in 100 ml Alkohol). Das entspricht einem Radikalgehalt von etwa 4%. Andere gleichartig hergestellte Präparate wiesen einen Gehalt von 2–4% an Dehydrierungsprodukt auf. Dies entspricht dem Radikalgehalt frisch hergestellter roter Lösungen. Die Radikalmischkrystalle gleichen im Habitus kryst. Tetraphenyl-pyrrol. Im DEBYE-SCHERRER-Diagramm liessen sich keine Unterschiede erkennen.

2. *Darstellung von 2:3-Di-(p-tolyl)-4:5-di-phenyl-pyrrol*

19.6 g Desoxybenzoin und 24.0 g *p*-Toluoin wurden mit 100 g Ammoniumacetat in 500 ml Eisessig 2.5 Stdn. unter Rückfluss erhitzt. Anschliessend fügten wir zur vollständigen Abscheidung des bereits teilweise ausgefallenen krystallisierten Rohproduktes 200 ml heisses Wasser hinzu. Nach Abkühlen erhielten wir 12 g schwach hellgrün gefärbte Krystalle (Ausb. 20% d.Th.). Zur Analyse krystallisierten wir zweimal aus Chloroform-Methanol um, wobei sich die Substanz in Form langer Nadeln abschied, und trockneten bei 100°/5 mm. Schmp. 196°.

$$C_{30}H_{25}N \quad (398.5) \quad \text{Ber. C } 90.41, \quad \text{H } 6.07, \quad \text{N } 3.51\%$$
$$\text{Gef. C } 89.96, \quad \text{H } 6.60, \quad \text{N } 3.50\%$$

Dieselbe Substanz erhält man in ungefähr der gleichen Ausbeute auch beim Erhitzen von Benzoin und Desoxytoluoin mit Ammoniumacetat in Eisessig.

---

[*] Dass durch Dehydrierung von Diphenyl-amin mit N,N-Diphenyl-N′-trinitrophenyl-hydrazyl Diphenyl-stickstoff entsteht, haben schon GOLDSCHMIDT UND RENN[5] beobachtet.

Literatur S. 328.

3. *Darstellung von Tetra-p-tolyl-pyrrol*

a. Aus *p*-Toluoin. 15 g *p*-Toluoin erhitzen wir in 400 ml Eisessig mit 4.2 g Zinkstaub und 40 g Ammoniumacetat 2½ Stdn. unter Rückfluss. Nach Beendigung der Reaktion fällten wir mit 100 ml heissem Wasser 5.5 g krystallisiertes Kondensationsprodukt (Ausb. 22 % d.Th.). Die Substanz wurde je einmal aus Äthanol und Chloroform-Methanol umgelöst und schmolz dann bei 173°. Feine Nadeln aus beiden Lösungsmitteln.

$$C_{32}H_{29}N \quad (427.2) \quad \text{Ber. C 89.88,} \quad \text{H 6.84,} \quad \text{N 3.28\%}$$
$$\text{Gef. C 90.01,} \quad \text{H 6.84,} \quad \text{N 3.42\%}$$

b. Durch Kondensation von Desoxytoluoin und *p*-Toluoin. 3.5 g Desoxytoluoin, 20 g Ammoniumacetat, 3.7 g *p*-Toluoin wurden in 100 ml Eisessig 2 Stdn. unter Rückfluss gekocht und anschliessend mit 25 ml heissem Wasser versetzt. Wir erhielten 5.3 g Rohprodukt, das aus Äthanol und Chloroform-Methanol umgelöst wurde. Die Substanz schmolz bei 173° und gab mit der unter a. hergestellten Verbindung keine Depression im Mischschmelzpunkt.

4. *Bildung von Tetra-p-tolyl-pyrazin aus Tetra-p-tolyl-pyrrol*

4.5 g Tetra-*p*-tolyl-pyrrol in 150 ml Eisessig versetzen wir bei einer Temperatur von 80° unter starkem Rühren anteilweise mit der gesättigten Lösung von 2 g $NaNO_2$ in Wasser. Es wurde noch eine Weile weitergerührt, wobei sich feine farblose Nädelchen abschieden. Diese lösten wir zur Analyse aus Eisessig um. Schmp. 292°, Literatur[7] 287°.

$$C_{32}H_{28}N_2 \quad (440.23) \quad \text{Ber. C 87.22,} \quad \text{H 6.41,} \quad \text{N 6.36\%}$$
$$\text{Gef. C 87.15,} \quad \text{H 6.41,} \quad \text{N 6.44\%}$$

Die Bildung der gleichen Substanz in geringer Menge beobachteten wir auch beim Erhitzen von Tetratolyl-pyrrol mit PbO_2 in Benzol und sonderbarerweise auch bei der Umsetzung von Ditolyl-diphenyl-pyrrol mit Bleitetra-acetat.

ZUSAMMENFASSUNG

1. Es werden Eigenschaften der roten Radikal-lösungen beschrieben, die man aus Tetraphenyl-pyrrol durch Einwirkung von Dehydrierungsmitteln erhält.
2. Es wird geschlossen, dass es sich um Tetraphenyl-pyrryl-Radikale mit 2-wertigem Stickstoff handelt, die in geringem Masse auch als Radikale mit 3-wertigem Kohlenstoff zu reagieren vermögen.
3. An Dehydrierungsvermögen übertreffen sie alle bisher bekannten Stickstoff-Radikale.

SUMMARY

1. The authors describe the properties of the red solutions of free radicals that are obtained by the action of dehydrogenators on tetraphenylpyrrole.
2. It is concluded that radicals of tetraphenyl-pyrryl with bivalent nitrogen are dealt with, which react similarly, but to a lesser degree, to radicals with trivalent carbon.
3. The dehydrogenating power of these radicals surpasses that of all other known nitrogen radicals.

RÉSUMÉ

1. Les auteurs décrivent les propriétés des solutions rouges de radicaux libres que l'on obtient par action des déshydrogénants sur le tetraphényl-pyrrol.
2. Ils concluent qu'il s'agit de radicaux tetraphényl-pyrryl à azote bivalent qui peuvent réagir également, en une faible mesure, comme radicaux à carbone trivalent.
3. Le pouvoir déshydrogénant de ces radicaux dépasse celui de tous les radicaux d'azote connus jusqu'à présent.

LITERATUR

[1] Dargestellt nach D. DAVIDSON, *J. Org. Chem.*, 3 (1938) 361.
[2] H. WIELAND, *Ann.*, 381 (1911) 200.
[3] R. KUHN UND H. KAINER, *Ann.*, 578 (1952) 226.
[4] O. DIMROTH, *Z. angew. Chem.*, 46 (1933) 571.
[5] ST. GOLDSCHMIDT UND K. RENN, *Ber.*, 55 (1922) 628, Fussnote 5.
[6] R. KUHN UND H. KAINER, *Chem. Ber.*, 85 (1952) 498.
[7] TH. CURTIUS UND R. KASTNER, *J. prakt. Chem.*, 2, 83 (1911) 230.

Eingegangen den 29. Juli 1953

EFFECTS OF INSULIN ON MELANOMA AND BRAIN METABOLISM

by

MARK WOODS, KENT WIGHT, JEHU HUNTER AND DEAN BURK

National Cancer Institute, National Institutes of Health,
Public Health Service, Department of Health, Education and Welfare
Bethesda, Maryland (U.S.A.)

INTRODUCTION

The prime importance of glycolysis in the metabolism of tumors was first recognized in the researches of OTTO WARBURG begun over 30 years ago. In 1930[32] he wrote, in summary, "*Glycolysis* is a property of all tumors, and very different types of tumors agree quantitatively, as regards glycolysis, to a considerable extent." Today, as the result of his continued researches and those of many others, WARBURG has reaffirmed that "shifting of the metabolism to the anaerobic state is the main biochemical difference between the tumor and normal cell"[33].

Since the primary known action of insulin is a stimulation of glucose uptake, and associated processes, the possible role of this hormone in tumor glycolysis is of special importance, particularly since tumors are geared to a glucose metabolism. While there is a considerable literature dealing with the effect of insulin on the *in vitro* metabolism of normal tissues, relatively little has been reported concerning its *in vitro* action on the metabolism of malignant tissues. In the present paper we report metabolic responses obtained following direct addition of insulin to reaction vessels containing freshly sectioned tissue. Such an approach has the advantage of exposing the tissue in question to the direct action of the hormone and related substances (*e.g.* zinc). Our studies have been limited chiefly to the malignant S–91 mouse melanoma of CLOUDMAN[6], and to whole brain preparations of normal mouse. Brain was compared with melanoma because both tissues possess a marked glucose metabolism; both display a considerable aerobic glycolysis; and, although the tumor melanoblast cannot be considered a nerve cell *per se*, it is in all probability of neural origin[11, 25]. The results obtained with brain do not demonstrate positive effects of added insulin but they do illustrate significant metabolic differences between the two types of tissues. The results with melanoma indicate that insulin plays an important role in determining the rate of glycolysis ($Q_{CO_2}^{N_2}$, $Q_{CO_2}^{O_2}$) as well as influencing certain other metabolic functions. Furthermore, the data from these *in vitro* experiments indicate that zinc plays a critical role in insulin action.

MATERIALS AND METHODS

The S–91 melanoma was maintained by intramuscular transplantation in dba mice as previously described[35], and was actively growing and readily transplantable*. Normal brains were usually

---

* The authors are indebted to Mr GEORGE HOBBY for his valuable assistance in maintaining the tumors used in this investigation.

obtained from Webster white mice of the N.I.H. strain; dba and C–57 black mice were used in some experiments. No differences in brain metabolism attributable to strain of mouse were noted in these experiments. In a number of experiments, the tumor-bearing mice were exposed to controlled tempera-tures for varying periods of time before the *in vitro* measurements. These are specifically described in the text. Tissues were sectioned by hand with a sharp, single-edge, safety razor blade, rapidly weighed on a torsion balance, and transferred to appropriate solutions in the respirometer vessels which were immersed in ice and water until transferred onto the manometers.

Anaerobic conditions were provided by gassing with a mixture of 95% N_2 and 5% CO_2 which had been passed, together, with a small amount of H_2 (*ca.* 1%), over hot copper to remove traces of O_2. In aerobic experiments 95% O_2 and 5% CO_2 were employed in the gas phase. Two media, which gave similar results, were used, Hank Simms* and Krebs-Ringer-bicarbonate**. A few experiments were al-so run in WARBURG-OKAMOTO solution***. Dextrose and $KHCO_3$ were added to these media as required. Unless otherwise stated all experiments were run at a level of 0.625% dextrose, a concentration found to give maximal rates of glycolysis in both brain and melanoma slices without significantly inhibiting respiration. Acid production was measured in terms of CO_2 released from the bicarbonate-buffered medium. Preliminary experiments in Hank-Simms medium with melanoma and brain slices showed that practically all of the manometrically indicated acid could be accounted for as lactic. 0.03 M $KHCO_3$ was routinely employed with 5% CO_2 in the gas phase to give an initial pH of *ca.* 7.6 at 38° C. pH determinations were frequently made of the vessel contents at the end of each run. Aerobic de-terminations were carried out with the Summerson differential manometer and modified Dixon-Keilin flasks.

Four types of insulin preparations were used†, (1) Iletin (insulin, Lilly) containing crystalline zinc-insulin and 0.2% phenol as a preservative; (2) zinc-insulin crystals (Lilly no. 535664); (3) zinc-insulin crystals (Lilly no. 499667) which had been treated with trypsin to destroy all of the hyper-glycemic factor (HGF); and (4) amorphous low-zinc (0.017%) insulin (Squibb no. 53 In-1). The sample of purified hyperglycemic factor contained only 0.05 units of insulin per mg. Inorganic zinc was supplied as $ZnSO_4 \cdot 7H_2O$, reported concentrations being for actual weight of zinc. Phenol (as separate from commercial insulin preparations) was reagent grade, Merck. All materials, except the commercial insulin solution, were in most cases added in distilled water (0.25 ml per 1.0 ml of medium) directly to the refrigerated respirometer vessels before placing them on the bath maintained at 38° C. In certain experiments the crystalline zinc-insulin was dissolved in 0.025 N NaOH and the pH immediately adjusted to *ca.* 7.0. This method of preparation gave clear solutions which were useful in making high dilutions of the hormone. The use of such preparations is specifically mentioned in the text.

The following symbols have been used to designate the metabolic activities measured: Q_{O_2} = microliters of oxygen consumed per mg initial dry weight per hour; $Q_{CO_2}^{O_2}$ = microliters of acid, in terms of CO_2, produced per mg initial dry weight per hour in the presence of oxygen; $Q_{CO_2}^{N_2}$, like the preceding, but in the absence of oxygen.

Comparative metabolism of melanoma and brain slices in Hank-Simms medium

The comparative behavior of brain and S–91 melanoma slices in Hank-Simms medium is illustrated in Table I. Values for embryonic brain slices (fetus *ca.* 10 days old) and slices of total embryo (fetus several days old) are given for comparison in the same medium. Contrary to generality, $Q_{CO_2}^{O_2}$ was greater then $Q_{CO_2}^{N_2}$ in adult brain (9.4 vs 2.3), which is all the more strkjing in view of the high Q_{O_2} (17.1) which would normally yield a positive rather than a negative Pasteur effect. Monkey brain (young adult female *Rhesus*)††, although showing a somewhat different quantitative pattern, behaved in a

---

* *Hank-Simms solution* (values refer to molarities): Hank's solution–3 parts: NaCl 0.137, KCl 0.005, $MgSO_4 \cdot 7H_2O$ 0.004, $MgCl_2 \cdot 6H_2O$ 0.005, $CaCl_2$ 0.001, $Na_2HPO_4 \cdot 12H_2O$ 0.00017, KH_2PO_4 0.00044; Simm's serum ultrafiltrate (prepared by Microbiological Associates, Bethesda, Md., from ox blood) 1 part $NaHCO_3$ was replaced by $KHCO_3$ and dextrose varied as indicated in the text. Phenol red (0.02 g/liter) was added as an indicator.

** *Krebs-Ringer-bicarbonate solution* (values refer to molarities): NaCl 0.141, KCl 0.005, $CaCl_2$ 0.003, KH_2PO_4 0.0014, $MgSO_4 \cdot 7H_2O$ 0.0014. $KHCO_3$ and dextrose added as indicated in the text.

*** *Warburg-Okamoto solution* (values refer to molarities): NaCl 0.148, $CaCl_2$ 0.002, KCl 0.003.

† We are indebted to Doctors H. A. CLOWES AND OTTO BEHRENS of Eli Lilly and Co. for the preparations of zinc-insulin crystals and the purified H.G.F. Dr. A. BORMAN of E. R. Squibb and Sons kindly supplied the amorphous low-zinc insulin preparation.

†† Data on comparative metabolism of various tissues of mouse and monkey were secured with Dr. ALEXIS SHELOKOV of the Laboratory of Infectious Diseases, National Microbiological Institute. These will be reported elsewhere.

References p. 346.

TABLE I

COMPARATIVE METABOLIC ACTIVITIES OF NORMAL MOUSE BRAIN AND S–91 MELANOMA SLICES IN HANK-SIMMS MEDIUM PLUS 0.03 M KHCO$_3$ AND 0.625% DEXTROSE. THE RESULTS OF SINGLE EXPERIMENTS UNDER THE SAME CONDITIONS WITH EMBRYONIC MOUSE BRAIN (*ca.* I WEEK OLD) AND TOTAL EMBRYO (LESS THAN I WEEK OLD) ARE SHOWN FOR COMPARISON

Gas phase and metabolic measurement	Brain			S-91 Melanoma			Embryonic brain	Total embryo
	Average	Range	No. of Expts.	Average	Range	No. of Expts.		
95% O$_2$; 5% CO$_2$								
$Q_{O_2}^a$	− 17.1	(15.3–20.5)	4	− 4.5	(3.8–5.2)	3	− 5.9	− 6.0
R.Q. (CO$_2$/O$_2$)	− 0.82	(0.72–0.93)	4	− 0.75	(0.58–0.91)	3	− 0.84	− 0.92
$Q_{CO_2}^{O_2\ a}$	+ 9.4	(5.7–13.0)	4	+ 4.6	(3.7–5.0)	3	+ 0.9[b]	+ 2.0
95% N$_2$; 5% CO$_2$								
$Q_{CO_2}^{N_2\ a}$	+ 2.3	(2.0–3.1)	10	+ 8.0	(7.5–8.8)	3	+ 4.3	+ 9.1
Pasteur effect		−300%			+43%		+70%	+78%

[a] All Q values expressed as μl/mg dry wt/hr. (Calculation based on 23% dry wt except melanoma calculations based on 20% dry wt).
[b] Became +5.1 in presence of 0.1 mg/ml Neotetrazolium where Q_{O_2} was −1.3 and R.Q. −1.2.

similar manner under the same experimental conditions ($Q_{O_2} = 7.2$, $Q_{CO_2}^{O_2} = 4.7$, and $Q_{CO_2}^{N_2} = 3.0$). Lactic acid determinations, which were made essentially by the method of BARKER-SUMMERSON[2], showed that with melanoma slices in Hank-Simms medium with 0.625% dextrose virtually all of the manometrically indicated acid could be accounted for as lactic. Thus in four experiments the average $Q_{CO_2}^{N_2}$ was 7.3 (range 4.5 to 8.8), and the average $Q_{lactic}^{N_2}$ was 7.3 (range 5.3 to 10.0). In the presence of oxygen the average $Q_{CO_2}^{O_2}$ was 4.3 (range 3.7 to 5.0) and the average $Q_{lactic}^{O_2}$ was 4.3 (range 4.1 to 4.7). Similarly in brain the $Q_{CO_2}^{N_2}$ in two experiments was 2.7 and 2.1 the respective lactic values, 2.1 and 2.1. In the second of these experiments $Q_{CO_2}^{O_2}$ was 5.7, and the $Q_{lactic}^{O_2}$ 4.0. All subsequent experiments were based upon measurements of CO$_2$ evolution only, and pH measurements were frequently made to provide a general check on the manometric data.

Action of phenol, magnesium, and insulin on brain slices

The $Q_{CO_2}^{N_2}$ of brain could be raised to the melanoma level by the combined effects of increasing the magnesium level from 0.01 mg to 0.4 mg per ml plus the addition of 0.25 ml of commercial insulin per ml of Hank-Simms medium to give a final concentration per ml of 4 units crystalline zinc-insulin and 0.4 mg phenol (the phenol present in commercial insulin as a preservative). Further experiments showed that this action of commercial zinc-insulin preparations, which was largely additive to the magnesium effect (Fig. 1), could be duplicated by the use of equivalent concentrations of phenol *without added insulin*. Furthermore, the crystalline, preservative-free zinc-insulin was without significant effect (Fig. 2). Both the usual zinc-insulin crystals, as well as the preparation free from hyperglycemic factor, gave negative results. The same negative results were also obtained when low-zinc insulin was used. However, without a single exception (over 20 experiments) addition of phenol (with or without insulin), and/or raising the magnesium level, increased the $Q_{CO_2}^{N_2}$ of brain although the magnitude of the stimulation varied in different preparations. Thus in 4 typical experiments

References p. 346.

with brain slices in Hank-Simms medium the average control $Q_{CO_2}^{N_2}$ was 2.4 (range 2.0 to 3.15) and the addition (before placing vessels at 38° C) of 0.4 mg of phenol per ml raised the $Q_{CO_2}^{N_2}$ to 5.25 (range 4.60 to 6.45). Addition of a commercial insulin preparation to give an equivalent concentration of phenol raised the $O_{CO_2}^{N_2}$ to a similar level, *i.e.* average 5.09 (range 4.7 to 6.0). In the absence of phenol, increasing the magnesium level from 0.01 mg to 0.4 mg per ml in three typical experiments increased the $Q_{CO_2}^{N_2}$ an average of 200% (range 131 to 268%). With the same preparations, an identical increase in magnesium level *in the presence of 0.4 mg phenol per ml*, gave an average

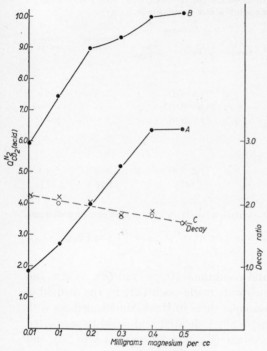

Fig. 1. Influence of magnesium level and phenol plus insulin (= commercial insulin) on rates of anaerobic acid production (solid lines) by mouse brain slices in Hank-Simms solution plus 0.03 M KHCO$_3$ and 0.625 % dextrose. B, with phenol, 0.4 mg and insulin, 4 units per ml (= commercial insulin); A, control minus phenol and insulin. The rate of decay in acid production (dotted line) is represented by the $Q_{CO_2}^{N_2}$ obtained for the period 0 to 66 minutes divided by the $Q_{CO_2}^{N_2}$ for the period 66 to 152 minutes. Gas phase 95% N$_2$ and 5% CO$_2$.

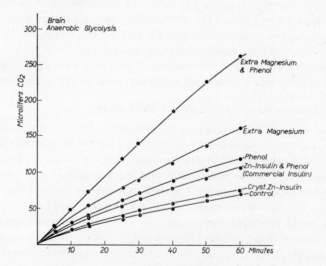

Fig. 2. The influence of crystalline zinc-insulin (4 units per ml), phenol (0.4 mg per ml), commercial regular insulin (4 units crystalline zinc-insulin and 0.4 mg phenol per ml), extra magnesium (0.48 mg magnesium per ml), and phenol plus extra magnesium (same respective concentrations) on rate of anaerobic acid production in brain (100 mg wet wt. of slices). Control level of magnesium = 0.016 mg per ml. In all cases Hank-Simms solution with 0.03 M KHCO$_3$, and 0.625% dextrose. Gas phase 95% N$_2$ and 5% CO$_2$.

increase of 110% (range 82 to 148%) over and above that caused by phenol alone. The combined effects of magnesium and phenol are more completely illustrated in Fig. 1 where the source of phenol was a commercial insulin preparation.

The stimulating action of phenol on $Q_{CO_2}^{N_2}$ of brain slices occurred only when it was added before the tissue had been incubated at 38° C. A delay of 20 minutes at 38° C before tipping the phenol was sufficient to eliminate the effect. Tissue exposed to commercial insulin preparations (plus phenol), and then rinsed once in insulin-phenol-free medium, behaved like untreated tissue both with respect to low $Q_{CO_2}^{N_2}$ in the absence of these substances and the occurrence of marked stimulation of acid production upon re-addition of phenol-insulin. Thus phenol seems to act as a stabilizing agent, presumably by preventing destruction of an enzyme, or enzymes, essential for maintenance of a high rate of acid production. In this connection it is of interest that addition of ATP (1 mg tetrasodium ATP per ml) to the reaction vessel had no significant effect on $Q_{CO}^{N_2}$ either in the presence or absence of extra magnesium, and/or phenol.

Action of phenol, magnesium, and insulin on melanoma slices

The responses of melanoma slices to phenol, magnesium, and insulin (Fig. 3) were in marked contrast to those obtained with brain. $Q_{CO_2}^{N_2}$ was not stimulated by phenol at any concentration tested (0.02 to 1.5 mg per ml). For example, in eight different experimental runs, involving five separate tumors, addition of 0.4 mg of phenol per ml gave an average lowering of $Q_{CO_2}^{N_2}$ of 15% (range 10 to 19 %). However, unlike the results obtained with brain slices, the addition of commercial insulin (to give a final concentration of 4 units of crystalline zinc-insulin and 0.4 mg phenol per ml) to melanoma preparations gave higher $Q_{CO_2}^{N_2}$ values than when equivalent phenol alone was added. When the $Q_{CO_2}^{N_2}$ plus commercial insulin was compared with that of the tissue plus phenol alone, it was found in five experiments (dextrose 0.625%) that the presence of insulin gave an average stimulation of 26% (range 6 to 55%). Because of the inhibiting effect of phenol alone, the effect of commercial insulin (with phenol as preservative) on $Q_{CO_2}^{N_2}$ of melanoma slices is more or less masked when comparisons are made with controls to which neither insulin nor phenol have been added.

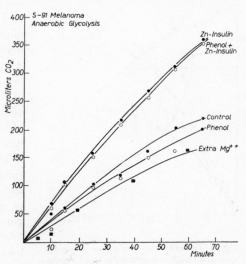

Fig. 3. Influence of crystalline zinc-insulin (4 units per ml), phenol (0.4 mg per ml), crystalline zinc-insulin plus phenol, and extra magnesium (0.48 mg additional per ml; control = 0.016 mg per ml) on anaerobic acid production in S–91 melanoma (100 mg wet wt. of slices). 0.625% dextrose, gas phase 95% N_2 and 5% CO_2.

In sharp contrast to brain, raising the magnesium level from 0.01 mg to 0.4 mg per ml did not increase the $Q_{CO_2}^{N_2}$ of melanoma slices. Instead the rate was decreased 0 to 25% (Fig. 3). Again in marked contrast to brain, the acid production by melanoma slices, was increased (Fig. 3) by the various preservative-free preparations of insulin. Crystalline zinc-insulin, rendered free of hyperglycemic factor by tryptic digestion, was as effective in stimulating acid production as was regular crystalline zinc-insulin. That HGF played no significant role in producing the observed effects was further evidenced by the fact that a preparation of purified factor (contained only 0.05 unit insulin per mg) at 2 γ per ml had no significant effect on $Q_{CO_2}^{N_2}$ in two experiments (0.9%); whereas HGF-free insulin in the same experiments gave 45% and 46% stimulation respectively. The remainder of this paper presents in detail the results obtained with preservative-free insulin, and/or varying concentrations of inorganic zinc.

Effect of glucose concentration

Glucose concentration had a marked effect on both the rate and the extent of response to insulin. This is illustrated by the results of an experiment shown graphically in Fig. 4. At a glucose level of 0.125% (equivalent to 312 μl lactic acid) the rate with insulin after 45 minutes was below that of the control (Fig. 4, A,A'), presumably due in part to glucose depletion. At the intermediate level of 0.225% glucose (Fig. 4, B,B') the rate with insulin remained above that of the control for over 90 minutes although there was a steady decline in the per cent stimulation. On the other hand at 0.625% glucose (Fig. 4, C,C') the per cent stimulation above the control was maximal and remained approximately constant for 60 minutes. A number of other experiments established the fact that under anaerobic conditions a high level of glucose was required to give maximal $Q_{CO_2}^{N_2}$ values, and maximal responses to insulin. BURK et al.[4] have shown that in other tissues the glycolytic system is stabilized under anaerobic conditions by glucose. In the present study, varying the glucose concentration from 0.125% to 0.625% had little effect (less than 5%) on the Q_{O_2} of brain or melanoma slices although $Q_{CO_2}^{O_2}$ was increased, particularly in brain. Because of these results 0.625% glucose was used routinely in the following experiments.

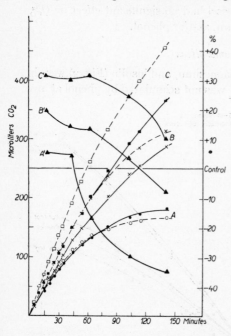

Fig. 4. The influence of glucose concentration and insulin on anaerobic acid production by S–91 melanoma slices in Hank-Simms medium (1.0 ml Hank-Simms plus 0.25 ml H$_2$O ± insulin). A, B and C show (by summation) microliters of CO$_2$ produced in time (solid line *minus* insulin, broken line *plus* 4 units crystalline zinc-insulin) by 100 mg wet weight of slices (left ordinate): A, with 0.125% dextrose, B, with 0.225% dextrose, and C with 0.625% dextrose. Curves A', B' and C' (right ordinate) represent *non-summative* plots of the percentage difference between the control and insulin-treated tissue (at the 3 glucose levels A, B and C respectively) for the time periods between successive points (heavy triangles). Gas phase 95% N$_2$ and 5% CO$_2$.

References p. 346.

Effect of insulin concentration

Crystalline zinc-insulin added in distilled water as the vehicle medium (0.25 ml water added per 1.0 ml Krebs-Ringer-bicarbonate, or Hank-Simms) was equally effective at final concentrations of 4.0 and 0.8 units per ml (*ca.* 0.15 to 0.03 mg insulin per ml). For example, in 3 experiments with melanoma from mice exposed to 35° C (see next section) the average $Q_{CO_2}^{N_2}$ without added insulin was 7.41 (range 6.0 to 9.4); with 4 units of crystalline zinc-insulin

10.88 (range 7.28 to 13.80); and at 0.8 unit per ml 11.15 (range 7.29 to 14.44). In a similar experiment in which crystalline zinc-insulin was compared with low-zinc insulin, the control $Q_{CO_2}^{N_2}$ was 9.4; with 4 and 0.8 units of crystalline zinc-insulin per ml, 13.80 and 14.44, respectively; and with the same levels of low-zinc insulin 13.47 and 13.54, respectively. The results of these, and other experiments, show conclusively that 0.8 unit of insulin per ml is approximately as effective as 4 units per ml in stimulating the $Q_{CO_2}^{N_2}$ of melanoma slices. However, crystalline zinc-insulin (unlike amorphous low-zinc insulin) is sparingly soluble in water. While the routine use of 4 to 0.8 units of insulin per ml in the present experiments assured a saturating concentration of insulin per vessel, it was desirable to determine the actual limiting concentrations capable of elevating $Q_{CO_2}^{N_2}$. For this purpose crystalline zinc-insulin was dissolved at alkaline pH (as described under methods) to give a clear solution which was immediately neutralized. Dilutions of such solution were added directly to the WARBURG vessels in the routine way. In two such experiments it was found that as little as 0.08 unit per ml ($= 3 \gamma$ per ml) was as effective as ten times this amount (42% and 39% average stimulation respectively). Other experiments confirmed this finding. Obviously the limiting concentration is below 0.08 unit per ml. Further experiments have indicated that the limiting concentration of insulin varies somewhere between 0.04 and 0.004 unit per ml (50 mg wet weight of tissue in a total fluid volume of 2.5 ml).

Solutions of zinc-insulin (0.15 units per ml) in 0.05 N NaOH were completely inactivated by heating for one hour at 100° C. While the extremely small amounts of insulin (3 γ or less per ml) that were effective in raising the $Q_{CO_2}^{N_2}$ would indicate a high degree of specificity, avidin, a protein unlikely to contain insulin, was run in comparison with the hormone. In two experiments, where the two proteins were compared at weights equivalent to 0.8 to 4.0 units of crystalline-zinc insulin, only the insulin significantly increased the $Q_{CO_2}^{N_2}$ (avidin 8 and 9%; insulin 37 and 47% respectively). Further work is needed to determine the conditions necessary to produce optimal sensitivity to the hormone. As will be described below, exposure of the melanoma-bearing mice to elevated temperatures (38° to 35° C) increases the subsequent *in vitro* reponse to insulin. Since in the present investigation it was desirable to maintain a saturating concentration of insulin; and to make additions in distilled water (*e.g.* zinc, phenol, magnesium, etc.), 1 to 4 units of insulin per ml were used in most experiments.

Effect of temperature on in vitro response to insulin*

When the $Q_{CO_2}^{N_2}$ values of a number of S–91 tumors from mice maintained at ambient room temperatures (24° C $\pm$ 4°) were compared, considerable inter-tumor variation in response to insulin was encountered. Thus, for example, in 20 experiments, involving 20 different tumors in Hank-Simms medium, the average $Q_{CO_2}^{N_2}$ without added insulin was 10.2, and with added insulin (4 units per ml) was 12.6 (average stimulation-24%). The ranges were 6.3 to 15.2 minus insulin and 7.6 to 19.6 plus insulin (0 to 50% stimulation). On the other hand when the tumor-bearing mice were held at controlled temperatures before making *in vitro* determination of tumor metabolism, the responses to insulin were much more uniform. For example, when the tumors were from mice exposed to

* The authors wish to acknowledge the assistance of Mrs. ELINOR BRENT in the conduct of these experiments.

References p. 346.

approximately 40° C for 13 to 17 hours prior to sacrifice (Table II), the percentage response to insulin was much greater than in tumor slices from comparable animals maintained for the same period at 18 to 20° C (47 *vs* 7%). In the table the $Q_{CO_2}^{N_2}$ values

TABLE II

$Q_{CO_2}^{N_2}$ VALUES OBTAINED IN FOUR GROUPS OF S–91 MELANOMAS FROM MICE EXPOSED TO HIGH (35° TO 40° C) OR LOW (18° TO 20° C) TEMPERATURES FOR INDICATED TIME PERIODS. IN EACH GROUP THE TUMORS HAVE BEEN ARRANGED IN ORDER OF ASCENDING MAGNITUDE OF $Q_{CO_2}^{N_2}$ OF THE CONTROLS (WITHOUT ADDED INSULIN). KREBS-RINGER-BICARBONATE, 0.625% DEXTROSE, 0.03 M KHCO$_3$ AND 95% N$_2$, 5% CO$_2$ IN ALL CASES

Hours exposed	$Q_{CO_2}^{N_2}$ Control	$Q_{CO_2}^{N_2}$ Plus insulin[b]	Per cent. stimulation	Hours exposed	$Q_{CO_2}^{N_2}$ Control	$Q_{CO_2}^{N_2}$ Plus insulin[b]	Per cent. stimulation
Animals exposed to 40° C ± 1°[a]				Animals exposed to 18–20° C ± 2°[a]			
17	7.72	12.25	59	17	12.00	12.29	3
17	8.27	11.29	37	16	14.79	15.37	7
16	10.50	16.35	56	16	15.45	18.16	17
13	12.41	18.36	47	17	15.51	15.28	−1
16	14.17	24.11	70	13	20.95	22.49	10
13	16.08	18.22	13	13	23.04	25.02	8
Average (N = 6)	11.52	16.76	47	Average (N = 6)	16.95	18.10	7.3
Animals exposed to 35° C ± 0.1°[c]				Animals exposed to 20° C ± 0.5°[c]			
20	6.85	11.66[d]	70	40	9.80	10.05[d]	3
20	6.89	13.71	98	40	11.66	12.05	3
20	8.66	12.57	45	17	11.66	13.28	14
91	9.27	14.16	52	17	13.49	13.83	2
17	9.35	13.07	39	17	13.61	15.66	14
18	9.82	14.07	43				
18	10.06	13.52	34				
40	10.52	14.38	37				
19	12.24	17.77	45				
Average (N = 9)	9.29	13.88	51.4	Average (N = 5)	12.08	12.97	7.2

[a] Experiments run from February 27 to March 19, 1953.
[b] 4 units low-zinc insulin plus 1.1 γ zinc per ml.
[c] Experiments run from May 14–28, 1953.
[d] Crystalline zinc-insulin (0.8 to 4 units per ml) in all but second tumor at 35° C which received 4 units low-zinc insulin per ml.

for the controls at all temperatures (minus added insulin) have been arranged in order of ascending magnitude. The general range of values in the 40° C series is obviously lower than in the corresponding low temperature series (average 11.52 *vs* 16.95). On the other hand in the presence of insulin the range of values in 40° C tumors is similar to the range of values in the low temperature series (average 16.95 *vs* 18.10). The data suggest that exposure of the animals to 40° C resulted in a lowering (average 32%) of the tumor $Q_{CO_2}^{N_2}$ and that this could be largely restored by insulin. In contrast to these results, slices

References p. 346.

of two S–91 tumors from mice maintained at 40° C for 255 hours had $Q_{CO_2}^{N_2}$ values of only 4.10 and 4.86 in the absence of additions, and only 3.08 and 4.4 respectively in the presence of 4 units of low-zinc insulin plus 1.1 γ inorganic zinc per ml. It is not known whether these tumors were zinc-inhibited (*cf.* later section and Table IV, columns 3 and 4) or not, but two "room temperature" tumors from the same transplant generation, and run simultaneously, showed $Q_{CO_2}^{N_2}$ values of 10.21 and 13.72 without insulin and 14.03 and 14.41 (respectively) with low-zinc insulin plus zinc. Very prolonged exposure to high temperature at least results in a marked lowering of tumor $Q_{CO_2}^{N_2}$, and is associated with pronounced suppression of tumor growth (Fig. 5). Melanoma-bearing mice held at 35° C for varying periods of time, and compared with mice held at a uniform temperature of 20° C, also showed much larger insulin-induced stimulations of $Q_{CO_2}^{N_2}$ than did the low temperature series (Table II). Here, too, the average control $Q_{CO_2}^{N_2}$ is lowest in the high temperature series, and following the addition of insulin, rises to that of the low temperature series. Again prolonged exposure of the tumors to high temperature (35° C) was associated with a further depression of both $Q_{CO_2}^{N_2}$ and growth. Thus in two tumors held for 44 days at 35° C there was a marked suppression of growth (Table III), and the $Q_{CO_2}^{N_2}$ values were low. In one of these tumors the $Q_{CO_2}^{N_2}$ was 6.83, and addition of 1 unit crystalline zinc-insulin per ml raised this value only 12%. The other tumor, which was the more fibrous of the two, had a $Q_{CO_2}^{N_2}$ of only 3.06. In the latter case insulin increased the rate of acid production 80% ($Q_{CO_2}^{N_2} = 5.50$).

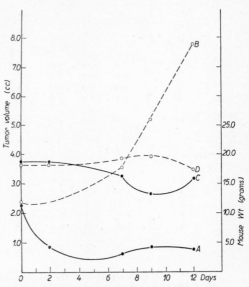

Fig. 5. Growth responses in dba mice bearing S–91 melanomas and exposed to different temperatures. A, average (4 mice) volume of tumors in mice exposed continuously to 40° C ± 1°; B, same as A but for mice held at 24° C ± 2° (average of 4 tumors except 12th day value based on 3); C, weight of mice held at 40° C minus respective tumor volumes X 1.1 (= approx. wt. of host mouse); D, same as C but for mice held at 24° C. Mice were maintained on Purina chow and water *ad lib* until the 9th day when they were also given whole-wheat bread and water *ad lib*.

Effect of temperature on tumor growth

That the high temperatures exert a marked effect on the general physiology of the tumor (either directly or over host mechanisms) is evidenced by the pronounced suppression of tumor growth. This is illustrated in Fig. 5 where the average tumor volumes (Curves A and B) have been plotted against the approximate weights of the host mice (Curves C and D). Table III illustrates the effect of exposure to 35° C on tumor growth. While the host mice in the 40° C experiment (Fig. 5) were active and vigorous at 12 days, tumor growth was markedly suppressed over this period following an initial pronounced regression in volume (Curve 4). The experiment was discontinued at 12 days. Other melanoma-bearing mice, maintained at 40° C for periods up to 10 days, behaved in a similar manner although detailed measurements of tumor size were not taken.

References p. 346.

TABLE III

GROWTH OF S–91 MELANOMAS OF THE SAME TRANSPLANT SERIES IN MALE DBA MICE AT 35° AND 25° C EXPRESSED IN APPROXIMATE TUMOR VOLUMES. EXPOSURE TO CONTROLLED TEMPERATURES BEGAN 20 DAYS AFTER TUMOR IMPLANTATION. MICE WERE MAINTAINED ON PURINA CHOW AND WATER AD LIB.

DAYS	0	3	7	10	14	19	22	25	28	31	35	39
Mice at 35° C					Volume of tumor in CC							
1	0.2	0.3	0.2	0.1	0.1	0.3	0.3	0.7	1.1	0.6	0.6	0.8
2	0.4	0.5	0.4	0.6	0.5	0.7	0.7	0.7	1.0	1.1	0.9	0.8
3	0.5	0.3	0.3	0.1	0.1[b]							
5[a]	5.1	3.0	1.8	1.5	1.4	0.9	0.8	1.0	0.9	0.9	0.7[c]	
Average	1.6	1.0	0.7	0.6	0.5	0.6	0.6	0.8	1.0	0.9	0.7	0.8
Mice at 25° C[d]					Volume of tumor in CC							
1	2.2	3.5	5.0	7.2	7.6	8.4	14.1					
2	1.7	2.3	3.5	6.8								
3	1.8	3.2	5.3	8.2	7.1	11.7	17.2					
4	1.1	2.3	2.9	3.1	3.6	7.6						
5	1.2	1.8	3.4	7.0	7.1	11.8	14.9	17.6	20.2	20.2		
Average	1.6	2.6	4.0	6.5	6.4	9.9	15.4	17.6	20.2	20.2		

[a] Mouse number 4 died on the second day.
[b] Died on 15th day as result of mechanical strangulation.
[c] Died on 36th day presumably as the result of exposure to 35° C.
[d] In all cases, death presumably due to tumor

In the 35° C series (Table III), tumor growth was also strongly suppressed. Metabolic determinations in slices of tumors of two of the 35° C mice surviving at 44 days showed that, as in the case of the tumors maintained for 12 days at 40° C, a pronounced reduction in $Q_{CO_2}^{N_2}$ had taken place (see previous section). The body weights of the host mice at 35° C, following an initial loss, leveled off at about 12 days and remained fairly constant until about 32 days when a further reduction in weight occurred. Deaths at 35° C in this series of 5 mice, which were presumably associated with exposure to high temperature, occurred on the second day (one mouse) and on the thirty-sixth day (one mouse). One mouse died on the fifteenth day as the result of mechanical strangulation. The control (25° C) tumors grew rapidly, deaths of host mice being attributable to this factor.

While it has long been known[12] that elevating the environmental temperature (29° to 37° C) of normal mice increases their sensitivity to insulin (as measured by convulsions), the present results show that exposure of melanoma-bearing mice to high temperatures (35° to 40° C) for only 13 to 17 hours is sufficient to markedly alter the *in vitro* response of the tumor to insulin. In this connection it may be of interest to note that body temperature measurements (rectal; determined by thermocouple) of melanoma-bearing dba mice (average weight of mouse plus tumor = 23 g) showed that after 3½ hours of exposure to 38° C the average body temperature in 7 mice was 39.2° C (range 38.4° to 39.5°); after 31 days exposure of 8 mice to 35° C, was 37.8° C (range 37.2° to 38.4°); and after 7 hours of exposure of 5 mice to 20° C, was 34° C (range 31.2 to 38.0). Nine melanoma-bearing mice maintained 14 days at 26° C (approximately

References p. 346.

equivalent to the average room temperature) had a mean body temperature of $37.5°$ C (range 36.50 to 38.40).

Response of brain in heat-treated mice

Since brain slices of normal mice uniformly failed to respond to insulin (by elevation of $Q_{CO_2}^{N_2}$) it was of interest to determine whether brain tissues from heat-treated mice bearing insulin-responsive melanomas would show an effect. In two experiments, involving mice held for *ca.* 19 hours at $35°$C, insulin (4 units crystalline zinc-insulin per ml) slightly inhibited $Q_{CO_2}^{N_2}$ of brain slices (4 and 17 % respectively); whereas tumor slices from the same animals showed marked *stimulation* (46 and 45 % respectively). A third experiment involving a melanoma-bearing mouse maintained at room temperature gave similar results except that the percentage stimulation in the tumor was not so large (brain —8%, tumor 18%).

The influence of inorganic zinc

Although crystalline insulin contains zinc (*ca.* 0.7%) the metal can be largely removed by dialysis and other means. However, since there are considerable stores of zinc in the body it is difficult, from *in vivo* experiments, to assess the requirement for zinc in insulin function. Nevertheless, because of the presence of zinc in freshly isolated insulin, the capacity of insulin crystals to combine with large quantities of zinc[13], and the relation of zinc content to the duration of insulin action following the injection of such crystals, it has been suggested that this element may have a special *in vivo* relation to action of the hormone[13].

The present results secured with the S–91 melanoma also suggest that zinc plays a special role in insulin action, and that the relative concentrations of the two substances are critical. Thus in a number of experiments with the S–91 melanoma, employing low-zinc insulin, crystalline zinc-insulin, and inorganic zinc it was found that the tumors fell into a graded pattern of response. This is best illustrated by comparing the two extremes in the response pattern (Table IV). In experiments A and B (Table IV), each involving slices of different individual tumors, the addition of inorganic zinc (as $ZnSO_4 \cdot 7H_2O$) at concentration of 1.1 γ^* to 8.0γ per ml (as zinc ions) did not cause significant changes in the $Q_{CO_2}^{N_2}$. However, both low-zinc insulin, and crystalline zinc-insulin increased the $Q_{CO_2}^{N_2}$. When 1.1 γ of inorganic zinc were added per 4 units of the low-zinc insulin, the $Q_{CO_2}^{N_2}$ was considerably higher than with insulin alone (Table IV, expts A and B). On the other hand when 8.0 γ of inorganic zinc were added per 4 units of low-zinc insulin, the stimulating effect of the insulin was largely abolished (Table IV). That crystalline zinc-insulin was not always equivalent to low-zinc insulin plus *added* zinc is indicated by the data in Table IV, experiment B.

In contrast to tumors of the type just described, those that lay at the other extreme of the response pattern (Table IV, expts C and D) showed inhibition of $Q_{CO_2}^{N_2}$ when either concentration of inorganic zinc alone was added. Furthermore, in the same tumors crystalline zinc-insulin was markedly less stimulatory than low-zinc insulin. The addition of even the lowest concentration of inorganic zinc (1.1 γ/ml) to low-zinc insulin practically abolished the insulin-induced stimulation of acid formation of these zinc-inhibited tumors. It might be concluded from the data (Table IV, C and D) that insulin counteracted

---

* 1.1 γ of zinc is approximately equivalent to the zinc content of 4 units of crystalline zinc-insulin.

References p. 346.

TABLE IV

RESPONSE OF S–91 MELANOMA SLICES TO ZINC, $\pm$ INSULIN, IN FOUR EXPERIMENTS, EACH INVOLVING
A DIFFERENT INDIVIDUAL TUMOR. THE VALUES REPRESENT PERCENTAGE STIMULATIONS OR INHIBITIONS
RELATIVE TO THE CONTROLS (WITHOUT ADDED INSULIN OR ZINC). CONTROL $Q_{CO_2}^{N_2}$ VALUES WERE 12.0 IN A,
12.6 IN B, 15.2 IN C, AND 10.6 IN D. 1.1 γ OF ZINC ION ARE APPROXIMATELY EQUIVALENT TO THE ZINC
PRESENT IN 4 UNITS OF CRYSTALLINE ZINC-INSULIN (ZINC CA. 0.7%). THE LOW-ZINC INSULIN HAD A
ZINC CONTENT OF CA. 0.017%. EXPERIMENTS A, B AND C IN HANK-SIMMS AND D IN KREBS-RINGER-
BICARBONATE. DEXTROSE 0.625%, 0.03 M KHCO$_3$, 95% N$_2$ AND 5% CO$_2$.

Added insulin (units per ml) and zinc (gamma per ml)	$Q_{CO_2}^{N_2}$ Not significantly lowered by inorganic zinc in absence of added insulin		$Q_{CO_2}^{N_2}$ Lowered by inorganic zinc in absence of added insulin	
	% Stimulation or inhibition		% Stimulation or inhibition	
	Expt. A	Expt. B	Expt. C	Expt. D
Zinc (1.1 γ)	9	−4	−37	−29
Zinc (8.0 γ)	0	5	−20	−31
Low-Zinc Insulin (4 u)	22	22	26	37
Low-Zinc Insulin plus 1.1 γ Zinc	34	40	−5	−20
Low-Zinc Insulin plus 8.0 γ Zinc	12	−1	−4	5
Crystalline Zinc-Insulin (4 u)	36	15	13	3

the inhibitory action of zinc. However, it should be noted that in the other response
pattern (Table IV, A and B) zinc alone, at 8.0 γ per ml, did not inhibit acid production
although it did markedly counteract the stimulatory effect of insulin when the two
were given simultaneously.

It is of interest that in zinc-inhibited tumors in the absence of added insulin the
inhibition was as great with *ca.* 1 γ of zinc per ml as with 4 to 8 γ of zinc. Thus in three
experiments the average inhibition with *ca.* 1 γ zinc per ml was 28% (range 15 to 41%)
and with 4 to 8 γ, 21% (range 15 to 31%). On the other hand in three experiments where
ca. 1 γ of zinc per ml did not significantly change the $Q_{CO_2}^{N_2}$ (−1% in all 3 experiments),
likewise 8 γ of zinc did not cause a significant change (average −2%, range −9 to 5%).
The data show that in those tumors where zinc (*in the absence of added insulin*) is
inhibitory, a concentration of only 1 γ zinc per ml is already saturating.

Some tumors were found to have patterns of response to zinc and insulin intermediate between those illustrated in Table IV. While many questions are left un-
answered, the data obtained indicate that zinc plays an important role in insulin
function (in so far as this can be determined from *in vitro* stimulation of anaerobic acid
production), and that the relative concentrations of the two substances are highly
critical. While HALLAS-MØLLER et al.[13] have reported that addition of phosphate
completely neutralizes the protracted effect (*in vivo* response) of an insulin crystal
suspension containing zinc, phosphate-zinc interaction can hardly be playing a major
role in the present experiments. In the first place, the wide range of response patterns to
zinc occurred in the presence of a uniform and low level of phosphate (*ca.* 0.001 M).
Secondly, in other experiments with S–91 melanoma, raising the phosphate level from
0.001 M to 0.005 M had no effect on either $Q_{CO_2}^{N_2}$ or on the percentage stimulation by
insulin.

References p. 346.

The influence of insulin on aerobic metabolism

Whenever insulin stimulated *in vitro* anaerobic acid production by S–91 melanoma slices, it was found that the $Q_{CO_2}^{O_2}$ was also increased if this was measured. Inorganic zinc alone, on the other hand, did not stimulate aerobic acid formation. Contrary to *in vitro* results secured with certain normal tissues insulin never increased the Q_{O_2}, and in fact sometimes decreased it (0 to *ca.* 25%).

In spite of the absence of respiratory stimulation, insulin frequently increased the absolute Pasteur effect ($Q_{CO_2}^{N_2} - Q_{CO_2}^{O_2}$), or depression of net acid formation due to the presence of O_2 (Table V, Fig. 6), and in no case was the absolute Pasteur effect significantly decreased by insulin.

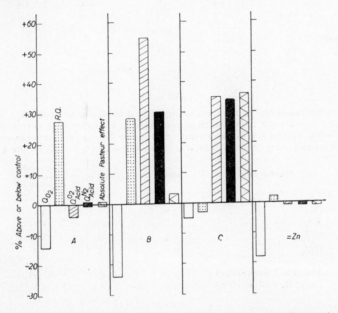

Fig 6. Comparison of 3 different patterns of response of S–91 melanoma slices to insulin. Each bar represents the percentage stimulation or inhibition relative to the control (minus insulin). A, with 4 units of crystalline zinc-insulin per ml (from data of Table VI); B, with 4 units of amorphous low-zinc insulin plus 1.1 γ zinc per ml (one experiment involving pooled slices from 3 tumors of the same transplant series pre-heated at 40° C for 16 hours); and C, with 4 units of crystalline zinc-insulin per ml (from average data of 3 experiments. Results obtained with 1.1 γ of inorganic zinc per ml (without added insulin) are shown to the right of C. All experiments with 0.625 % dextrose, 0.03 M KHCO₃, 95 % N₂ and 5 % CO₂.

There are numerous reports[1, 14, 16] that insulin administration to tissue slices *in vitro* raises the R.Q. This effect was obtained in melanoma, but to a variable extent. Table VI shows that this elevation of R.Q. can occur without concomitant increase in mano-metrically measurable acid formation, and that the effect is attributable to insulin rather than to zinc *per se*. This is further borne out by similar results obtained with low-zinc insulin in the absence of added zinc. The general range of responses observed, in terms of per cent stimulation or inhibition, under both aerobic and anaerobic conditions is illustrated in Fig. 6.

References p. 346.

TABLE V

RESPONSE OF S–91 MELANOMA SLICES TO CRYSTALLINE ZINC-INSULIN (4 UNITS PER ML) IN 3 DIFFERENT EXPERIMENTS. EXPERIMENT I IN HANK-SIMMS WITH POOLED SLICES FROM TWO TUMORS OF THE SAME TRANSPLANT SERIES (38 DAYS OLD), EXPERIMENT II IN HANK-SIMMS WITH POOLED SLICES FROM THREE TUMORS OF THE SAME TRANSPLANT SERIES (45 DAYS OLD), AND EXPERIMENT III IN WARBURG-OKAMOTO WITH POOLED SLICES FROM TWO TUMORS 27 AND 45 DAYS OLD RESPECTIVELY. 0.625% DEXTROSE, 0.03 M KHCO$_3$, 95% N$_2$, 5% CO$_2$ IN ALL CASES.

Metabolic factor	Experiment I		Experiment II		Experiment III	
	Control	Plus insulin	Control	Plus insulin	Control	Plus insulin
QO_2	−4.4	−4.4	−4.8	−4.5	−3.2	−3.1
R.Q.	−0.96	−0.92	−1.0	−0.95	−0.90	−0.89
$Q_{CO_2}^{O_2}$	2.2	3.4	2.5	2.9	2.4	3.3
$Q_{CO_2}^{N_2}$	11.3	15.1	5.7	6.9	6.4	9.5
Absolute Pasteur Effect (μl CO$_2$)	366	489	121	153	164	250

TABLE VI

METABOLIC PATTERN OBSERVED IN S–91 MELANOMA WHICH SHOWS THAT ELEVATION OF THE R.Q. CAN OCCUR WITHOUT CONCOMITANT INCREASE IN MANOMETRICALLY MEASURABLE ACID FORMATION. HANK-SIMMS MEDIUM WITH POOLED SLICES FROM THREE TUMORS OF THE SAME TRANSPLANT SERIES (44 DAYS OLD). DEXTROSE 0.625%, 0.03 M KHCO$_3$ AND GAS PHASE EITHER 95% O$_2$, 5% CO$_2$ OR 95% N$_2$, 5% CO$_2$.

Metabolic factor	Control	1.12 Zinc/ml	Plus 4 units crystalline Zn-insulin/ml
QO_2	−3.6	−3.1	−3.1
R.Q.	−0.87	−0.85	−1.11
$Q_{CO_2}^{O_2}$	2.4	2.3	2.3
$Q_{CO_2}^{N_2}$	9.0	8.5	9.0
Absolute Pasteur effect	263 μl	245 μl	264 μl
Per cent, Pasteur effect	73%	73%	74%

DISCUSSION

Recent work[10, 20, 21, 22] has shown that tissue slices and homogenates of various normal adult tissues can be made to show a vigorous glycolysis if hexose diphosphate and co-factors (ATP, DPN, niacinamide, magnesium, phosphate) are supplied in sufficient amount. However, one marked difference (aside from a higher Q_{O_2}) between these tissues and malignant tissues is the greater capacity of the latter to utilize glucose as the substrate for anaerobic glycolysis. Adult brain is often cited as a non-malignant tissue possessing a considerable capacity to glycolyse glucose *in vitro*. However, we have found that under certain *in vitro* conditions, where the anaerobic glycolysis of tumors remains at a high level, that of brain decays rapidly to a low level, although aerobically a high glycolysis is maintained. Thus, part of the difference between the metabolism of adult brain and certain tumors, *e.g.* melanoma, lies not so much in the absence of potential glycolytic capacity in the brain as in the relative instability of the glycolytic metabolism of this tissue under certain anaerobic conditions. It is probable that this reflects the

References p. 346.

relative inability of *adult* brain to maintain vigorous phosphorylation of glucose under anaerobic conditions (see MEYERHOF AND WILSON[23, 24]), an ability much more inherent in tissues adapted to a more anaerobic environment as *e.g.*, embryonic tissues and tumors. In the present study we were able to raise the $Q_{CO_2}^{N_2}$ of brain to the melanoma level, but only following addition of high levels of magnesium and phenol.

Insulin is of peculiar interest to the cancer problem because of its role (direct or indirect) in the stimulation of glycolysis[19]. Whether this stimulation results from action on an intracellular enzyme or inhibitor[7] or occurs through a mere speeding up of entry of glucose into the cell[29, 34] cannot be fully decided at present. The work of RYER[26], in which insulin and/or thyroxine was administered *in vivo* to rabbits bearing the Brown-Pearce epithelioma, shows that tumor metabolism can be markedly affected by insulin injections. Both respiration and glycolysis were increased in the liver and tumor tissues which were subsequently measured *in vitro*.

In the present study, insulin was administered only after the tissues were placed in the respirometer vessel so that any metabolic changes noted must have been due to the immediate action of the hormone. Most investigators have measured insulin action on excised tissues in terms of glucose disappearance and glycogen formation although lactic acid formation and respiratory CO_2 (from labeled glucose) have also been followed (*cf.* [18, 19, 30]). Our interest has been primarily in determining the effect of insulin on over-all metabolism, particularly anaerobic and aerobic acid formation. While the results are more or less in line with those of other investigators (who used normal instead of malignant tissues) certain differences do occur.

BALMAIN *et al.*[1], and HILLS *et al.*[16], have reported that insulin *in vitro* enhances the R.Q. of lactating mammary gland tissues of rats. This effect, which seems to be due to acceleration of fatty acid synthesis, did not occur in a phosphate medium and appeared in bicarbonate medium only in the presence of acetate and glucose. Under the latter conditions *an increased O_2 uptake also occurred*. We observed marked enhancement of R.Q. in melanoma in both Hank-Simms and Krebs-Ringer-bicarbonate media as the result of treatment with both low-zinc, and crystalline zinc-insulin. The response, however, was variable. In our experiments, glucose was the only added substrate, and the reasons for this variability are not clear. Unlike the results with normal tissues, we have never obtained an insulin-induced increase in the Q_{O_2} of melanoma. In spite of this, insulin frequently increased the absolute Pasteur effect. These partly atypical results with tumor may be related to the well-known respiratory defect in oxidative reserve characteristic of malignancies generally[17]. At this point we wish to comment, somewhat parenthetically, on the question of this respiratory defect in tumor cells.

WARBURG suggested many years ago[32] that "the aerobic glycolysis of the tumor cell is derived in any case from a disturbance of the respiration". Although certain tumors have relatively high oxidative quotients, aerobic glycolysis is present *if there is an adequate supply of glucose* (*cf.* BURK[3]). In such cases, from a *relative* standpoint, the respiration is certainly low in relation to the glycolytic capacity.

The role of mitochondria in mediating the oxidative processes of cellular metabolism has become increasingly clear since the original discovery by WARBURG[31] that the Atmungsferment, and other associated enzymes, are carried on the cytoplasmic particulates. Recent work[10] has indicated that mitochondria may also play a more active role in glycolysis than had been generally accepted. Furthermore, these sub-cellular organelles have been shown to possess extra-nuclear hereditary factors which through their

References p. 346.

mutation become the continuing cause of self-perpetuating cellular abnormalities[36-38]. Very similar cellular abnormalities can also result from the action of viruses on mitochondrial development and function[36]. In the latter case, however, the continuing presence of the virus is required since the mitochondria are not hereditarily changed. Is it not possible that the lack of *oxidative reserve*, or conversely the *glycolytic excess*, which characterizes the tumor cell, may be the result of metabolic imbalance brought about either by mitochondrial mutation, or by the action of a virus on these organelles? Unfortunately, it has not yet been possible to subject animal mitochondria to genetic tests as in the case of higher plants[37]. However, observations in mouse melanomas of variable pigment content, while not conclusive, are at least consistent with the view that mitochondria may act as genetic determiners in mammalian tumors[8, 15]. Recently SCHNEIDER et al.[28], as a result of studies on carcinogenesis, have stated that "— the data available at present support the concept that the mitochondria are involved in the carcinogenic process in liver". The data from aberrant plant mitochondrial elements suggest that similar modifications in homologous structures of animal cells could, from the genetic standpoint, be the *continuing cause* of the respiratory defects and glycolytic unbalance of malignant cells.

The reactions of melanomas from mice exposed to high temperatures (40° and 35° C) suggest that the capacity of the tumor to maintain a high rate of anaerobic glycolysis may be dependent on the available supply of insulin. This is suggested by the fact that the lowered $Q_{CO_2}^{N_2}$ of tumors from animals exposed to high temperatures for only 13 to 20 hours (Table II) was raised by insulin to levels characteristic of tumors that had not been exposed to high temperatures. Thus one immediate result of exposure to elevated temperature may be a reduction (absolute or relative) in the amount of insulin in the tumor. This might be the result of a diminished blood circulation in the tumor (this was evidenced by a decreased amount of blood in the excised tissues), to decreased secretion of the hormone, or to some combination of these and other factors (*e.g.* altered pituitary function[7, 19].

Since insulin has been reported to stimulate growth of hypophysectomized rats[27] it seems possible that this hormone might play a role in tumor growth. In view of the marked effect of high temperature on melanoma growth and $Q_{CO_2}^{N_2}$, it is of particular interest to determine to what extent these factors may be interrelated. In this connection it should also be noted that the apparent insulin deficiency of the heat-treated tumors (as indicated by insulin-reversible lowering of $Q_{CO_2}^{N_2}$) may be the expression of an increased concentration of insulin-reversible glycolytic inhibitors such as have been reported in the pituitary and adrenals[7]. Further experiments are in progress to determine the extent and persistence of the temperature-induced growth suppression as well as to further define the associated metabolic changes and their relation to insulin. The apparent critical relation between zinc and insulin concentrations with respect to $Q_{CO_2}^{N_2}$ is of general interest in connection with the mechanism of insulin action, but may also have some special significance with respect to tumor metabolism.

References p. 346.

SUMMARY

Both brain and melanoma slices displayed similar $Q_{CO_2}^{O_2}$ values, but marked differences occurred in $Q_{CO_2}^{N_2}$ under certain conditions. Thus, the two tissues responded differently to added magnesium, phenol, and insulin. The first two substances markedly increased the $Q_{CO_2}^{N_2}$ of brain but slightly inhibited that of melanoma. The $Q_{CO_2}^{N_2}$ of brain slices was not increased by insulin but that of melanoma was (*ca.* 40%).

As little as 0.003 mg (0.1 units) of crystalline zinc-insulin per ml was sufficient to give maximal stimulation. Crystalline zinc-insulin freed of hyperglycemic factor was as effective as regular crystalline zinc-insulin in increasing the $Q_{CO_2}^{N_2}$ of melanoma slices. Hyperglycemic factor largely freed of insulin had no appreciable effect on $Q_{CO_2}^{N_2}$. Zinc appears to play a critical role in connection with the influence of insulin on $Q_{CO_2}^{N_2}$ of melanoma slices. The relative concentrations of the two substances are critical. Under aerobic conditions insulin variably increased the R.Q., $Q_{CO_2}^{O_2}$, and absolute Pasteur effect of melanoma. Q_{O_2} (respiration) was never increased, but was sometimes decreased.

Exposure of melanoma-bearing mice to 35° or 40° C, for 13 hours or more, was associated with a marked diminution in the $Q_{CO_2}^{N_2}$ of the tumor slices as compared to tumor slices from mice exposed to *ca.* 20° C. Insulin increased (average 49%) the $Q_{CO_2}^{N_2}$ of slices from the heat-treated tumors to a level approximately equal to that of slices from 20° C tumors where insulin gave only slight stimulation (average 7%); additional (12 to 44 days) exposure to 35° or 40° C resulted in marked suppression of tumor growth and further decline in the $Q_{CO_2}^{N_2}$.

RÉSUMÉ

Les valeurs de $Q_{CO_2}^{O_2}$ sont les mêmes pour des coupes de cerveau et pour des coupes de mélanome, mais les valeurs de $Q_{CO_2}^{N_2}$ diffèrent nettement dans certaines conditions. Par exemple les deux tissus réagissent de façon différente à l'addition de magnésium, de phénol et d'insuline. Les deux premières substances augmentent nettement le $Q_{CO_2}^{N_2}$ du cerveau mais inhibent légèrement celui du mélanome. L'insuline n'augmente pas le $Q_{CO_2}^{N_2}$ des coupes de cerveau mais augmente celui du mélanome (de 40% en moyenne).

Il suffit de 0.03 mg (0.1 unité) d'insuline-zinc cristallisée par ml pour provoquer la stimulation maximum. L'insuline-zinc cristallisée dépourvue de facteur hyperglycémiant augmente autant le $Q_{CO_2}^{N_2}$ des coupes de mélanomes que l'insuline-zinc cristallisée ordinaire. Le facteur hyperglycémiant débarrassé en grande partie de l'insuline n'affecte pas sensiblement le $Q_{CO_2}^{N_2}$. Il semble que le zinc joue un rôle essentiel dans l'action de l'insuline sur le $Q_{CO_2}^{N_2}$ des coupes de mélanome. Les concentrations relatives des deux substances sont importantes. En aérobiose l'insuline augmente plus ou moins le Q.R., le $Q_{CO_2}^{O_2}$ et l'effet Pasteur absolu du mélanome. Le Q_{O_2} (respiration) n'est jamais augmenté, mais quelquefois diminué.

Le $Q_{CO_2}^{N_2}$ de coupes tumorales prélevées sur des souris maintenues à 35° ou 40° C, pendant au moins 13 heures, est nettement inférieur à celui de coupes prélevées sur des souris maintenues à 20° C. L'insuline augmente (de 49% en moyenne) le $Q_{CO_2}^{N_2}$ des coupes de tumeurs exposées à la chaleur jusqu'à une valeur à peu près égale à celle de coupes de tumeurs maintenues à 20° C sur lesquelles l'insuline n'est que légèrement stimulante (en moyenne 7%); en prolongeant pendant 12 à 44 jours l'exposition à 35° ou à 40°, la croissance des tumeurs est nettement inhibée et le $Q_{CO_2}^{N_2}$ encore diminué.

ZUSAMMENFASSUNG

Sowohl Gehirn- wie Melanomaschnitte zeigten ähnliche $Q_{CO_2}^{O_2}$-Werte, unter gewissen Bedingungen jedoch traten in den $Q_{CO_2}^{N_2}$-Werten beträchtliche Unterschiede auf. Die beiden Gewebe verhalten sich so zugefügten Magnesium, Phenol und Insulin gegenüber verschieden. Die beiden ersten Substanzen verursachten einen beträchtlichen Anstieg des $Q_{CO_2}^{N_2}$ im Gehirn und eine geringe Erniedrigung in den Melanoma. Der $Q_{CO_2}^{N_2}$ von Gehirnschnitten stieg bei Zugabe von Insulin nicht an, aber dagegen bei Melanoma (*ca.* 40%).

Schon 0.003 mg (0.1 Einheiten) kristallisierten Zinkinsulins per ml war genügend um maximale Stimulation hervorzurufen. Kristallines vom hyperglycämischen Faktor befreites Zinkinsulin war genau so wirksam wie reguläres kristallines Zinkinsulin bei der Erhöhung des $Q_{CO_2}^{N_2}$ in Melanomaschnitten. Zum grössten Teil von Insulin befreiter hyperglycämischer Faktor zeigte keinen merklichen

Effekt auf $Q_{CO_2}^{N_2}$. Zink scheint eine entscheidende Rolle zusammen mit dem Einfluss von Insulin auf den $Q_{CO_2}^{N_2}$ von Melanomaschnitten zu spielen. Die relative Konzentration der zwei Substanzen ist entscheidend. Unter aerobischen Bedingungen verursachte Insulin ein wechselndes Ansteigen des R.Q., des $Q_{CO_2}^{O_2}$ und des absoluten Pasteureffektes bei Melanoma. Q_{O_2} (Respiration) nahm in keinen Fall zu, dagegen manchmal ab.

Setzte man Mäuse mit Melanoma 13 Stunden oder länger einer Temperatur von 35–40° aus, so trat eine bemerkenswerte Verminderung des $Q_{CO_2}^{N_2}$ der Tumorschnitte auf verglichen mit den Tumorschnitten von Mäusen, die einer Temperatur von 20° C ausgesetzt waren. Mit Insulin nahm der $Q_{CO_2}^{N_2}$ der Schnitte von hitzebehandelten Tumoren bis zu einem ungefähr mit den Schnitten von Tumoren, die bei einer Temperatur von 20° gehalten wurden und bei denen Insulin nur eine geringe Stimulierung hervorrief (durchschnittlich 7 %) gleichen Stand zu (durchschnittlich 40 %). Ein zusätzliches Aussetzen von Temperaturen von 35–40° (12 bis 44 Tage) ergab eine beträchtliche Unterdrückung des Tumorwachstums und ein weiteres Absinken des $Q_{CO_2}^{N_2}$.

REFERENCES

[1] J. BALMAIN, T. H. FRENCH AND S. J. FOLLEY, *Nature*, 165 (1950) 807.
[2] S. B. BARKER AND W. H. SUMMERSON, *J. Biol. Chem.*, 138 (1941) 535.
[3] DEAN BURK, *Cold Spring Harbor Symposia Quant. Biol.*, 7 (1939) 420.
[4] D. BURK, H. SPRINCE, J. M. SPANGLER, E. A. KABAT, J. FURTH AND A. CLAUDE, *J. Nat. Cancer Inst.*, 2 (1941) 201.
[5] I. L. CHAIKOFF, *The Harvey Lectures*, pg. 99. Academic Press, N.Y. (1953).
[6] A. M. CLOUDMAN, *Science*, 93 (1941) 380.
[7] S. P. COLOWICK, G. T. CORI AND M. W. SLEIN, *J. Biol. Chem.*, 168 (1947) 583.
[8] H. G. DU BUY, M. W. WOODS, DEAN BURK AND M. D. LACKEY, *J. Nat. Cancer Inst.*, 9 (1949) 325.
[9] H. G. DU BUY, M. W. WOODS AND M. D. LACKEY, *Science*, 111 (1950) 572.
[10] H. G. DU BUY, M. W. WOODS AND J. L. SHOWACRE, *Pigment Cell Growth*, pg. 335. Academic Press, N.Y. (1953).
[11] G. P. DUSHANE, *The Biology of Melanomas*, p.1. Spec. Publ. N.Y. Acad. of Sci. 4 (1948).
[12] C. W. EMMENS, *Hormone Assay*, p. 71. Academie Press, N.Y. (1950).
[13] K. HALLAS-MØLLER, K. PETERSEN AND J. SCHLICHTKRULL, *Science*, 116 (1952) 394.
[14] N. HAUGAARD AND J. B. MARSH, *J. Biol. Chem.*, 194 (1952) 33.
[15] M. L. HESSELBACH, *Pigment Cell Growth*, p. 189. Academic Press, N.Y. (1953).
[16] G. A. HILLS AND W. C. STADIE, *J. Biol. Chem.* 194 (1952) 25.
[17] J. G. KIDD, R. J. WINZLER AND D. BURK, *Cancer Res.*, 4 (1944) 547.
[18] M. E. KRAHL AND C. R. PARK, *J. Biol. Chem.*, 174 (1948) 939–46.
[19] M. E. KRAHL, *Annals, N.Y. Acad. Sci.*, 54 (1951) 531.
[20] G. A. LEPAGE, *J. Biol. Chem.*, 176 (1948) 1009.
[21] G. A. LEPAGE AND W. C. SCHNEIDER, *Ibid.*, 176 (1948) 1021.
[22] G. A. LEPAGE, *Cancer Res.*, 10 (1950) 77.
[23] O. MEYERHOF AND J. R. WILSON, *Arch. Biochem.*, 21 (1949) 1.
[24] O. MEYERHOF AND J. R. WILSON, *Ibid.*, 21 (1949) 22.
[25] M. E. RAWLES, *Pigment Cell Growth*, p. 1. Academic Press, N.Y. (1953).
[26] R. RYER, PhD Thesis, Dept. of Vital Economics, The Univ. of Rochester, Rochester, N.Y., 1942.
[27] J. SALTER AND C. H. BEST, *Federation Proc.*, 12 (1953) 122 (abstr.).
[28] W. C. SCHNEIDER, G. H. HOGEBOOM, E. SHELTON AND M. J. STRIEBICH, *Cancer Res.*, 13 (1953) 285.
[29] S. SOSKIN AND R. LEVINE, *Carbohydrate Metabolism*. Rev. Ed. Univ. of Chicago Press, Chicago, Ill., 1952.
[30] W. C. STADIE, *Annals N.Y. Acad. Sci.*, 54 (1951) 531.
[31] OTTO WARBURG, *Arch. ges. Physiol.*, 154 (1913) 599.
[32] OTTO WARBURG, *The Metabolism of Tumors*. Constable, London, 1930.
[33] OTTO WARBURG, 1952, Private communication.
[34] A. WICK AND D. R. DRURY, Abstr. no. 113 (p. 46C), Abstracts, Div. of Biol. Chem., A.C.S. March, 1953.
[35] M. W. WOODS, H. G. DU BUY, D. BURK AND M. HESSELBACH, *J. Nat. Cancer Inst.*, 9 (1949) 311.
[36] M. W. WOODS AND H. G. DU BUY, *Am. J. Botany*, 38 (1951) 419.
[37] M. W. WOODS AND H. G. DU BUY, *J. Nat. Cancer Inst.*, 11 (1951) 1105.
[38] M. W. WOODS, J. L. SHOWACRE AND H. G. DU BUY, *J. Wash. (D.C.) Acad. Sci.*, 42 (1952) 169.

Received July 30, 1953

AN ELECTROCHEMICAL DEMONSTRATION OF THE ENERGY CYCLE
AND MAXIMUM QUANTUM YIELD IN PHOTOSYNTHESIS*

by

KURT DAMASCHKE, FRITZ TÖDT, DEAN BURK** AND OTTO WARBURG

Max Planck Institute for Cell Physiology, and Material-prüfungsamt, Berlin-Dahlem (Germany)

A new and rapid electrochemical method with a time period of less than one second has been applied to a study of the oxygen exchanges occurring in *Chlorella* cultures during varying periods of darkness and of illumination with measured quantities of visible light. It has been possible to show that an initial photochemical reaction takes place with a high quantum efficiency, and that this photo reaction is followed by a back reaction of enhanced oxygen consumption with a time period that may vary from seconds to a few minutes. The overall efficiency of net oxygen production in this cycle approaches, under suitable experimental conditions, the theoretical limit set by the first and second laws of thermodynamics, namely, 2.5 to 3 quanta of light per molecule of oxygen gas produced.

METHODS

The electrochemical measurement of dissolved oxygen was carried out by the method of TÖDT[1,2] in glass vessels of the type illustrated in Fig. 1. Such vessels had a volume of 80 ml or more, and a diameter of 6 cm, and hence an area of 28 cm² on the bottom surface, which the measured light entered and covered to the extent of at least 95%. At the top edge of a given vessel there were three inlets with glass-ground joints, two inlets for holding electrodes, and a third inlet for holding either a simple stopper or a microburette used in connection with electrode calibration for oxygen response.

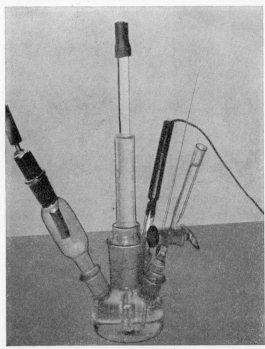

Fig. 1. Vessel for electrochemical measurement of oxygen exchange in photosynthesis and respiration.

* The substance of this paper was presented in a lecture entitled *Thermodynamik und Kinetik der Photosynthese* given by DEAN BURK on July 6, 1953 at the Max Planck Institute for Medical Research, Heidelberg, at the invitation of Prof. RICHARD KUHN, Director.

** Foreign Member, Kaiser Wilhelm Institut for Cell Physiology, Berlin-Dahlem, and Head of Cytochemistry Section, National Institutes of Health, United States Public Health Service, Bethesda, Md. (U.S.A.)

References p. 355.

The electrodes employed in a given vessel were (a) polarizable, a platinum wire of approximately 0.5 cm length and 0.03 cm diameter, and (b) unpolarizable, a cast-iron electrode of high carbon and copper content, selected for stability, of approximately 2 cm length and 4 cm² surface area, and immersed in saturated KCl solution contained in a glass tube at the end of which was a semi-permeable clay diaphragm heat-sealed to the glass end. At the top center of the vessel was a ground glass joint for holding a stirring device consisting of a quartz tube some six inches in length containing a close fitting water-sealed quartz tube, at one end of which were four paddles at right angles to each other, and at the other end of which was a short piece of rubber tubing connected with an A.C. synchronous motor turned at a high constant speed of 1500 r.p.m. to provide maximum electrode response, which, in the absence of stirring, could be 10–50 times as small. The platinum micro-electrode was placed in the culture medium as close to the paddles of the stirrer as feasible, in order to take maximum advantage of the stirring. When in use, a vessel was completely filled with liquid medium (*Chlorella* suspension), and contained no gas phase.

Calibration of the platinum electrode for response to oxygen was carried out in one or both of two ways. For higher oxygen pressures, the current was measured in solutions saturated with air, yielding values of 50 to 100 μ Amp. for 21% of 1 atm. O_2, the actual value in any one electrode depending mainly upon the size of the electrode. At lower oxygen pressures, small quantities of air-saturated suspension medium of known oxygen content (6.3 μl/ml at 20° C) were admitted by means of the micro-burette, which contained a long open capillary permitting a forced extrusion of an equal volume of liquid. By this second method, it was always possible to make a calibration under the same conditions, and at essentially the same time, as the experimental measurements of photosynthesis or respiration (see Fig. 4 as example). With micro-electrodes of platinum the two methods of calibration gave identical results, that is, galvanometer readings were directly proportional, within experimental error, to oxygen content up to air-saturation, in the diffusion-current-region of the current-voltage curve employed, where current is virtually independent of potential.

Current measurements below 5 μ Amp. were usually made with a 200 mm scale Bruno Lange Multiflex Galvanometer No. 3 with a sensitivity of $2 \cdot 10^{-9}$ Amp./mm that permitted distinctions of ca. 0.0003 μl O_2/ml solution to be made, corresponding to changes of ca. 0.001% of O_2 saturation at 1 atm. O_2 pressure. This was a far greater sensitivity than could be obtained with the most sensitive polarographic or other physical or chemical method available. By using larger electrodes, this sensitivity could be increased several fold further. At current values above 5 μ Amp., either shunted, or less sensitive, galvanometers were employed, but in all cases the time response for small changes in oxygen concentration was ordinarily less than one second.

The galvanometric responses were measured not only visually (see Figs. 2, 5, 6), but were usually also recorded mechanically, by means of either the *Photoregistrier-apparat* (see Fig. 3) of Bruno Lange, or, most frequently, his *Linienschreiber* (see Fig. 4), both of which have a time response of less than one second. In the latter recording instrument, the writing pen was activated over its 200 mm ride by means of a selenium cell in front of the light spot of the galvanometer, and the pen wrote upon a drum that revolved once per exactly 120 seconds over a distance of 27.8 cm.

The *Chlorella* cultures employed in this study were cultivated in the several ways described in the accompanying publication[3], for one to three days, after which they

References p. 355.

were centrifuged and taken up in a medium of the following composition: $7.25 g$ KH_2PO_4, $0.5 g$ Na_2HPO_4, $2.5 g$ $MgSO_4.7H_2O$, and $1 g$ $NaCl$ per 1000 ml twice-distilled water (pH 5.5). Heavy metal or other salts (especially of calcium) that deposit on a platinum electrode are to be avoided, and may be removed, if necessary, by brief immersion of the electrode in concentrated nitric acid or chromic acid, followed by distilled water rinsing.

The experimental vessel, filled completely with *Chlorella* suspension, was maintained at constant temperature (20° C) in a water bath, and illuminated from below with monochromatic light prepared and measured bolometrically as described by WARBURG[3]. Respiration-compensating light was supplied either by means of the same beam or by means of a supplementary, nearly collimated beam of white light obtained from a secondary lamp source, which, in the latter instance, was not measured The *Chlorella* suspensions usually contained 5% CO_2, but 10, 20, and 50% CO_2 were also studied, supplied in N_2 containing variable amounts of O_2 up to 21%, but usually 0.1–2%.

O_2-PRESSURE

Since the electrochemical method is more sensitive at lower oxygen pressures (lower current values), we first determined how far the oxygen pressure can be lowered before a decrease in the normal, dark rate of oxygen consumption by the *Chlorella* becomes notable. We found that, under our experimental conditions, especially with our great stirring velocity, that the respiration remained constant down to at least 0 05% of O_2 saturation at 1 atm. Down to a pressure of 0.1% O_2, there was thus, in practice, no danger that a change in the rate of respiration could be caused by low oxygen pressure.

We have tested this last important condition in special cases. Thus, in Curve 1, Fig 4, a known quantity of oxygen was added *by means of the microburette* to a *Chlorella* suspension held with a constant white light at respiration-compensation at 0.15% O_2, and after the given O_2 addition compensation remained (respiration *not* increased). Two

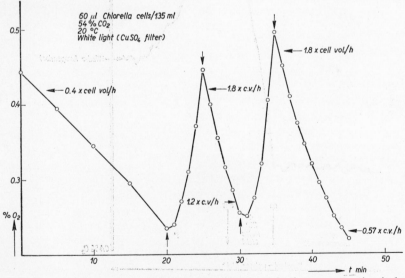

Fig. 2. The photosynthetic cycle, in *Chlorella* cells, without respiration compensation (galvanometer read visually).

References p. 355.

minutes later, after bringing the pO_2 back to ca. 0.15% by shutting off the compensating illumination for somewhat less than a minute, an equivalent amount of oxygen was added to the *Chlorella* suspension *by means of extra red light*, and *now* the respiration increased (compensation decreased) during, and due to, the course of the back reaction in the photosynthetic cycle (Curve 2).

Or, as in Fig. 2, the respiration of a *Chlorella* suspension was first measured as an initial oxygen pressure P_o (here 0.445%) fell to a pressure P (here 0.235%) over a virtually linear time course. Illumination was then given until the pressure was returned, by oxygen production in photosynthesis, to P_o. Now, upon darkening, much more oxygen was consumed per minute (4.5 times) than previously at the same pressure P_o, clearly indicating a light-induced reaction of increased oxygen consumption *not* ascribable to low oxygen pressure alone.

THE PHOTOSYNTHETIC ENERGY CYCLE

Fig. 2 and 5, 3, and 4 present typical galvanometric results, respectively obtained visually, photographically, and by pen-recording, that show various time courses of the

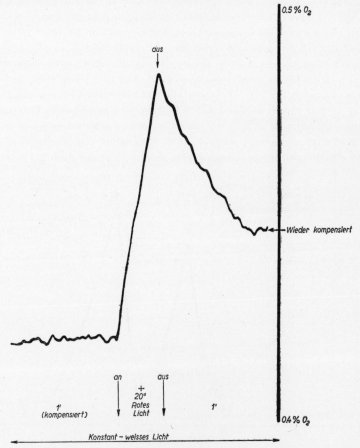

Fig. 3. Photographic record of galvanometric observations on the photosynthetic cycle, with respiration compensated.

References p. 355.

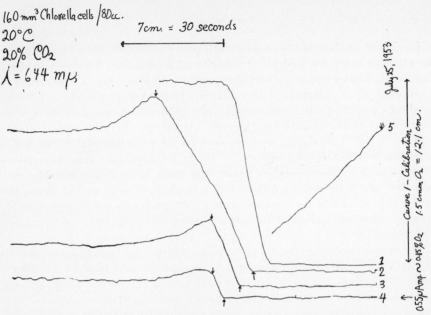

Fig. 4. Photograph of work sheet obtained with *Linienschreiber* recording of galvanometric observations on the photosynthetic cycle, with respiration compensated (also illustration of method of
calibrating electrodes for response to oxygen pressure change).

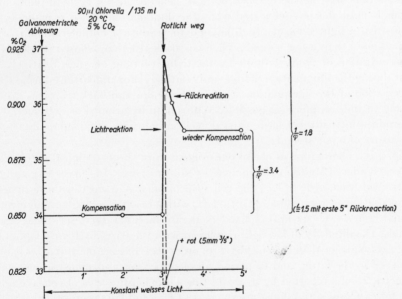

Fig. 5. The photosynthetic cycle, with respiration compensated (galvanometer read visually).

photosynthetic cycle under various conditions, as observed either without (Fig. 2) or
with (Figs. 3, 4, 5) compensation of respiration by a supplementary source of light.

References p. 355.

Back reaction of enhanced oxygen consumption

The initial respiratory curve shown in Fig. 2 had already been proceeding linearly from 4% to 0.445% for a period of many hours in darkness, without any intervening illumination. After each of the two illuminations shown in Fig. 2, the rate of oxygen consumption, upon cessation of illumination, proceeded at $1.8/0.4 = 4.5$ times the normal rate, a marked enhancement, and a very clear demonstration of the light-induced back reaction of the photosynthetic cycle. As shown after the second illumination period, more than ten minutes were required for the back reaction, in this instance, to run its course before re-establishment of the basic respiratory rate. The pressure fall during the back reaction was more nearly first order, as compared with the zero order time course of the normal respiratory fall in oxygen pressure. In Fig. 2, the intensity of white light employed for the two 5 minute illuminations was high enough to result in typical induction periods in the photo phases, following the long initial period of dark adaptation.

The increase in oxygen consumption induced by the light reaction can also be shown with particular beauty if the *Chlorella* cell suspension is first brought to compensation of respiration (Figs. 3, 4, 5). When additional light is turned on briefly, and then off, any increased rate of back reaction immediately makes itself evident by a *fall* in oxygen pressure in the system upon cessation of the additional illumination, and the time taken to return to the state of compensation is a measure of the time period of the back reaction of the cycle under the conditions of the experiment. In our experience, this may vary from a few seconds up to a minute or more, depending upon a variety of conditions that need not be detailed here. In general, such a cycle of photo and back reactions is most sharply delineated when the illumination period is made as short as possible with a light intensity high enough to produce a notable amount of oxygen within no more than a few seconds. Then the back reaction, whose rate depends upon the concentration of products built by the light reaction, becomes relatively less important during the illumination period, and relatively more important during the period after cessation of the illumination; that is, the photo and back reactions are thereby separated in time as much as possible. With photo-flash bulbs of extremely high but undetermined intensity per flash, typical cycle curves were obtained qualitatively with single flashes of 0.001 second.

Fig. 4 is a photograph of one of our original work sheets obtained with the *Linien-schreiber* recorder of Multiflex Galvanometer No. 3 response. In Curves 2, 3, and 4, which must be read from right to left, the cell suspension was in each instance first brought to compensation at approximately 0.15% O_2 with a beam of white light, and then given extra red light ($\lambda = 644$ mμ) of fixed moderate intensity for respectively 28, 8, and 3 seconds. The intensity of red light employed with the partially light-adapted cultures in Fig. 4 was smaller than that in Fig. 2, in order to avoid the photosynthetic induction phases seen in the latter, and to permit an electrochemical demonstration (confirming manometric results reported by us many times previously[4, 5, 6, 7]) of concave downward photo curves whose initial slopes are steepest at first and fall progressively to a constant steady-state value as the rate of the back reaction rises to a constant value. This rise in back reaction rate is indicated not only by the fall in slope as illumination proceeds, but also by the increasingly greater initial negative slopes observed when the red light is turned off in Curves 4, 3, and 2, respectively. Curve 1 in Fig. 4 is the calibration

References p. 355.

curve already referred to on page 349, and its variable slope in the ascending portion is merely an incidental expression of the slightly uneven rate of addition of the oxygen from the calibrated microburette. Curve 5 is a partial recording of the fall in oxygen pressure that was taken when the compensating white light was turned off, between Curves 2 and 3, in order to return the oxygen pressure in the medium to ca. 0.15% of saturation at 1 atm. O_2.

Quantum requirements with short illuminations

As already indicated, the quantitative aspects of the photosynthetic cycle can in general best be studied by using relatively short illumination periods. In Fig. 5 is shown an experiment in which the quantum requirement observed was 1.8 per molecule of O_2 produced as *positive pressure alone*, uncorrected for any back oxidation reaction occurring, during a 5 second illumination period with 5 μl of red light ($\lambda = 644$ mμ). A conventional correction for back oxidation, made by adding algebraically the back reaction observed in the first 5 seconds after turning off the red light, yielded a quantum requirement of 1.45. The quantum requirement for the *net* gain of O_2 in the entire cycle (5 seconds illumination with red light, followed by 20 seconds without red light, until re-establishment of compensation) was 3.4 $h\nu/O_2$. Similar experiments were also performed for 10 and 30 second illumination periods of red light, with results summarized as follows:

	Quantum requirement ($h\nu/O_2$)		
Time of illumination (seconds)	Light reaction (Positive O_2 alone)	Light reaction Corrected for back reaction	Cycle (Net gain after return to compensation)
30	2.35	2.15	3.4
10	2.0	1.7	3.3
5	1.8	1.45	3.4

These results are a confirmation of the manometric results of 1950[4], with the difference that the back reaction is here somewhat faster, with *Chlorella* cultures grown somewhat differently. With the electrochemical method employed, one can fortunately measure rapid photo and back reactions not possible with manometry.

From these quantitative data, it is again evident that, for a given and appropriate light intensity, the quantum requirement for the positive production of oxygen in the light reaction becomes less as the time period of illumination is shortened, and falls below the conventionally assigned thermodynamic limit of 2.7 $\pm$; the shorter the illumination period the less will be the relative effect of the back reaction in reducing the observed yield of O_2 during the actual illumination period itself. The net gain of oxygen in the entire cycle of light and dark reactions was, however, independent of the period of illumination here given.

The rate of back oxygen consumption for the first 10 seconds after turning off the red light in the foregoing experiments was of the order of three times the cell volume per hour, or five times the normal rate of respiration observed in total darkness just before the photosynthetic experiments described were carried out.

References p. 355.

STEADY-STATE EFFICIENCIES

In Fig. 6 is illustrated an application of the electrochemical method of TÖDT to the determination of steady-state quantum efficiencies at light intensities up to many

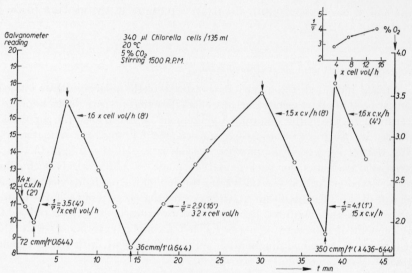

Fig. 6. Quantum yields at high light intensities, in the virtual steady-state (galvanometer read visually).

times that needed for respiration compensation. The quantum requirement, calculated in the usual manner to include respiration correction, was 2.9 at the lowest intensity employed, and 4.1 at the highest. At the highest level of light intensity, the calculated quantum requirement is not greatly changed if the dark oxygen consumption is left out of the calculation (4.5 instead of 4.1), since the dark respiration is only one tenth of the total photosynthesis. This result is in agreement with the similar manometric results reported in the accompanying paper[3]. In Fig. 6 the oxygen exchanges in photo-synthesis and in respiration are both reported in terms of "times cell volume per hour" for purposes of facilitated comparison.

SUMMARY

1. The electrochemical method of TÖDT for the determination of oxygen gas has been applied to the measurement of (1) the quantum requirement of photosynthesis and (2) the course of the light reaction and the dark back-oxidation over very short time periods (seconds).

2. With this new and independent, galvanometric method, the earlier results obtained by us with manometry have been confirmed, that is, attainment of a limiting quantum requirement of about 3 in the cycle of light and dark reactions. All significant objections raised regarding the time lag of manometry, as used by us, are thereby refuted.

3. Quantum requirements with single illumination periods as short as 5 seconds have been reported, and much shorter periods are shown possible.

4. The new electrochemical method opens up a field of investigation closed, on a time basis, to manometry. Nevertheless, manometry, with which the energetics of photosynthesis was discovered, can never be given up: for it alone of all methods gives information about both gases, oxygen and carbon dioxide.

References p. 355.

RÉSUMÉ

1. La méthode électrochimique de Tödt pour la détermination de l'oxygène gazeux a été appliquée à la mesure 1° du nombre de quanta requis par la photosynthèse et 2° de la marche de la réaction qui a lieu à la lumière et de celle qui a lieu à l'obscurité (réoxydation) pendant des périodes très courtes (secondes).

2. A l'aide de cette méthode galvanométrique, nouvelle et indépendante, nous avons pu confirmer nos résultats obtenus préalablement par manométrie, c. à d. que le nombre de quanta requis atteint une limite qui est de 3 environ pour le cycle de réactions à la lumière et à l'obscurité. Toutes les objections soulevées contre la période de retard de notre méthode manométrique se trouvent ainsi réfutées.

3. Nous avons déterminé le nombre de quanta pour une seule période d'illumination de 5 secondes et montré que des périodes encore beaucoup plus courtes sont possibles.

4. La nouvelle méthode électrochimique donne accès à un nouveau domaine de recherches que l'on ne pouvait atteindre par manométrie. Cependant, la méthode manométrique qui avait permis de découvrir l'énergétique de la photosynthèse, ne pourra jamais être abandonnée car, parmi toutes les méthodes, elle est la seule qui nous renseigne sur les deux gases, oxygène et dioxyde de carbone.

ZUSAMMENFASSUNG

1. Die elektrochemische Methode von Tödt zur Bestimmung von gasförmigem Sauerstoff wurde auf die Messung (1) des Quantenbedarfs der Photosynthese und (2) des Verlaufs der Lichtreaktion und der Dunkelreaktion (Rückoxydation) während sehr kurzer Zeiträume (Sekunden) angewandt.

2. Mit dieser neuen und unabhängigen galvanometrischen Methode wurden die früheren von uns durch manometrische Messungen erhaltenen Ergebnisse bestätigt, nämlich die Erreichung eines Grenzquantenbedarfs von ungefähr 3 im Cyclus der Licht- und Dunkelreaktion. Alle bedeutenden, auf Grund der Zeitverschiebung bei der von uns benützten manometrischen Messung erhobenen, Einwände wurden hierdurch widerlegt.

3. Es wurde der Quantenbedarf für einfache Beleuchtungsperioden von 5 Sekunden berichtet und es wurde gezeigt, dass noch viel kürzere Beleuchtungsperioden möglich sind.

4. Die neue elektrochemische Methode eröffnet ein für manometrische Untersuchungen wegen der erforderlichen Zeit unerschlossenes Gebiet. Nichts-destoweniger können manometrische Untersuchungen, mit denen die energetischen Beziehungen der Photosynthese entdeckt wurden, nie aufgegeben werden, denn von allen Methoden geben sie allein sowohl über Sauerstoff wie über Kohlendioxyd Aufschluss.

REFERENCES

[1] F. Tödt, in *Handbuch der Analytischen Chemie*, Teil III, Bd. VIa, p. 24 (Springer-Verlag, Berlin, 1953).
[2] F. Tödt, G. Teske, F. Windisch, W. Heumann and Chr. Goslich, *Biochem. Z.*, 323 (1952) 192.
[3] O. Warburg, *Biochim. Biophys. Acta*, 12 (1953) 356.
[4] D. Burk and O. Warburg, *Z. f. Naturforschung*, 6b (1951) 12.
[5] O. Warburg, *Z. Elektrochem.*, 55 (1951) 285.
[6] D. Burk, J. Cornfield and M. Schwartz, *Scientific Monthly*, 73 (1951) 213.
[7] D. Burk, *Federation Proc.*, 12 (1953) 611.

Received July 31st, 1953

MESSUNG DES QUANTENBEDARFS DER PHOTOSYNTHESE FÜR SEHR DÜNNE ZELLSUSPENSIONEN

von

OTTO WARBURG

(mit GÜNTHER KRIPPAHL, WALTER SCHRÖDER UND WOLFGANG BUCHHOLZ)

Max Planck Institut für Zellphysiologie, Berlin-Dahlem (Germany)

Um die Bestimmungen des Quantenbedarfs weiter zu vereinfachen, sind wir mit den Zelldichten soweit heruntergegangen und haben dabei die Zellen so stark belichtet, dass die Atmung zu einem Korrectionsglied wurde, das für viele Zwecke vernachlässigt werden konnte. Dann war es nicht mehr notwendig, die Belichtung zwecks Atmungsmessung zeitweise zu unterbrechen; oder die Atmung zu kompensieren und zeitweise den Kompensationsgrad zu messen; sondern die Zellen wurden in den Manometergefässen einfach solange kontinuierlich belichtet, zum Beispiel 6 Stunden, bis die manometrischen Ausschläge gross geworden waren, zum Beispiel 100 und 50 mm. Dann wurde aus der Lichtabsorption und den entwickelten positiven Drucken, also unter Vernachlässigung der Atmung, die Ausbeute berechnet (Fig. 1). Wir fanden bei diesem Verfahren den Quantenbedarf zwischen 5.5 und 3.5, bei einer positiven Sauerstoffentwicklung gleichdem 10- bis 20-fachen Zellvolumen pro Stunde; während der Sauerstoffverbrauch in längeren Dunkelzeiten meistens nur das 1-fache Zellvolumen pro Stunde betrug. Im allgemeinen vermehrten sich die Zellen während der Ausbeutebestimmungen.

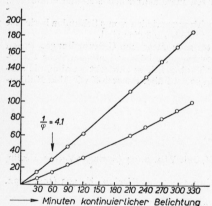

Fig. 1. Bestimmung des Quantenbedarfs unter Vernachlässigung der Atmung. 2-Gefässmethode. Obere Kurve kleines Gefäss. Untere Kurve grosses Gefäss. Stundenumsatz 18-faches Zellvolumen. Daten am Schluss dieser Arbeit. λ 546 mm. $J = 92 \, \mu l$ Quanten pro Minute. Anfangs-Absorption 6.2 %.

Vielfach haben wir bei einer Sauerstoffentwicklung gleich dem 40-fachen Zellvolumen pro Stunde einen Quantenbedarf von 4, unter Vernachlässigung der Atmung, gefunden, ein Ergebnis, das man noch vor wenigen Jahren für unmöglich gehalten hätte und das den Fortschritt unserer Methoden — physikalisch und biologisch — zeigt. Die Sauerstoffentwicklung dieser Zellen bei Lichtsättigung betrug das 60-fache Zellvolumen pro Stunde.

Optische Anordnung

Als Lichtquellen bei der Messung der Photosynthese dienten Quecksilber- und Cadmium-Quecksilber-Hochdrucklampen, für deren Anfertigung wir der Osram-

Studiengesellschaft in Berlin zu grossem Dank verpflichtet sind. Wir isolierten daraus mit Interferenzscheiben und Filtern die Wellenlängen 366, 436, 480, 578 und 644 mμ. Zur Belichtung der Manometergefässe wurde auf ihrem Boden eine viereckige Blende abgebildet; 7/8 der Grundfläche wurde dabei belichtet. Diese weitgehende Ausleuchtung der Manometergefässe wurde dadurch ermöglicht, dass die Spiegel, die das Licht in die Manometergefässe reflektierten, nicht mehr fest montiert waren, sondern sich synchron mit den Manometergefässen bewegten. Dann konnte, trotz 7/8 Ausleuchtung, beim Schütteln der Gefässe kein Licht verloren gehen. Die neue Anordnung hat den Vorteil, dass die Flächenintensität bei gleicher Gesamtintensität etwa 7-mal kleiner ist, dass also die Wirkungen des Lichts bis zu höheren Intensitäten linear bleiben. Die Trennung des Lichtstrahls in 2 gleiche Teile geschah nicht mehr mit 4 Prismen, sondern mit einem teildurchlässigen Spiegel, wobei die geteilten Strahlen mit Irisblenden bolometrisch auf gleiche Intensitäten justiert wurden. Die neue Anordnung hat den Vorteil, dass Lage-änderungen des Lichtbogens die Verteilung des Lichts auf die beiden Strahlen weniger ändern können, aber den (geringeren) Nachteil, dass die Teildurchlässigkeit der Spiegel für die verschiedene Wellenlängen verschieden ist, sodass bei einem Wechsel der Wellen-längen die beiden Teilstrahlen neu justiert werden müssen.

Messung der Lichtabsorption

Zur Messung der Lichtabsorption wurde teils das Transmissionsactinometer, teils die ULBRICHT'sche Kugel nach der Vorschrift von DRESLER[1] benutzt, wobei auch die Korrektur für die Mehrfach-Absorption mit monochromatischem Licht bestimmt wurde. Während der Absorptionsmessung wurde der in der Kugel montierte Trog wie bei der Messung der Photosynthese bewegt. Da Actinometer und Kugel genau die gleichen Absorptionen ergaben, wurde später, aus Gründen der Zeitersparnis, der ULBRICHT'schen Kugel der Vorzug gegeben. War dabei die Absorption einer Zellsuspension zu gering, so wurde die Suspension konzentriert, zum Beispiel auf das 3-fache und das 6-fache. Mit Hilfe der 3 Punkte $c = 0$, $c = 3$ und $c = 6$ wurde dann eine Absorptionskurve gezeichnet, aus der die gesuchte Absorption entnommen wurde. Dieses Verfahren wurde zum Beispiel im grün angewandt, während im rot und im blau die Absorptionen direkt gemessen wurden, da sie hinreichend gross waren, wenn in die Versuchsgefässe 5 μl Zellen eingefüllt wurden.

Gasgemische

Da Sauerstoff und Stickstoff in den Stahlflaschen Spuren von Stickoxyden bilden können, die für Zellen giftig sind, so empfehlen wir, sowohl bei den Kulturen, als auch bei den Messungen, den Stickstoff durch Argon zu ersetzen.

Schüttelgeschwindigkeit

Wir haben beobachtet, dass es *Chlorella* gibt, die die für die Manometrie notwendige grosse Schüttelgeschwindigkeit in langen Versuchen nicht gut verträgt. Wir schütteln deshalb bei den Bestimmungen des Quantenbedarfs dünner Zellsuspensionen die Mano-metergefässe während des grösseren Teils der Versuchszeit so langsam, dass die Zellen eben in Suspension bleiben und schütteln immer nur 3 Minuten lang vor der mano-metrischen Ablesung so schnell, wie es die Manometrie verlangt.

Literatur S. 359.

Züchtung der Chlorella

DANIELS, EMERSON UND JAMES FRANCK haben oft hervorgehoben, dass es gleichgültig ist, wie man die *Chlorella* züchtet. Dies stimmt, solange man sich mit einem Quantenbedarf von 20 bis 12 zufrieden gibt. Verlangt man aber maximale Ausbeuten, so ist nichts wichtiger, als die Methode der Züchtung. In der Tat ist heute, wo die physikalischen Methoden zur Messung des Quantenbedarfs bis zur Vollkommenheit entwickelt sind, die reproduzierbare Züchtung von Zellen bestimmter Eigenschaften das Hauptproblem der Energetik der Photosynthese.

Bei unsern neuen Züchtungsversuchen eliminierten wir das Brunnenwasser und ersetzten es durch doppelt destilliertes Wasser, dem wir meistens die Mikroelemente nach ARNON[2], zusetzten. Im übrigen enthielt 1 Liter Kulturlösung 5 g $MgSO_4$ 7 H_2O, 2.5 g KH_2PO_4, 2 g NaCl, 2 g KNO_3 und 2 g $Ca(NO_3)_2$ 4H_2O. Die Zelldichten bei der Ernte betrugen 1 bis 2 μl Zellen/ml.

Alle unsere Kulturen erhielten Tageslicht. Zum Teil züchteten wir an einem Südfenster unter Zusatz von Metallfadenlicht, zum Teil an einem Nordfenster unter Zusatz des Lichts der Xenon-Hochdrucklampe, die in der letzten Zeit von der Osram-Studiengesellschaft in Berlin entwickelt worden ist. Diese Lampe, die heisser als die Sonne ist, strahlt ein Kontinuum mit dem Maximum im himmelblau aus. Besonders im Winter, wenn das Tageslicht schwach war, haben wir sehr gute Erfahrungen mit der Xenon-Hochdrucklampe gemacht.

Änderungen des pH

Da sich bei langen Versuchen pH und damit die Retention der Kohlensäure in den Messgefässen ändert, so muss Klarheit darüber herrschen, wie pH-Änderungen die Manometrie beeinflussen können, zumal EMERSON darüber physikalisch unrichtige Ansichten geäussert hat.

Bei jedem pH liefern die Gleichungen der 2-Gefässmethode, ohne Berücksichtigung der Retention der Kohlensäure, völlig korrekt sowohl Entwicklung oder Verbrauch des Sauerstoffs als auch Entwicklung oder Verbrauch der *freien* Kohlensäure; dies gilt auch dann, wenn sich pH während der manometrischen Messungen beliebig ändert. Nur wenn man auch die Aenderungen der *gebundenen* Kohlensäure kennen lernen will — also gewissermassen nicht nur das physikalische sondern auch das chemische

$$\gamma = \frac{CO_2}{O_2}$$ — nur dann muss man die Retention in die Gleichungen der 2-Gefässmethode einführen.

Man überzeuge sich von der Richtigkeit des gesagten, indem man experimentell oder in Gedanken die 2-Gefässmethode auf die Karbonatgemische anwendet. Im Fall der die CO_2 vollständig retinierenden Gemische findet man dann mit den *zwei* Gefässen genau dieselbe Sauerstoffentwicklung wie mit dem *einen* Gefäss:

$$x_{O_2} = H'xK'_{O_2} = HxK_{O_2} = h'xk'_{O_2} = hk_{O_2} \text{ und immer } \gamma = \varphi_{O2}.$$

Beispiel

Versuch vom 26.6.53. Wellenlänge 546 mμ. 1-tägige Kultur in Kultursalzlösung mit Mikroelementen. Nordzimmer, Xenonlicht. Vermehrung von 60 auf 160 μl Zellen im 250 ml-Kolben. Kulturlösung (ohne Zentrifugieren) direkt zum Versuch benutzt. Je 7 ml Suspension mit je 4.5 μl Zellen in die Gefässe v = 20.75 und v = 16.5 ml eingefüllt. 20°. Gasraum 5.5 % CO_2-Luft. Eingestrahlte Intensität 92 μl Quanten pro Minute. Absorption zu Beginn des Versuchs 6.2 %.

Literatur S. 359.

	Kleines Gefäss mm abgelesen	Grosses Gefäss mm abgelesen
30'	+ 14.5	+ 7.0
60'	+ 30.0	+ 15.0
90'	+ 45.5	+ 23.5
120'	+ 62.5	+ 32.0
211'	+ 113.0	+ 60.5
241'	+ 132.0	+ 70.5
271'	+ 149.0	+ 80.0
301'	+ 168.0	+ 89.5
331'	+ 186.0	+ 99.5

Für die ersten zwei Stunden ergibt die Rechnung ohne Berücksichtigung der Atmung

$$x_{O_2} = +167 \, \mu l; \quad x_{CO_2} = -185 \, \mu l \quad \gamma -1.11$$

$$\frac{1}{\varphi} = \frac{120 \times 92 \times 0.062}{167} = \frac{684}{167} = 4.1$$

Der Versuch ist in Fig. 1 graphisch dargestellt. D-er Stundenumsatz in den ersten zwei Stunden beträgt das 18-*fache* des Zellvolumens. Mit einer Atmung von 4.5 μl pro Stunde würde in den ersten beiden Stunden

$$\frac{1}{\varphi} = \frac{684}{167 + 9} = 3.88.$$

ZUSAMMENFASSUNG

Die Methoden zur Messung des Quantenbedarfs der Photosynthese sind weiter vereinfacht worden. Insbesondere ist nunmehr die Atmung auf ein zu vernachlässigendes Korrektionsglied heruntergedrückt worden. Mit der neuen Anordnung wird bestätigt, dass der Quantenbedarf pro Molekül Sauerstoff bei maximaler Ausnutzung der Lichtenergie, kleiner als 4, wahrscheinlich kleiner als 3 ist.

SUMMARY

Methods of determining the number of quanta required for photosynthesis have been further simplified. In particular, respiration has become negligible. With the help of the new technique it has been confirmed that the number of quanta required per oxygen molecule, the illuminating energy being used maximum, is less than 4, probably less than 3.

RÉSUMÉ

Les méthodes de mesure du nombre de quanta requis par la photosynthèse ont été simplifiées davantage. En particulier, la respiration est devenue négligeable. A l'aide du nouveau dispositif il a été confirmé que le nombre de quanta requis par molécule d'oxygène, l'énergie lumineuse étant utilisée au maximum, est plus petit que 4, probablement plus petit que 3.

LITERATUR

[1] *Handbuch der Lichttechnik*, herausgegeben von R. SEWIG, Springer, Berlin, 1938, S. 348.
[2] D. I. ARNON, *Am. J. Botany*, 25 (1938) 322.

Eingegangen den 5. August 1953

AUTHOR INDEX

SUBJECT INDEX